Material Science and Metallurgy

U. C. Jindal

Delhi • Chennai • Chandigarh

Assistant Editor–Acquisitions: Gauravjeet Singh Reen
Associate Editor–Production: Vipin Kumar

ISBN: 978-81-317-5911-0

First Impression

Published by Dorling Kindersley (India) Pvt. Ltd, licensees of Pearson Education in South Asia.

Head Office: 7th Floor, Knowledge Boulevard, A-8(A), Sector 62, Noida 201 309, UP, India.
Registered Office: 11 Community Centre, Panchsheel Park, New Delhi 110 017, India.

Composition: County Caramels
Printer: HT Media Limited, Noida

*Dedicated to
the almighty and my parents.
Their blessings have made everything possible.*

Contents

Preface

The study of material science and metallurgy is an essential prerequisite for a successful mechanical engineer in order to study the behaviour of engineering materials under various mechanical, thermal and electrical processes before practical use of the material is made.

The content of the book has been designed by taking into account the syllabi prescribed by universities, technical institutions, and competitive examinations conducted by examining bodies such as the UPSC, GATE, PSUs, AMIE etc. This book is useful to undergraduate students as well.

The book is divided into 21 chapters. The first two chapters deal with atomic models, atomic arrangements and crystal structure. Chapters 3 and 4 deal with deformation in materials under mechanical loading and consequently with the study of mechanical properties.

The chapter on diffusion describes various diffusion processes in detail while chapters on phase diagrams and phase transformations deal with changes in phases with respect to temperature, that is eutectic, eutectoid and peritactic reactions. The chapter on phase transformation actually deals with phase transformations in steel depending upon temperature and rate of heating/cooling. Chapter 8 deals with various heat treatment processes such as annealing, tempering, normalizing and hardening which is useful for all mechanical engineers at all levels.

There are chapters on metal alloys, organic materials, ceramic materials and composite materials relative to mechanical engineering field. The study of corrosion and wear of materials is useful for making selection of materials for use under various environmental and industrial conditions. Electrical conducting, semi-conducting and insulating materials are also studied in brief as far as their utility in mechanical engineering applications is concerned. Magnetic and dielectric properties of the materials are also included in the book.

The chapters are self-contained. Each chapter ends with a detailed list of key points to remember, review questions, multiple choice questions to help students test their grasp of concepts and then proceed to solve practice problems.

Every care has been taken by the publisher and me to weed out any typographical error or miscalculation in numerical problems. However, I will be happy to receive feedback and suggestions.

U.C. Jindal

Dr U. C. Jindal is former Professor and Head of the Department of Mechanical Engineering, Delhi College of Engineering. He completed his MTech from IIT Kanpur and did his PhD on Experimental Stress Analysis from the University of Delhi. For the last 45 years Dr Jindal has been involved in teaching, research and development activities in the mechanics group of subjects—engineering mechanics, strength of materials, machine design, theory of machines and materials science. He is the author of nine books, and has also published numerous research papers in the fi eld of stress analysis, material testing, stress concentrations, adhesives and composite materials in various national and international journals. Dr Jindal was awarded the Toshiba Anand Prize in 1978 for original research in Theory and Practice of Standardization. He is a life member of the Indian Society for Construction Materials and Structures, New Delhi.

1

ATOMIC STRUCTURE

1.1 INTRODUCTION

Up to the end of nineteenth century even the prominent scientists doubted the presence of an atom, but in 1899, J.J. Thomson proposed the existence of an atom and found that electrons are constituents of all matter. Now a days everybody realizes the existence of atoms, which are the building blocks of all the materials. Today, even an individual atom can be identified and photographed; through the light an atom emits. Atoms are stable and exist for billions of years without any change. They can combine together to form solids and can interact with other atoms to make compounds. Atoms can also emit or absorb light.

In an atom, there is a nucleus containing protons (positively charged particles) and neutrons (without any charge) surrounded by electrons (negatively charged fine particles) moving in orbits. The number of protons is equal to the number of electrons to balance the charge. Neutrons are slightly heavier than protons, i.e. 1.008 times heavier.

The charge on an electron is $e = 1.602 \times 10^{-19}$ C (Coulomb). The diameter of the nucleus is extremely small and it is of the size of 10^{-4} of an atom.

The atomic number is the number of electrons or protons in an atom. The mass number of an atom is equal to the sum of the number of protons plus neutrons. The 'atomic weight' of an atom is equal to the sum of the number of protons plus neutrons. Most elements have fractional atomic weights due to the existence of different 'isotopes' of the same element.

The atomic weight of an element is the 'average relative weight' of its atom as compared to the weight of an atom of oxygen, which is taken as 16.

1.2 ISOTOPES

All atoms of the same element having different weights are known as 'isotopes' and their atomic numbers are the same. Following are a few examples of isotopes:

1. Hydrogen exists in three isotopic forms as hydrogen (atomic weight 1), deuterium (atomic weight 2) and tritium (atomic weight 3). All the three isotopes of hydrogen contain one proton and one electron, but different number of neutrons.

2. Chlorine has two isotopes with atomic weights 35 and 37, i.e. Cl_{35}, Cl_{37} present in the ratio of 3:1.

$$\text{Average atomic weight of chlorine} = \frac{3 \times 35 + 1 \times 37}{4}$$

$$= 35.5$$

1.3 ISOBARS

Atoms with same mass but different chemical elements are called 'isobars'. The atomic weight of argon is 39.95 and that of calcium is 40.05, both weights are approximately 40.

1.4 AVOGADRO'S NUMBER

Avogadro's number is the number of atoms in exactly 12 g of carbon-12, which is a universal constant, given by $N_a = 6.02 \times 10^{23}$ atoms/mol.

It is the sum of the atomic weights of the atoms making one molecule of an element. This chapter discusses the atomic models (structure of an atom comprising electrons, protons and neutrons), electron configurations and periodic table.

1.5 ATOMIC MODEL

First atomic model was proposed by J.J. Thomson in 1899 and he concluded that electron is a constituent of all matter. J.J. Thomson clearly identified the electron of mass 9.1085×10^{-31} kg at rest with a negative charge of 1.602×10^{-19} C. His proof on existence of electrons became an essential pre-requisite for the subsequent models on structure of atoms, each model removing the anomalies of previous models. In chronological order, the following atomic models were developed.

1. Thomson model
2. Rutherford's nuclear atomic model
3. Bohr atomic model
4. Sommerfeld–Wilson atomic model
5. Vector model or modern model

These models will be discussed in detail one by one.

1.5.1 Thomson Model

Thomson considered atom as a sphere, which consists of positively charged matter with negatively charged electrons to balance the positive charge. Using spectroscopy, he computed the total number of electrons in an atom. By using different materials for the filament wire, he found that the same value is always obtained for charge to mass ratio, i.e. e/m ratio of electron charge to mass.

However, the atomic model presented by Thomson could not explain spectral series of hydrogen atom.

Figure 1.1 gives the atomic model of Thomson, showing electrons (negatively charged fine particles) in positively charged matter.

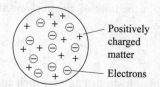

Figure 1.1 *Thomson's Atomic Model*

However, the most important achievement of Thomson was the identification of electrons present in the matter along with mass of each electron and negative charge in Coulombs of each electron.

1.5.2 Rutherford's Nuclear Atomic Model

On the basis of differential scattering experiments, Rutherford proposed a model of an atom consisting of a nucleus and electrons moving very rapidly around different orbits as shown in Figure 1.2. He suggested that the nucleus of an atom is very small compared to the size of the atom. The positive charge is concentrated in the nucleus. The electrons are moving at high speed in orbits and attain the centrifugal force. He also suggested that the 'force of attraction' between negatively charged electrons and positively charged nucleus was balanced by the centrifugal force attained by the electrons.

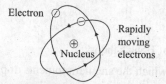

Figure 1.2 *Rutherford's Nuclear Model*

However, if an electron moves in a circular orbit of radius r, with a constant linear velocity v, then it is subjected to two forces: one acting inwards (centripetal force) and the other acting outwards (centrifugal force).

Short comings of Rutherford Model

The electrons move in the Coulomb field of nucleus, in space like a planetary motion. An electron moving in a curved path is accelerating, but the accelerating charged particles radiate electromagnetic waves and lose energy. If Newton's laws of motion and Maxwell electromagnetic equations are applied to an atom of Rutherford model, then in about 10^{-10} s, all the energy of the electron would be radiated away and the electrons would collapse into the nucleus as shown in Figure 1.3.

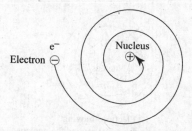

Figure 1.3 *Collapsing of an Electron into Nucleus*

Therefore, Rutherford model defies the laws of classical mechanics and the nuclear atomic model suggested by Rutherford is defective.

1.5.3 Bohr Atomic Model

In 1913, Neil Bohr proposed a model of hydrogen atom, which could correctly explain the spectrum of hydrogen atom.

While accepting the Rutherford model of nucleus and moving electrons around the nucleus, he proposed that the electrons are moving in 'orbits' around the nucleus. In case of hydrogen, Bohr proposed that the nucleus contains one proton and one electron revolving round the nucleus. He assumed that electron is a particle, which orbits around the nucleus 'in a circular path'. The electrons are moving in a definite planetary system (in circular orbits) of fixed energy levels known as 'energy states', and there is a definite value of 'potential energy' associated with each orbit. More than one energy level is possible for any electron of the atom.

The energy levels can be determined on the condition that the angular momentum of the electron moving in a circular orbit can take values of $L = nh/2\pi$, where $n = 1, 2, 3$, a positive integer and h is the Planck's constant.

When an electron changes its position from one orbit to another, 'electron can emit' or 'absorb energy'.

Postulates of Bohr's Theory

Following are the three postulates of Bohr's theory:

1. Only 'those orbits' occur for which the angular moments of planetary electrons are integral multiples of $h/2\pi$.
2. No electron radiates energy as long as it remains in one of the orbital energy states. Radiation takes place when one electron goes from a higher energy state to a lower energy state.

   The energy of quantum of radiation, $h_f = E_{n2} - E_{n1}$, energy difference of the states, where n_2 is the higher energy level and n_1 is the lower energy level.

   The energy difference released from the atom in the form of light waves is called a 'photon'.

   So light is not emitted from an electron when it is moving in one of its fixed orbits, but only when it jumps from one orbit to another.
3. The centripetal force on a revolving atom is equal to the inward 'electrostatic force'. This postulate prevents the electron from spiralling towards the nucleus or going away from it to escape. Figure 1.4 shows the Bohr's model of atom with nucleus at the centre and electrons moving in circular orbits with radii of orbits $r_1, r_2, r_3, \dots$ and $n = 1, 2, 3, \dots$

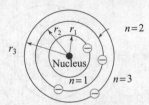

Electrons moving
along circular orbits around the nucleus

Figure 1.4 *Bohr's Atomic Model*

Limitations of Bohr's Theory of Atomic Model

Even though the model gives the idea of quantized atomic energy, it is unsatisfactory for the following reasons:

1. The assumption that the electrons make only circular orbits is arbitrary.
2. The systems cannot be generalized with two or more electrons.
3. There is no method to calculate the rate of transition between different energy levels.
4. The model is unable to handle unbound systems.
5. Bohr's model deals only with the quantum number (principal quantum number n).

Bohr's Theory for Hydrogen Atom

Hydrogen has an atomic number equal to 1, i.e., $Z = 1$, consists of one proton in the nucleus and one electron around it in a circular orbit of radius r. The nucleus is 1836 times heavier than an electron, therefore, it can be assumed to be at rest.

For example, m = mass of electron, then

$$\text{Centripetal force on electron} = \frac{mv^2}{r} \tag{1.1}$$

$$= \frac{mv_n^2}{r_n} \quad \text{(in } n \text{ orbit),}$$

F = electrostatic force of attraction between proton and electron

$$= \frac{Ze^2}{4\pi \varepsilon_0 r^2} \tag{1.2}$$

$$= \frac{Ze^2}{4\pi \varepsilon_0 r_n^2} \quad \text{(in } n \text{ orbit),}$$

where

$$\frac{1}{4\pi \varepsilon_0} = 9 \times 10^9 \text{ MKS units}$$

$Z = 1$ for hydrogen atom
As per Newton's third law of motion

$$\frac{mv_n^2}{r_n} = \frac{Ze^2}{4\pi \varepsilon_0 r_n^2} \tag{1.3}$$

$$\text{Angular momentum of orbitive electron} = \frac{nh}{2\pi}$$

(The angular momentum of electron should be an integral multiple of $h/2$, where h is the Planck's constant.)

$$\text{Angular momentum} = mv_n r_n = \frac{nh}{2\pi} \tag{1.4}$$

Hence, $n = 1, 2, 3, \ldots$ is an integer, defining the number of orbits.

Kinetic energy of electron,

$$E_k = \frac{1}{2}mv_n^2 = \frac{Ze^2}{8\pi \varepsilon_0 r_n} \qquad \text{[From Eq. (1.3)]} \tag{1.5}$$

Potential energy,

$$E_p = -eV$$

= nuclear charge × electrical potential

$$= \frac{-Ze^2}{4\pi\varepsilon_0 r_n}$$

Potential,

$$V = \frac{eZ}{4\pi\varepsilon_0 r_n} \qquad (1.6)$$

Total energy = kinetic energy + potential energy

$$= E_k + E_p$$

$$= \frac{Ze^2}{8\pi\varepsilon_0 r_n} - \frac{Ze^2}{4\pi\varepsilon_0 r_n}$$

$$= -\frac{Ze^2}{8\pi\varepsilon_0 r_n} \qquad (1.7)$$

Moreover, from Eq. (1.4)

$$mv_n r_n = \frac{nh}{2\pi}$$

$$mv_n^2 = \frac{Ze^2}{4\pi\varepsilon_0 r_n} \qquad \text{[From Eq. (1.3)]}$$

Eliminating mass m from these two equations, we get

$$\frac{mv_n r_n}{mv_n^2} = \frac{nh}{2\pi} \times \frac{4\pi\varepsilon_0 r_n}{Ze^2}$$

$$v_n = \frac{Ze^2}{2\varepsilon_0 nh} \qquad (1.8)$$

and

$$r_n = \frac{nh}{2\pi} \times \frac{1}{mv_n} = \frac{nh}{2\pi} \times \frac{2\varepsilon_0 nh}{mZe^2}$$

$$= \frac{\varepsilon_0 n^2 h^2}{\pi m Ze^2}$$

Putting the value of r_n, in term of mass, energy E can be calculated by

$$E = -\frac{Ze^2}{8\pi\varepsilon_0} \times \frac{\pi m Ze^2}{\varepsilon_0 n^2 h^2} = -\frac{mZ^2 e^4}{8\varepsilon_0^2 n^2 h^2}$$

Putting the values of m, e, h, ε_0, where

$$m = 9.1085 \times 10^{-31} \text{ kg}$$

$$e = 1.602 \times 10^{-19} \text{ C}$$

$$\varepsilon_0 = 8.854 \times 10^{-12}$$

Planck's constant,

$$h = 6.62 \times 10^{-34}$$

Energy,

$$E = \frac{9.1085 \times 10^{-31} \times Z^2 \times (1.602 \times 10^{-19})^4}{8 \times (8.854 \times 10^{-12})^2 \, n^2 \, (6.62 \times 10^{-34})^2} \ \text{J}$$

$$= \frac{9.1085 \times 6.58643 \times 10^{-107} \, Z^2}{8 \times 78.3933 \times 43.8244 \times 10^{-92} \, n^2}$$

$$= \frac{54.9925 \times 10^{-15} \, Z^2}{27484.3 \, n^2}$$

$$= \frac{21.828 \times 10^{-19} \, Z^2}{n^2} \ \text{J}$$

But

$$1 \ \text{eV} = 1.6 \times 10^{-19} \ \text{J}$$

So

$$E = \frac{13.6 Z^2}{n^2} \ \text{eV}$$

In the first orbit $\quad\quad\quad\quad n = 1, \ E_1 = -13.6 Z^2 \ \text{eV}$

In the second orbit $\quad\quad\quad n = 2, \ E_2 = -3.4 Z^2 \ \text{eV}$

In the third orbit $\quad\quad\quad\; n = 3, \ E_3 = -1.52 Z^2 \ \text{eV}$

Example 1.1   As per Bohr's theory, the radius of the first orbit of electron in a hydrogen atom is 0.529 Å. What is the radius of the second orbit in a singly ionized helium atom?

Solution:

$$r_n = \frac{\varepsilon_0 n^2 h^2}{\pi m Z e^2} = C \times \frac{n^2}{Z}$$

where C is a constant $= \varepsilon_0 h^2 / \pi m e^2$, having all fixed values, $r_n = 0.529$ in the first orbit, $z = 1$ in hydrogen atom and $C = 0.529$Å as $n = 1$ and $z = 1$.

In helium atom, there are two electrons, $z = 2$ and $n = 2$.

$$r_2 \text{ for helium} = C \times \frac{n^2}{Z} = 0.529 \times \frac{2^2}{2}$$

$$= 1.058 \ \text{Å}$$

Exercise 1.1   Calculate the velocity of an electron in a hydrogen atom as per Bhor's first orbit. Taking following values

$$h = 6.626 \times 10^{-34} \ \text{Js}$$

$$\varepsilon_0 = 8.85 \times 10^{-12} \ \text{F/m}$$

Hint

$$v_n = \frac{Z e^2}{2 \varepsilon_0 n h} \quad\quad\quad\quad\quad\quad\quad\quad\text{[From Eq. (1.8)]}$$

Ans. [2.188×10^6 m/s]

Orbital Frequency of an Electron (as per Bohr's Theory)

The orbital frequency can be defined as the number of revolutions an electron makes around the nucleus per second.

$$r_n = \text{radius of a particular orbit}$$

$$\omega = \text{angular velocity in radius/s}$$

$$f_n = \text{frequency}$$

Now, linear velocity in an orbit, $v_n = r_n \omega$

$$= 2\pi f_n r_n \qquad (1.9)$$

Now,

$$v_n = \frac{Ze^2}{2\varepsilon_0 nh}$$

$$r_n = \frac{\varepsilon_0 n^2 h^2}{\pi m Z e^2}$$

Substituting these values in Eq. (1.9), we get

$$\frac{Ze^2}{2\varepsilon_0 nh} = 2\pi f_n \times \frac{\varepsilon_0 n^2 h^2}{\pi m Z e^2}$$

or frequency,

$$f_n = \frac{m Z^2 e^4}{4\varepsilon_0^2 n^3 h^3}$$

Example 1.2 Calculate the orbital frequency of an electron in n orbit if

$$m = 9.1085 \times 10^{-31} \text{ kg}$$

$$e = 1.602 \times 10^{-19} \text{ C}$$

$$\varepsilon_0 = 8.854 \times 10^{-12} \text{ F/m}$$

$$h = 6.626 \times 10^{-34} \text{ Js}$$

Solution:

Frequency,

$$f_n = \frac{9.1085 \times 10^{-31} \times Z^2 \times (1.602 \times 10^{-19})^4}{4 \times (8.854 \times 10^{-12})^2 \, n^3 \times (6.626 \times 10^{-34})^3}$$

$$= \frac{59.9925 Z^2 \times 10^{-107}}{313.573 \times 10^{-24} \times n^3 \times 290.907 \times 10^{-102}}$$

$$= \frac{59.9925 Z^2 \times 10^{-107}}{9.122 \, n^3 \times 10^{-122}}$$

$$= 6.576 \times 10^{15} \frac{Z^2}{n^3}$$

Exercise 1.2   Calculate the orbital frequency of an electron in the Bohr's first orbit for a hydrogen atom.

Hint $$[(f_n = 6.576 \times 10^{15} \, Z^2/n^3)]$$

Ans. $[6.576 \times 10^{15} \text{ Hz}]$

Example 1.3   A hydrogen atom exits with an electron in the third orbit, $n = 3$ state. The electron comes down to orbit $n = 2$. What is the (a) energy of the photon emitted, (b) frequency of photon and (c) wave length of photons?

Solution:

We know that the energy of electron/photon

$$E = \frac{-13.6Z^2}{n^2} \text{ eV}$$

For hydrogen, $Z = 1$ and orbit $n = 3$

$$E_3 = \frac{-13.6 \times Z^2}{3^2} = \frac{-13.6 \times 1}{9} = -1.511 \text{eV}$$

If $n = 2,$

Similarly, $$E_2 = \frac{-13.6 \times 1^2}{2^2} = -3.4 \text{eV}$$

Energy of the photon transmitted $= E_3 - E_2$

$$= -1.511 - (3.4)$$

$$= +1.889 \text{eV}$$

Energy of the photon emitted $= 1.889 \times (1.602 \times 10^{-19})$ J

$$= 3.02618 \times 10^{-19} \text{ J}$$

Frequency of the photon emitted,

$$f = \frac{\text{energy of photon emitted}}{\text{mass of an electron}}$$

$$= \frac{3.02618 \times 10^{-19}}{6.626 \times 10^{-34}} = 4.567 \times 10^{14} \text{ Hz}$$

Wave length of the photon

$$\lambda = \frac{c}{f} = \frac{3 \times 10^8 \text{ m/s}}{4.567 \times 10^{14} \text{ /s}} = \frac{\text{velocity of light}}{\text{frequency}}$$

$$= 0.657 \times 10^{-6} \text{m}$$

or

$$= 0.657 \mu\text{m}$$

Exercise 1.3   Show that the energy of an electron jumping from orbit number 3 to 1 and energy emitted by an electron jumping from orbit number 2 to 1 are at the rate of 32/27.

Hint $$[(E_3 - E_1)/(E_2 - E_1)]$$

1.5.4 Sommerfeld–Wilson Atomic Model

In order to account for observed radiations for atoms having two or more planetary electrons and to explain fine structure, Sommerfeld and Wilson considered many modifications in Bohr's model. Sommerfeld proposed elliptical orbits in addition to circular orbits, which is possible as per Newtonian mechanics, and in order to achieve this he introduced 'second quantum number' l, which is analogous to the angular momentum number l and retained the quantum number n are also which is redefined as the total momentum.

As a result of Sommerfeld theory, an electron of hydrogen can move to any one of the orbits, i.e., $n = 1, 2, 3$ and so on and these are the possible orbits.

For $n = 1$, second quantum number $l = 0$. Figure 1.5 shows the ground state $n = 1, l = 0$.

For $n = 2, l = 0$, an elliptical orbit $2s$, $n = 2, l = 1$, a circular orbit. Figure 1.6 shows the orbits s and p.

For $n = 3, l = 2$, a circular orbit $3d$, $n = 3, l = 1$, an elliptical orbit, $n = 3, l = 0$, an elliptical orbit as shown in Figure 1.7.

For $n = 1$, second quantum number $l = 0$.
Figure 1.5 shows the ground state $n = 1$ and $l = 0$.

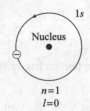

Figure 1.5 *Ground State*

For $n = 2, l = 0$, an elliptical orbit $2s$, $n = 2, l = 1$, a circular orbit. Figure 1.6 shows the orbits s and p.

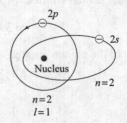

Figure 1.6 *Orbits s and p*

For $n = 3, l = 2$, a circular orbit $3d$, $n = 3, l = 1$, an elliptical orbit $3p$, $n = 3, l = 0$, an elliptical orbit $3s$ as shown in Figure 1.7.

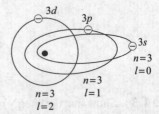

Figure 1.7 *Orbits s, p, d*

Electron orbits

The diameters of the circular orbits are given by Bohr's theory and are equal to the major axes of elliptical orbits. The second quantum numbers are designated as shown in Table 1.1.

Table 1.1 *Second Quantum Numbers*

$l=0$	$l=1$	$l=2$	$l=3$
s	P	d	F

All orbits with the same value of n (principal quantum number) have the same total energy. Each of the allowed orbits of this model of an atom becomes a subshell into which electrons are added to build the elements of the periodic table. Maximum number of electrons in any subshell $= 2(2l + 1)$, that is, if $s = 1$, $l = 0$, maximum number of electrons are 2. If $p = 2$, $l = 1$, maximum number of electrons are 6. If $d = 3$, $l = 2$, maximum number of electrons are 10 as will be obvious from electron configuration for different elements.

1.5.5 Vector Model or Quantum Model

Vector model is based on quantum mechanics and is also known as 'quantum model'. All the quantized principal terms are represented by vectors. Many investigators have determined the 'structural separations' of various energy levels using this model, while Sommerfeld atomic model does not explain the effects of magnetic and electric fields on spectral lines.

New model takes into account the electron spin, at the same time retaining the Sommerfeld feature of planetary momentum of electrons in different orbits (circular as well as elliptical).

In the new model, two new quantum numbers, the magnetic spin quantum number (m_s) and the magnetic orbital quantum number (m_l) along with the principal quantum number (n) and the orbital or azimuthal quantum number (l) can be used to specify the state of electrons (Table 1.2).

Note that there are $2n^2$ states in a shell, but $2(2l + 1)$ states in a subshell.

Table 1.2 *Electron States of an Atom*

Quantum Number	Symbol	Allowed Values	Related to
Principal	n	1, 2, 3	Distance from the nucleus
Orbital	l	0, 1, 2 – $(n-1)$	Orbital angular momentum
Orbital magnetic	m_l	0, ±1, ±2	Orbital angular momentum (z component)
Spin magnetic	m_s	±1/2	Spin angular momentum (z component)

1.6 ELECTRON CONFIGURATIONS

Electron orbits are not well-defined rings. As per quantum mechanics, electrons have the properties of particles and are similar to those of energy waves.

Electronic configuration of an atom is defined by the quantum numbers. The quantum numbers and electron configurations are used in various ways in engineering materials. For example', the electron configuration of carbon atom determines the molecular bonding characteristics in the case of polymers.

Some general rules about electronic configuration of atoms are listed as follows:

1. Electrons associated with an atom occupy orbitals and subshells with orbitals.

2. The exact location of electrons in orbitals are defined by four quantum numbers that refer to the

   (a) energy of the electron (principal quantum number),
   (b) shape of an orbital (angular momentum quantum number),
   (c) orientation of an orbital (magnetic quantum number), and
   (d) spin of an electron (spin quantum number).

3. No two electrons can have same four quantum numbers, i.e. they cannot be at the same place at the same time—as per Pauli's exclusion principle.

4. When two electrons reside in the same orbitals, their spins must be paired.

5. The number of electrons in a given orbital is $2n^2$, where n is the principal quantum number, that is, if

$n = 1$,	only 2 atoms in s subshell
$n = 2$,	only 8 atoms in sp subshells
$n = 3$,	only 16 atoms in spd subshells
$n = 4$,	only 32 atoms in $spdf$ subshells and so on

6. When two atoms interact to form a compound, the electrons move into the unoccupied orbitals rather than moving into the partially occupied orbitals.

7. The outermost or valence electrons largely determine the chemical behaviour of the elements.

Table 1.3 shows the electron configurations for various elements:

1. Elements, symbol, atomic number
2. Principal quantum numbers, n
3. Number of electrons in subshells s, p, d, f
4. Electron configurations in principal orbits and subshells s, p, d, f

1.7 PERIODIC TABLE

As per the electronic configuration, all the elements are classified in periodic table. These elements are arranged by increasing atomic number. There are seven horizontal rows called 'periods'. Elements arranged in a given column or group have similar valence electron structure. However, the chemical and physical properties gradually change while moving horizontally across each period.

Group 0—right most group shows inert gases (e.g. He, Ne, Ar, Kr. ..., Rn).

Group VII A—gases like F, Cl, Br, I, A$_r$ are sometime termed as halogens.

Group I A–II A—alkali and Alkaline earth metals (e.g. Li, Na, K, Be, Mg, Ca, ...)

Group III B–II B—transition metals.

Group III A, IV A, V A——display properties that intermediate between metals and non-metals by virtue of the valence electrons (e.g. B, Si, Ge, ...).

Table 1.3 *Electron Configurations for Various Elements*

		Principal Quantum Number (n) Increasing Energy							
		1	2	3	4	5	6	7	
		Number of Electrons in Subshell ($2n^2$)							
Element	**At. No**	**s**	**sp**	**spd**	**spdf**	**spdf**	**spdf**	**s**	**Electron Configuration**
Hydrogen, H	1	1							$1s^1$
Helium, He	2	2							$1s^2$
Lithium, Le	3	2	1						$1s^2 2s^1$
Beryllium, Be	4	2	2						$1s^2 2s^2$
Boron, B	5	2	2 1						$1s^2 2s^2 2p^1$
Carbon, C	6	2	2 2						$1s^2 2s^2 2p^2$
Nitrogen, N	7	2	2 3						$1s^2 2s^2 2p^3$
Oxygen, O	8	2	2 4						$1s^2 2s^2 2p^4$
Fluorine, F	9	2	2 5						$1s^2 2s^2 2p^5$
Neon, Ne	10	2	2 6						$1s^2 2s^2 2p^6$
Sodium, Na	11	2	2 6	1					$1s^2 2s^2 2p^6 3s^1$
Magnesium, Mg	12	2	2 6	2					$1s^2 2s^2 2p^6 3s^2$
Aluminium, Al	13	2	2 6	2 1					$1s^2 2s^2 2p^6 3s^2 3p^1$
Silicon, Si	14	2	2 6	2 2					$1s^2 2s^2 2p^6 3s^2 3p^2$
Phosphorous, P	15	2	2 6	2 3					$1s^2 2s^2 2p^6 3s^2 3p^3$
Sulphur, S	16	2	2 6	2 4					$1s^2 2s^2 2p^6 3s^2 3p^4$
Chlorine, Cl	17	2	2 6	2 5					$1s^2 2s^2 2p^6 3s^2 3p^5$
Argon, Ar	18	2	2 6	2 6					$1s^2 2s^2 2p^6 3s^2 3p^6$
Potassium, K	19	2	2 6	2 6	1				$1s^2 2s^2 2p^6 3s^2 3p^6 4s^1$
Calcium, Ca	20	2	2 6	2 6	2				$1s^2 2s^2 2p^6 3s^2 3p^6 4s^2$
Scandium, Sc	21	2	2 6	2 6 1	2				$1s^2 2s^2 2p^6 3s^2 3p^6 3d^1 4s^2$
Titanium, Ti	22	2	2 6	2 6 2	2				$1s^2 2s^2 2p^6 3s^2 3p^6 3d^2 4s^2$
Vanadium, V	23	2	2 6	2 6 3	2				$1s^2 2s^2 2p^6 3s^2 3p^6 3d^3 4s^2$
Chromium, Cr	24	2	2 6	2 6 5	1				$1s^2 2s^2 2p^6 3s^2 3p^6 3d^5 4s^1$
Manganese, Mu	25	2	2 6	2 6 5	2				$1s^2 2s^2 2p^6 3s^2 3p^6 3d^5 4s^2$
Iron, Fe	26	2	2 6	2 6 6	2				$1s^2 2s^2 2p^6 3s^2 3p^6 3d^6 4s^2$
Cobalt, Co	27	2	2 6	2 6 7	2				$1s^2 2s^2 2p^6 3s^2 3p^6 3d^7 4s^2$
Nickel, Ni	28	2	2 6	2 6 8	2				$1s^2 2s^2 2p^6 3s^2 3p^6 3d^8 4s^2$
Copper, Cu	29	2	2 6	2 6 10	1				$1s^2 2s^2 2p^6 3s^2 3p^6 3d^{10} 4s^1$
Zinc, Zn	30	2	2 6	2 6 10	2				$1s^2 2s^2 2p^6 3s^2 3p^6 3d^{10} 4s^2$
Gallium, Ga	31	2	2 6	2 6 10	2 1				$1s^2 2s^2 2p^6 3s^2 3p^6 3d^{10} 4s^2 4p^1$
Germanium, Ge	32	2	2 6	2 6 10	2 2				$1s^2 2s^2 2p^6 3s^2 3p^6 3d^{10} 4s^2 4p^2$
Arsenic, As	33	2	2 6	2 6 10	2 3				$1s^2 2s^2 2p^6 3s^2 3p^6 3d^{10} 4s^2 4p^3$
Xenon, Xe	54	2	2 6	2 6 6	2 6 10 – 2 6				$1s^2 2s^2 2p^6 3s^2 3p^6 3d^6 4s^2 4p^6$ $4d^{10} 5s^2 5d^6$
Tungsten, W	74	2	2 6	2 6 10	2 6 10 142 6 4–2				$1s^2 2s^2 2p^6 3s^2 3p^6 3d^{10} 4s^2 4p^6$ $4d^{10} 4f^{14} 5s^2 5p^6 5d^4 6s^2$

The groups of elements in the separate horizontal blocks called the lanthanide series and actinide series actually belong to periods 6 and 7, respectively, but listing them in their respective periods would make the table unbalanced in shape.

Table 1.4 *Periodic Table of Elements*

Periodic Table of Elements ⟶ Nonmetal

Atomic number of each element is shown

1 H	II A	III B	IV B	V B	VI B	VII B	VIII			I B	II B	III A	IV A	V A	VI A	VII A	2 He
3 Li	4 Be					Metal	Non-Metal	Inter-mediate				5 B	6 C	7 N	8 O	9 F	10 Ne
11 Na	12 Mg	III B	IV B	V B	VI B	VII B	VIII	I B	II B			13 Al	14 Si	15 P	16 S	17 Cl	18 Ar
19 K	20 Ca	21 Sc	22 Ti	23 V	24 Cr	25 Mn	26 Fe	27 Co	28 Ni	29 Cu	30 Zn	31 Ga	32 Ge	33 As	34 Se	35 Br	36 Kr
37 Rb	38 Sr	39 Y	40 Zr	41 Nb	42 Mo	43 Tc	44 Ru	45 Rh	46 Pd	47 Ag	48 Cd	49 In	50 Sn	51 Sb	52 Te	53 I	54 Xe
55 Cs	56 Ba	57-71 Lanthauide series	72 Hf	73 Ta	74 W	75 Re	76 Os	77 Ir	78 Pt	79 Au	80 Hg	81 Tl	82 Pb	83 Bi	84 Po	85 At	86 Rn
87 Fr	88 Ra	89-103 Actinide series															

Lanthanide series		57 La	58 Ce	59 Pr	60 Nd	61 Pm	62 Sm	63 Eu	64 Gd	65 Tb	66 Dy	67 Ho	68 Er	69 Tm	70 Yb	71 Lu
Actinide series		89 Ac	90 Th	91 Pa	92 U	93 Np	94 Pu	95 Am	96 Cm	97 Bk	98 Cf	99 Es	100 Fm	101 Md	102 No	103 Lr

Dr. Mendeleev, a Russian scientist, is the author of this periodic table (Table 1.4).

Elements in the periodic table with electronic number greater than 92 do not exist is the nature. They are produced by nuclear reactions.

KEY POINTS TO REMEMBER

- Atomic number = number of electrons = number of protons
- Atomic weight (amu) = protons + neutrons
- Electron mass, $m = 9.11 \times 10^{-31}$ kg
- Planck's constant, $h = 6.63 \times 10^{-34}$ Js
- Velocity of light in a vacuum, $c = 3 \times 10^8$ cm/s
- Electron charge $e = 1.602 \times 10^{-19}$ C
- Avogadro's number, $N_A = 6.033 \times 10^{23}$ molecules/mol

❏ Thomson model—an atom, a sphere in which electrons are dispersed in positively charged matter.

❏ Rutherford's model—a very small positively charged nucleus surrounded by moving electrons at high speed. He suggested that the force of attraction between negatively charged electrons and positively charged nucleus was balanced by the centrifugal force attained by the electrons.

❏ Bohr atomic model—electrons move only in circular orbits; electrons emit or absorb energy when they change position from one orbit to another.

❏ The electrostatic force between proton and electron, $F = Ze^2/4\pi\varepsilon_0 r^2$, where Z is the number of electrons, e is the electron charge, r is the radius, ε_0 is the permittivity of free space, $1/4\pi\varepsilon_0 = 9 \times 10^9$ in MKS units.

❏ Energy,

$$E = \frac{mZ^2 e^4}{8\varepsilon_0^2 h^2 h^2},$$

where m = mass = $9.1085b \times 10^{-31}$ kg
  h = Planck's constant = 6.62×10^{-34}

❏ Sommerfeld–Wilson atomic model takes into account principal quantum number (n), the second quantum number (l), circular orbits and elliptical orbits. Vector model on quantum model takes into account.

n = principal quantum number
l = second (azimuthal) quantum number
m_1 = orbital magnetic quantum number
m_s = magnetic spin quantum number

MULTIPLE CHOICE QUESTIONS

1. How many isotopes of hydrogen exist in nature?

 (a) 4   (c) 2
 (b) 3   (d) None of these

2. What is the average atomic weight of chlorine?

 (a) 36.5   (c) 35.5
 (b) 36.0   (d) None of these

3. Match the list of elements with atomic number

A	B
I Fluorine	19
II Potassium	24
III Chromium	9
IV Zinc	30

	I	II	III	IV
(a)	9	19	24	30
(b)	19	9	30	24
(c)	19	24	30	9

 (d) None of these

4. What is the electron configuration of potassium?

 (a) $1s^2 2s^2 2p^6 3s^2 3p^6 3d^1$
 (b) $1s^2 2s^2 2p^6 3s^2 3p^5 3d^2$
 (c) $1s^2 2s^2 2p^6 3s^2 3p^6 4s^1$
 (d) None of these

5. What is the mass of one electron?

   (a) 9.11×10^{-30} kg   (c) 9.11×10^{-32} kg

   (b) 9.11×10^{-31} kg   (d) None of these

6. For a hydrogen atom, energy level of an electron in the second orbit is

   (a) 13.6 eV   (c) 1.52 eV

   (b) 3.4 eV   (d) None of these

7. If l is the orbital quantum number, how many electrons can be present in a subshell of l orbital quantum number

   (a) $2(l + 1)$ (c) $2(2l - 1)$

   (b) $2(2l + 1)$ (d) None of these

Answers

1. (b)   2. (c)   3. (a)   4. (c)   5. (b)   6. (b)   7. (b)

REVIEW QUESTIONS

1. Differentiate between Thomson atomic model and Rutherford's atomic model.

2. Write electronic configuration of the following elements:

Fe, Ni and W.

3. Discuss briefly various quantum numbers.

4. What are the merits and demerits of Bohr's model and Sommerfeld model of atomic structure?

5. What is the maximum number of electrons in a subshell?

6. What are group III A and group IV A elements? What are their characteristics?

7. Define the followings:

Nucleus, proton, neutron and molecule.

8. What is the difference between atomic weight and atomic number?

9. Why Thompson model of atomic structure is not accepted?

10. State Bohr's postulates.

ATOMIC BONDING AND CRYSTAL STRUCTURE

2

2.1 INTRODUCTION

The properties of any material are highly dependent on the type of bond between the atoms and the arrangement of atoms in the unit cell of a lattice in the crystal. Most of the solid materials are either crystalline (e.g. copper, aluminium, zinc and iron) or non-crystalline, i.e. amorphous (e.g. glasses, plastics and wood) in nature. Graphite is soft and greasy, while diamond is the hardest material, even though both are made of carbon atoms. The change in the behaviour of same carbon atom in graphite and diamond is directly attributed to the type of interatomic bonding.

Many mechanical properties such as strength, ductility and hardness depend upon the geometry of the crystal, i.e. how the atoms are arranged in the unit cell, which is repeated orderly in a three-dimensional structure called 'lattice'. Unit cells are of different shapes such as cubic, hexagonal and tetragonal, and the arrangement of atoms in a unit cell plays the most important part of deciding the properties of solids.

This chapter discusses various directions in crystal and identification of various planes using Miller indices. Important directions in crystal along which the linear atomic density is maximum and the plane on which planar atomic density is maximum are characterized so as to find the crystallographic slip lines and slip planes.

Generally, the solids are polycrystalline, yet single crystals exist in nature and can also be grown artificially in a laboratory.

Common structures of crystalline solids such as simple cubic, body-centred cubic, hexagonal, close packed and face-centred cubic will be discussed in details. Packing factors of these structures, along with linear atomic density along various directions and planar atomic density on various planes will be discussed so as to identify the planes and directions of interest. The density calculations of various solids will also be dealt with. The mechanical properties of single crystals also form a part of this chapter.

2.2 CLASSIFICATION OF MATERIALS

Materials are generally classified as (1) crystalline and (2) non-crystalline or amorphous. Metals are mostly crystalline, e.g. copper, zinc, aluminium, iron, chromium and so on, while non-metals like wood, plastic and paper are non-crystalline.

Crystalline solids have periodically repeated arrangement of atoms and are further classified as (1) monocrystalline, i.e. single crystal and (2) polycrystalline.

Most of the materials in engineering applications are polycrystalline, while monocrystalline material which has single crystal such as single crystal of 'quartz' is used in producing ultrasonic waves and a single crystal of silicon is employed in making semiconductor strain gauge or is used in electronic microcircuits.

The smallest visible part of a material is made up of a large number of crystals. The crystals are of different shapes and sizes and are separated by grain boundaries. These crystals are randomly oriented. Each crystal is composed of basic structural elements called 'unit cells', as shown in Figure 2.1(a) and (b).

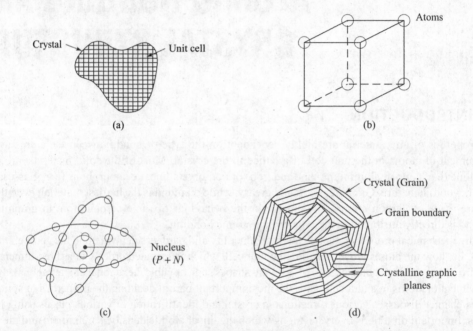

Figure 2.1 *Atomic Structure (a) Crystal and Unit Cell (b) Unit Cell (c) Electron Orbits and Nucleus (d) Polycrystalline Material*

The atomic structure consists of a nucleus (containing protons and neutrons) surrounded by oscillating electrons in orbits as shown in Figure 2.1(c).

Figure 2.1(d) shows a visible part of a solid; when seen under a microstructure, crystals (or grains) separated by grain boundaries can be observed. The crystals are randomly oriented as shown by random orientation of crystallographic planes in the crystals.

2.3 ATOMIC STRUCTURE

The nucleus of an atom contains protons and neutrons, and it is surrounded by electrons moving in orbits. Both electrons and protons are electrically charged: -1.6×10^{-19} C for electrons and $+1.6 \times 10^{-19}$ C for protons. Both protons and neutrons in the nucleus have approximately the same mass, i.e. 1.67×10^{-27} kg, but the mass of one electron is approximately 9.11×10^{-31} kg.

The number of protons present in the nuclei gives the atomic number (Z), which is equal to the number of electrons.

$Z = 1$ for hydrogen

$Z = 84$ for plutonium, the element with highest atomic number

Mass of one atom = sum of the masses of protons and neutrons

$A = Z + N$ = protons + neutrons

2.3.1 Isotope

Although the number of protons remains the same for all atoms of a given element, the number of neutrons may vary. The atoms of the same element having two or more different atomic masses are called 'isotopes'. The atomic weight of an element corresponds to the *weighted average* of the atomic masses of the naturally occurring isotopes of the atoms.

Atomic mass unit (amu) is used to calculate the atomic weights. 1 amu = $1/12 \times$ atomic mass of most common isotope of carbon (12 C), i.e. $A = 12$. The atomic weight of an element or the molecular weight of a compound may be specified on the basis of amu per atom (or molecules) or mass per mole of the material.

In one mole of a material, there are 6.023×10^{23} (Avogadro's number) atoms or molecules.

1 amu/atom or molecule = 1 g/mol.

Example: Atomic weight of aluminium is 26.98 amu/atom or 26.98 g/mol.

2.4 SPACE LATTICE

Space lattice is defined as an infinite array of points in three-dimensional space, in which each point is identically located with respect to the other points. A study of space lattice is helpful in understanding the crystal structure of the existing materials.

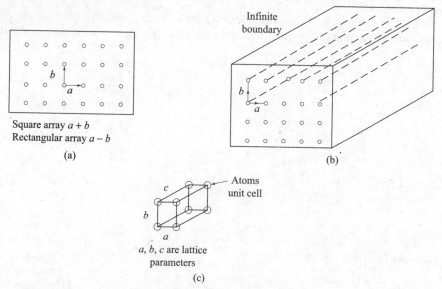

Infinite boundary

Square array $a + b$
Rectangular array $a - b$

(a)

(b)

Atoms
unit cell

a, b, c are lattice parameters

(c)

Figure 2.2 *(a) Two-dimensional Array (b) Three-dimensional Space Lattice (c) Three-dimensional unit cell*

Repeated translational movement of three non-coplanar vectors (a, b, c) results into a three-dimensional space lattice.

In a cubic array, $\qquad\qquad\qquad\qquad\qquad\qquad a = b = c$

In a non-cubic array, $\qquad\qquad\qquad\qquad\qquad a \neq b \neq c$

The *smallest unit* formed by joining these identically spaced points is known as '*unit cell*', formed by three geometrical vectors a, b and c [Figure 2.2(a)–(c)].

Example: For element polonium (Po), there is a simple cubic array with atoms at the corners as shown in Figure 2.3(a). Hexagonal array represents the sheet form structure of graphite as shown in Figure 2.3(b).

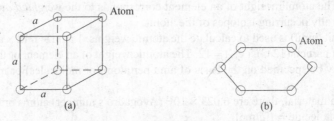

(a)   (b)

Figure 2.3 *(a) Cubic Array a = b = c for Polonium (b) Hexagonal Array Sheet Structure for Graphite*

2.5 BASIS

Basis is defined by the way of filling up of points of space lattice by atoms. Space lattice combined with basis generates a unit cell.

Unit cells are monoatomic (one atom occupies each lattice point), diatomic (two atoms occupy each lattice point) and multiatomic (many atoms occupy each lattice point) as shown in Figure 2.4(a)–(c).

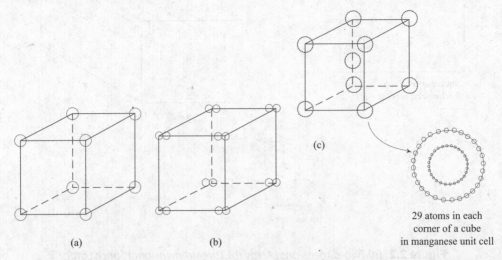

(c)

29 atoms in each corner of a cube in manganese unit cell

(a)   (b)

Figure 2.4 *(a) Monoatomic Unit Cell (b) Diatomic Unit Cell (c) Multiatomic Unit Cell*

2.5.1 Basis for Some Materials

Basis for some materials are listed in Table 2.1.

Table 2.1 *Basis for Some Materials*

Element	Symbol	
Polonium	Po	1 atom per lattice point
Aluminium	Al	1 atom per lattice point
Chromium	Cr	1 atom per lattice point
Silicon	Si	2 atoms per lattice point
Manganese	Mn	29 atoms per lattice point and 29 atoms at body centre
Proteins (combinations of amino acids)	—	Thousands of atoms per lattice point

Diatomic and multiatomic crystals are known as molecular crystals. In manganese (Mn) unit cell, there are 29 atoms at each corner and 29 atoms at the body centre of the cube (Figure 2.5). In a unit cell of manganese, there are

$$29 \times \frac{8}{8} + 29 \text{ (at body centre)} = 58 \text{ atoms}$$

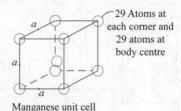

29 Atoms at each corner and 29 atoms at body centre

Manganese unit cell

Figure 2.5 *Manganese Unit Cell*

2.6 BRAVAIS CRYSTAL STRUCTURE

Geometrics of the crystal are defined in terms of linear dimension a, b and c, along the three axis, x, y and z, and by three angular parameters, α, β and γ, i.e. angle between x–y, y–z and z–x axis as shown in Figure 2.6.

Lattice parameters a, b and c along x, y and z are also shown in Figure 2.6.

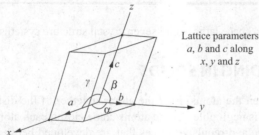

Lattice parameters a, b and c along x, y and z

Figure 2.6 *α, β and γ Angles Between x–y, y–z and z–x Axis*

Table 2.2 *Bravais Crystal System*

Unit Cell	Space Lattice	Abbreviation	Example
1. Cubic $a=b=c$	1. Simple cubic 2. Body-centred cubic 3. Face-centred cubic	SC BCC FCC	Po Li, Na, Cr, Mo, W, Fe Ni, Cu, Ag, Al, Au, Pb
2. Tetragonal $a=b\neq c$ $\alpha=\beta=\gamma=90°$	4. Simple tetragonal 5. Body-centred tetragonal	ST BCT	 —White Sn
3. Orthorhombic $a\neq b\neq c$ $\alpha=\beta=\gamma=90°$	6. Simple orthorhombic 7. End-centred orthorhombic 8. Body-centred orthorhombic 9. Face-centred orthorhombic	SO ECO BCO FCO	Sb, Bi S, Ga
4. Rhombohedral $a=b=c$ $\alpha=\beta=\gamma\neq90°$	10. Simple rhombohedral	SR	
5. Hexagonal $a=b\neq c$ $\alpha=120°$ $\gamma=90°$ (Figure 2.7)	11. Hexagonal	H	Se, graphite, La

Figure 2.7

6. Monoclinic $a\neq b\neq c$ $\alpha=\beta=90°$ $\gamma\neq90°$	12. Simple monoclinic (points at eight corners of unit cell) 13. End-centred monoclinic (points at eight corners and at two face centres opposite to each other)	SM ECM	Rochelle salt S
7. Triclinic $a\neq b\neq c$ $\alpha\neq\beta\neq\gamma\neq90°$	14. Simple triclinic (points at eight corners of unit cell)		Triclinic crystal structure is least symmetric

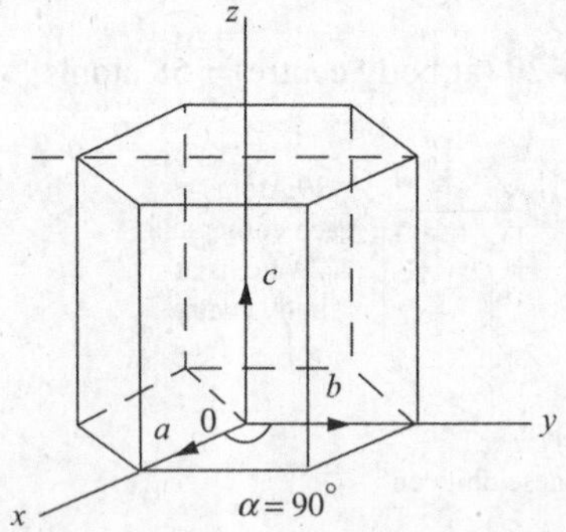

Bravais has classified 14 space lattices into seven crystal structure systems, as described in Table 2.2.

2.7 ATOMIC BONDING IN SOLIDS

Interatomic forces (between the atoms) bind the atoms together. If the distance between the atoms is large, then the interaction is negligible. As the atoms come closer, each atom exerts forces on the other atoms. These are attractive and repulsive forces that are developed between them. The magnitude of each force is a function of the interatomic distance.

Origin of the force P_A, force of attraction depends upon the type of bonding that exist between the two atoms. The magnitude of the force varies with the distance. Finally, the outer shells of the two atoms begin to overlap and a strong repulsive force P_R comes into play.

Net force between two atoms

$$P_N = P_A + P_R$$

At,

$$r = r_0, P_N = 0$$

A state of equilibrium exists between two atoms, i.e. force of attraction and force of repulsion [Figure 2.8(a)] balance each other. The centres of two atoms will remain separated by r_0, i.e. equilibrium spacing.

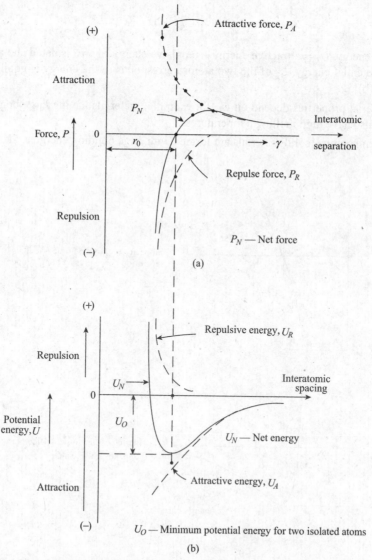

Figure 2.8 *(a) Net Force Versus Interatomic Distance (b) Potential Energy Versus Interatomic Distance*

For many atoms, $r_0 \cong 0.3$ nm (3 Å)

In the equilibrium position, the two atoms will counteract any attempt to separate them by an attractive force P_A or to push them closer by a repulsive force, P_R.

Potential energy between the two atoms is minimum at equilibrium spacing.

Potential energy, $U = \int P dr$

$$U_N = \int_\alpha^r P_N dr = \int_\alpha^r P_A dr + \int_\alpha^r P_R dr$$

$$= U_A + U_R$$

Net potential energy, U_N = attractive energy + repulsive energy of two isolated and adjacent atoms. The minimum potential energy, U_0 of the two atoms corresponds to the energy at equilibrium spacing of r_0 [Figure 2.8(b)].

1. Many material properties depend on U_0, for example, materials having large bonding energies, typically, also have high melting temperatures.

2. At room temperature, solid materials are formed with large bonding energies.

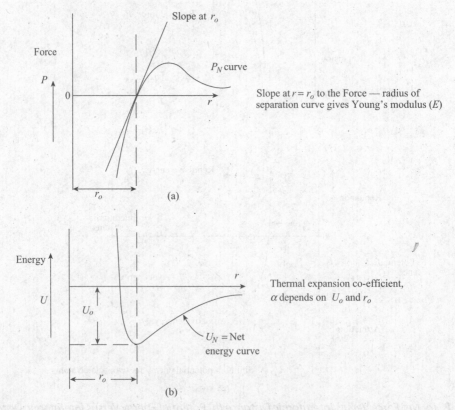

Figure 2.9 *(a) Net Force Versus Interatomic Distance Curve (b) Net Energy Versus Interatomic Curve*

3. For small energies, a gaseous state is formed.
4. For liquid substances, bonding energy is between high energies for solid materials and small energies for gaseous substances.
5. Young's modulus (E) or stiffness of the material is dependent on the slope of the force versus interatomic separation curve, i.e. slope at r_0 defines Young's modulus (E) at atomic scale as shown in Figure 2.9(a).
6. Coefficient of thermal expansions α, depends on minimum potential energy, U_0 and equilibrium interatomic spacing, r_0 as shown in Figure 2.9(b).

2.8 PRIMARY INTERATOMIC BONDING

There are three types of primary bonding: (1) ionic bonding, (2) covalent bonding, and (3) metallic bonding.

2.8.1 Ionic Bonding

Ionic bonding is found in compounds that are composed of both metallic and non-metallic elements. Atoms of metallic elements easily give up their valency electrons to the non-metallic atoms. In this process, all the atoms require stable or insert gas configuration and in addition an electrical charge; that is, they become 'ions'. The atom that contributes the electrons is left with a net positive charge and is called a 'cation', while the atom that accepts the electrons acquires a net negative charge and is called an 'anion'. The oppositely charged ions are then attracted each other and produce the ionic bond. For example, attraction between sodium and chloride ions produces sodium chloride.

Figure 2.10 shows the formation of ionic bond in sodium chloride. Ionic bonds have the following characteristics:

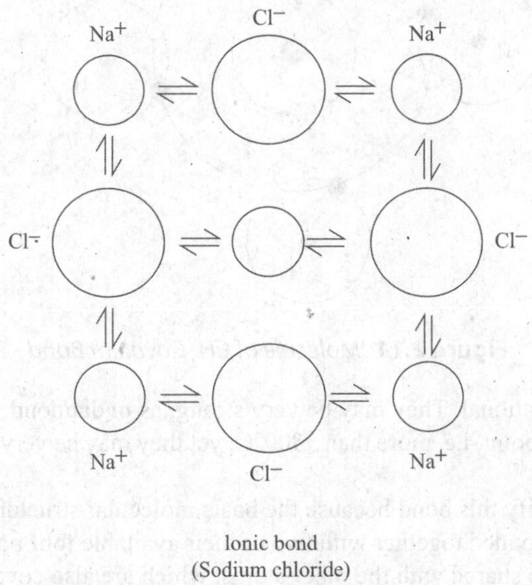

lonic bond
(Sodium chloride)

Figure 2.10 *Formation of Ionic Bond in Sodium Chloride*

1. They are brittle in nature, i.e. when force is applied to a sodium chloride crystal, the electrical balance is upset and the material breaks.
2. They are poor in electrical conductivity (electrical charge is transferred by the movement of entire ions, which do not move as easily as electrons).
3. Many ceramic materials and minerals are at least partly bonded by ionic bonds.
4. Ionic bonding is non-directional, i.e. magnitude of bond is equal in all directions.
5. Ionic material is stable.

Other solids having ionic bonds are potassium oxide (K_2O), cupric oxide (CuO), chromous oxide (CrO_2), molybdenum fluoride (MoF_2) and so on.

2.8.2 Covalent Bonding

In covalent bonding stable electron configurations are assumed by sharing of electrons between the adjacent atoms. Two atoms that are covalently bonded will contribute each other at least one electron to the bond and the shared electrons may be considered belonging to both the atoms.

Molecules of CH_4 carbon atom have four valency electrons, whereas each of four hydrogen atoms has a single valency electron. Now, carbon has four additional shared electrons (one from each hydrogen atom) for a total of eight valency electrons. The number of covalent bonds that are possible for a particular atom is determined by the number of valence electrons (Figure 2.11).

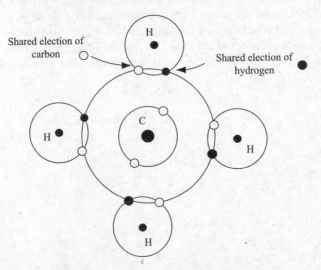

Figure 2.11 *Molecule of CH_4 Covalent Bond*

Covalent bonds are directional. They may be very strong, as in diamond, which is the hardest material and has a high melting point, i.e. more than 3500°C, yet they may be very weak as in bismuth, which melts at 270°C.

Polymeric materials typify this bond because the basic molecular structure is a long chain of carbon atoms that are covalently bonded together with two of their available four bonds per atom. The remaining two bonds normally are shared with the other atoms, which are also covalently bonded.

It is possible to have interatomic bonds that are partially ionic and partially covalent and in fact very few compounds exhibit pure ionic or pure covalent bonding.

Example: A silicon atom, which has a valence of 4, obtains eight electrons in its outer energy shell by sharing its electrons with four surrounding silicon atoms (Figure 2.12).

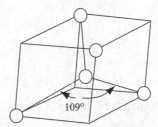

Figure 2.12 *Covalent Bonds Silicon-tetrahedral Structure*

Each silicon atom is bonded to four neighbouring atoms by four covalent bonds. This arrangement produces a tetrahedron, with angles of 109° between covalent bonds. Diamond develops tetrahedral bond angle of 109.5°. For methane (CH_4) also, the bond angle is 109°.

2.8.3 Metallic Bonding

Metallic materials have one, two or at the most three valence electrons. These valence electrons are not bound to any particular atoms in the solid and are more or less free to drift throughout the entire space of the metal. These free electrons form a *sea of electrons* surrounding the metallic atoms. The remaining non-valence electrons and atomic nuclei form the core of positively charged ions. The net positive charge is equal in magnitude to the total valence electrons charge per atom. The free electrons shield the positively charged ion-cores from mutually repulsive electrostatic forces. Metallic bond is non-directional. Free electrons *act as an adhesive* to hold ion-cores together (Figure 2.13).

Metals are good conductors of heat and electricity due to the presence of free electrons. Ionic- and covalent-bonded materials are electrical and thermal insulators because of the absence of free electrons.

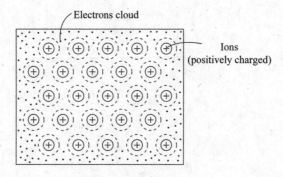

Figure 2.13 *Metallic Bond*

2.8.4 Molecules

A molecule may be defined as a 'group of atoms' that are bonded together by strong primary bonds (Figure 2.14).

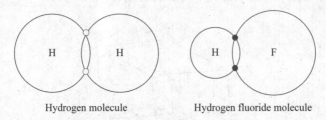

Hydrogen molecule   Hydrogen fluoride molecule

Figure 2.14 *Group of Atoms*

2.8.5 Van der Waals Bonding

Van der Waals bonds join molecules or groups of atoms by *weak electrostatic attractions*. Many plastics, ceramics, water and many other molecules are permanently polarized, i.e. some portions of the molecule tend to be positively charged, while other portions are negatively charged. The electrostatic attraction between the positively charged ions of one molecule and the negatively charged ions of another molecule weakly bond the two molecules together. Van der Waals bond is a secondary bond, but within the molecule or group of atoms these are joined by strong covalent or ionic bonds. Heating water to the boiling point breaks the Van der Waals bonds and changes water to steam. These bonds can dramatically change the properties of the materials. For example, long-chain molecules of polyvinyl chloride (PVC) are bonded to one another by Van der Waals bonds. PVC can be reformed significantly by breaking only the Van der Waals bonds.

In the case of H_2O, the nucleus of hydrogen, which has a proton (positively charged) is attracted towards the unshared, negatively charged electrons of oxygen as shown in Figure 2.15. Due to these attractions, molecules of water are held together.

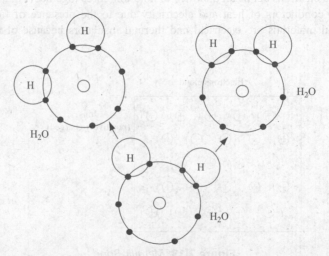

Figure 2.15 *Hydrogen Nucleus Attracted Towards Unshared Electrons of Oxygen*

2.9 STRUCTURES OF CRYSTALLINE SOLIDS

Solid materials may be classified according to the repetitive order in which the atoms or ions are arranged with respect to one another and the arrangement of atoms or ions in the unit cell. A periodic array exists over a long range. Upon solidification from molten state, the atoms position themselves in a repetitive three-dimensional network in which each atom is bonded to its nearest neighbouring atoms.

All metals, many ceramic materials and some polymers form crystalline structures under normal solidification process. For non-crystalline materials, long-range atomic order is absent; these are amorphous materials.

Some of the properties of crystalline solids depend on the crystal structure of the material. There are a large number of different crystal structures, all having long-range atomic order, varying from relatively simple structures for metals to exceedingly complex structures for some ceramic and polymeric materials.

A crystalline structure is represented by a combination of *atomic hard spheres model,* in which the spheres that represent nearest neighbouring atoms are touching one another. Many a times, the term 'space lattice' is used in the context of crystal structure, lattice or three-dimensional array of points that coincides with the position of atoms (i.e. centres of spheres).

2.9.1 Unit Cells

A unit cell is selected to represent the symmetry of crystal structure, where all atom positions in the crystal may be generated by translation of the unit cell by integral distances along each of the edges.

A unit cell is the basic structural unit or a building block in the crystal structure and defines the crystal structure by virtue of its geometry and the atomic positions within the crystal.

Atomic bonding in the group of materials is metallic and therefore non-directional. Consequently, there are no restrictions as to the number and positions of the neighbouring atoms (touching atoms); this leads to a large number of nearest neighbours, which is responsible for dense atomic packing for most of the metallic crystal structures.

Three relatively simple structures are found for most of the common metals: face-centred cubic(FCC), body-centred cubic(BCC) and hexagonal close packed(HCP).

Important parameters like crystal structure, atomic weight, atomic number and atomic radii for commonly used elements are given in Table 2.3.

2.9.2 Face-centred Cubic (FCC) Structure

In an FCC structure, each corner atom is shared among eight units cells, whereas face-centred atom belongs to two unit cells. Elements, which possess FCC structures are copper, gold, aluminium, lead, nickel, silver, platinum and so on. Two important properties of any crystal structure are (1) co-ordination number and (2) atomic packing factor (APF). For Metals, each atom has the same number of nearest neighbour or touching atoms, which is co-ordination number. For FCC, the co-ordination number is 12. Figure 2.16(a) shows the arrangement of atoms in an FCC structure and Figure 2.16(b) shows that the co-ordination number of FCC is 12.

Now, let us analyze how many atoms touch the atom A marked in Figure 2.16(a)

1. Four corner atoms along the half plane of atom *A*.
2. Four face-centred atoms touch the lower half surface of atom *A*.

Table 2.3 *Important Parameters of Common Elements*

Element	Symbol	Atomic Weight (g/mol)	Atomic Number	Atomic Radius (nm)	Structure
Aluminium	Al	26.98	13	0.143	FCC
Boron	B	10.81	5	0.023	Rhomb
Carbon	C	12.011	6	0.071	Hex
Chromium	Cr	52.00	24	0.125	BCC
Cobalt	Co	58.93	27	0.125	HCP
Copper	Cu	63.54	29	0.128	FCC
Gold	Au	196.97	79	0.144	FCC
Germanium	Ge	72.59	32	0.122	Dia. Cubic
Magnesium	Mg	24.31	12	0.160	HCP
Iron (α)	Fe	55.85	26	0.124	BCC
Lead	Pb	207.2	82	0.175	FCC
Manganese	Mn	54.94	25	0.112	BCC
Molybdenum	Mo	95.94	42	0.136	BCC
Nickel	Ni	58.70	28	0.125	FCC
Platinum	Pt	195.09	78	0.139	FCC
Phosphorous	P	30.97	15	0.109	Ortho
Silver	Ag	107.87	47	0.144	FCC
Silicon	Si	28.09	14	0.118	Dia. cubic
Tin	Sn	118.69	50	0.151	Tetra
Tungsten	W	183.85	74	0.137	BCC
Titanium	Ti	47.88	22	0.145	HCP
Vanadium	V	50.94	23	0.132	BCC
Zinc	Zn	65.39	30	0.133	HCP
Zirconium	Zr	91.22	40	0.159	HCP

3. Four face-centred atoms touch the upper half surface of atom A, of the unit cell above the unit cell shown in the figure.

So, the number of atoms in each unit cell of FCC structure

$$= 8 \times \frac{1}{8} \text{(at corners)} + 6 \times \frac{1}{2} \text{(at face centres)}$$

$$= 4$$

Parameter a of unit cell, $\sqrt{2}a = 4r$, where r is the atomic radius or $a = 2\sqrt{2}r$.

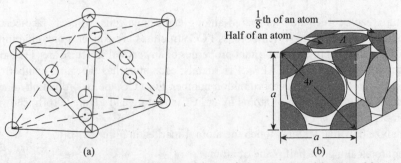

(a)   (b)

Figure 2.16 *(a) FCC Structure (b) FCC Structure (Showing Touching Neighbouring Atoms)*

2.9.3 Body-centred Cubic (BCC) Structure

In a BCC structure, there are atoms at each of eight corners. Each atom at the corner is shared by eight unit cells. One atom is located at the body centre of the unit cell as shown in Figure 2.17(a). Figure 2.17(b) shows that body centre atom of the unit cell is touching eight nearest neighbouring atoms.

Number of atoms in each BCC unit cell

$$= 8 \times \frac{1}{8} \text{ (corner)} + 1 \text{(at centre)}$$

$$= 2$$

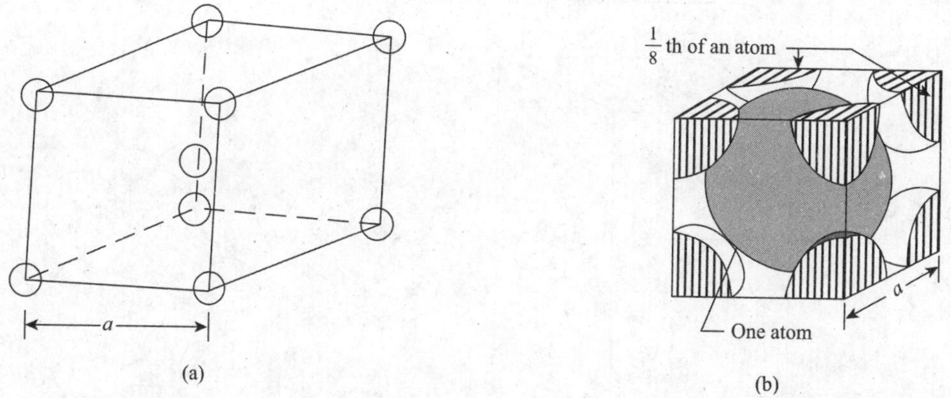

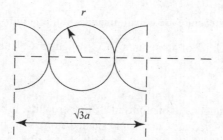

(a)   (b)

Figure 2.17 *(a) Body-centered Cubic (b) BCC Body-centered Atom is Touched by Eight Corner Atoms*

Along the body diagonal, the atoms are arranged as shown in Figure 2.18. Along the body diagonals, three atoms touch each other as shown in Figure 2.18.

Lattice parameter

$$\sqrt{3}\,a = 4r$$

$$a = \frac{4}{\sqrt{3}}r = 2.31 \times r$$

where r is the atomic radius. Chromium, iron (α), tungsten and vanadium are metals with BCC structure.

Figure 2.18 *Body Diagonal of BCC*

2.9.4 Hexagonal Close-packed (HCP) Structure

In an HCP structure, top and bottom faces of the unit cell consist of six atoms that form regular hexagon and surround a single atom at the centre of the face. Another plane that provides three additional atoms to the unit cell is situated between the top and the bottom planes. The atoms in the mid plane have nearest neighbours in both the adjacent two-plane (top and bottom faces) sides of hexagon a and the height of HCP cell is $c = 1.633a$, as shown in Figure 2.19(a). Moreover, Figure 2.19(b) shows that one atom at the centre of the top face is surrounded by six neighbouring atoms in the plane of the face and three central atoms of the lower unit cell and three central atoms of the upper unit cell. Therefore, the co-ordination number of HCP is 12.

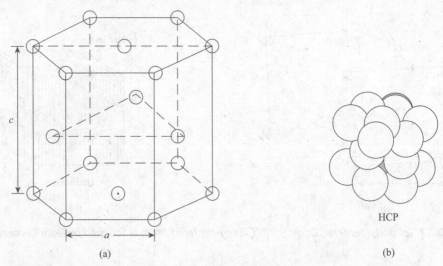

(a)   (b)

Figure 2.19 *(a) HCP Unit Cell (b) Touching Atoms in HCP Unit Cell*

Number of atoms in an HCP unit cell

$$= 2 \times 6 \times \frac{1}{6} \text{ (corner atoms at the top and bottom)}$$

$$+ 2 \times \frac{1}{2} \text{ (face-centred atoms at the top and bottom faces)}$$

$$+ 3 \text{ atoms in the central plane of unit cell}$$

$$= 6$$

Examples of metals with HCP structure are cobalt, magnesium, titanium, zinc and zirconium.

Example 2.1 Show the packing of atoms in a BCC structure. Calculate tpacking factor of a BCC crystal structure.

Solution:

Figure 2.20(a) shows the arrangement of atoms in a BCC structure. In reality, atoms touch each other, represented by spheres of atomic radius. Completely shaded atom is the body-centred atom. If we visualize the body diagonal, then all corner atoms touch the body-centred atom as shown by the diagonal.

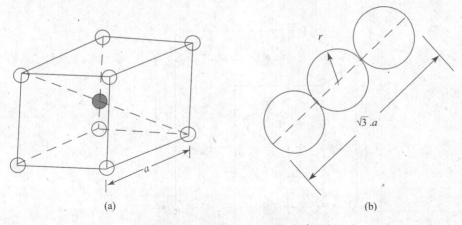

(a)   (b)

Figure 2.20 *Body Diagonal of BCC*

Length of diagonal $= \sqrt{a^2 + a^2 + a^2}$

$$= \sqrt{3}\,a \qquad\qquad\qquad\qquad \text{[Figure 2.20(b)]}$$

Radius of atom, $r = \dfrac{\sqrt{3}\,a}{4}$

$$= 0.4330a$$

Number of atoms in one unit lattice $= 2$

Volume of atoms $= 2 \times \dfrac{\pi 4}{3} \times r^3 = \dfrac{8\pi}{3} \times (0.433a)^3$

$$= 0.680a^3$$

Packing factor, APF $= \dfrac{0.680a^3}{a^3} = 0.680$

Example 2.2   Show the packing of atoms in an HCP structure. Explain the co-ordination number of an HCP structure. Calculate its packing factor, if $c = 1.633a$.

Solution:

Figure 2.21 shows the hexagonal close-packed structure (HCP), in which there are six atoms surrounding the central atom (shaded) on the top surface or the bottom surface. There are three body-centred atoms 2, 3 and 4 (shown by complete dark spheres). One central atom at the top is touched by six surrounding atoms of the same top surface and by three body-centred atoms of the unit cell as shown plus by three more body-centred atoms of the unit cell above the unit cell shown; so, 12 atoms touch the central top surface atom. Therefore, the co-ordination number of an HCP structure is 12.

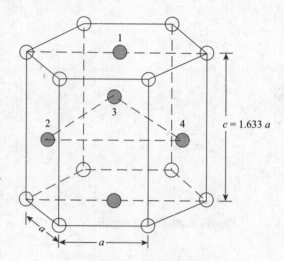

Figure 2.21 *HCP Structure*

Number of atoms in one unit cell

$$= 6 \times \frac{1}{6}(\text{top surface}) + 6 \times \frac{1}{6}(\text{bottom surface})$$

$$+ \frac{1}{2}(\text{top surface}) + \frac{1}{2}(\text{bottom surface})$$

$$+ 3 \text{ body-centred atoms} = 6$$

In reality, atoms touch each other as shown in Figure 2.22. It shows how the atoms touch each other on the top or bottom hexagonal surfaces.

Side of hexagonal $= a$

Surface area $= \frac{1}{2} \times a \times 0.866a \times 6 = 2.598a^2$

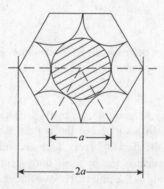

Figure 2.22 *Top Plane of HCP*

Volume of unit cell, $V_c = 2.598a^2 \times c = 2.598 \times 1.633a^3 = 4.242534a^3$

Radius of atoms, $r = \dfrac{2a}{4} = 0.5a$

Volume of one atom $= \dfrac{4}{3}\pi r^3 = \dfrac{4}{3} \times \pi(0.5a)^3 = \dfrac{\pi}{6}a^3$

Volume of six atoms of unit cell $= \dfrac{\pi}{6} \times 6 \times a^3 = \pi a^3$

Packing factor, APF $= \dfrac{\pi a^3}{4.242534a^3} = 0.740$

Example 2.3   What is the packing factor of diamond? Mass of carbon is 12 amu and lattice size is 0.3569 nm. Diamond is having a cubic unit cell. What is the density of diamond?

Solution:

The strength of covalent bonds and the arrangement by which atoms are held in structure make diamond a very hard and strong material with a high melting point.

There are four atoms (within the unit cell) marked 1–4, six atoms at the centre of six faces (marked 5–10) and eight atoms at corners (marked 11–18) (Figure 2.23).

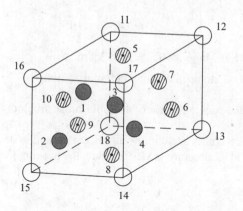

Figure 2.23 *Diamond - Atomic Structure*

Effective number of atoms in a diamond cubic unit cell $= \dfrac{1}{8} \times 8 + \dfrac{1}{2} \times 6 + 4 = 8$

Volume of each spherical atom $= \dfrac{4}{3}\pi r^3$,

where r is the atomic radius of carbon atom.

Radius of atom, $r = a\sqrt{3}/8$, where a is the lattice parameter.

Volume of atoms in unit cell $= 8 \times \dfrac{1}{3}\pi r^3 = \dfrac{32}{3}\pi r^3$

$$= \dfrac{32}{3} \times \pi \left(\dfrac{a\sqrt{3}}{8}\right)^3$$

$$= \frac{32}{3} \times \frac{\pi \times 3\sqrt{3}}{5/2} \times a^3 = 0.340a^3$$

Volume of unit cell $= a^3$

$$\text{Packing factor} = \frac{0.34a^3}{a^3} = 0.340$$

$$\text{Density} = \frac{\text{mass of atoms in unit cell}}{\text{volume of unit cell}}$$

Mass of one carbon atom $= 12$ amu

$$= 12 \times 1.660 \times 10^{-27} \text{ kg}$$

$$= 1.992 \times 10^{-26} \text{ kg}$$

Volume of one lattice $= a^3$

$$= (0.3569 \times 10^{-9})^3$$

$$= .04546 \times 10^{-27} \text{ m}^3$$

Density $= 1.992 \times 10^{-26} \times 8/0.04546 \times 10^{-27} = 3505 \text{ kg/m}^3$

Note that there are eight carbon atoms in one unit cell of diamond.

Exercise 2.1   Show that the packing factor of a simple cubic structure is 0.52.

Exercise 2.2   Show clearly with a sketch how atoms are packed in an FCC structure. Explain how co-ordination number of an FCC structure is 12. Calculate the packing factor for FCC structure.

Ans. [0.74]

2.10 DENSITY

A knowledge of crystal structure of a metallic solid permits the calculation of true density ρ, by using the relationship
    Density,

$$\rho = \frac{nA}{V_c N_A}$$

where n is the number of atoms in a unit cell, A is the atomic weight in g/mol, V_c is the volume of unit cell in cm^3 and N_A is the Avogadro's number, 6.023×10^{23} atoms/mol.

Example 2.4   Iron has an atomic radius of 0.124 nm (1.24 Å) and a BCC structure, with an atomic weight of 55.85 g/mol. Calculate the density of iron.

Solution:

BCC structure, $n = 2$, number of atoms per unit cell

$A_{Fe} = 55.85$ g/mol., atomic weight

Unit cell volume, $V_C = a^3$, where $\sqrt{3}a = 4r$, where r is the atomic radius.

$$V_C = a^3 = \left(\frac{4r}{\sqrt{3}}\right)^3 = 12.3171 r^3$$

$$= 12.3171 \times (1.24 \times 10^{-8} \text{ cm})^3$$

$$= 23.484 \times 10^{-24} \text{ cm}^3$$

Avogadro's number,

$$N_A = 6.023 \times 10^{23} \text{ atoms/mol}$$

$$V_C N_A = 23.484 \times 10^{-24} \times 6.023 \times 10^{23}$$

$$= 14.144$$

Density,

$$\rho = \frac{nA_{Fe}}{V_C N_A} = \frac{2 \times 55.85}{14.1444}$$

$$= 7.897 \text{ g/cc}$$

Example 2.5   Zinc has an atomic radius of 0.133 nm (1.33 Å) with an HCP structure, and atomic weight of 65.39 g/mol. Calculate the density of zinc.

Solution:

In HCP crystal volume, $V_C = 4.82185a^3$, where a is the side of an hexagon, C/a ratio is 1.856

$a = 2r$, where r is the atomic radius of the element,

$$V_C = 4.82185 \, (2r)^3 = 38.575r^3$$

$$V_C = 4 \, 38.575 \, (1.33 \times 10^{-8} \text{ cm})^3$$

$$= 90.753 \times 10^{-24} \text{ cm}^3$$

$$N_A = \text{Avogadro's number}$$

$$= 6.023 \times 10^{23} \text{ atoms/mol}$$

$$= 6.023 \times 10^{23} \times 90.753 \times 10^{-24} \text{ cm}^3$$

$$= 54.66 \text{ cm}^3$$

Number of atom per unit cell of HCP,

$$n = 6$$

Density,

$$\rho = \frac{n \times A_{ZN}}{N_A V_C}$$

$$= \frac{6 \times 65.39}{54.66}$$

$$= 7.17 \text{ g/cc}$$

Note that density given in the commercial table is only 7.13.

Exercise 2.3   Copper has an atomic radius of 0.128 nm (1.28 Å), an FCC crystal structure and an atomic weight of 63.5 g/mol. Determine its density.

Ans. [8.89 g/cc]

Exercise 2.4   Gold has an atomic weight of 196.97 g/mol, while its atomic radius is 0.144 nm (1.44 Å) and an FCC structure. Determine the density of gold.

Ans. [19.364 g/cc]

Example 2.6   Calculate the number of atoms per unit cell of a metal having lattice parameter of 0.29 nm and a density of 7.868 g/cc. Atomic weight of the metal is 55.85 g/mol and Avogadro's number is 6.023×10^{23}. What is the crystal structure of the metal?

Solution:

Lattice parameter,

$$a = 0.29 \text{ nm} = 2.9 \text{ Å}$$

$$= 2.9 \times 10^{-8} \text{ cm}$$

Density,

$$\rho = 7.868 \text{ g/cc}$$

Atomic weight of metal,

$$A = 55.85 \text{ g/mol}$$

Avogadro's number,

$$N_A = 6.023 \times 10^{23} \text{ atoms/mol}$$

Density,

$$\rho = \frac{nA}{N_A V_C}$$

where

$$V_C = \text{volume of unit cell}$$

$$a^3 = (2.9 \times 10^{-8})^3 = 24.389 \times 10^{-24} \text{ cm}^3$$

$$n = \text{number of atoms}$$

$$= \frac{\rho N_A V_C}{A} = \frac{7.868 \times 6.023 \times 10^{23} \times 24.389 \times 10^{-24}}{55.85}$$

$$= \frac{115.5769}{55.85} = 2.069 \simeq 2$$

If the number of atoms per unit cell is two, it means that it is a BCC structure since the density 55.85 g/mol is that of iron (α); therefore, it is a BCC structure of Fe (α).

Exercise 2.5   A material with an FCC structure has a density of 6.25 g/cc and a molecular weight of 60.2 g/mol. Calculate the lattice parameter a, if Avogadro's number is $N_A = 6.02 \times 10^{23}$ atoms/mol.

Ans. [1.857 Å]

2.11 ALLOTROPY OR POLYMORPHISM

Some metals as well as non-metals may have more than one crystal structure, a phenomenon known as 'polymorphism'. When this is observed in elemental solids, the condition is known as 'allotropy'. The prevailing crystal structure depends on both the temperature and the external pressure. Following are few examples:

1. For carbon, graphite is a stable polymorph at ambient temperature, while diamond is formed at extremely high pressures and temperatures.

   In the graphite, the carbon atoms are arranged in sheets of regular hexagons with each carbon atom bonded together to three other carbon atoms with a bond angle of 120°.

   A diamond structure is composed of two FCC lattices displaced from each other by one fourth of a body diagonal. There are eight atoms in a unit cell, i.e. eight atoms at eight corners, six at six faces and four inside at one fourth of the distance. The total number of atoms per unit cell,

$$n = 8 \times \frac{1}{8} + 6 \times \frac{1}{2} + 4 = 8$$

2. For pure iron, BCC crystal structure occurs at ambient temperature, but FCC structure occurs at 912°C.

   Most often, a modification of the density and other physical properties accompanies a polymorphic transformation.

3. For silica, simplest polymorph of SiO_2 is 'cystobalite', which is stable at high temperature. The other two polymorphs of silica are tridymite and quartz. All the three polymorphs of SiO_2 have their SiO_2 tetrahedrals linked together in different ways.

   Quartz $\xrightarrow{\text{867°C}}$ Tridynite $\xrightarrow{\text{1470°C}}$ Crystobalite $\xrightarrow{\text{1726°}}$ Molten state

   (SG = 2.65)   (SG = 2.26)   (SG = 2.32)

   SG: Specific Gravity.

2.12 CRYSTALLOGRAPHIC DIRECTIONS

Many a times, it is necessary to specify a particular crystallographic direction or a crystallographic plane. Three integers or indices are used to designate a direction or a plane. The basis for determining indices is the unit cell with co-ordinate axis x, y and z. For same unit cell, as in a hexagonal structure, the three axis are not mutually perpendicular.

Crystallographic direction is defined as a line between two points or a vector. The three-directional indices are determined as follows:

1. A vector of convenient length is positioned such that it passes through the origin of the co-ordinate system.

2. The length of projection of vector on each of the other three axis (x, y and z) is determined. These are measured in the terms of lattice parameters (a, b and c) (Figure 2.24).

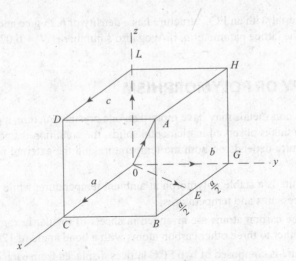

Figure 2.24 *Unit Cell with Lattice Vectors a, b, c*

3. These three numbers are multiplied or divided by a *common factor* so as to reduce them to the smallest integer values.

4. The three indices not separated by commas

   U—reduced projection along x

   V—reduced projection along y

   W—reduced projection along z

Let us consider a unit cell *ABCD*, *OGHL*, with space lattice vectors a, b, c, and co-ordinate axis x, y, z passing through O. Direction of *OE*, passing through origin O and point E is $(a/2, b, 0)$. Projections of vector *OE* on x, y, z axis are $(a/2, b, 0)$, divided by lattice vectors we get [1/2, 1, 0] and multiplying by 2, we get indices [1 2 0].

Crystallographic direction of *OE* is [1 2 0]. Similarly, consider vector *OA* with projections on x, y, z axis equal to $(a\ b\ c)$, respectively, divided by respective lattice vectors a, b, c, we get [1 1 1].

Crystallographic direction of *OA* is [1 1 1]. Similarly, crystallographic directions of lines *OB*, *OC*, *OL* and *OD* are

$$OB\ [1\ 1\ 0]$$
$$OC\ [1\ 0\ 0]$$
$$OL\ [0\ 0\ 1]$$
$$OD\ [1\ 0\ 1]$$

Example 2.7   Find the direction [1 $\bar{2}$ 0] in a unit cell.

Solution:

In this case, the projection on y-axis is in negative direction and the projection on x-axis is half the projections on y-axis; in this $\bar{2}$, bar on 2 indicates negative direction.

Figure 2.25 shows a line *OM*, where projections on x, y, z axis are $+a/2$, $-b$, 0, respectively.

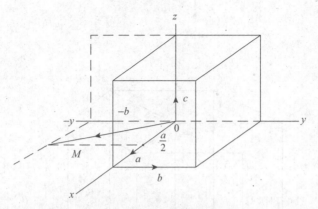

Figure 2.25 *Direction [1 2̄ 0]*

Dividing by space lattice parameters a, b, c, respectively, we get $[1/2 \quad \bar{1} \quad 0]$. Multiplying each by 2, we get direction $[1 \quad \bar{2} \quad 0]$ for line *OM*.

Exercise 2.6 Draw the crystallographic direction [1 3 3].

[Ans. Figure 2.26]

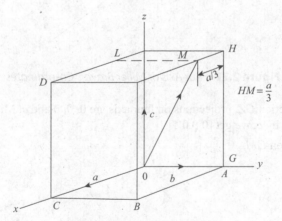

Figure 2.26 *For Example 2.6*

2.12.1 Crystallographic Direction in a Hexagonal Crystal

In the case of hexagonal crystals, there are four axis a_1, a_2, a_3 and z as shown in Figure 2.27. These are also called Miller Bravais co-ordinates. The three axis a_1, a_2 and a_3 are all contained within a single plane (called basal plane as shown) and are at an angle of 120° to one another.

Four axis are $0a_1$, $0a_2$, $0a_3$ and $0z$ side of hexagonal a, height of hexagonal crystal c, so lattice parameters are a, a, a and c as shown in Figure 2.27.

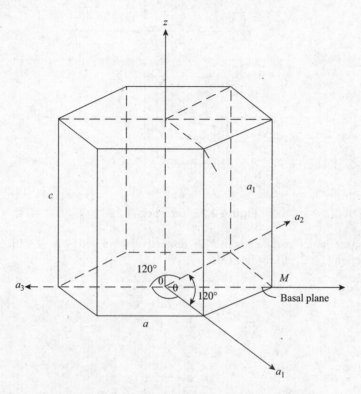

Figure 2.27 *Four Axis or Miller Bravais Co-ordinates*

Example 2.8 In direction *OZ*, projections on four axis are 0, 0, 0 and *c*. Miller indices for direction *OZ* is [0 0 0 *c*]. Dividing by *c*, we get [0 0 0 1].

Let us find out direction *OM*.

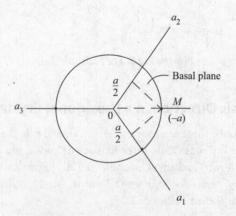

Figure 2.28 *For Example 2.8*

Projections of vector OM on

axis $oa_1 + a/2$

axis $oa_2 + a/2$

axis $oa_3 - a$

axis oz 0 (Figure 2.28)

Solution:

Directions $[a/2 \ a/2 \ \bar{a} \ 0]$, multiplying throughout by $2/a$, we get $[1 \quad 1 \quad \bar{2} \quad 0]$ in direction OM.

Direction OL

Projections of vector OL on

axis $0a_1 \rightarrow OM = 0.866a$

axis $0a_2 \rightarrow O$

axis $0a_3 \rightarrow OK = -0.866a$

axis $0Z \rightarrow 0$

Direction $[0.866a \quad 0 \ldots -0.866a \quad 0]$ (Figure 2.29)

Dividing throughout by $0.866a$, we get direction OL $[1 \quad 0 \quad \bar{1} \quad 0]$.

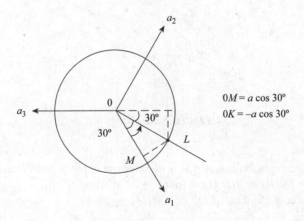

$0M = a \cos 30°$

$0K = -a \cos 30°$

Figure 2.29 *For Direction [1 0 $\bar{1}$ 0]*

Exercise 2.7   Mark the direction $[1 \quad \bar{1} \quad 0 \quad 0]$ in basal plane of a hexagonal crystal.

2.13 CRYSTALLOGRAPHIC PLANES

In all but hexagonal crystal system, crystallographic planes are specified by three Miller indices, i.e. (h k l). Any two planes parallel to each other are equivalent and have identical indices.

The procedure for determining Miller indices for planes: Following are the major steps to be followed:

1. If a plane passes through the selected origin, then either *another parallel plane* must be constructed within the unit cell *or a new origin* must be established at the corner of another unit cell.

2. At this point, the crystallographic plane either intersects or parallels each of the three axis. The length of the planar intercept for each axis is determined in terms of lattice parameters *a*, b and c.

3. The reciprocals of three numbers (i.e. planar intercepts) are taken. A plane that parallels an axis may be considered to have an infinite intercept and therefore a zero index (reciprocal of infinity).

4. These three numbers (if necessary) are changed to the set of smallest integer by multiplication or division by a common factor.

5. Finally, integer indices not separated by commas are enclosed within parenthesis (h k l).

Example: Figure 2.30 represents a unit cell of parameters *a*, *b* and *c*. Let us find Miller indices of plane *AOFG*, which is passing through the origin *O*. Therefore, consider a plane *EBHD*, which is parallel to plane *AOFG*.

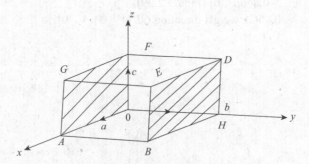

Figure 2.30 *Planes (0 1 0)*

The plane *EBHD* intercepts the *y*-axis at *H*, with intercept *b*, but is parallel to *x* and *z* axis. Therefore, Miller indices of plane *EBHD* or *AOFG* are (a/∞ b/b c/∞) or (0 1 0).

Similarly, Miller Indices of plane *GEDF* or *ABHU* are (0 0 1).

Example 2.9 Consider another example of a unit cell with lattice parameter (*a*, *b*, *c*) as shown in Figure 2.31.

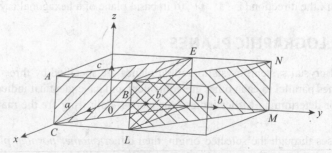

Figure 2.31 *For Example 2.9*

Solution:

Miller Indices of crystallographic plane *ACDE* intercepts on three axis are (a, b, ∞). Miller Indices of plane are $(a/a \quad b/b \quad c/\infty)$ or (1 1 0). If plane *BLMN* is parallel to *ACDE*, then Miller indices of this plane are also (1 1 0). If we consider a third plane passing through the origin *O*, but parallel to plane *ACDE*, then Miller Indices for this plane also will be (1 1 0).

Example 2.10 Let us consider unit cell with parameters (a, a, a) as shown in Figure 2.32.

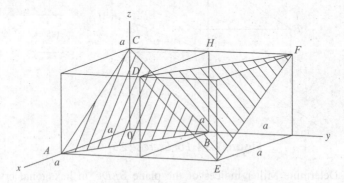

Figure 2.32 *For Example 2.10*

Solution:

The intercepts of the plane *ABC* (plane not passing through the origin *O*) are a, a, a on x, y, z axis, respectively. Miller indices of plane *ABC* are $(a/a \quad a/a \quad a/a)$ or (1 1 1). Plane *DEF* has planar intercepts as $(a, a, -a)$ taking origin at *H*. Miller Indices of this plane are also (1 1 $\bar{1}$). Please note that in place of a negative sign a bar is put on top of the index.

Exercise 2.8 Mark the plane with Miller indices (1 $\bar{1}$ 0) on a unit cell with parameters (a, a, a).

Ans. [Figure 2.33]

Ans.

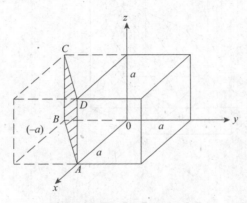

Figure 2.33 *For Exercise 2.8*

Exercise 2.9 Give Miller indices of the plane *ABCD* shown in Figure 2.34. [Hint take origin at *C*].

Ans. [1 $\bar{1}$ 2]

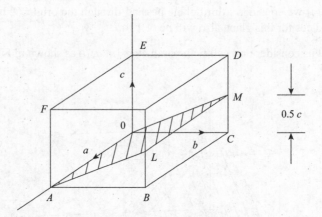

Figure 2.34 *For Exercise 2.9*

Example 2.11 Determine Miller indices of the plane *BEDC* in hexagonal crystal, as shown in Figure 2.35. Edges *BC* and *ED* are parallel to axis a_2. Intercept on axis a_1 is $+a$, intercept on axis a_2 is update, intercept on axis a_3 is $-a$, and intercept on axis oz is $+c/2$.

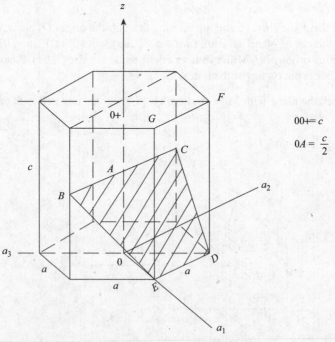

Figure 2.35 *Plane [1 0$\bar{1}$ 2]*

Solution:

Miller indices of the given plane is

$$\left(\frac{a}{a} \ \frac{a}{\infty} \ \frac{a}{-a} \ \frac{c}{c/2}\right)$$

or

$$(1 \quad 0 \quad \bar{1} \quad 2)$$

Exercise 2.10   Find Miller indices of the plane EDFG of a hexagonal crystal, as shown in Figure 2.35 in Example 2.11.

Ans. [1 0 $\bar{1}$ 0]

2.14 ATOMIC ARRANGEMENTS

The atomic arrangement on any crystallographic plane depends on the crystal structure. A family of planes consists all planes, which are graphically equivalent meaning thereby that they have the same atomic packing and are designated by braces {1 0 0}, {0 1 0}, {0 0 1} as shown in Figure 2.36.

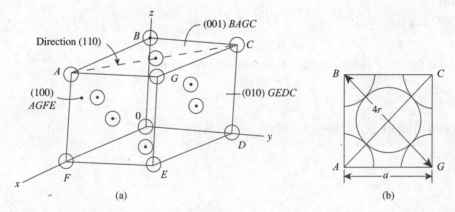

Figure 2.36 *(a) FCC Crystal Structure (b) Atomic Arrangement on All Six Faces of FCC Structure*

Lattice parameter of FCC structure $= a$

Radius of atoms, $r = \dfrac{\sqrt{2a}}{4} = 0.3535a$

Area of face $= a^2$

Area of atoms $= 2\pi r^2 = 2\pi \ (0.3535a)^2$

$$= 0.785a^2$$

Planar density of (0 0 1), (0 1 0), (1 0 0) planes of FCC structure $= 0.785a^2/a^2 = 0.785$

$$= 78.5 \text{ per cent}$$

Linear density of line AC or [1 1 0] $= \dfrac{4r}{\sqrt{2}a} = \dfrac{4 \times 0.3535a}{\sqrt{2}a}$

$$= 1.0 = 100 \text{ per cent}$$

2.14.1 Linear and Planar Atomic Densities

Directional equivalency is related to the atomic linear density in the sense that the equivalent directions have identical linear densities. The direction vector is positioned so as to pass through the atom centres and the fraction of line intersected by these atoms is equal to the linear density.

The crystallographic planes that are equivalent have the same atomic planar density. The plane of intersect is positioned so as to pass through the atom centres and the planar density is simply the fraction of total crystallographic plane area that is occupied by the atoms, as planar density of (0 1 0) plane of FCC structure is 0.785 or 78.5 per cent.

The linear and planar densities are one- and two-dimensional analogs of the atomic packing factor.

Example 2.12 Calculate the linear density of [1 0 0] direction of BCC.

Solution:

In a BCC unit cell,

$$\sqrt{3}a = 4r$$

where a is the lattice parameter and r is the radius of the atoms.

$$r = \dfrac{\sqrt{3}a}{4} = 0.433a$$

along [1 0 0] direction, i.e. along x-axis (Figure 2.37)

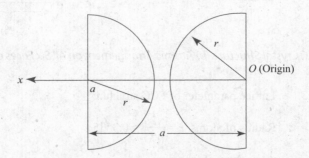

Figure 2.37 *Linear Density Along [1 1 0] in BCC*

Linear density along [1 0 0] direction $= \dfrac{(0.433a) \times 2}{a}$

$$= 0.866 \text{ or } 86.6 \text{ per cent}$$

Example 2.13 Calculate the planar density of (1 1 0) plane of FCC structure.

Solution:

Dimensions of (1 1 0) plane are $\sqrt{2}a$ and a as shown in Figure 2.38.
Plane (1 1 0) of FCC

$$\text{Atomic radius, } r = \frac{\sqrt{2}}{4}\, a = 0.3535a$$

$$\text{Area of plane} \quad = \sqrt{2}a \times a\,\sqrt{2}a^2$$

$$\text{Area of atoms} \quad = 2\pi r^2 = 2\pi(0.3535a)^2$$

$$= 0.785a^2$$

$$\text{Planar density of atoms} = \frac{0.785a^2}{\sqrt{2}a^2}$$

$$= 0.555 = 55.5 \text{ per cent}$$

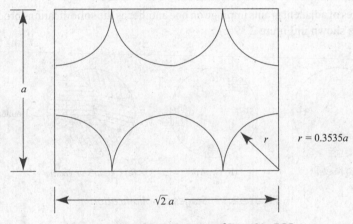

Figure 2.38 *Planar Density of [1 1 0] in FCC*

The linear and planar densities are important considerations relative to the process of slip that is the mechanism by which the atoms deform plastically. Slip occurs on most packed crystallographic planes, and in such planes, along the directions of the greatest atomic packing.

If FCC crystal plane (1 0 0) is more densely populated than the plane (1 1 0), slip direction in (1 0 0) plane is [1 1 0].

Both FCC and HCP crystal structures have the atomic packing factor of 0.74, which is the most efficient packing of equal-sized atoms or spheres.

Example 2.14 Topaz, an orthorhombic semiprecious stone, has a ratio of lattice parameter $a:b:c$ of 0.529:1:0.477. Find the Miller indices of the face whose intercepts are as follows (0.264:1.0:0.238).

Solution:

Miller indices of the plane are
$$\begin{pmatrix} \dfrac{0.529}{0.264} & \dfrac{1.0}{1.0} & \dfrac{0.477}{0.238} \end{pmatrix}$$

or
$$(2\ 1\ 2)$$

Exercise 2.11   For an orthorhombic crystal structure having lattice parameter a, b and c, the intercepts for a plane are $-a/2$, $+b/3$, $+c$. What are the Miller indices of the plane?

Ans. [$\bar{2}$ 3   1]

2.15 CRYSTAL GROWTH OF POLYCRYSTALLINE MATERIALS

Most of the crystalline solids are composed of a collection of many small crystals or grains so that material is termed as polycrystalline.

Various stages of solidification process are as follows:

1. Small nuclei are formed at various positions as shown in Figure 2.39(a).
2. Small grains grow by successive addition of solid particles of metal from the surrounding liquid of atoms to the structure of each nucleus as shown in Figure 2.39(b).
3. The boundaries of adjacent grains impinge on one another as the solidifications process approaches completion as shown in Figure 2.39(c).

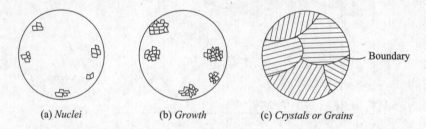

(a) *Nuclei*   (b) *Growth*   (c) *Crystals or Grains*

Figure 2.39 *Stages of Solidification*

For many polycrystalline materials, the crystallographic orientations of the individual grains are totally random. Under these circumstances, even though each grain may be anisotropic, a specimen consisting of grain aggregate behaves isotropically. Moreover, the magnitude of a measured physical property represents some average of directional values.

2.16 SINGLE CRYSTAL

For a crystalline solid, when the periodic and repeated arrangement of atoms is perfect or extends throughout the entire region of the specimen without interruption, the result is a single crystal. All unit cells interlock in the same way and have the same orientation. Single crystals exist in nature, but they may also be produced artificially.

If the boundary of a single crystal is permitted to grow without any external constraints, the crystal will assume a regular geometric shape having faces flats as with some of the gem stones, the very shape is indicative of the crystal structure. In electronic microcircuits, single crystals of silicon and germanium are employed. The physical properties of single crystals of same substance depend on the crystallographic directions in which the measurements are taken.

Table 2.4 shows the effect of crystallographic direction of crystal growth on the modulus of elasticity of metals. Materials for which measured properties are independent of the direction of measurement are isotropic materials, such as tungsten as shown in Table 2.4.

Table 2.4 *Modulus of Elasticity in GPa in Different Directions of Some Metals*

Structure	Metal	[1 0 0]	[1 1 0]	[1 1 1]
FCC	Aluminium	63.7	72.6	76.1
FCC	Copper	63.7	130.3	191.1
BCC	Iron	125.0	210.4	191.1
BCC	Tungsten	384.6	384.6	384.6

2.16.1 Bragg's Law

Determination of Crystal Structure

X-ray diffraction technique or radiography has been used to reveal the internal details of crystal structure of metals such as type of unit cell, atomic arrangement, imperfections in unit cell, impurity atoms, orientation of polycrystalline materials, choice of preferred orientation of crystals and so on.

Bragg's law of X-ray diffraction helps in determining interplanar distances between parallel planes.

A crystal contains innumerable number of atoms and X-rays are reflected from parallel planes as shown in Figure 2.40, which shows parallel planes with spacing d_{hkl} where h, k and l are intercepts of plane on three co-ordinate axis, and h, k and l are integers. Figure 2.40 shows three planes, i.e. 1, 2 and 3.

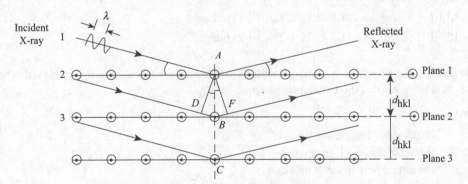

Figure 2.40 *Incident and Reflected X-rays*

Ray 1 incident on plane 1 at an angle θ, reflected from A at an angle θ.
Ray 2 incident on plane 2 at an angle θ, reflected from B at an angle θ.
Ray 3 incident on plane 3 at an angle θ, reflected from C at an angle θ.

Extra distance covered by ray 2, in addition to the distance covered by ray 1, is $DB + BF$, where

$$DB + BF = d_{hkl}\sin\theta + d_{hkl}\sin\theta$$
$$= 2d_{hkl}\sin\theta$$

If $2d_{hkl}\sin\theta = n\lambda$, where $n = 1, 2, 3, \ldots$, rays 2 and 1 will be in phase.

$n = 1$, for first order of reflections
$n = 2$ for second order of reflection
$n = 3$ for third order of reflection

$\sin\theta$ cannot be greater than 1, so

$$2d_{hkl} = \lambda, \text{ for single degree}$$

If $d_{hkl} = 3$ Å, then maximum value of wave length of X-ray, $\lambda = 6$ Å. The wave length of X-ray must be less than 6 Å.

For a plane (hkl), perpendicular distance of the plane from the origin will be $= \dfrac{a}{\sqrt{h^2 + k^2 + l^2}}$, where a is the lattice parameter and h, k and l are the intercepts (in integer) on the three axis of the plane (hkl). If

1. $h^2 + k^2 + l^2 = 1$, it means $1^2 + 0^2 + 0^2 = 1$, plane will be (1 0 0), (0 1 0), (0 0 1) (0 $\bar{1}$ 0) and so on.
2. $h^2 + k^2 + l^2 = 2$, indicates (1 1 0), (1 0 1), (1 $\bar{1}$ 0) planes.
3. $h^2 + k^2 + l^2 = 3$, indicates (1 1 1), (1 $\bar{1}$ 1), ($\bar{1}$ 1 1) planes.
4. $h^{2+} k^{2+} l^2 = 4$, indicates (2 0 0), (0 2 0), (0 $\bar{2}$ 0) planes.
5. $h^2 + k^2 + l^2 = 5$, indicates (1 2 0), (2 1 0), (2 0 1), (2 0 $\bar{1}$) planes.
6. $h^2 + k^2 + l^2 = 6$, indicates (1 1 2), (2 1 1), (1 $\bar{2}$ 1), (1 $\bar{2}$ 1) planes.
7. $h^2 + k^2 + l^2 = 7$, cannot exist.
8. $h^2 + k^2 + l^2 = 8$, indicates (2 2 0), (0 2 2), (0 $\bar{2}$ 2) planes.
9. $h^2 + k^2 + l^2 = 9$, indicates (1 2 2), (2 1 2), ($\bar{2}$ 1 2) planes.

Example 2.15 X-rays with a wavelength of 0.58 Å are used for calculating d_{200} in nicked. The reflection angle is 9.5°. What is the lattice parameter a?

Solution:

X-ray wave length, $\lambda = 0.58$ Å
$\theta = 9.50°$ for $n = 1$, first order
a = lattice parameter of unit cell
Interplanar distance, $d = \dfrac{a}{\sqrt{h^2 + k^2 + l^2}}$
d_{200} = mean distance for (2 0 0 plane),
where h = 2, k = 0, l = 0.
$$d_{200} = \dfrac{a}{\sqrt{2^2 + 0^2 + 0^2}} = \dfrac{a}{2} = 0.5a$$

As per Bragg's law, $2d \sin \theta = n\lambda$

$$2 \times d \times \sin 9.5° = 1 \times \lambda$$
$$2 \times \frac{a}{2} \times 0.165 = 0.58 \text{ Å}$$
$$a = \frac{0.58}{0.165} = 3.515 \text{ Å}$$

Example 2.16 For a certain BCC crystal, the (1 1 0) plane has a separation of 1.54 Å, These planes are indicated with X-rays of wavelength 1.54 Å. How many orders of Bragg's reflection can be observed in this case.

Solution:

Interplanar distance, $d = 1.54$ Å
X-ray wave length, $\lambda = 1.54$ Å
For maximum order of Bragg's reflection, maximum value of reflections angle $\theta = 90°$.
Number of orders as per Bragg's law, $n = \dfrac{2d \sin\theta}{\lambda}$

$$n - \frac{2 \times 1.54 \text{ Å} \times \sin 90°}{1.54 \text{ Å}} = 2$$

Example 2.17 Determine the interplanar spacing when an X-ray beam of wavelength 1.54 Å is directed towards the crystal at an angle of 20.3° to the atomic plane.

Solution:

X-ray wave length, $\lambda = 1.54$ Å
$\theta = 20.3°$
Order, $n = 1$
By Bragg's law, $2d \sin\theta = n\lambda = 1\lambda$
$2 \times d \times \sin 20.3° = 1.54$ Å

$$d = \frac{1.54 \text{ Å}}{2 \times 0.347} = 2.22 \text{ Å}$$

Example 2.18 An X-ray beam of wave length 0.2 Å is incident on a crystal at an angle of incidence equal to 8.5°, when first-order diffraction occurs. Determine the glancing angle (or incident angle) for the third-order diffraction and the interplanar spacing in crystal.

Solution:

X-ray wave length, $\lambda = 0.82$ Å
$\theta = 8.50°, n = 1$
$2d \sin\theta = \lambda$ for $n = 1$
$2 \times d \times \sin 8.5° = 082$

$$d = \frac{0.82 \text{ Å}}{2 \times 0.1478} = 2.774 \text{ Å}$$

Interplanar spacing, $\qquad$ $d = 2.774$ Å

If $\qquad$ $n = 3$, $\sin\theta_3/\sin\theta = 3/1$, when $\theta_1 = \theta = 8.5°$

$\qquad\qquad\qquad\qquad$ $\sin\theta = 3 \times \sin\theta_1 = 3 \times 0.1478 = 0.4434$

Angle of incidence, $\qquad$ $\theta_3 = 20°19'15'$

Exercise 2.12 X-rays of wave length 1.542 Å are diffracted by (1 1 1) planes in a crystal at an angle of 30°, in the first order. Calculate the interatomic spacing.

Ans. [1.542 Å]

Exercise 2.13 Calculate the Bragg angle of (1 1 1) planes of a cube (lattice parameter $a = 3.57$ Å) crystals that are exposed to X-rays of wave length 1.54 Å.

Ans. [20°57']

Exercise 2.14 For BCC iron, calculate (1) the interplannar spacing and (2) the diffraction angle for (2 1 1) set of planes. The lattice parameter for iron is 2.87 Å. Also assume that the monochromatic radiation having a wave length of 0.1542 nm (1.542 Å) is used and order of reflection is 1.

Ans. [1.17 Å 41°13'17"]

Exercise 2.15 Bragg angle corresponding to a reflection from a plane for which $h^2 + k^2 + l^2 = 8$ is formed to be 17°. Determine the lattice parameter of the crystal if X-rays of wave length 0.71 Å are used. Determine also the Miller indices of the reflecting planes.

Ans.[3.42 Å, (2 2 0), (2 0 2), (2 0 $\bar{2}$) planes so on]

KEY POINTS TO REMEMBER

❑ The physical and mechanical properties of solids are very much dependent on minimum potential energy between the atoms, type of interatomic bonding and the arrangement of atoms in a crystal structure.

❑ Each crystal is composed of basic structural elements called unit cells.

❑ The atoms of the same element having two or more different atomic masses are called isotopes.

❑ Space lattice is defined as an infinite array of points in a three-dimensional space, in which each point is identically located with respect to the other.

❑ Manganese: There are 29 atoms per lattice point and 29 atoms at the body centre.

❑ Common crystal structures are BCC, FCC and HCP atoms.

❑ For many atoms, equilibrium spacing between the two atoms, i.e. $r_0 = 0.3$ nm.

❑ The minimum potential energy of two atoms corresponds to the energy of equilibrium spacing of r_0.

❑ In ionic bonding, oppositely charged ions are attracted to one another and produce ionic bonding.

❑ Ionic bonds are brittle in nature, and poor in electrical and thermal conductivities.

❑ In covalent bond, each of the two atoms that are covalently bonded will contribute at least one electron to the bond and the shared electrons may be considered belonging to both the atoms.

❑ In metallic bonding, positively charged metal ions are surrounded by electron cloud, forming strong metallic bond.

❑ Metals are good conductors of heat and electricity due to the presence of electron cloud.

❑ Vander Waals bonds join molecules or groups of atoms by weak electrostatic attractions.

❑ A crystalline structure is represented by a combination of hard spheres model, in which spheres representing nearest neighbouring atoms touch one another.

❑ The number of atoms in FCC unit cell is 4, APF = 0.74 and the co-ordination number is 12.

❑ The number of atoms in BCC unit cell is 2, APF = 0.68 and the co-ordination number is 8.

❑ The number of atoms in HCP unit cell is 6, APF = 0.74, and the co-ordination number is 12.

❑ Diamond has a cubic unit cell; four atoms within the unit cell, eight atoms at corners and six atoms at six face centres. Effective number is 8 and the packing factor is 0.34.

❑ Density $r = (nA)/(V_C N_A)$, where n is the number of atoms in a unit cell, A is the atomic weight in g/mol, V_C is the volume of the unit cell in cm³ and N_A is Avogadro's number, 6.023×10^{23} atom/mol.

❑ Some metals as well as non-metals may have more than one crystal structure, a phenomenon known as polymorphism.

❑ To determine the Miller indices of a direction, the direction vector must pass through the origin or a new origin can be established. The projections of direction vectors on three axis are noted.

❑ To determine the Miller indices of a plane, the plane must not pass through the origin, or else another parallel plane can be drawn. The intercepts made by the planes on the three axis are noted down.

❑ In a hexagonal crystal, there are four axis (a_1, a_2, a_3, z).

❑ The crystallographic planes that are equivalent have the same atomic planar density.

❑ Slip occurs on most densely packed crystallographic planes and in such planes along the direction of greatest atomic packing.

❑ The boundary of a single crystal is permitted to grow without any external constraint.

❑ The physical properties of single crystals of some materials depend on the crystallographic direction in which the measurements are made.

❑ Bragg's law $2d_{hkl}\sin\theta = n\lambda$, where d_{hkl} is the planar distance of plane with intercepts h, k, l, n is the order of reflection and λ is the wave length of X-ray.

MULTIPLE CHOICE QUESTIONS

1. The number of nearest neighbouring atoms in FCC crystal is
   (a) 6   (c) 12
   (b) 8   (d) None of these

2. The Miller indices of a set of parallel planes, which make intercepts in the ratio of $3a:4b$ on the x and y axis and are parallel to z-axis (with a, b and as lattice parameters) are
   (a) [0 4 3]   (c) [3 3 0]
   (b) [4 3 0]   (d) [3 4 0]

3. Ratio of packing factor of an FCC crystal to the packing factor of a single cubic crystal is
   (a) 1.0   (c) 0.702
   (b) 1.423   (d) None of these

4. In a unit cell of silver, the atoms occupy what percentage space per unit cell
   (a) 80%   (c) 74%
   (b) 68%   (d) 52%

5. In the covalent bond of methane, bond angle is 109°. What is the bond angle in the covalent bond of silicon
   - (a) 104°
   - (b) 107°
   - (c) 109°
   - (d) 109.5°

6. How many atoms are there in an HCP crystal structure?
   - (a) 8
   - (b) 6
   - (c) 4
   - (d) None of these

7. Crystal structure of zinc is HCP. What is c/a ratio for zinc unit cell?
   - (a) 1.633
   - (b) 1.75
   - (c) 1.856
   - (d) None of these

8. How many carbon atoms are there in a unit cell of diamond?

   - (a) 8
   - (b) 6
   - (c) 4
   - (d) None of these

9. In which crystallographic direction, copper has maximum value of modulus of electricity?
   - (a) [1 0 0]
   - (b) [1 1 1]
   - (c) [1 1 0]
   - (d) None of these

10. Which one of the following metals is truly isotropic?
    - (a) Tungsten
    - (b) Copper
    - (c) Aluminium
    - (d) None of these

11. The interatomic equilibrium spacing between two atoms is generally
    - (a) 0.3 nm
    - (b) 4 nm
    - (c) 0.5 nm
    - (d) None of these

Answers

1. (c)   2. (b)   3. (b)   4. (c)   5. (c)   6. (b)   7. (c)   8. (a)   9. (b)
10. (a)   11. (a)

REVIEW QUESTIONS

1. What are single crystal, polycrystalline and amorphous solids?

2. What are isotopes? Give examples.

3. What are space lattice, unit cell and lattice parameters? Explain.

4. What do you understand by Basis?

5. Differentiate among cubic, tetragonal and orthorhombic unit cells with the help of sketches.

6. Describe the dependence of material properties on minimum potential energy of two atoms bound together.

7. Explain with the help of examples ionic bonding and covalent bonding.

8. Explain how metallic bonds are formed and why are they stronger than other types of bonds?

9. Explain with the help of a sketch, co-ordination number of an FCC crystal structure.

10. Differentiate among atomic packing factor, planar and linear atomic densities.

11. Explain how the density of a material is determined.

12. What do you understand by allotropy and polymorphism?

13. With the help of a neat sketch show crystallographic axis of a hexagonal structure.

14. Describe the process of solidification of metals.

15. What is a single crystal? Why the mechanical properties are dependent on direction of crystal growth?

PRACTICE PROBLEMS

1. If the atomic radius of aluminium is 0.143 nm, calculate volume of its unit cell.

Ans. $[6.616 \times 10^{-29} \text{ m}^3]$

2. Calculate the radius of iridium atom, having an FCC crystal structure, a density of 22.4 g/cc and atomic weight of 192.2 g/mol.

Ans. [0.136 nm]

3. Sketch a unit cell for the orthorhombic crystal structure and within that cell sketch $(0\ \bar{1}\ 1)$ direction and $(0\ 0\ 2)$ plane. (Take a, b, c as lattice parameters.)

4. Make a unit cell with $a = 0.3$ nm, $b = 0.5$ nm and $c = 0.3$ nm, and mark the direction $(1\ \cdot1\ \bar{4})$ and plane $(1\ 0\ \bar{2})$.

5. Within a cubic unit cell, sketch $(\bar{1}\ \bar{2}\ 1)$ and $(0\ \bar{1}\ \bar{2})$ directions.

6. Compute and compare the linear densities of [1 0 0] and [1 1 1] directions of FCC.

7. Compute and compare the linear densities of [1 1 0] and [1 1 1] of BCC.

8. Calculate the planar density of HCP plane (0 0 0 1)

9. Below are listed the atomic weight, density and atomic radius for three hypothetical materials. For each, determine whether its crystal structure is FCC, BCC or HCP and justify your determination.

Material	Atomic Weight (g/mol)	Density (g/cc)	Atomic Radius (nm)	
A	24.31	1.74	0.160	HCP
B	107.87	10.49	0.144	FCC
C	22.99	0.971	0.186	BCC

10. Draw the planes (1 2 2) and (2 3 1) in a cubic system.

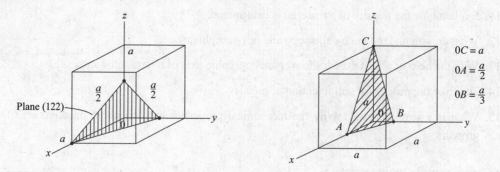

$0C = a$
$0A = \frac{a}{2}$
$0B = \frac{a}{3}$

11. Draw the planes ($\overline{1}$ 2 2) and ($\overline{2}$ 3 1) in a cubic system.

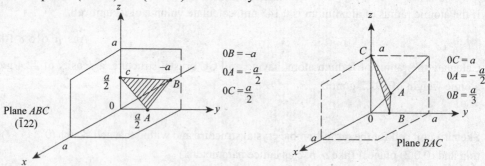

$0B = -a$
$0A = -\frac{a}{2}$
$0C = \frac{a}{2}$

$0C = a$
$0A = -\frac{a}{2}$
$0B = \frac{a}{3}$

12. Prove that the Miller indices for the directions OM in a hexagonal crystal as shown in Figure. 2.41 is [$\overline{1}$ $\overline{1}$ 2 2].

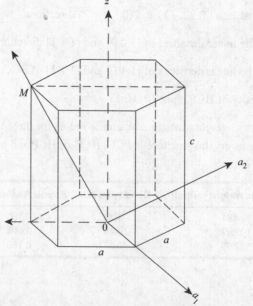

Figure 2.41 *Miller Indices of Hexagonal Crystal*

13. (a) Mark the direction ($\bar{1}$ 2 0) in a cubic crystal. (b) What is the direction of the line shown in Figure 2.42?

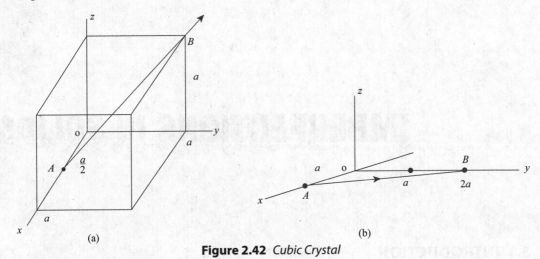

(a)   (b)

Figure 2.42 *Cubic Crystal*

14. In a hexagonal crystal mark the planes ($\bar{1}$ 0 1 0) and (1 0 $\bar{1}$ 0).

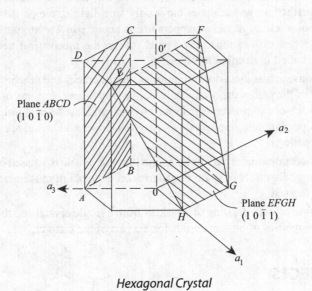

Hexagonal Crystal

IMPERFECTIONS IN SOLIDS

3.1 INTRODUCTION

The study of imperfections in crystalline materials is of utmost importance because the mechanical properties such as strength, hardness and ductility are strongly dependent on imperfections. These are classified as point imperfections, line imperfections, stacking faults and volume imperfections. The influence of point imperfections as vacancies plays only a negligible role on the strength of a material because the presence of vacancy at room temperature is about 1 in 10^7 atomic sites. But line imperfections as edge and screw dislocations play a vital role in the mechanical behaviour of crystalline materials and will be studied in detail in this chapter.

Volume imperfections such as inclusions, impurities, voids, cracks and notches are detrimental to the mechanical behaviour of the materials. Many a times, impurity atoms or atoms of alloying elements are intentionally added to achieve improvements in the physical and mechanical properties, for example, a small percentage of copper in gold improves its strength. Copper and nickel are completely soluble in each other in any proportions.

The response of dislocations under externally applied stresses is also discussed in detail. Despite metal deformation as twinning, the effect of grain boundaries on dislocation movement and low-angle grain boundaries are also discussed.

The growth of a single crystal, drawing of whiskers from a single crystal and the properties of whiskers in comparison to properties of bulk materials form a part of the chapter.

3.2 POINT DEFECTS

Simplest point defect is a vacancy site or a vacant lattice site, i.e. an atom missing from the array of unit cells. All crystalline solids contain vacancies and the presence of vacancies increases the entropy of the crystal.

Number of equilibrium vacancies,

$$N_e = N \exp\left(\frac{-Q_v}{kT}\right)$$

where N is the total number of atomic sites, Q_v is the energy required to create a vacancy and k is the Boltzmann constant

$$= 1.38 \times 10^{-23} \text{ J/atom–K}$$
$$= 8.62 \times 10^{-5} \text{ eV/atom–K}$$

T is the absolute temperature in K.

For most of the metals, the fraction of vacancies N_e/N just below the melting temperature is of the order of 10^{-4}, i.e. one lattice site out of 10,000 is missing.

A self-interstitial is an atom from the crystal that is crowded into an interstitial site, a small void space that under ordinary conditions is not occupied. In metals, self-interstitial atom introduces relatively large distortions in the surrounding lattice because the atom is substantially larger than the available interstitial space. Formation of this defect is not highly probable and so exists in very small concentrations, significantly much lower than for vacancies.

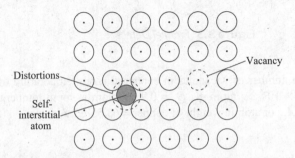

Figure 3.1 *Vacancy and Self-interstitial Point Defects*

Figure 3.1 shows point defects in lattices, a vacancy and a self interstitial atom occupying space between four atoms and causing distortions in the surrounding atoms.

Point defects may arise either by imperfect packing during the crystallization process or from thermal energy of atoms at high temperature. The vacancies are drastically reduced at low temperature or at room temperature.

3.2.1 Schottky Defect

The removal of a positively charged ion to create a vacancy must be counter–balanced by the removal of a negatively charged ion in order to maintain neutrality. A pair of two vacancies (positively charged ion + negatively charged ion) is known as Schottky defect. As in the case of a sodium chloride crystal, the removal of a positive sodium ion is balanced by the removal of a negative chlorine ion in order to maintain neutrality (Figure 3.2).

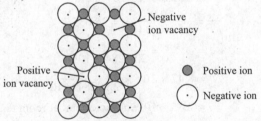

Figure 3.2 *Schottky Defect*

3.2.2 Frenkel Defect

Frenkel defect is related to interstices. If an interstitial ion moves from a normal point to an interstitial point, then the defect is known as Frenkel defect. In Figure 3.3, an ion moves from normal position at A to interstitial position at B.

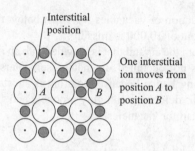

Interstitial position

One interstitial ion moves from position A to position B

Figure 3.3 *Frenkel Defect*

Example 3.1   Calculate the number of vacancies in copper at room temperature of 20°C. Assume Boltzmann constant, $k = 8.62 \times 10^{-5}$ eV/atom–K, $Q_v = 0.9$ eV/atom at room temperature, density of copper, $\rho = 8.94$ g/cc at 20°C, A_{Cu} or atomic weight of copper = 63.55 g/mol.

Solution:

Number of regular lattice sites,

$$N = \frac{N_A \times \rho}{A_{Cu}}$$

$$= \frac{6.023 \times 10^{23} \times 8.94}{63.55}$$

$$= 8.47 \times 10^{22} \text{ atoms/cm}^3$$

Number of vacancies in copper,

$$N_e = N \exp\left(\frac{-Q_v}{kT}\right)$$

$$T = 273 + 20 = 293°K$$

$$k = 8.62 \times 10^{-5} \text{ eV/atom–K}$$

$$kT = 293 \times 8.62 \times 10^{-5}$$

$$= 2.5256 \times 10^{-2} \text{ eV/atom}$$

$$\frac{Q_v}{kT} = \frac{0.9}{2.5256 \times 10^{-2}} = 35.635$$

$$e^{\frac{Q_v}{kT}} = e^{-35.635} = \frac{1}{2.99284 \times 10^{15}}$$

$$N_e = 8.47 \times 10^{22} \times \frac{1}{2.99284 \times 10^5}$$

$$= 2.83 \times 10^7 \text{ vacancies/cm}^3 \text{ at room temperature of } 20°C$$

Students can work out the number of vacancies at higher temperature and may observe that vacancies increase at higher temperature.

Example 3.2 Calculate the equilibrium number of vacancies per cc for copper at 1000°C. The energy per vacancy formation is 0.9 eV/atom, atomic weight = 63.55 g/mol and density at 1000°C is 8.4 g/cc. What is the ratio of N_e and N?

$$\text{Ans. } [2.186 \times 10^{19} \text{ vacancies/cc}, 2.746 \times 10^{-4}]$$

Example 3.3 An analysis of 100 g sample of pure iron (BCC) showed that 0.01 g of carbon atoms were present in the interstices of pure iron. How many carbon atoms are present in 10,000 unit lattices of iron?

Solution:

Sample size = 100 g

Mass of iron atoms = 99.99 g

Mass of carbon atoms = 0.01 g

Molecular weight of iron = 55.8 g/mol

Molecular weight of carbon = 12 g/mol

Avogadro's number = N_A = 6.023 × 10²³ atoms/mol

Number of iron atoms = $\dfrac{99.99}{55.8} \times 6.023 \times 10^{23}$

$= 10.793 \times 10^{23}$ atoms

Number of carbon atoms = $\dfrac{0.01}{12} \times 6.023 \times 10^{23}$

$= 5.019 \times 10^{20}$ atoms

Number of iron atoms per unit cell of BCC structure = 2

Number of iron atoms in 10,000 unit lattices = 2 × 10,000

$= 20,000$ atoms

Number of carbon atoms = $20,000 \times \dfrac{5.019 \times 10^{20}}{10.793 \times 10^{23}}$

$= 9.3 \approx 10$ carbon atoms

3.3 IMPURITIES IN SOLIDS

Impurities or foreign atoms are always present in metals. These impurities exist in crystalline materials as point defects. Even if a metal is refined to the level of 99.9999 per cent, impurity atoms are present to the order of 10^{22}–$10^{23}/m^3$ of refined metal. Generally, the common metals like iron, copper and aluminium are not highly pure. Moreover, in alloys impurity atoms are intentionally added to impart desired properties to the metal. Quite often, alloying is used in metals to improve mechanical properties such as strength, hardness and ductility, to resist corrosion.

The addition of impurity atoms to a metal results in the formation of a solid solution and a new second phase is produced, depending upon the type of impurity, concentration of impurity and the temperature of the alloy. There are solute and solvent materials. Solvent represents the element or compound that is present in greater amount. The solvent atoms are called host atoms. The 'solute' is used to denote an element or a compound present in smaller concentration.

3.3.1 Solid Solution

A solid solution is formed when the solute atoms added to the host atoms of a material maintain the crystal structure and no new crystal structure is formed. The impurity atoms are randomly and uniformly dispersed within the solid.

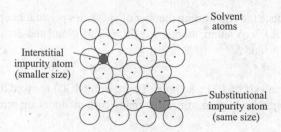

Figure 3.4 *Solid Solution*

The impurity atoms take up the substitutional position or interstitial position as shown in Figure 3.4. The substitutional impurity atoms are of the same size and the interstitial impurity atoms of smaller size. as carbon atom (of smaller size) takes interstitial position in iron atoms (of bigger size).

There are several features of the solute and solvent atoms that determine the degree to which the solute atoms are dissolved in solvent atoms, which are as follows:

1. *Atomic size factor:* The difference in the atomic radius between the two types of atoms is less than ±15 per cent, otherwise solute atoms will create lattice disorders or a new phase formation.

2. *Crystal structure:* The crystal structure of both solute and solvent atoms should be the same.

3. *Electronegativity:* If one of the element is more electropositive and the other is more electronegative, greater is the possibility that they together form an intermetallic compound, instead of substitutional solid solution.

4. *Valences:* Other factors being equal, a metal will have more tendencies to dissolve another metal of higher valency than one of a lower valency.

Example: Copper and nickel are completely soluble in one another in all proportions (Refer to Table 3.1).

Table 3.1 *Properties of Copper and Nickel Atoms*

Metal	Atomic Radii (nm)	Structure	Electronegativity	Valency
Cu	0.128	FCC	1.9	+1
Ni	0.125	FCC	1.8	+2

For interstitial solid solution, the impurity atoms fill the voids or interstices between the host atoms. For metals having high packing factors, the interstitial positions are relatively small. Therefore, the atomic radius of an interstitial impurity atom must be much smaller than that of a host atom. Normally, the maximum allowable concentration of the interstitial impurity atoms is low (less than 10 per cent). Generally, these interstitial impurity atoms introduce some lattice strains on the adjacent host atoms.

Example: Carbon forms an interstitial solid solution in iron and the maximum concentration of carbon is 2 per cent. The atomic radius of carbon is 0.071 nm and iron is 0.124 nm.

Weight per cent of one metal,

$$W_1 = \frac{m_1}{m_1 + m_2} \times 100$$

where m_1 and m_2 represent the mass of elements 1 and 2, respectively.

3.3.2 Atom per cent

Atom,

$$nm_1 = \frac{m_1}{A_1} = \frac{\text{mass in grams}}{\text{atomic weight for element}} \text{ for element 1}$$

$$nm_2 = \frac{m_2}{A_2}, \text{ for element 2}$$

Atom per cent,

$$C_1 = \frac{nm_1}{nm_1 + nm_2} \times 100$$

Atom per cent computation can also be worked out on the basis of the number of atoms instead of moles, since 1 mol of all substances contain the same number of atoms.

Example 3.4   What is the composition in atom per unit of an alloy, which consists of 90 per cent by weight of Ag and 10 per cent by weight of Cu.

Atomic weights of silver and copper are

$$A_{Ag} = 107.87 \text{ g/mol and } A_{Cu} = 63.55 \text{ g/mol}$$

Solution:

W_{Ag} is the weight per cent of silver = 90 per cent
W_{Cu} is the weight per cent of copper = 10 per cent
C_{Ag} is the atom per cent of silver
C_{Cu} is the atom per cent of copper

$$C_{Ag} = \frac{W_{Cu} \times A_{Ag}}{W_{Ag} \times A_{Cu} + W_{Cu} \times A_{Ag}} \times 100$$

$$= \frac{90 \times 63.55}{90 \times 63.55 + 10 \times 107.87}$$

$$= \frac{5719.5}{5719.5 + 1078.7} \times 100 = \frac{5719.5}{6798.2} \times 100$$

$$= 84.13 \text{ per cent}$$

C_{Cu} is the atom per cent of copper

$$C_{Cu} = \frac{W_{Cu} \times A_{Ag}}{W_{Ag} \times A_{Cu} + W_{Cu} \times A_{Ag}} \times 100$$

$$= \frac{10 \times 107.87}{5719.5 + 1078.7} \times 100 = \frac{1078.7}{6798.2} \times 100$$

$$= 15.87 \text{ per cent}$$

3.4 LINE DEFECTS

A linear disorder in the atomic arrangement, which can easily occur on the slip plane within the crystal is known as a dislocation (i.e. atoms dislocated from their normal lattice sites). The dislocation is a one-dimensional defect or line defect and an important crystal imperfection responsible for changes in the mechanical properties of the solid.

Moreover, it is responsible for the deformation of the metals by slip phenomenon. The dislocations are formed in the process of solidification; but they are increased during plastic deformation at yield point, strain hardening and creep and fatigue loading of a material.

The dislocation is a line defect or one-dimensional defect around which some of the atoms are dislocated from the normal lattice sites.

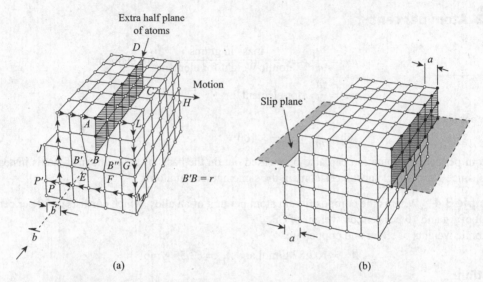

Figure 3.5 *(a) Edge Dislocation (b) Movement of Edge Dislocation*

The simplest type of dislocation is the edge dislocation, as shown in Figure 3.5(a). The dislocation is the extra half plane of atoms squeezed into the crystal lattices. Just above the edge *BC*, of extra half plane, the atoms are squeezed together and below the edge the atoms are put in a state of compression ($r < r_0$). The edge *BC*, i.e. rows along *E* and *F*, come under tension ($r > r_0$), the bond distance *r* is greater than normal value r_0 and the distorted configuration extends all along edge *BC* in the crystal. The potential energy increases for an increase as well as decrease in the bond lengths, *r* (i.e. interatomic distance) so that there is extra strain energy due to distortion in the region surrounding the edge (*BC*) of an incomplete plane (*ABCD*).

As the region of maximum distortion surrounds the extra half plane, the distortion represents a line imperfection and is called an edge dislocation, denoted by ⊥.

Depending upon whether the extra plane starts from the top or bottom of the crystal, the two configurations are referred to as positive and negative edge dislocations, respectively, and are represented by ⊥ and ⊤. Plane *J BCGH K* (*K* not shown in the figure) is called slip plane. The region above the slip plane is called slipped part and the region of crystal below the slip plane is called *unslipped part* [Figure 3.5(b)].

3.4.1 Burger's Circuit and Burger's Vector

Let us start from point *P* in Figure 3.5(a). Going upward by four steps and going towards right by six steps, we reach the point *L*. Coming down by four steps, we reach the point *M*, then moving towards left by six steps, we reach the point *P'*. This circuit is called Burger's circuit and closing side *PP'* is known as *Burger's vector $\bar{b}$*. In an ideal crystal without the edge dislocation, Burger's vector, $\bar{b} = 0$.

Burger's circuit has been drawn clockwise, viewing in the direction of arrow marked along edge $\overrightarrow{BC}$ (edge of dislocation).

Burger's vector PP for an edge dislocation (*BC*) is perpendicular to the dislocation edge *BC*. When metals are deformed, the atoms making up the crystalline structure rearrange to accommodate the deformation by various mechanisms. The dislocation motion is a primary mechanism. When dislocation occurs towards right [Figure 3.6(a)], it (extra half plane) reaches the outer surface of the crystal, causing a slip step by one lattice parameter *a* or by Burger's vector. The extra half plane will project out from a free surface [Figure 3.6(b)].

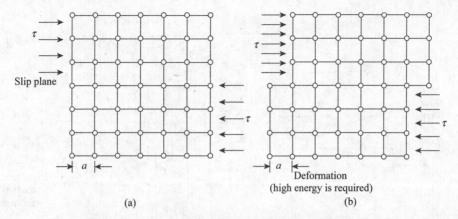

Figure 3.6 *(a) Perfect Crystal (b) High Energy is Required*

If a shearing stress is applied to a perfect crystal, all the atomic bonds along the slip plane would be broken and new bonds are formed. It takes a lot of energy to deform a perfect crystal and to reform all the bonds at once along the slip plane [Figures 3.7(a) and (b)]. However, if the crystalline array has dislocations, the material may deform under an applied shear stress by only breaking and reforming one bond at a time as the dislocation occurs along the slip plane.

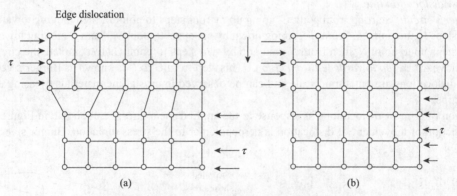

Figure 3.7 *(a) Crystal with an Edge Dislocation*
(b) Only One Row of Bonds is Broken and Reformed at once

3.4.2 Screw Dislocation

This is another type of line defect or line imperfection. In this case, there is no extra half plane of atoms (as in the case of edge dislocation), but a screw dislocation (atoms distorted along an helix of a screw) is formed when a part of the crystal displaces angularly over the remaining part, as if a shear stress has produced this dislocation. As shown in Figure 3.8, the angular displacement is similar to the movement of a screw when it is turned. Screw dislocations are symbolically represented by ⊕ or ⊕ and are referred to as clockwise or anticlockwise or positive or negative screw dislocations. Part *MNB′C* of a crystal has displaced over part *FGHJ* from right to left.

In slip plane *MODG*, the distance *D′G* is displaced to new position *D′C* (Figure 3.8). Dislocation has occurred in the slip plane. Screw dislocation line *l* is marked in the direction of arrow *l*.

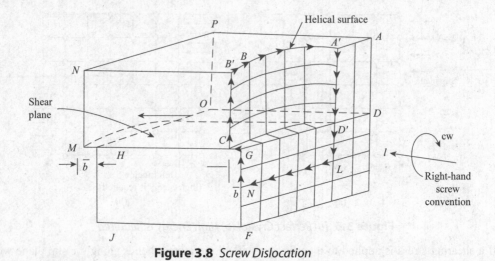

Figure 3.8 *Screw Dislocation*

The atomic bonds in the vicinity of dislocation line undergo thorough shear deformation. This gives rise to the development of shear stress and shear strain field.

Burger's circuit is shown using right-hand screw rule. In this case, *Burger's vector $\bar{b}$ is parallel to the screw dislocation line.*

Burger's circuit: Starting from point *C*, going up by four steps to point *B'*, then moving towards right by five steps to the point *A'*. From *A'* coming down by six steps to point *L*, from *L* moving towards left by five steps up to point *N*, then from *N* going up by two steps to point *G*. To complete the circuit, one has to move *extra step towards left from G to C*. This step from *G* to *C* is known as Burger's vector $\bar{b}$.

The dislocations are on atomic scale and can be observed in crystalline materials by using electron microscope.

Motion of a screw dislocations in response to the applied shear stress, τ, is shown in Figure 3.9(a). The direction of movement of dislocation is perpendicular to the stress direction. Burger's vector $\bar{b}$ is

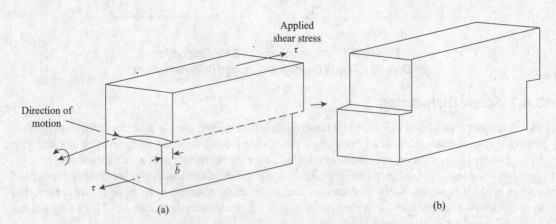

Figure 3.9 *(a) Applied Shear Stress on a Screw Dislocation*
(b) Formation of a Step on the Surface of a Screw Dislocation

parallel to dislocation line [Figure 3.9(b)]. Most of the dislocations found in the crystals are neither pure edge nor pure screw dislocations, but a combination of both which are known as mixed dislocations. The direction of motion of the mixed dislocation line is neither perpendicular nor parallel to the applied shear stress, but lies some where in between (Figure 3.10).

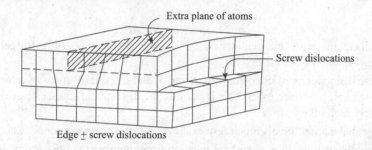

Figure 3.10 *Mixed Dislocation*

All crystalline materials contain some dislocations that are introduced during solidification, during plastic deformation of the material and due to thermal stress developed during quenching operations. The number of dislocations or dislocation density in a material is expressed as total dislocation length per unit volume, or equivalently the number of dislocations present on a unit area of crystalline material. The dislocation density as low as 10^3 mm/mm^3 is typically found in crystals solidified under carefully controlled conditions.

For a heavily deformed material, the dislocation density can be as high as 10^{10} mm/mm^3. The Heat treatment processes of annealing or normalizing reduce the dislocation density to the order of 10^5–10^6 mm/mm^3.

During plastic deformation, the number of dislocations increases exponentially. The Grain boundaries, internal defects, surface irregularities as scratches and notches act as stress concentrations and serve as sites for the formation of dislocations and the existing dislocations get multiplied.

Mixed dislocations generally emerge at the curved boundaries on which the directional continuity gets changed, such as holes, notches and cuts in the material.

3.5 CHARACTERISTICS OF DISLOCATIONS

The properties and behaviour of dislocations are characterized by certain geometries, which are as follows:

1. A crystal normally consists of a large number of dislocations. Hence, there exist numerous Burger's vectors. The sum of these vectors meeting at a point called nodal point inside the crystal remains zero.

2. A dislocation does not abruptly end within the crystal. It vanishes either at the nodal point or on the *surface* of the crystal.

3. A dislocation under the influence field may close on as a *loop*. The profile of the loop may be circle or edge.

4. The distortional energy associated with dislocations may be the source of crystal's instability. The distortional energy is produced due to tensile and compressive stresses/strains field around the edge dislocation and due to shear stress–shear strain field in the case of screw dislocations.

5. The elastic strain energy is directly proportional to the square of the Burger's vector $\bar{b}$,

$$u = \frac{\pi}{8} Gb^2 \simeq \frac{Gb^2}{2}$$

where G is the shear modules of the material.

6. The dislocations may have Burger's vectors of full lattice translation (a) or partial translation of a, i.e.

$$a, 2a, 3a, \ldots \text{ or } a/2, a/3, \ldots$$

7. The dislocations have inherent tendency to keep smallest possible Burger's vector, which enhances the stability of the crystal.

8. Two edge dislocations of opposite sign ⊥ and ⊤ and of equal Burger's vector and on the same slip plane cancel out each other. This is because the distortional strain energy fields superimpose and cancel each other.

9. The edge dislocation travels much faster (about 50 times) than the *screw dislocations*.

10. The edge dislocations in a crystal are much more in number than the screw dislocations in any crystalline material.

11. Due to plastic deformation of the crystal, the dislocations get multiplied.

3.6 SOURCES OF DISLOCATIONS

There are two main sources of dislocations in crystals: (1) mishandling during grain growth, i.e. during solidification process and (2) mechanical deformation during metal working processes as rolling, extrusions, drawing and spinning.

The crystals are obtained by the process of crystallization, i.e. molten metal is solidified. Recovery, recrystallization and *grain growth are* the essential features of a manufacturing process. It is almost impossible to achieve perfections in grain growth, hence dislocations occur in crystals.

Mechanical deformation is another source of dislocations. The mechanical processes such as rolling, extrusion, forging and wire drawing greatly increase the dislocation density in the crystals. These mechanical deformations may be geometrically linear, angular or complex.

The effects of dislocations are detrimental to the mechanical properties of crystalline materials such as

1. The mechanical strength is reduced.
2. The ductility of the material is reduced due to strain hardening.
3. The surface properties of the materials such as corrosion resistance are influenced negatively.
4. However, the density of the material is negligibly affected.

The following remedial measures are suggested to minimize the occurrence of dislocations:

- Use of thermal energy such as annealing process for reduction of dislocation density.
- Careful control of various parameters during crystallization process, i.e. grain growth.
- Prevention of undesired mechanical deformations.
- Use of the material in whisker's form, in which the dislocations are reduced to a minimum level.

On heating the crystals to a high temperature, many dislocations are either annihilated among themselves or are driven out of the crystal surfaces.

3.7 STACKING OF CLOSE-PACKED STRUCTURES

The FCC and HCP structures can be built up from a stacking of close-packed planes of spheres. Figure 3.11 shows that there are two ways in which spheres can be stacked.

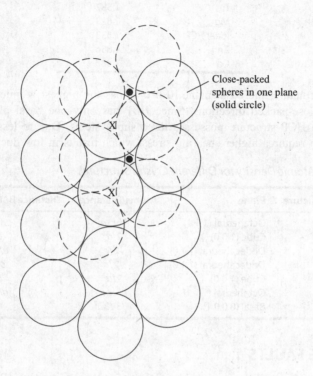

Close-packed spheres in one plane (solid circle)

Figure 3.11 *Stacking of Close-packed Spheres*

The first layer of spheres is arranged in such a way that each sphere is surrounded by six other spheres and each touching the other (shown by a layer of solid circles). A second layer of close-packed spheres can be placed over the bottom layer so that the *centres* of the atoms in the second plane cover one half of the number of valleys in the bottom layer (dotted circles in Figure 3.11). There are two ways of adding spheres to get a *third close-packed plane*. Although the spheres in the third layer must fit into the valleys in the second plane, they may lie either over the valleys not covered in the first plane (the dots in the figures) or directly above the atoms in the first plane (the crosses).

The first possibility results in the staking sequence *ABC ABC* — which is found for the (III) planes of an FCC structure. The other possibility results in the stacking sequence *AB AB*—, which is found for the (0 0 0 1) basal plane of the HCP structure. For ideal HCP packing ratio $c/a = \sqrt{8}/3 = 1.633$. Actual HCP metals deviate from the ideal c/a ratio (Table 3.2).

Both FCC and HCP structures are close-packed structures with $APF = 0.74$. However, in BCC unit cell, $APF = 0.68$ and in simple cubic unit cell, $APF = 0.52$.

Plastic deformation is confined to planes of higher density of atoms per unit area. Moreover, the planes of greatest atomic density also are most widely spaced for the crystal structures (Table 3.3).

Table 3.2 *c/a Ratio for Various Metals*

Metal	c/a ratio
Be	1.568
Ti	1.587
Mg	1.623
Ideal HCP	1.633
Zn	1.856
Cd	1.886

In HCP crystal structure, the basal plane (0 0 0 1) has the highest atomic density and the axes [1 1 2 0] are the close-packed directions. Since HCP has only one basal plane per unit cell and three directions, the HCP structure possesses three slip systems. Due to less number of slip systems, the dislocation requires higher shearing stress, which results in low ductility in HCP crystals.

Table 3.3 *Atomic Density for Different Crystal Structures*

Crystal Structure	Plane	Atoms/Distance	Distance Between Planes
FCC	Octahedral (1 1 1)	$4/\sqrt{3}a^2$	$a/\sqrt{3}$
	Cube (1 0 0)	$2/a^2$	$a/2$
	Dodecahedral (1 1 0)	$\sqrt{2}/a^2$	$a/2\sqrt{2}$
BCC	Dodecahedral (1 1 0)	$\sqrt{2}/a^2$	$a/\sqrt{2}$
	Cube (1 0 0)	$1/a^2$	$a/2$
	Octahedral (1 1 1)	$1/\sqrt{3}a^2$	$a/2\sqrt{3}$
HCP	Basal (0 0 0 1)	$1/3\sqrt{3}a^2$	c

3.8 STACKING FAULTS

For an FCC structure, the stacking sequence of planes of atoms is given by *ABC/ABC/ABC* as shown in Figure 3.12(a). Due to plastic deformation fault in the stacking sequence is produced as shown in

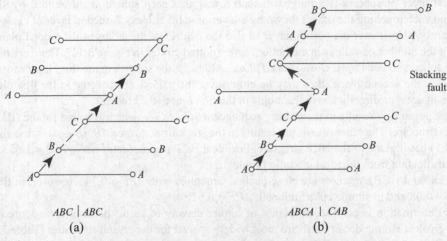

ABC | ABC
(a)

ABCA | CAB
(b)

Figure 3.12 *Deformation Fault in FCC*

Figure 3.12(b), i.e. *ABCA/CAB*. Slip on the (III) plane in an FCC lattice produces a deformation stacking fault by the process shown in Figure 3.12(b), and stacking sequence becomes *ABCA/CAB*.

Another way by which a stacking fault occurs in an FCC metal is by sequence shown in Figure 3.13. Stacking sequence *ABC/ACB/CA* is called 'twin stacking fault'. The three layers, *ACB*, constitute the twin.

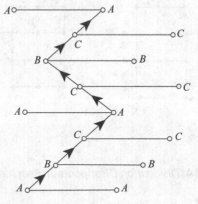

ABC |ACB | CA

Figure 3.13 *Twin Stacking Fault*

From the point of view of dislocation theory, a stacking fault in an FCC metal can be considered to be an extended dislocation consisting of a thin hexagonal region bounded by partial dislocations.

It is more difficult to form stacking faults in a BCC lattice than in close-packed FCC and HCP structures. The stacking faults enter during the plastic deformation of metals in a number of ways. Metals with wide stacking faults strain-harden more rapidly and form an annealing twin easily.

3.9 BEHAVIOUR OF DISLOCATIONS

The response of the dislocations under externally applied stress is listed as follows:

1. Glide motion of dislocation
2. Climb up or climb down motions
3. Cross slip in dislocations
4. Dislocations pile up
5. Jogs or jumps of dislocations
6. Dislocation interactions with point imperfections
7. Frank Read source of dislocations

3.9.1 Glide Motion

Only edge dislocation and mixed dislocations can have glide motion, i.e. crystal glides over the slip plane [Figure 3.14(a)]. The dislocation moves or glides over the slip plane and disappears when it reaches free surface as shown in Figure 3.14(b). There is no gliding motion of screw dislocation.

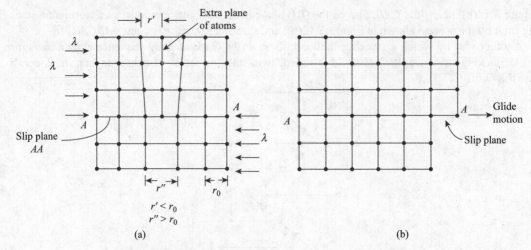

Figure 3.14 *Dislocation Disappears on Reaching the Surface*

3.9.2 Dislocation Climb

A plane perpendicular to the glide plane is a climb plane and an edge dislocation can climb up or down. So, edge dislocations can go up or come down in the climb plane. The movement of atoms and vacancies at high temperature is the cause of this motion.

A crystal contains an edge dislocation AB and a vacancy along the row at V [Figure 3.15(a)]. When the row of atoms at B shifts to vacancy site V, the extra plane AB of atoms shrinks due to subtraction of row of atoms at B. The edge dislocation climbs up as shown in Figure 3.15(b). In the climb down process, there is an increase in the row of atoms below edge dislocations, thereby vacancies are filled or formed as the case may be.

Screw dislocation cannot climb up or climb down. The edge dislocation climb is a diffusion-controlled process.

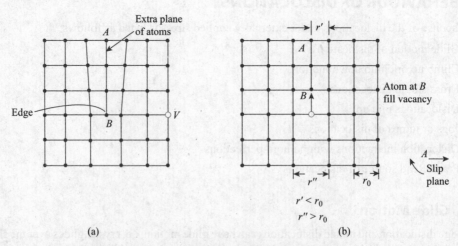

Figure 3.15 *(a) A Crystal with Edge Dislocation AB and Vacancy at V*
(b) Vacancy at V is Filled Up

The positive climb causes the vacancies to annihilate while the negative climb generates vacancies. The climb motions require more energy than glide motions, because these are associated with migration of vacancies. Stress helps the climb motion. A compressive stress causes a positive climb and a tensile stress causes a negative climb.

The dislocation climb is necessary for polygonization and creep processes. Creep occurs due to diffusion of vacancies.

3.9.3 Cross Slip

A characteristic of FCC crystal lattice is that any Burger's vector is common to two slip planes. The screw dislocations have no fixed glide plane, and can surmount obstacles by gliding into another slip plane having a common slip direction. This is the process of *cross slip*.

A screw dislocation can gross slide or cross slip from one slip plane to another as shown in Figure 3.16. The screw dislocation first glides, then cross slips to a non-parallel plane $(1\,\bar{1}\,1)$. In the double cross slip process, it again cross slips back to (1 1 1) plane, which is parallel to the initial plane (Figure 3.16). Cross slip is easier in metals with high stacking fault energy.

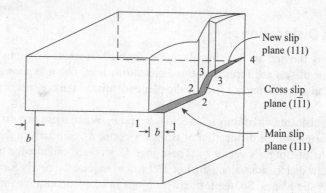

Figure 3.16 *Cross Slip*

3.9.4 Dislocations Pile Up

During plastic deformation, when dislocations travelling on a slip plane, the dislocations of opposite nature annihilate each other on the same slip plane, but the dislocations of same nature (all positive as shown) pile up as they reach the obstacle, i.e. hard grain boundary. The distance between the dislocations goes on decreasing and are most tightly packed near the obstacle (Figure 3.17).

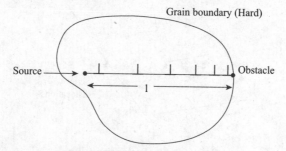

Figure 3.17 *Dislocation Pile Up*

The number of dislocations n that are gathered or pile up is given by relations

$$n = \frac{K\pi\tau_a l}{Gb}$$

where l is the distance along the slip plane from source to obstacle.

K is a factor

= 1 for screw dislocations

= $(1 - v)$ for edge dislocations, where v is Poisson's ratio

τ_a is the average resolved shear stress in the slip plane, G is the shear modulus of the material and b is the Burger's vector.

If the source is situated at the centre of the grain of average diameter d, the number of dislocations is given by

$$n = \frac{K\pi\tau_a d}{4Gb}$$

Since the source is located at the centre, there will be a back stress on the source.

Total Burger's vector = nb. Force on the dislocations at the piled up end = $nb\tau_a$

3.9.5 Jogs in Dislocations

If the dislocations moving in the slip plane cut through other dislocations intersecting the active slip plane, jogs or offsets are formed in the dislocations line. *The jogs formed in this case are edge dislocations*, because their Burger's vectors are perpendicular to the original dislocation line *DD* shown in Figure 3.18.

There are two dislocations of Burger's vectors b_1 and b_2. When these two dislocations intersect, a jog or step of b_2 is formed in the dislocation of Burger's vector b_1. Similarly, a jog or step of b_1 is formed in the dislocations of Burger's vector b_2. These jogs formed are called edge dislocations. Any further movement of screw dislocations along the line *DD* would require the newly formed edge components to move out of their slip planes. So, the formation of jogs in screw dislocations impedes their motion and may even lead to the formation of vacancies and interstitials, if the jogs are forced to move further. The jogs in edge dislocations do not impede their motion.

As the dislocation can move from one plane to another, similarly it can also jump from one plane to another by creating a step or a jog. The jog is treated as a short dislocation. Figure 3.19 shows CB_1, as jog in edge dislocation BC, jumped to position B_1C_1.

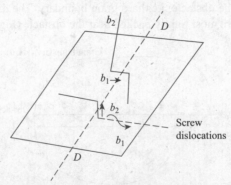

Figure 3.18 *Dislocation Jog*

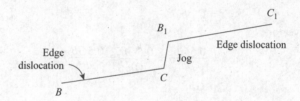

Figure 3.19 *Dislocation Jog*

3.9.6 Interaction of Dislocation with Point Imperfections

Point imperfections (i.e. vacancies) are thermodynamically stable, but dislocations are not. Dislocations interact with point imperfections provided that energies of both, i.e. point imperfections and disloca-tions, lower down. The observations for this interaction are as follows:

1. Vacancy diffusion helps in dislocation climb.
2. Substitutional impurity atoms interact with edge dislocation and stress–strain field around dislo-cation is changed.
3. Smaller substitutional atom reduces energy of interacting system.
4. Large substitutional atom destabilizes the system.
5. Interstitial atom fits into large spaced region of edge dislocation, as carbon occupies interstitial positions in iron (BCC) atoms, causing discontinuous yielding in mild steel.

3.9.7 Frank Read Source

Sources (for dislocations) originally present in the metal could produce new dislocations by the process of slip. But the surface displacement at a slip band is due to the movement of about 1000 dislocations over a slip plane. During cold working of a metal, severe strain hardening takes place due to the multi-plication of the dislocation density. So, there is some process by which each source could produce large amount of slip before it becomes immobilized. There must be a process of generating dislocations so as to produce high density of dislocation.

Figure 3.20(a) shows nodes A and A', or the impurity atoms A and A'. The dislocation line leaves the slip plane at A and A', so that it is immobilized at these points. If a shear stress τ acts in the slip plane, the dislocation line $AA' = 1$ bulges out and produces slip. For a given stress τ, the dislocation line will assume a certain radius ρ, say $\rho = 1/2$, so that ρ has a minimum value.

Line tension,

$$\Gamma = 0.5\ Gb^2,$$

where G is shear modulus.

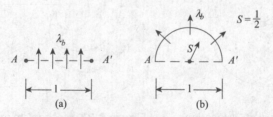

Figure 3.20 *(a); (b) Bulging of Dislocation Line*

$$\tau = \Gamma/\rho b,$$

where b is Burger's vector.

$$\tau = \frac{0.5Gb^2}{\rho b} = \frac{0.5Gb}{\rho} = \frac{0.5Gb}{l} \times 2$$

$$= \frac{Gb}{l}$$

where l is the distance between the nodes. If the shear stress is raised above the critical value, the dislocations become unstable and expand as shown in Figure 3.20(c). It shows the expanded loop.

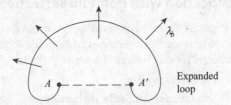

Figure 3.20 *(c) Expanded Loop*

The loop can continue to expand over the slip under the increasing stress. The section AA' will soon straighten out under the influence of applied stress τ and line tension Γ, and the Frank Read source will be in position to repeat the process.

Figure 3.21 shows that the dislocation has almost double back on itself. Figure 3.22 shows the repetition of Frank Read source dislocations. In the final stage, a circular dislocation loop is generated. Repetition of the process results in infinite number of loops, which move out and disappear at the free surface.

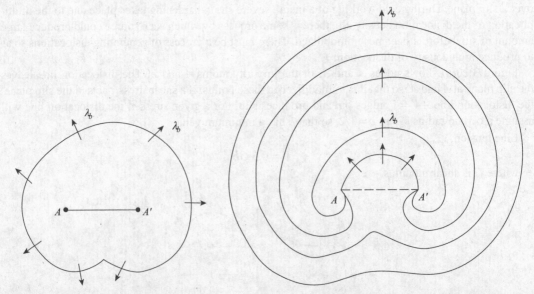

Figure 3.21 *Double Back of Dislocation*   **Figure 3.22** *Mechanism of Frank Read Source*

3.10 TWINNING

Metal deformation also takes place by the process of twinning. In twinning, a portion of the crystal takes up an orientation that is related to the orientation of the rest of the untwinned lattice, in a definite symmetrical way.

The twinned portion of the crystal is a mirror image of the parent crystal. The *plane of symmetry* between the two portions is called *twinning plane*.

Figure 3.23 shows the atomic picture of a twinning process. Low index planes (planes of maximum atomic density) are oriented at an angle to the polished plane *PS*. The twining plane is perpendicular to the plane of the paper. If a shear stress, *τ*, is applied, the crystal will twin about the twinning plane. Region *B*, to the right of the twin plane is undeformed. To the left of this plane, planes of atoms have sheared in such a way that the lattice becomes a mirror image across the twin plane. Region *A* is the mirror image of region *B*. Each atom in the twinned region moves by a shear stress, a distance proportional to its distance from the twin plane. Open circles represent atoms that have not been moved, and solid circles are the final positions of the atoms in the twinned region. Twin is visible on the polished surface.

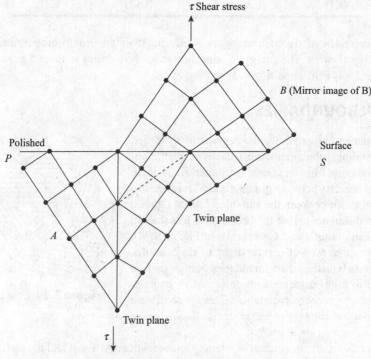

Figure 3.23 *Twinning*

Twinning differs from slip in many ways:

1. In slip, orientations of the crystal above and below the slip plane is the same after deformation, but twinning results in an orientation difference across the twin plane.
2. Slip occurs in discrete multiples of atomic spacing, but in twinning, the atom movements are much less than an atomic distance.

3. Slip occurs on relatively wide spread planes, but in the twinned region every atomic plane is involved in the deformation.

4. Twins can be formed within a time as short as a few microseconds, while for slip there is a delay time of several milliseconds before a slip band is formed.

Twins may be produced by mechanical deformation or as a result of annealing, which is followed after plastic deformation. So, there are mechanical twins and annealing twins. Mechanical twins are produced in BCC or HCP crystals under conditions of rapid rate of loading and decreased temperature. Gold–silver alloys twin readily when deformed at low temperature. Mechanical twins are produced in copper at 4K.

Common twin planes and twin directions are given in Table 3.4.

Table 3.4 *Twin Planes / Twin Directions of Various Crystal Structures*

Crystal Structure	Example	Twin Plane	Twin Direction
BCC	α Fe, Ta	(1 1 2)	(1 1 1)
HCP	Zn, Cd, Mg, Ti	(1 0 $\bar{1}$ 2)	($\bar{1}$ 0 1 1)
FCC	Ag, Au, Cu	(1 1 1)	(1 1 2)

Twins do not extend beyond a grain boundary. Annealing twins are usually broader and with straighter sides than mechanical twins. The energy of annealing twins boundaries is about 5 per cent of the grain boundary energy. Most FCC metals form annealing twins.

3.11 GRAIN BOUNDARIES

The grain boundaries are generally the regions of disturbed lattices. The crystallographic orientation (planes of maximum atomic density) changes from one grain to another. High-angle grain boundary (boundary between grains A and B) represents a region of random misfit between the adjoining crystal lattices. If the orientation difference across the boundary is less than $1°$ (boundary between grains A and C as shown in Figure 3.24), boundary may be composed of regular array of dislocations.

High-angle grain boundaries are boundaries of high surface energy. Because of high surface energy (along such bounda-ries), these boundaries serve as preferential sites for solid state reactions. *The concentrations of solute atoms are higher at the boundary than in the interior of grain.*

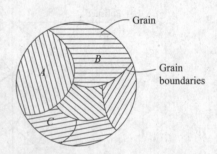

Figure 3.24 *Grain Boundaries*

The grain boundaries are the sources of strength and weakness. At about half the melting temperature, increase in strain rate increases the strength. At high temperatures and low strain rate (as in the case of creep process), deformation is localized at the grain boundary, grain boundary sliding and stress–induced migrations take place and finally the fracture takes place. In comparison to single crystal, polycrystalline materials exhibit a high rate of strain hardening, and with the help of a high precision microscope one can view that slip stops at the grain boundary. The dislocations pile up at the grain boundary producing back stress, which opposes the generation of Frank Read sources.

3.12 LOW-ANGLE GRAIN BOUNDARIES

Within a grain of high energy boundary, there are subgrains of low energy sub-boundaries in which difference in orientation across this boundary may be at the most a few degrees. So, within a grain, there is a network of subgrains of low-energy boundaries, which can be detected by X-ray technique. Figure 3.25(a) shows sub-boundaries of subgrains with a small angle between the two sub-boundaries. Figure 3.25(b) shows the sub-boundaries formed together by an array of edge dislocations.

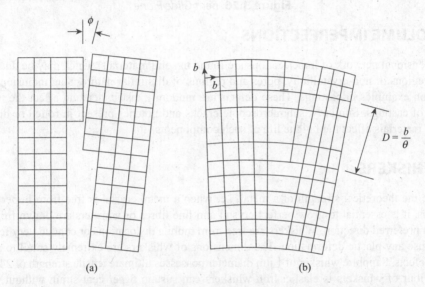

Figure 3.25 *(a) Low-angle Subgrain Boundaries*
(b) Array of Dislocation Along Low-angle Brain Boundary

Relationship between θ and spacing between dislocations

$$\theta = 2 \tan^{-1}\frac{b}{2D} \approx \frac{b}{D}$$

where b is the magnitude of Burger's vector.

If the angle is low, so that spacing between dislocations, i.e. D is large, it is possible to observe that the sub-boundary is composed of a row of etch pits with each etch pit as site of dislocation. The sub-boundaries in a crystal can be produced in many ways:
  i) During crystal growth
  ii) During high-temperature creep deformation

If a single crystal is bent to a relatively small curvature and then annealed, bending results in the introduction of an excess number of dislocations of the same sign as shown in Figure 3.26(a).

The dislocations are distributed along that bent glide planes as shown in Figure 3.26(a). When the crystal is heated, dislocations group themselves with low energy configuration of a low-angle boundary by dislocation climb as shown in Figure 3.26(b). The resulting structure is a polygon-like network of low-angle grain boundaries. The term is known as 'polygonization'.

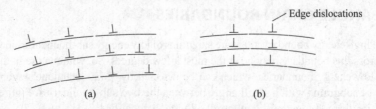

Figure 3.26 *Bent Glide Plane*

3.13 VOLUME IMPERFECTIONS

Three-dimensional network of imperfections are found in solid materials, which may be due to foreign particles, regions of non-crystallinity, pores and regions of dissimilar nature. Slag inclusion and pores are common examples in castings. These defects are randomly distributed and affect the mechanical properties of castings. Similarly, submicroscopic cracks and notches present in rolled or drawn poly-crystalline materials affect the fatigue life of such components.

3.14 WHISKERS

To achieve the theoretical strength of a metal, i.e. when a metal crystal is free from imperfections or dislocations, it is essential to grow perfect crystal and fine fibres or whiskers are drawn from a single crystal in a preferred direction. Whiskers are free from mobile dislocations or contain very few dislocations to cause any plastic deformation. The dimensions of whiskers are extremely small to allow little room for defects. Sapphire whisker of 1 μm diameter possesses ultimate tensile strength of 24,000 MPa. The behaviour of whiskers is elastic. Iron whiskers can sustain 5 per cent strain without permanent deformation, while bulk iron sets in at 0.2 per cent strain only. Metal oxide whiskers can be deformed up to 3–4 per cent without permanent set. The strength of a metal whisker varies inversely with its diameter.

Whiskers are available from metallic, non-metallic, organic and inorganic materials. The defects such as grain boundaries are fully eliminated as whiskers are drawn from a single crystal. Table 3.5 shows a comparison of strength, Young's modulus and elastic deformation for whiskers and bulk materials.

Table 3.5 *Comparison of Strength, Young's Modulus and Elastic Deformation for Whiskers and Bulk Materials*

Material	Strength MPa Bulk	Strength MPa Whisker	E GPa Bulk	E GPa Whisker	Elastic Deformation % Bulk	Elastic Deformation % Whisker
Graphite	2600	19,700	27	703	—	—
Silicon carbide	10,000	20,700	450	840	—	—
Tungsten	1500	14,000	400	2400	0.01	0.3
Mild steel	420	12,800	210	1000	0.2	5.0
Alumina	5000	14,000	390	2250	—	2.0

KEY POINTS TO REMEMBER

❑ There are vacancy and self-interstitial point defects in a crystal. Self-interstitial point defect distorts the lattice around the atom.

❑ Number of equilibrium vacancies,

$$N_e = N \exp\left(\frac{-Q_v}{kT}\right)$$

where N is the total number of atomic sites, Q_v is the energy required to create a vacancy, k is the Boltzmann constant and T is the absolute temperature of the material.

❑ The impurity atoms in solids take up the substitutional or interstitial positions.

❑ Copper and nickel are completely soluble in one another in all proportions.

❑ Extra plane of atoms inserted in perfect crystal lattices is known as edge dislocation.

❑ Under external shear stress, edge dislocation glides over the slip plane.

❑ Zones of compression and tension are developed around edge dislocation.

❑ Screw dislocation is formed when a part of the crystal displaces angularly over the remaining part.

❑ In screw dislocation, Burger's vector is parallel to dislocation.

❑ In mixed dislocations, there are screw and edge dislocations present in the crystal.

❑ For heavily deformed metal, dislocation density can be as high as 10^{10} mm/mm^3.

❑ Strain energy per unit length of dislocation $u = Gb^2/2$, where G is the shear modulus and b is Burger's vector.

❑ Edge dislocations are much more in number than screw dislocations in a metal.

❑ Edge dislocations travel much faster than screw dislocations.

❑ Mishandling during grain growth and mechanical deformation are the sources of dislocations.

❑ Twinned portion of the crystal is a mirror image of the parent crystal. The plane of symmetry between the two planes is called twinning plane.

❑ Twins can be produced by mechanical deformation or by annealing.

❑ Gold–silver alloys twin readily when deformed at low temperature.

❑ Twins do not extend beyond grain boundary.

❑ An edge dislocation climbs up or climbs down when a ray of vacancy is filled by atoms at the edge of dislocation.

❑ A screw dislocation can surmount obstacles by gliding into another slip plane having a common slip direction—process is known as cross slip.

❑ Dislocations pile up as they reach hard obstacle as grain boundary.

❑ Frank Read source generates dislocations so as to increase the density of dislocations.

❑ Grain boundaries are the regions of disturbed lattices. High-angle grain boundaries represent regions of misfit between the adjoining crystal lattices.

❑ The strength of metal whiskers varies inversely with its diameter.

❑ Whiskers are drawn from a single crystal.

❑ Sapphire whisker of 1 μm diameter possesses ultimate strength of 24,000 GPa.

❑ Within a grain, there is a network of subgrains of low energy boundaries.

❑ Polygonization takes place in dislocations grouping themselves into low energy configuration of sub-boundaries.

MULTIPLE CHOICE QUESTIONS

1. Which of the following statements is correct?

   (A) Self-interstitial atom produces large distortions in the surrounding lattice

   (B) Presence of equilibrium number of vacancies adversely affects the mechanical strength of a metal

   (a) Only A   (c) Both A and B

   (b) Only B   (d) Neither A nor B

2. For most metals, the fraction of equilibrium number of vacancies N_e to total atomic sites is

   (a) 10^{-3} (c) 10^{-5}

   (b) 10^{-4} (d) None of these

3. Why copper and nickel are completely soluble in each other?

   (a) The atomic radius of nickel and copper is the same

   (b) Both have same crystal structure

   (c) Valence electrons for both are the same

   (d) None of these

4. Which of the following statements is correct?

   (A) In edge dislocation, Burger's vector is perpendicular to edge dislocation.

   (B) Under applied shear stress, edge dislocation glides over slip plane.

   (a) Both A and B   (c) Only B

   (b) Only A   (d) Neither A nor B

5. Which is the incorrect statement?

   (A) Cross slip takes place in screw dislocations.

   (B) Atomic bonds in the vicinity of screw dislocations undergo thorough shear deformation.

   (C) Burger's vector is perpendicular to screw dislocations.

   (a) Both A and B   (c) Both B and C

   (b) C only   (d) None of these

6. By what process the dislocation density is drastically reduced?

   (a) Plastic deformation

   (b) Annealing

   (c) Tempering

   (d) None of these

7. If b is Burger's vector and G is the shear modulus, elastic strain energy per unit volume is

   (a) $Gb^2/2$ (c) $Gb^2/3$

   (b) $Gb/3$ (d) None of these

8. Which of the following statements is correct?

   (A) Most FCC metals form annealing twins.

   (B) Mechanical twins are produced in BCC or HCP crystals.

   (a) Both A and B   (c) B only

   (b) A only   (d) Neither A nor B

9. Ratio of E of a whisker of mild steel to E of a bulk material is

   (a) 4   (c) 50

   (b) 5   (d) 60

10. In low-angle grain boundary, spacing between edge dislocation is given by

(a) b/θ

(b) θ/b

(c) $\theta/2b$

(d) None of these

where b is Burger's vector and θ is the angle between sub-boundaries.

Answers

1. (a)   2. (b)   3. (b)   4. (a)   5. (b)   6. (b)   7. (a)   8. (a)   9. (b)   10. (a)

═══ REVIEW QUESTIONS ═══

1. What are the different types of point defects?

2. Explain the difference between Schottky and Frenkel defects.

3. What is the ratio of equilibrium number of vacancies and total number of atomic sites in a metal near melting point?

4. What do you understand by solid solution? What is the type of solid solution of nickel and copper?

5. What type of solid solution exists between iron and carbon?

6. What are the different types of line defects? Explain with the help of neat sketches.

7. What are the basic differences among edge, screw and mixed dislocations?

8. Take an edge dislocation and describe Burger's circuit and Burger's vector in this?

9. Write a short note on characteristics of dislocations.

10. What do you understand by stacking fault in close-packed structures?

11. Explain the process of twinning, how it is different from a slip?

12. Explain climb, jog and cross slip in dislocations.

13. Explain the process of dislocation generation by Frank Read source.

14. Why Young's modulus and strength are much more for whiskers than for bulk materials?

15. What is polygonization in low-angle subgrain boundaries?

PRACTICE PROBLEMS

1. What is the composition in weight per cent of an alloy, which consists of 15 per cent Cu and 85 per cent of Pt by atoms. Take atomic weights, $A_{Cu} = 63.55$ g/mol., $A_{Pt} = 195.09$ g/mol.

    Ans. [94.56 per cent, 5.44 per cent]

2. Determine the composition in atom per cent of an alloy that consists of 97 per cent by weight of aluminium and 3 per cent by weight of copper. Atomic weights are $A_{Cu} = 63.55$ g/mol, $A_{Al} = 26.98$ g/mol

    Ans. [Al, 98.7 per cent, Cu 1.3 per cent]

3. Calculate the energy for vacancy formation in silver, if the number of equilibrium vacancies at 800°C is 3.6×10^{23}/m³. The atomic weight of silver is 107.9 g/mol and the density at 800°C is 9.5 g/cm³

    Ans [$Q_v = 1.10$ eV/atom]

4. What is the composition in weight per cent of an alloy that consists of 6 atom per cent of Pb and 94 atom per cent of Sn?

    Ans. [90 per cent, 10 per cent]

5. What is the composition in atom per cent of an alloy that contains 98 g of tin and 65 g of lead?

    Ans. [72.5 per cent, 27.5 per cent]

6. Calculate the number of atoms per cubic metre in aluminium.

    Ans. [6.02×10^{28} atom/m³]

4

PLASTIC DEFORMATION IN CRYSTALLINE MATERIALS

4.1 INTRODUCTION

The most ideal representation of a material is in the form of its single crystal. The mechanical behaviour of a single crystal is described on the basis of crystal structure and defects in the crystal. However, the use of single crystal is limited to electronic and semiconductor devices as single crystals of germanium and silicon are grown in laboratory and the chips are cut in preferred orientations.

But in a polycrystalline material, a grain or crystal is not free to deform independently because of the constraints imposed on it by the surrounding crystals, which may have different crystallographic orientations. Even if slip has started in one crystal, it is not carried through another crystal because the surrounding crystal may have different slip planes and different slip directions.

The first part of this chapter deals with slip systems of a single crystal and the critical resolved shear stress and tensile test on a single crystal.

In the second part, yield point phenomenon of polycrystalline metals is discussed. Yield point elongation at lower yield point, strain ageing and hardening due to point defects are discussed. The strength at yield point and increase in yield point due to strain hardening are important considerations in the industrial applications of low carbon steels. Strengthening mechanisms in metals, grain size reduction, solid solution hardening, strain hardening and precipitation hardening are explained in detail in this chapter.

Finally, there is a discussion on the recovery of original structure of the metal, by relieving the internal stresses and reducing the lattice distortions (due to cold work) by the process of annealing. Recrystallization and grain growth to achieve ductility and toughness for a material are also the important contents of this chapter.

4.2 SLIP IN PERFECT LATTICE

Slip takes place when one plane moves over another plane. Figure 4.1(a) shows perfect lattice structure without any imperfections. If shear stress τ is applied, then the plane 1–1 slips over another plane 2–2, say by a distance x as shown in Figure 4.1(b). Moreover in the y-direction, atoms are displaced from distance

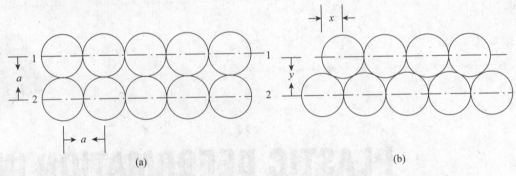

Figure 4.1 *(a) Perfect Lattice (b) One Plane Slips over Another Plane*

a to y, as shown, where a is the lattice parameter. Please note that $y < a$, atoms of plane 1–1 occupy the positions in the valleys of atoms of plane 2–2. Shear stress is zero, when the atoms occupy the stable positions at the centre of the valleys or when one atom comes at the top of another atom as in perfect lattice. So, there is variation of shear stress τ as distance x varies from 0 to $a/2$ and $a/2$ to a as shown in Figure 4.2.

Figure 4.2 shows the variation of shear stress τ with respect to displacement x, which can be written as

$$\tau = \tau_m \frac{\sin 2\pi x}{a}$$

where τ_m is the maximum shear stress.

We have $\tau \simeq \tau_m (2\pi x/a)$, where values of x/a are very small, and $\tau = G \times \gamma$, as per Hooke's law (= shear modulus × shear strain). But shear strain $\gamma = x/y$. Putting these values, we get

$$\tau = G \times \frac{x}{y} = \tau_m \times \frac{2\pi x}{a}$$

$$\tau_m = \frac{Ga}{2\pi y} \tag{4.1}$$

If $\qquad\qquad a = y$, then $\tau_m = \dfrac{G}{2\pi}$

The theoretical shear stress of a crystal required to produce plastic deformation is $G/2\pi$. This theoretical value of τ_m is very much higher (about 100 times) than the observed shear stress in metal crystals, because of some other slip mechanisms such as dislocation. A realistic curve between τ and x is shown in Figure 4.2.

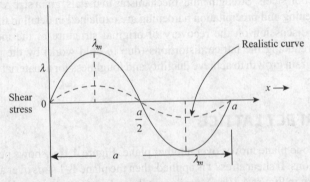

Figure 4.2 *Variation of Shear Stress τ versus Displacement x*

Tyson has used computer for the prediction of maximum shear stress for various crystal structures as follows:

$$\tau_m = \frac{G}{16} \quad \text{for FCC structure}$$

$$= \frac{G}{8} \quad \text{for simple cubic}$$

$$= \frac{G}{4} \quad \text{for covalently bonded, such as diamond}$$

4.3 SLIP SYSTEMS

Dislocations do not move with the same degree of ease on all crystallographic planes of atoms and in all crystallographic directions. Ordinarily, there is a preferred plane (slip plane) and a specific direction (slip direction) in a slip system.

For a particular crystal structure, the slip plane is the plane that has the densest atomic packing (having the greatest planar density). The slip direction corresponds to the direction in this plane that is most closely packed with the atoms.

The most close packed direction in an FCC structure is [1 1 0] where the most densely packed planes (1 1 1) exist. There are four slip (1 1 1) planes of which each contains three [1 1 0] directions. There are $3 \times 4 = 12$ slip systems.

In a BCC, the most closed packed direction is [1 1 1]. There are three planes in BCC with relatively high packing densities: (1 1 0), (1 0 0) and (1 1 2) planes. As the (1 0 0) planes do not contain the [1 1 1] directions, there are two slip planes, i.e. (1 1 0) and (1 1 2). There are six (1 1 0) planes with two [1 1 1] directions in each, totalling $6 \times 2 = 12$ slip systems. Moreover, there are also 12 systems of the type (1 1 2) planes and [1 1 1] directions.

4.3.1 HCP Crystal

There are three most closely packed directions lying in the closed packed basal plane (0 0 0 1) and slip direction [1 1 2 0]. There are only three slip systems in an HCP crystal.

Slip is more difficult in low-density planes because atoms are far apart and the slip distances are large. Table 4.1 gives an overview of the slip systems in common crystal structures.

Table 4.1 *Slip Systems in Common Crystal Structures*

Crystal Lattice	Metals	Slip Planes	Slip Directions	Slip Systems Number
BCC	Fe, W, V, Cr, Mo	(1 1 0), (1 1 2) and (1 1 3) (less common)	[1 1 1] and [1 1 1]	$6 \times 2 = 12$
FCC	Al, Cu, Ni, Ag, Pt	(1 1 1)	[1 1 0]	$4 \times 3 = 12$
HCP	Mg, Co, Zn, Ti, Zr	(0 0 0 1)	[1 1 2 0]	$3 \times 1 = 3$

4.4 CRITICAL RESOLVED SHEAR STRESS FOR SLIP

The amount of slip taking place in a single crystal depends on the magnitude of the shearing stress produced by an external force, geometry of the crystal structure and the orientation of the active slip planes with respect to the shearing stress.

Slip begins when the shearing stress on the slip plane in the slip direction reaches a threshold value called the *critical resolved shear stress*, and this depends mainly on the composition of the metal and the temperature.

It is obvious that different tensile loads are required to produce slip in single crystals of different orientation, but it can be rationalized by a critical resolved shear stress.

First of all, it is necessary to determine from X-ray diffraction (i) the orientation with respect to the tensile axis of the plane on which the slip first appears and (ii) the slip direction.

Figure 4.3 shows a single crystal of cylindrical shape, with a cross-sectional area A. The angle between the normal to the slip plane and the tensile axis is φ (Figure 4.3). The angle, which the slip direction makes with the tensile axis is α.

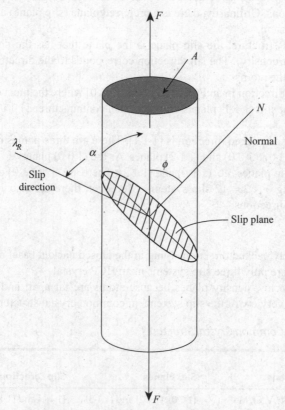

Figure 4.3 *Critical Resolved Shear Stress, τ_R*

Area of the plane $= \dfrac{A}{\cos \varphi}$

Component of the axial load F acting in the slip direction is $F \cos \alpha$. Therefore, the critical resolved shear stress is given by

$$\tau_R = \frac{F \cos \alpha}{A/\cos \varphi} = \frac{F}{A} \cos \varphi \cos \alpha$$

The law of critical resolved shear stress is best demonstrated by HCP crystals, where the limited number of slip systems allows large difference between the slip plane and the tensile axis (angle φ). In FCC metals, due to high symmetry, the variation in critical resolved shear stress is only two times, because of the differences in orientation of the slip plane and the tensile axis. In BCC crystals, there are large number of available slip systems and there is less variation in resolved shear stress.

When a small amount of impurities is added, there is an increase in the critical resolved shear stress. A large increase in the resistance to slip is produced by alloying gold with silver. These atoms are alike and they form a solid solution over the complete range of compositions. In a solid solution, where the solute atoms differ considerably in size from the solvent atoms, an even greater increase in critical resolved shear stress is observed.

The magnitude of critical resolved shear stress of a crystal is determined by the interaction of its population of dislocation with each other and with defects such as vacancies and interstitial and impurity atoms. This stress is greater than the stress required to move a simple dislocation, but it is very much lower than the stress required to produce a slip in a perfect lattice.

Micron diameter single crystal filaments or whiskers can be grown dislocation-free, which have the strengths approximately equal to the strengths of a perfect crystal.

4.4.1 Tensile Test on Single Crystals

Single crystals are subjected to simple uniaxial tensile load to study their mechanical properties. The resolved shear stress τ_R is plotted against *glide strain*, which is the relative displacement of two parallel slip planes separated by a unit distance. Suppose the orientation of the slip plane and the slip direction with respect to the tensile axis are known, both before and after deformation. Say α_0 and α_1 are the initial and final angles between the slip directions and the tensile axis, and β_0 and β_1 are the initial and final angles between the slip plane and the tensile axis glide strain, then

$$\gamma = \frac{\cos \alpha_1}{\sin \beta_1} - \frac{\cos \alpha_0}{\sin \beta_0}$$

In the ordinary tensile test, the movement of the crossheads of the testing machine is along one axis. The specimen is constrained at the grips, and it is not allowed to deform freely as shown in Figure 4.4(a). Instead, it deforms in the manner shown in Figure 4.4(b). Near the centre of the gauge length, the slip planes rotate as the single crystal is extended, so as to align themselves parallel with the tensile axis.

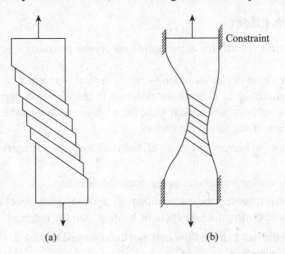

Figure 4.4 *(a) Tensile Deformation of Single Crystal without Constraint*
(b) Rotation of Slip Planes due to Constraint

Near the grips, bending of the slip planes is superimposed on the rotation. The amount of rotation towards the tensile axis increases with the extent of deformation; change in gage length $L_0 \rightarrow L_1$ is related to the change in the angle between the slip planes and the tensile axis, i.e., $\beta_0 \rightarrow \beta_1$.

$$\frac{L_1}{L_0} = \frac{\sin \beta_0}{\sin \beta_1}$$

The deformation behaviour of the single crystal is studied more efficiently by loading the crystal in shear. Shear strain is applied by a couple acting parallel to the active slip system. The crystal can be oriented so that the maximum shear occurs on any desired slip system. The resolved shear stress and shear strain are measured directly from the test.

4.5 STRAIN HARDENING OF SINGLE CRYSTAL

Strain hardening means that the shear stress required to produce deformation continuously increases with increasing strain. The increase in stress required to cause slip because of previous deformation is known as strain hardening. The increase in stress due to strain hardening can be as high as 100 per cent in a single crystal of good ductility.

The following are the reasons for strain hardening:

1. The dislocations intersecting with each other and with barriers, which are microscopic precipitate particles and foreign atoms.
2. Other barriers arising from the fact that glide dislocations on intersecting slip planes may combine with one another to produce new dislocation that is not in a slip direction.
3. Strain hardening due to dislocation pile up at barriers in the crystal.
4. The generation of dislocation due to Frank–Read source by which a large amount of slip could be produced by a single dislocation.
5. The dislocations treading through the acting slip plane, which are often called dislocation forests, and the strain hardening process is referred to as intersection of a forest of dislocation.

4.5.1 Bauschinger's Effect

Zinc crystal (HCP structure) is ideal for experiments on crystal plasticity, because they slip only on a basal plane.

By applying the shear stress in one direction $(+\tau)$, the crystal is strained up to B as shown in Figure 4.5. It is loaded from point B up to C and then reloaded in the direction opposite to the original slip direction, i.e. shear stress $-\tau$. Now, the crystal yields at a lower stress than the yield stress when it was first loaded. This is because of the following factors:

1. Back stress developed at barrier as a result of dislocations pile up at barriers during the first loading cycle.
2. Back stress aid dislocation movement in the opposite direction.
3. When slip direction is reversed, the dislocations of opposite nature develop and they cancel some dislocations produced during the first cycle of loading, and the material is softened.

These reasons explain the fact that the flow curve in the reverse direction lies below the curve for continued flow in the original direction.

Lowering of yield stress when deformation in one direction is followed by deformation in the opposite direction is called *Bauschinger's effect*.

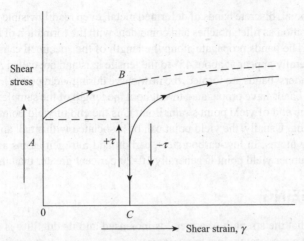

Figure 4.5 *Stress–strain Curve (Complete Reversal of Stress)*

4.6 YIELD POINT PHENOMENON

Many materials, especially low-carbon steels, show a localized heterogeneous type of transition from elastic deformation to plastic deformation, which produces a yield point in the stress–strain curve. The metals having a yield point exhibit a flow curve as shown in Figure 4.6.

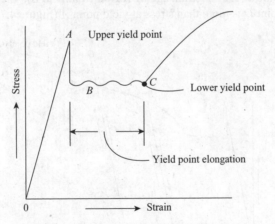

Figure 4.6 *Stress–strain Curve for Mild Steel*

The load increases gradually from O to A, with the elastic strain. At the point A, load suddenly drops down to B, and further deformation takes place with more or less constant load at B, with a considerable deformation from B to C, at which the load again starts increasing. Load at A is known as upper yield point (Figure 4.6), load at B is called lower yield point and the heterogeneous elongation from B to C is known as yield point elongation. So, the transition from elastic to plastic deformation is heterogeneous for many ductile materials. In some cases, yield point elongation is as large as 10 per cent. In addition to low-carbon steel, yield points have been observed in polycrystalline materials such as titanium, molybdenum and aluminium alloys and in single crystals of iron, cadmium, zinc and α and β brass.

At the upper yield point, discrete bands of deformed metal, even readily visible to the eye, appear at the sites of stress concentration as fillet, notches and coincident with the formation of bands, the load drops to the lower yield point. The bands propagate along the length of the specimen causing yield point elonga- tion. These bands generally appear at about 45° to the tensile axis and are called *Luders' bands*, stretcher lines. When several Luders' bands are formed, the flow curve during yield point elongation becomes irreg- ular. After the Luders' bands have propagated throughout the length of the sample, the stress will increase with strain, marking the end of yield point strain. Point *C* is the end of yield point strain and is known as point of strain hardening. Usually, the yield point can be associated with small amounts of interstitials or substitutional impurity atoms. In low-carbon steel, carbon and nitrogen atoms are responsible for yield point elongation. The upper yield point is generally 10–20 per cent greater than the lower yield point.

4.7 STRAIN AGEING

Strain ageing means that the strength of a metal is increased and its ductility is decreased, if after cold working it is heated at a moderately low temperature.

A metal (say low-carbon steel) is strained, from 0 to *A*, an elastic strain. At *A* stress drops to lower yield point stress and after subjected to yield point elongation, stress increases to stress at *B*. The metal is cold worked up to stress and strain at *B* (region I). Now, the metal is unloaded and then reloaded without any appreciable delay or any heat treatment (region II). *On reloading, the yield point does not occur,* because the dislocations have been torn away from the atmosphere of carbon and nitrogen atoms. Now, say the specimen is strained up to point *C* and unloaded. It is reloaded after several days at room temperature or several hours at 150°C (strain ageing region from *D* to *E*). The yield point will reappear and then stress at yield point *D* is more than stress at yield point *A* (Figure 4.7).

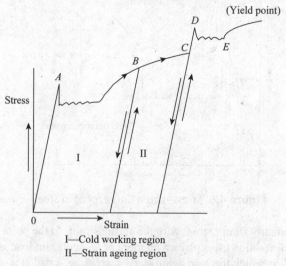

I—Cold working region
II—Strain ageing region

Figure 4.7 *Strain Ageing*

The reappearance of yield point is due to the *diffusion of carbon and nitrogen atoms to the disloca- tions* during the ageing period to form new atmospheres of interstitials (of carbon and nitrogen atoms) anchoring the dislocations. Nitrogen has a higher solubility and diffusion coefficient and produces less complete hardening during precipitation.

In deep drawing operation of steel, strain ageing must be eliminated as reappearance of yield point produces *stretcher strains*. To control strain ageing, it is necessary to reduce the amount of carbon and nitrogen in solution by adding elements such as aluminium, vanadium, titanium and boron. The usual industrial solution is to deform the metal to point *B* by roller levelling or skin-pass rolling, and then to use the steel immediately before it can age.

For plain carbon steels, discontinuous yielding occurs in the temperature region of 250–400°C. This temperature zone is known as *blue brittle region,* because steel heated in this temperature region shows a decreased tensile ductility and decreased notch impact strengths.

Strain ageing is different from quench ageing, which occurs in low-carbon steels. Quench ageing is a type of true precipitation hardening that occurs on quenching the steel from the temperature of maximum solubility of carbon and nitrogen in ferrite, and plastic deformation is not necessary to produce quench ageing.

4.8 HARDENING DUE TO POINT DEFECTS

If the lattices are *bombarded with fast neutrons* having energies of 2 million electron volts, atoms are forced into interstitial positions in the lattice, which increases the hardness and strength of the metal. In copper crystals, a dose of 10^{18} neutrons per square centimetre increases its yield strength by 10 times.

In metals, which show a ductile to brittle transition such as steel, prolonged nuclear irradiation can appreciably raise the transition temperature.

Only vacancies can be produced by rapidly quenching a pure metal, so that there is no precipitation of second phase, from a temperature near its melting point. The vacancy concentration of about 10^{-4} can be achieved by quenching. Soft metals such as aluminium, zinc and copper can be hardened by quenching, introducing a randomly distributed population of vacancies. Quench hardening results in increase in yield stress and decrease in rate of strain hardening. A greater quench hardening results if ageing treatment is also done after quenching. Ageing permits the migration of vacancies to dislocations, where they interact and impede the dislocation movement.

The plastic deformation produces point defects, mainly the vacancies. These point defects are produced by the intersection of dislocations. The vacancy formation is important in the study of fatigue and creep behaviour of the metals.

4.9 MECHANISM OF STRENGTHENING IN METALS

Hardness and strength of metals are related with the ease with which the plastic deformation is made to occur. By reducing the mobility of dislocations, the mechanical strengths can be enhanced, i.e. more mechanical force is required to initiate plastic deformation. Virtually, all strengthening techniques depend on a simple principle:—'restricting or hindering the dislocation motions renders a material harder and stronger'.

The strengthening mechanisms for single-phase metals are as follows:

1. Grain size reduction
2. Solid solution alloying
3. Strain hardening
4. Precipitation hardening

4.9.1 Grain Size Reduction

The grain boundaries act as barriers to dislocation motion for the following two reasons:

1. As two grains are of different orientations, as shown below, and dislocation passing from grain A to B will have to change its direction of motion, this becomes more difficult as the crystallographic misorientation increases.

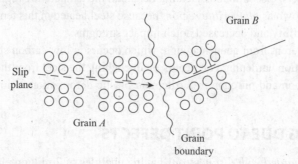

2. The atomic disorder within a grain boundary region will result in discontinuity in slip planes from one grain to another.

A fine-grained material (smaller grains) is harder and stronger than the one which is coarse grained, as the total grain boundary area to impede dislocation motion increases in fine-grained material.

The effect of grain size is largest on the properties, which are related to early stages of deformation, because at this stage grain boundary barriers are most effective. The yield strength is more dependent on the grain size than the effect of grain size on the tensile strength.

For most metals, yield stress is related to the grain size by equation,

$$\sigma_y = \sigma_0 + \frac{K_y}{\sqrt{D}} \qquad \text{[Hall Patch equation]}$$

where σ_y is the yield stress, σ_0 is the friction stress opposing motion of a dislocation, K_y is a constant, which depends upon the extent to which the dislocations are piled up at barriers and D is the grain diameter.

This equation was first proposed for low-carbon steels. The intercept σ_0 is a measure of stress required to drive a dislocation against the resistance of impurities, precipitate particles, subgrain boundaries and so on.

Moreover, the grain size reduction improves not only the strength but also the toughness of many alloys. The strengthening effect for a given grain size depends on the magnitude of constant K_y. In general, K_y tends to be larger for BCC metals as compared to that for FCC or HCP metals.

Following are the values of K_y for various materials:

- BCC iron: 0.71 MN m$^{-1.5}$
- FCC copper: 0.11 MN m$^{-1.5}$
- FCC aluminium: 0.07 MN m$^{-1.5}$

Figure 4.8 shows variation of σ_y with respect to grain size for 70/30 Cu–Zn brass. Heating a metal or an alloy above the recrystallization temperature and then cooling at a faster rate develop fine grains in crystal structure, and the strength and hardness of the metal alloy increase.

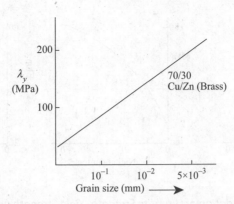

Figure 4.8 *Variation of Yield Stress with Respect to Grain Size*

4.9.2 Solid Solution Alloying

Another technique of strengthening and hardening metals is alloying them with impurity atoms that make either substitutional or interstitial solid solution. Solute atoms in general are either smaller or larger in size than the atoms of parent (solvent) metal. Smaller atoms produce a local tensile field in the crystal, whereas larger atoms produce a local compressive stress field. In both cases, the stress field of a moving dislocation interacts with the stress field produced by the solute atoms. This increases the stress required to move the dislocation, so solid solutions are stronger than pure metals. Silver and gold are completely soluble in each other and make a solid solution for all compositions, but maximum yield strength is developed when composition is 50/50 Au/Ag.

The strengthening effect is due to the fact that a solute atom depends on several factors:

1. Larger concentration of solute atom produces more obstacles to dislocation movement, and strength is proportional to $\sqrt{C}$, where C stands for concentration.

2. Size difference between the solute and the solvent atoms. As the size difference increases, the intensity of stress field around the solute atom increases and resistance to movement of dislocation also increases.

3. The nature of stress field produced by solute atoms.

Substitutional solutes produce spherical distortion, which is much less effective than the non-spherical distortion produced by interstitial atoms.

Example: Carbon and nitrogen atoms in ferrite produce tetragonal distortion, and the strength of ferrite increases linearly with increasing concentration of carbon and nitrogen. The occurrence of a yield point in iron is known to be associated with interstitial solute atoms.

The strengthening effect of solute atoms can be increased by forcing increased solubility by non-equilibrium methods. A supersaturated solution can be produced by quenching from a high temperature where solubility is more. On quenching, an austenite supersaturated martensite structure is producedThe stress field around carbon atoms in martensite effectively hinders dislocation motion; a brittle but hard martensite is obtained, which requires tempering to regain some ductility.

Figure 4.9 (*a, b, c*) shows that the nickel concentration in copper increases its ultimate strength and yield strength, but decreases its ductility.

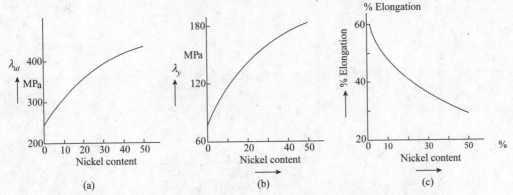

Figure 4.9 *Variation of Ultimate Strength, Yield Strength and Percentage Elongation with Nickel Content*

In brief, the effects of solid solution are as follows:

1. Alloys are stronger than pure metals because the impurity atoms that go into solid solution impose lattice strains on the neighbouring host atoms. The lattice strain field interactions between dislocation and impurity atoms restrict the movement of dislocations.
2. Resistance to slip is greater when the impurity atoms are present because the overall lattice strain must increase to tear away dislocations.

4.9.3 Strain Hardening

Strain hardening is the increase in applied stress for continuous slip or increase in stress with increase in shear strain. This occurs due to interaction of dislocations (during their movement) with other dislocations and other barriers and dislocation movement is impeded.

In a single crystal also there is strain hardening, but to a very small amount. In polycrystalline materials, there is mutual interference between the adjacent grains and multiple slips occur readily and appreciable strain hardening takes place. The plastic deformation, which is carried out in a temperature region and over a time period such that strain hardening is not relieved is known as *cold work*.

An annealed metal contains 10^6–10^8 dislocations/cm^2. If this annealed metal is plastically deformed severely, then dislocation density increases to 10^{12} dislocations/cm^2. The variations of dislocation density occur from high value in distorted grain boundaries to low value in perfect lattice region.

Most of the energy consumed in deforming a metal by cold working is converted into heat; however, some energy is stored in the lattice as an increase in internal energy. The stored energy depends on the following factors:

1. Magnitude of stored energy depends on melting point of metal and number of solute additions.
2. Amount of stored energy depends upon on the type of the process as wire drawing, extrusion, etc.
3. Stored energy increases with strain up to a limiting value of saturation of solute atoms.
4. It increases with decreasing temperature of deformation.
5. Major part of the stored energy is due to production and interaction of dislocations during cold working.
6. Vacancies account for a part of stored energy for metals deformed at very low temperatures.

Strain hardening or cold working is an important industrial process, which is used to harden metals or alloys that are not heat treatable, i.e. they do not respond to any heat treatment process. The rate of strain hardening can be estimated from the slope of the flow curve. In mathematical terms

$$\sigma = Ke^n$$

where σ is the stress, K is the stress at $n = 0.0$ and $n =$ the strain hardening coefficient.

This equation is valid only from the beginning of plastic flow to the maximum load at which necking starts in specimen.

Figure 4.10 shows the typical variation of strength and ductility with increasing amount of cold work. Cold work produces elongation of the grains in the principal direction of working as in the case of wire drawing. Principal direction of cold working is the axis of the wire being drawn.

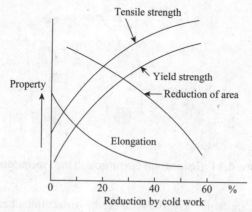

Figure 4.10 *Variation of Mechanical Properties with Cold Working*

Steel, brass and copper increase in yield and tensile strengths with increasing cold work, but the ductility of these metals gets reduced.

Torsteel used as reinforcing bars for concrete is *cold twisted to increase its yield strength*. Under controlled conditions, heavy cold working operations can increase the strength of iron to nearly the strength of perfect crystal. Main disadvantage of cold working is the decrease in ductility. Moreover, cold working is also detrimental as it raises the ductile to brittle transition temperature of steels.

4.9.4 Precipitation Hardening

Precipitation hardening is produced by solution treating and quenching an alloy in which a second phase is in solid solution at the elevated temperature, but precipitates during quenching and ageing at lower temperature. The age hardening of aluminium alloys and copper–beryllium alloys are common examples.

For precipitation hardening to occur, the second phase must be soluble at an elevated temperature but must exhibit decreasing solubility with decreasing temperature. Usually, there is atomic matching or coherency between the lattices of the precipitate and the matrix. The formation of a coherent precipitate in a precipitation hardening system as Cu–Al occurs in many steps, i.e.

1. after quenching from solid solution, the alloy contains regions of solute segregation (or clustering),

2. clustering may produce local strain and the hardness is higher than that of the solid solution, and

3. with additional ageing, hardness is increased further.

The dislocation motion is impeded by fully or partially coherent precipitates but eventually the dislocations shear through the particles. For a non-coherent precipitate, the slip lines do not cut through the particles. Instead, the dislocation lines bend to avoid the particles.

The dislocation model of precipitation hardening considers that second phase particles act as obstacles to the movement of dislocations. A moving dislocation has two options, i.e. (i) to cut through the precipitates and (ii) to bypass the precipitate by bending around them.

When the precipitate particle size is about 50 Å, and particles are coherent with the matrix, dislocation cuts through the particle by creating a step at the interface as shown in Figure 4.11.

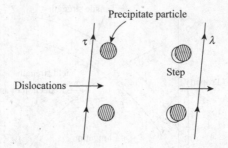

Figure 4.11 *Dislocation Cuts through the Precipitate Particles*

When the particle sizes are larger, say 100–500 Å, the dislocations bend around and bypass them. The shear stress required to bend the dislocation and to bypass the precipitate particles varies inversely with the inter-particle spacing *S*, as shown in Figure 4.12.

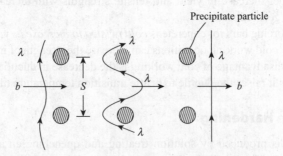

Figure 4.12 *Bending and Bypassing the Particle*

Since the fine particles are more closely spaced, the distribution of fine precipitate effectively increases the stress to bend and pass. Precipitate particles of size greater than 1000 Å are bypassed with ease and little hardening takes place.

Large non-deforming particles are present in many two-phase systems and dislocations moving in the matrix easily bypass them. In such cases, the yield strength tends to be low, but the tensile strength increases because the stresses from dislocation loops tend to elastically strain these rigid particles to conform to the plastically deforming matrix.

4.10 RECOVERY, RECRYSTALLIZATION AND GRAIN GROWTH

All the three phenomena, i.e. recovery, recrystallization and grain growth, are highly associated with the heat treatment process of annealing, which is done after the metal is cold worked. During cold working, severe plastic deformation takes place, consequently, the crystal structure is damaged, lattices are highly distorted and metal becomes hard but brittle, which is undesirable. During plastic deformation, several defects such as vacancies, interstitial atoms, stacking faults, twin boundaries, etc. are introduced in the metal. Following are the effects of plastic deformation:

1. Yield strength, tensile strength, hardness and electrical resistance of metals are increased.
2. Ductility, formability, and plasticity of metal are reduced.
3. Dislocations get multiplied, residual stresses are developed.

Take a metal deforming process as wire drawing, in which the wire is passed through a die, by a pulling force a wire is drawn out of the die, grains are elongated in the direction of the applied force, severe plastic deformation takes place, which increases the yield point, and more stress is needed to continue the process due to strain hardening. To recover the original properties of the metal, annealing is done after two stages of wire drawing.

Equilibrium is achieved in three stages, i.e. recovery, recrystallization and grain growth.

4.10.1 Recovery

During recovery (after cold working operation), metal is heated to a temperature $0.1\ T_{mp}$, i.e. 10% of melting point temperature. The following objectives are achieved:

1. Internal stresses developed during cold working are relieved.
2. Distortion in lattice is reduced.
3. Electrical resistivity is reduced.
4. Ductility and elastic limit are improved.
5. Dislocations rearrange themselves.
6. Surplus point defects as vacancies are reduced.

Mechanism of Recovery Recovery takes place at low temperature by motion of vacancies, i.e. by migration of point defects to grain boundaries and dislocations. At intermediate temperature, recovery mechanism is dislocation movement without climb, cancellations of dislocations of opposite nature.

At high temperatures, recovery mechanisms are dislocation movement with climb, disappearance of boundary between two subgrains (known as coalescence) and polygonization (which helps in softening of metals by reduction in dislocation density).

By recovery, stresses are relieved from cold-worked condition of metals, which prevent stress corrosion cracking. For complete removal of residual stresses, high recovery temperature is required. High-temperature treatment is useful for cast or welded parts.

4.10.2 Recrystallization

Temperature of recrystallization is $0.3\ T_{mp}$ to $0.5\ T_{mp}$ (melting temperature); when the metal is heated from the recovery stage, deformed grains are replaced by new strain-free grains. During recrystallization, following changes take place in the metals:

1. The mechanical properties are abruptly changed, i.e. increase in ductility and decrease in electrical resistivity. But the strengths and hardness are decreased
2. Distorted grains disappear and new equiaxed grains are formed.

3. Internal stresses are further reduced.
4. Slip bands formed during plastic deformation disappear.
5. No change in crystal structure.
6. Grain refinement occurs.
7. Dislocation density is reduced from 10^{10}–10^{12}/cm^2 to 10^6/cm^2.

The driving force to produce new grain structure is the difference in internal energy between the strained and unstrained materials. The new grains form as very small nuclei and grow until they completely replace the grains of the parent metal. Recrystallization of cold-worked metals may be used to refine the grain structure.

Recrystallization is a process, which depends on both time and temperature. The degree of recrystallization increases with time.

The influence of temperature is demonstrated in Figure 4.13, which plots strength and ductility of a brass alloy at various annealing temperatures. The grain structures found at various stages of the process are also presented.

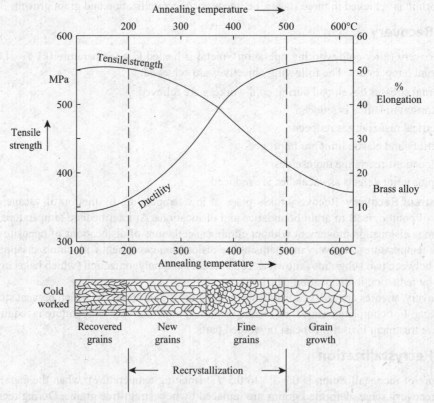

Figure 4.13 *Influence of Temperature on Strength and Ductility*

The recrystallization behaviour of a particular metal alloy is sometimes specified in terms of temperature of recrystallization; the temperature at which recrystallization just reaches completion in

1 hr. The recrystallization temperature for the brass alloy shown is 450°C. Typically, it lies between 0.3 T_{mp} and 0.5 T_{mp} (absolute melting temperature) of a metal or an alloy and depends on several factors including the amount of prior cold work and purity of metal, time, composition and initial grain size.

4.10.3 Laws of Crystallization

1. Some minimum deformation is necessary (2–8%) for recrystallization.
2. Smaller the degree of deformation, higher the temperature required to initiate recrystallization.
3. Increase in annealing time decreases the temperature required for recrystallization. But temperature is more important than time.
4. Final grain size depends mainly on the degree of deformation and less dependent on the grain size.
5. New grains do not grow into deformed grains.
6. Recrystallization proceeds more rapidly in pure metals than in alloys.

Full annealing restores the material to *strain-free lattice structure*.

The plastic deformation carried out at temperatures above the recrystallization temperature is a process termed as *hot working*. The material remains relatively soft and ductile during hot working because it does not strain harden.

Table 4.2 gives the recrystallization temperatures and melting temperatures for various metals and alloys.

Table 4.2 *Recrystallization and Melting Temperatures for Various Metals and Alloys*

Metal or Alloy	Recrystallization Temperature (°C)	Melting Temperature (°C)
Tin	−4	232
Zinc	10	420
Aluminium	80	660
Copper	120	1085
Brass (60 Cu/40 Zinc)	475	900
Nickel	370	1460
Iron	450	1540
Tungsten	1200	3400

4.10.4 Grain Growth

Grain growth can be defined as the phenomenon by which two grains of metal or alloy join together to form a bigger grain. During the grain growth, the fine-grained metal becomes coarse grained.

When the metal is held for a longer time at a temperature above the recrystallization temperature, grain size increases. Small grains disappear as they are merged in larger grains and grains become coarser and coarser. Yet, the metals with fine grains are harder and stronger as compared with coarse-grained metal. Softening is associated with grain growth.

An energy is associated with grain boundaries. As the grains increase in size, the total boundary area decreases, resulting in the reduction in total energy. This is the driving force for the grain growth.

Grain growth occurs by the migration of grain boundaries. Larger grains grow at the expense of smaller grains that shrink. So, the average grain size increases with time, and at any particular instant, there exists a range of grain sizes. Boundary motion is just the short-range diffusion of atoms from one side of the boundary to the other side.

For many polycrystalline materials, average grain diameter d varies with time, t, by the relation

$$d^n - d_0^n = Kt$$

where d_0 is the initial average grain diameter at time, $t = 0$, and K and n are time-dependent constants ($n = 2$, or greater than 2).

The mechanical properties at room temperature of a fine-grained metal are usually superior (i.e. higher strengths and toughness) to those of coarse grained ones.

KEY POINTS TO REMEMBER

❑ In a single crystal, maximum shear stress required to produce deformation is $G/2\pi$, where G is shear modulus.

Computer results of Tyson give the following values of τ_m, maximum shear stress:

$$\tau_m = \frac{G}{16} \text{ for FCC structure}$$

$$= \frac{G}{8} \text{ for simple cubic structure}$$

$$= \frac{G}{4} \text{ for covalently bonded diamond structure}$$

❑ Slip systems in BCC and FCC crystals are 12 and in HCP crystal are only 3.

❑ Critical resolved shear stress is

$$\tau_R = \frac{F}{A} \cos \phi \cos \alpha$$

where F is the tensile force, A is the area of cross-section of specimen, ϕ is the angle between normal to slip plane and tensile area, and α is the angle of slip direction with tensile axis.

❑ Reasons for strain hardening:
- Dislocations intersecting each other
- Intersecting slip planes
- Dislocations pile up at grain boundary
- Generation of dislocations due to Frank–Read source
- Dislocation forest treading through the active slip plane

❑ *Bauschinger's effect:* Dislocations are lined up at grain boundary, when load is reversed, back stress helps dislocation movement in the opposite direction and yield stress is reduced during reverse loading.

❑ *Yield point elongation:* Heterogeneous elongation at lower yield point.

❑ Yield point elongation causes Luders' bands.

❑ The upper yield point stress is generally 10–20% greater than the lower yield point stress.

❑ After cold working, the metal is heated at moderately low temperature for several hours, and the strength of the metal is increased, which is known as strain ageing.

❑ If the lattices are bombarded with fast neutrons having energies 2 million electron Volts, atoms are forced into interstitial positions in the lattice, which increases the hardness and strength of the metals.

❑ Strengthening mechanisms are (i) grain size reduction, (ii) solid solution alloying, (iii) strain hardening and (iv) precipitation hardening.

❑ Heating a metal or alloy above the recrystallization temperature and then cooling at a faster rate develops fine grains in a metal; the strength and hardness of the metal are increased.

❑ Impurity atoms make either substitutional or interstitial solid solution with the parent metal; the strength and hardness of the metal increase.

❑ Strain hardening is the increase in applied stress for continuous slip or increase in stress with increase in shear strain. This is due to the interactions of dislocations with other dislocations and barriers.

❑ For precipitation hardening, the second phase is soluble at elevated temperature, but its solubility in parent metal decreases with decreasing temperature.

❑ Dislocations either cut through the precipitated particles or bend or bypass the precipitate particles.

❑ During recovery (after cold-working operation) metal is heated to a temperature 0.1 times the melting point temperature. Internal stresses are relieved, distortion in lattice is reduced and the dislocations rearrange themselves.

❑ Temperature of recrystallization is 0.3–0.5 times the melting point temperature.

❑ During recrystallization, ductility is improved, internal stresses are further reduced, grain refinement occurs and dislocation density is reduced.

❑ Full annealing restores the material to strain-free lattice structure.

❑ During grain growth, fine-grained metal becomes coarse grained. Small grains disappear and merge with large grains.

MULTIPLE CHOICE QUESTIONS

1. To cause slip in perfect lattice, maximum shear stress for a crystal structure is $G/16$. What is the type of crystal structure?
   - (a) Simple cubic
   - (c) Diamond structure
   - (b) FCC
   - (d) None of these

2. How many slip systems are present in an HCP crystal structure?
   - (a) 3
   - (c) 12
   - (b) 6
   - (d) None of these

3. If F is the tensile force applied on a sample of single crystal with an area of cross-section A, ϕ is the angle of slip plane with tensile axis and α is the angle which the slip direction makes with the tensile axis, what is critical resolved shear stress?
   - (a) $\dfrac{F}{A\sin\phi\cos\alpha}$
   - (c) $\dfrac{F}{A\cos\phi\cos\alpha}$
   - (b) $\dfrac{F}{A\sin\phi\sin\alpha}$
   - (d) None of these

4. Which one of the following is not the reason for strain hardening?
   - (A) Dislocations intersecting with each other
   - (B) Dislocations of opposite sign cancel each other
   - (C) Generation of dislocation due to Frank–Read source
   - (D) Dislocations pile up at grain boundary
   - (a) A
   - (c) C
   - (b) B
   - (d) D

5. During strain ageing,
   - (a) Strength and ductility of the material increase
   - (b) Strength of material increases but ductility decreases
   - (c) Strength and ductility of the material decrease
   - (d) None of these

6. In metals subjected to cold working, strain hardening effect is due to
   - (a) Twinning mechanism
   - (b) Dislocation mechanism
   - (c) Fracture mechanism
   - (d) None of these

7. Which one of the following is not the reason for strain hardening?

(a) Dislocations pile up at grain boundary

(b) Annihilation of dislocations of opposite nature

(c) Dislocation interaction with each

(d) All the above

8. Reason for Bauschinger's effect is

(a) Back stress aids dislocation movement during reverse loading

(b) Slip direction is reversed during reverse loading

(c) Some dislocations are cancelled during reverse loading

(d) All the above

9. Reappearance of higher yield point after strain ageing is due to

(a) Cold working of the metal

(b) Nitrogen has higher solubility in iron than solubility of carbon

(c) Diffusion of nitrogen and carbon atoms into the dislocations

(d) None of the above

10. Which is a correct statement?

(a) After annealing, dislocation density is slightly increased

(b) Most of the energy consumed in cold working is converted into heat

(c) Fine-grained structure is tougher than coarse-grained structure

(d) None of the above

11. Size of precipitation particle is 150 Å. What is the type of dislocation movement?

(a) Dislocation cuts through the precipitates

(b) Dislocation bends around the precipitate and bypasses it

(c) Precipitate acts as rigid obstacle and dislocation bypasses it

(d) None of these

12. During recovery, what happens to the metal?

(a) Internal stresses are completely relieved

(b) Distortions in lattice are reduced

(c) Vacancies are moderately increased

(d) None of these

Answers

1. (b) 2. (a) 3. (c) 4. (b) 5. (b) 6. (b) 7. (b) 8. (d) 9. (c) 10. (b)
11. (b) 12. (b)

REVIEW QUESTIONS

1. Explain the process of slip in a single crystal. Derive expression for maximum shear stress for plastic deformation.

2. What do you mean by a slip system? How many slip systems are there in an HCP crystal? Give Miller indices for slip directions and slip plane.

3. What is critical resolved shear stress? Derive expressions for critical resolved shear stress for a single crystal.

4. Explain Bauschinger's effect?

5. Explain the difference between upper yield point and lower yield point. Give reasons for this difference.

6. With the help of a neat sketch, explain strain ageing process.

7. What do you understand by hardening due to point defects?

8. Explain the mechanism for grain size reduction?

9. What is the difference between solid solution hardening and precipitation hardening?

10. What are the applications of precipitation hardening?

11. Explain how the mechanical properties are dependent on strain hardening.

12. Explain the process of recovery.

13. Explain recrystallization during annealing.

14. Describe the process of grain growth.

15. How does grain diameter depend upon the time of growth? Explain.

5

MECHANICAL PROPERTIES

5.1 INTRODUCTION

The mechanical behaviour of a material reflects the relationship between its response (deformation) to an applied load (or force) such as strength, ductility, hardness, stiffness and toughness. These are known as mechanical properties. These properties play a vital role in the analysis and development of structures, machines and engineering and commercial products. These components are subjected to natural or applied loads under varying conditions of temperature and environment. Determination of mechanical properties through various tests is of utmost importance to design engineers. There are two types of tests: destructive and non-destructive. This chapter explains the destructive test, in which the material is subjected to loads or moments for the ultimate failure of the material. Many components are subjected to stress reversals and time-dependent strain, so in this chapter properties of fatigue and creep will also be thoroughly discussed. Moreover, the role of materials and metallurgical engineers is to produce and fabricate materials to meet service requirements as predicted by stress analysis.

5.2 TENSION TEST

An engineering tensile test is widely used to provide information on the strength of the material under uniaxial tensile load, as an acceptance text for specification of the material as yield point strength, ultimate strength, percentage elongation and percentage reduction in the area. A specimen of the material is subjected to a continually increasing uniaxial tensile force and simultaneous observation of elongation is made. Load divided by the original area of cross section gives the engineering stress and change in length divided by the original length gives the engineering strain at any instant. From the values of stress and strain from start up to fracture, a graph between stress (σ) and strain (ϵ) is plotted as shown in Figure 5.1.

Stress and strain used in this curve are average longitudinal stress and average linear strain.

$$\epsilon = \frac{\delta}{L_0} = \frac{\text{change in length}}{\text{original length}}$$

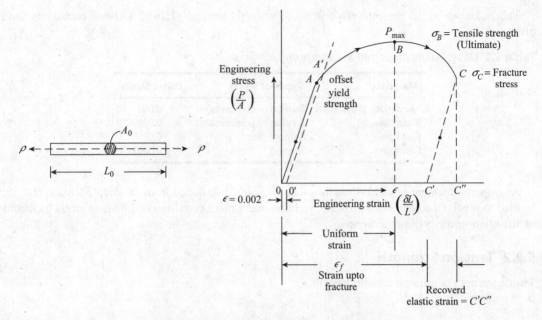

Figure 5.1 *Engineering Stress–strain Curve*

$$\sigma = \frac{P}{A} = \frac{\text{load at any instant}}{\text{original area of cross section}}$$

The shape and magnitude of stress–strain curve of any metal depends on its composition, heat treatment, prior history of plastic deformation, strain rate, temperature and so on.

Following are the important parameters that can be determined from the stress–strain curve using original length, final length, original diameter and final diameter at fracture section:

1. Yield strength
2. Tensile strength
3. Per cent elongation (for ductility)
4. Per cent reduction in the area (for degree of cold working)

5.2.1 Yield Strength

The yield strength is the load corresponding to a small specified plastic strain divided by the original cross-sectional area.

$$\sigma_{yp} = \frac{P_{\epsilon = 0.002}}{A_0}$$

There are practical difficulties in the measurement of elastic limit or proportional limit, so offset yield strength is noted at ϵ strain $= 0.002$. A line is drawn parallel to OA (Figure 5.1) from the point O, where $00' = 0.002$. This line intersects the stress–strain curve at A'. Then

$$\sigma_{yp} = \frac{P \text{ at } A'}{A_0, \text{ area of cross section (original)}}$$

This is known as 0.2 per cent proof stress offset yield strength. Table 5.1 shows commonly used offset values.

Table 5.1 *Offset Values for Common Engineering Materials*

Materials	Types of Stress	Offset Strain
Aluminium alloys, steel	Tension or compression	0.002
Brass, bronze	Tension or compression	0.0035
Cast iron	Compression	0.005
Concrete	Tension	0.0002

An important feature of yield strength is that the value determined from the simple tension test can be used to predict the conditions for static yielding under more complex conditions of stress by means of distortion-energy yielding criterion.

5.2.2 Tension Strength

Tensile strength or ultimate tensile strength,

$$\sigma_{ut} = \frac{P_{max}}{A_0}$$

For ductile materials, σ_{ut} is a measure of the maximum stress that a metal can withstand under uniaxial loading only. This strength is of little significance when theories of failure are considered. In the recent approach, the design is based on yield strength. Yet, tensile strength is useful for the purpose of material specifications.

For brittle materials, tensile strength is a valid criterion for the design of machine members.

5.2.3 Percentage Elongation

Percentage elongation $= \dfrac{L_f - L_0}{L_0} = \epsilon_f$, strain at fracture,

where

L_f = final gage length at fracture
L_0 = initial or original gage length
ϵ_f = strain at fracture

Figure 5.1 shows that at the time of fracture of specimen into two pieces, there is elastic recovery of some strain, and fracture strain is only OC'.

The elongation of specimen is uniform along the gauge length up to the maximum load, P_{max}. Beyond this point, necking begins and deformation is no longer uniform along the length of the specimen.

$$\epsilon_f = \epsilon_\epsilon \text{ up to } P_{max} + \epsilon', \text{ beyond } P_{max}$$

So (5.1)

$$= b + c\frac{\sqrt{A_0}}{L_0}$$

This relationship is given by Barba and hence b and c are called Barba's constants. A_0 is the original area of cross section and L_0 is the original length of the specimen.

However, to have an estimate on the property of ductility of the material, per cent elongation is always based upon total elongation ϵ_f. It is noted by putting the broken pieces of tensile specimen together and measuring the final change in length.

5.2.4 Reduction in Area

Per cent reduction in the area,

$$q = \frac{A_0 - A_f}{A_0} \times 100$$

where

$$A_0 = \text{original area of cross section}$$

$$= \frac{\pi}{4} d_0^2$$

$$A_f = \frac{\pi}{4} d_f^2, \text{ for circular section}$$

The determination of the reduction in the area in a thin sheet specimen is difficult, because for rectangular samples the area after fracture may be approximated by

$$A_f = \frac{b'}{3} (t_c + 2t_e)$$

where b' is the breadth of specimen at breaking, t_c is the thickness at the centre of the specimen and t_e is the thickness at the ends of the specimen.

$$A_0 = b \times t$$

$$= \text{original breadth} \times \text{original thickness of rectangular specimen}$$

The elongation and reduction in the area are usually not directly useful to the designer. A qualitative indication of formability of a metal can be obtained from these parameters.

A reduction in the area indicates material quality and is the most structure-sensitive parameter.

5.2.5 Modulus of Elasticity

The slope of the initial linear portion OA of stress–strain curve is the modulus of elasticity, or Young's modulus, a measure of stiffness of the material. Modulus of elasticity is required for computing deflections in beams and other members. It is an important design value. It is a measure of binding forces between the atoms. It is the most structure-insensitive mechanical property. It is slightly affected by alloying elements, heat treatment or cold work.

The modulus is usually measured at elevated temperature by a dynamic method, which measures mode and frequency of vibration of a metal specimen. Typical values of carbon steel at different temperatures are given in Table 5.2.

Table 5.2 *Materials Young's Modulus (GPa)*

Materials	Room Temp.	200°C	420°C	540°C	650°C
Carbon steel	207	186	155	135	125

5.2.6 Resilience

The ability of a material to absorb energy when deformed elastically and to return the same when unloaded is termed as 'resilience'. This energy up to the elastic limit (σ_e) per unit volume is known as 'modulus of resilience'.

Strain energy per unit volume, $\qquad u = \dfrac{\sigma \varepsilon}{2}$, at any stage upto elastic limit

$$u = \frac{\sigma^2}{2E}$$

Modulus of resilience, $\qquad\qquad u = \dfrac{\sigma_e^2}{2E}$

This equation shows that the ideal material for resisting energy load applications where material must not undergo permanent deformation such as mechanical spring should have high elastic limit stress σ_e or yield point stress σ_{yp} and low modulus E.

Table 5.3 shows Young's modulus and the yield point stress for some common engineering materials.

Table 5.3 *Young's Modulus and Yield Point Stress for Some Common Engineering Materials*

Material	E (GPa)	σ_{yp} (MPa)
Medium-carbon steel	207	310
High-carbon spring steel	207	960
Duralumin	70	125
Copper	160	30

5.2.7 Toughness

The toughness of a material is its ability to absorb strain energy in the plastic range, i.e. up to fracture. The ability to withstand occasional stresses (due to shock loads) above the yield stress without fracture

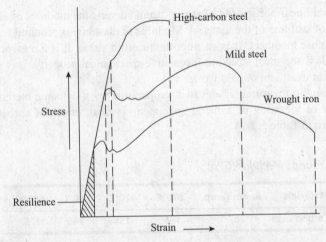

Figure 5.2 *Comparison of Stress–strain Curves for High-carbon Steel, Mild Steel and Wrought Iron*

is especially desirable in parts such as railway couplings, gears, chains, crane hooks and so on. The total area under the stress–strain curve in terms of strain energy is a measure of toughness.

Figure 5.2 shows stress–strain curves for wrought iron, mild steel and high-carbon steel. Although strength of high-carbon steel is maximum, its toughness is minimum out of these three, as the area under stress–strain curve is maximum for wrought iron.

The area under the elastic curve is maximum for high-carbon steel, therefore, it has maximum resilience. The spring steel is made from high-carbon steel, which has higher yield strength. Mild steel is used as a structural steel, with higher toughness. But the parts like railway couplings and crane hooks are made from wrought iron. So toughness is a parameter, which combines both strength and ductility.

Example 5.1 A round specimen of wrought iron of diameter 12.5 mm and gauge length of 100 mm was tested in tension up to fracture. Following observations were obtained.

$$\text{Load up to yield point} = 29.5 \text{ kN}$$
$$\text{Maximum load} = 44 \text{ kN}$$
$$\text{Load at the time of fracture} = 37 \text{ kN}$$
$$\text{Diameter at neck} = 9.2 \text{ mm}$$
$$\text{Total extension in specimen} = 28.5 \text{ mm}$$

From the data, calculate (a) yield strength, (b) ultimate strength, (c) actual breaking stress, (d) percentage elongation and (e) modulus of resilience at yield point stress.

$$E = 200 \text{ kN/mm}^2$$

Solution:

Original diameter,

$$d_0 = 12.5 \text{ mm}$$

Original area of cross section,

$$A_0 = \frac{\pi}{4} d_0^2 = \frac{\pi}{4} \times 12.5^2 = 122.72 \text{ mm}^2$$

Yield point load = 29.5 kN

(a) Yield strength,

$$\sigma_{yp} = \frac{29.5 \text{ kN}}{A_0} = \frac{29.5 \times 1000}{122.72} = 240.4 \text{ MPa}$$

Maximum load,

$$P_{max} = 44 \text{ kN}$$

(b) Ultimate strength,

$$\sigma_{ut} = \frac{44000}{122.72} = 358.54 \text{ MPa}$$

Diameter at neck = 9.2 mm

Area at neck,

$$A_n = \frac{\pi}{4} \times 9.2^2 = 66.476 \text{ mm}^2$$

Load at the time of fracture = 37 kN

(c) Actual breaking stress,

$$\sigma_f = \frac{37000}{66.476} = 556.6 \text{ MPa}$$

Initial gauge length, $L_0 = 100$ mm

Total extension, $\delta = 28.5$ mm

(d) Percentage elongation $= \frac{28.5}{100} \times 100 = 28.5$ per cent

(e) Modulus of resilience $= \frac{\sigma_{yp}^2}{2E} = \frac{240.4^2}{2 \times 200 \times 1000} = 0.1445 \text{ Nm/mm}^3$

5.2.8 True Stress–Strain Curve

When a tensile test specimen is subjected to continually increasing load, there is simultaneous elonga-tion and the area of cross section also continually changes. Therefore, engineering stress–strain curve is not the true indication of the deformation characters of a metal because it is based on original dimen-sions. Moreover, at the maximum load point, necking starts and cross-sectional area decreases rapidly at this stage. In reality, the metal continues to strain harden all the way up to fracture, and the stress required to cause further deformation goes on increasing. So, true stress is based on the actual area of

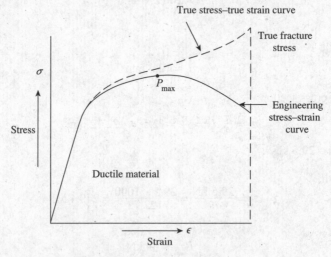

Figure 5.3 *Stress–strain Curves*

cross section and taking true stress into account, stress–strain curve increases continuously up to frac-ture. If the strain measurement is also based on instantaneous length measurements, the curve becomes true stress–true strain curve.

Figure 5.3 shows engineering stress–strain and true stress–true strain curves for a ductile material. True stress is the load at any instant divided by the cross-sectional area of the specimen at that instant

$$\sigma_T = \frac{P}{A_i}$$

True strain $\epsilon_T = \int_{L_0}^{L} \frac{\Delta L_i}{L_i}$, change in length up to a particular instant divided by the length of the speci-

men at that instant.

$$\epsilon_T = \ln \frac{L}{L_0}$$

$$= \ln \left[\frac{L_0 + \Delta L}{L_0} \right] = \ln \left[1 + \frac{\Delta L}{L_0} \right]$$

where $\frac{\Delta L}{L_0} = \epsilon$, engineering strain

True strain,

$$\epsilon_T = \ln (1 + \epsilon)$$

During plastic deformation, volume remains constant, so $A_0 L_0 = AL$.

True strain,

$$\epsilon_T = \ln \frac{L}{L_0} = \ln \frac{A_0}{A}$$

True stress,

$$\sigma_T = \frac{P}{A_i} = \frac{P}{A_0} \times \frac{A_0}{A_i}$$

But

$$\frac{A_0}{A_i} = \frac{L_i}{L_0} = \frac{L_0 + \Delta L}{L_0} = (1 + \epsilon)$$

where ϵ is engineering strain.

So true stress,

$$\sigma_T = \frac{P}{A_0} (1 + \epsilon)$$

$$= \sigma (1 + \epsilon) = \text{engineering stress} (1 + \text{engineering strain})$$

At Maximum Load

True stress at maximum load corresponds to true tensile strength.

$$\sigma_{uT} = \frac{P_{max}}{A_m} = \frac{\text{maximum load}}{\text{area of cross section at maximum load}}$$

It is usually desirable to express the stress–strain curve by a relationship as follow:

$$\sigma_T = K \epsilon_T^n$$

where n is the strain hardening exponent and K is the strength coefficient.

Example 5.2   A cylindrical test sample of diameter 12.8 mm is tested in tension up to fracture and found to have engineering fracture strength $\sigma_f = 450$ MPa. If the diameter of cross-sectional area at fracture is 10.7 mm, determine

(a) The ductility in terms of per cent reduction in the area
(b) True stress at fracture
(c) True fracture strain

Solution:

$$A_0 = \text{original area of cross section} = \frac{\pi}{4} \times 12.8^2$$

$$= 128.68 \text{ mm}^2$$

A_f = area of cross section at fracture

$$= \frac{\pi}{4} \times 10.7^2$$

$$= 89.92 \text{ mm}^2$$

Per cent reduction in area

$$= \frac{A_0 - A_f}{A_0} = \frac{128.68 - 89.92}{128.68} \times 100$$

$$= 30.12 \%$$

True fracture stress,

$$\sigma_{Tf} = \frac{\sigma_f A_0}{A_f} = \frac{450 \times 128.68}{89.92}$$

$$= 643.98 \text{ MPa}$$

True fracture strain,

$$\epsilon_{Tf} = 2\ln\left(\frac{d_0}{d}\right) = 2\ln\left(\frac{12.8}{10.7}\right)$$

$$= 0.358$$

The values of K and n vary from one alloy to another.

Table 5.4 gives the values of K and n for some common metals/alloys.

Table 5.4 *Values of Constants K and n for Some Common Metals/Alloys*

Material	K (MPa)	n
Low carbon steel	530	0.26
Alloy steel (4340)	640	0.15
Stainless steel (304)	1275	0.45
Aluminium (annealed)	180	0.20
Aluminium alloy (2024)	690	0.16
Copper (annealed)	315	0.54
Brass (70 Cu, 30 Zn)	895	0.49

Example 5.3 Assuming that the true stress–strain curve follows the relationship $\sigma_T = \sigma_0 + K\epsilon_T^n$, where σ_T is the true stress, σ_0 is the flow stress at plastic strain = 0, ϵ_T is the true plastic strain and n is the strain hardening exponent. Show that the rate of strain hardening $d\sigma_T/\sigma\epsilon_T$ is a function of n, σ_T, σ_0 and ϵ_T. Estimate the value of $d\sigma_T/\sigma\epsilon_T$, where $n = 0.3$, $\sigma_T = 300$ MPa, $\sigma_0 = 200$ MPa and $\epsilon_T = 0.05$.

Solution:

$$\sigma_T = \sigma_0 + K\,\epsilon_T^n \qquad\qquad (5.2)$$

$$\frac{d\sigma_T}{d\epsilon_T} = 0 + Kn\epsilon_T^{n-1} = Kn\epsilon_T^{n-1} \qquad\qquad (5.3)$$

From Eq. (5.2)

$$K = \frac{\sigma_T - \sigma_0}{\epsilon_T}$$

Putting the values in Eq. (5.3),

$$\frac{d\sigma_T}{d\epsilon_T} = \left(\frac{\sigma_T - \sigma_0}{\epsilon_T^n}\right)\left(n\epsilon_T^{n-1}\right) = \frac{(\sigma_T - \sigma_0)n}{\epsilon_T}$$

Now, $n = 0.3$, $\sigma_T = 300$ MPa, $\sigma_0 = 200$ MPa and $\epsilon_T = 0.05$

$$\frac{d\sigma_T}{d\epsilon_T} = \frac{(300 - 200) \times 0.3}{0.05} = 600 \text{ MPa}$$

5.3 HARDNESS

Hardness is a measure of a material's resistance to localized plastic deformation (a small dent or a scratch). There are three general types of hardness measurements depending upon the manner in which the test is conducted, which are as follows:

1. Scratch hardness
2. Indentation hardness
3. Rebound or dynamic hardness

Scratch hardness is primarily of interest for mineralogists. Various minerals are rated on their ability to scratch one another. Hardness is measured by Moh's scale. As per this scale, talc is the softest mineral, which has a scratch hardness of 1 and a scratch hardness of 10 is given to diamond, annealed copper-3 and Martensite-7. Moh's scale of scratch hardness is not suitable for metals and a different scratch hardness test is performed by a diamond stylus, making a scratch across the surface under a definite load, and depth or width of scratch is used as hardness measure. This type of hardness test is used for measuring relative hardness of microconstituents.

In dynamic hardness measurement, indenter is dropped onto the metal surface and the hardness is expressed as the energy of impact. The share scleroscope, a dynamic hardness tester, measures the hardness in terms of the height of rebound.

5.3.1 Brinell Hardness Test

In 1990, J.A. Brinell conducted hardness test by indenting the metal (steel) surface by a hardened steel ball of 10 mm diameter at a load of 3000 kg. For soft metals, the load is reduced to 500 kg to avoid a large impression. For very hard metals, a tungsten carbide ball is used to minimize distortion of the indenter. The load is applied for about 30 s, and the diameter of the indent is measured with a low power microscope, after the removal of the load.

Brinell hardness number is expressed as

$$\text{BHN} = \frac{P}{(\pi D/2)\left(D - \sqrt{D^2 - d^2}\right)}$$

where P is the applied load in kg, D is the diameter of the ball in mm and d is the diameter of indentation in mm as shown in Figure 5.4. However, BHN is not a satisfactory physical concept, because it does not give mean pressure over the surface of indentation.

Maximum error in BHN test occurs in the measurement of diameter of impression d. After the load is removed, there is elastic recovery, and the radius of curvature of the indentation will be larger than that of spherical ball indenter. Harder the metal, greater will be the elastic recovery. Moreover, the elastic recovery affects the depth of impression. However, two types of localized deformations occur around

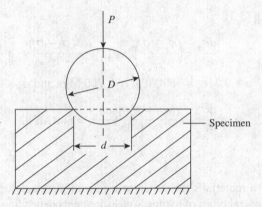

Figure 5.4 *Brinell Hardness Test*

the indentation: (1) ridging or piling up while a lip of metal forms around the edge of impression—common in cold-worked metals [Figure 5.5(a) and (b)] and (2) sinking in, in which there is depression of the metal at the rim of indentation [Figure 5.5(b)]. This type of behaviour is common in annealed metals, which have a high degree of strain hardening.

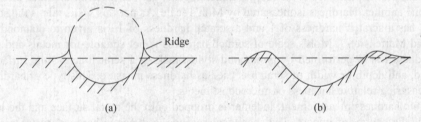

Figure 5.5 *(a) Ridging or Pile up (b) Sinking in*

If the indentation by a spherical ball is analysed, then for an ideal plastic metal with no strain hardening, highest pressure occurs just below the surface of the content at a depth of $d/2$, where d is the diameter of impression.

The pressure at this point is $0.47\,p_m$, where p_m is the mean pressure over the circle of contact. As per maximum shear stress theory, the criterion for plastic flow is

$$0.47\,p_m = 0.5\,\sigma_{yp}$$

where σ_{yp} = yield stress in tension or compression

or

$$p_m \simeq 1.1\,\sigma_{yp}$$

Therefore, the deformations under the indenter are elastic, until the mean pressure reaches $1.1\,\sigma_{yp}$. As the load is increased further, p_m increases and the plastically deformed region grows until it contains the entire region of contact.

Best analysts say

$$p_m \simeq 2.66\,\sigma_{yp}$$

$$\simeq 2.8\,\sigma_{yp} \text{ (fully plastic region)}$$

Most Brinell hardness tests are carried out under conditions where full plasticity is reached. A useful engineering correlation between BHN and σ_{ut} of heat-treated plain carbon steels and the medium alloy steels is developed

$$\sigma_{ut} = 3.5 \text{ (BHN) in MPa}$$

5.3.2 Vicker's Hardness Test

In Vickers's hardness test, a square-based diamond indenter is used. The included angle between the opposite faces of a pyramid is 136°. This angle approximates the best desirable ratio of indentation diameter to ball diameter in BHN test. Because of its shape, it is called 'diamond indenter'. A diamond pyramid hardness test or Vicker's Pyramid Number (VPN) is as follows:

$$\text{VPN} = \frac{\text{load}}{\text{surface area of indentation}}$$

To measure the surface area of indentation, the length of the diagonal of the impression is measured.

$$\text{VPN} = \frac{2P\sin\left(\frac{\theta}{2}\right)}{L^2} = \frac{1.854P}{L^2},$$

where P is the applied load in kg, L is the average length of diagonals in mm and θ is the angle between the opposite faces of diamond = 136°. VPN test is widely accepted for research work, because it provides a continuous scale of hardness.

VPN from 5 (for very soft material) to 1500 (for very hard materials) loads are generally used with this test range from 1 to 120 kg, depending upon the hardness of the metal to be tested. However, this test is not recommended for routine hardness check up because it is slow and requires careful surface preparation of the sample and there is an error in diagonal measurement.

A perfect indentation from a square pyramid diamond indenter will be a perfect square, but there are variations in indentation as shown in Figure 5.6.

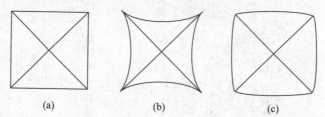

(a)   (b)   (c)

Figure 5.6 *(a) Perfect Indentation (b) Pin Cushion Indentation (c) Barrelled Indentation*

Pin cushion-type [Figure 5.6(b)] indentation is the result of sinking in of the metal around the flat forces of the pyramid (observed in annealed metals). The barrel-shaped [Figure 5.6(c)] indentation is found in cold-worked metals due to ridging or a piling up of the metal around the faces of the indenter.

5.3.3 Rockwell Hardness Test

This is the most widely accepted test, due to its speed of measurement, freedom from personal error and small size of indentation ability to distinguish small hardness differences. This test can be used for finished products, because of very small size of indentation. The test utilizes the depth of indent under constant load as a measure of hardness.

A minor load of 10 kg is first applied to set the specimen. This minimizes the amount of surface preparations required and the depth of indentation is automatically recorded on a dial gauge in terms of hardness number. Dial contains 100 divisions, each representing a penetration of 0.002 mm. BHN and VPN are in terms of kg/mm^2, but Rockwell hardness numbers are purely temporary.

The indentors used in Rockwell test are as follows:

1. Spherical and hardness steel balls of size 1/16 in. and 1/8 in.

2. A diamond cone of 120° (called a Brale indenter)

Major loads are 60, 100 and 150 kg for Rockwell *A*, *B* and *C*, respectively. Generally, three scales (*A*, *B* and *C*) are provided for metallic samples, but many other scales are available for special purposes.

Rockwell hardness test is a very useful and reproducible one, provided a number of precautions are taken to perform the test, as surface of the specimen should be flat and perpendicular to the indenter, and it should be clean, dry, smooth and free from oxide.

5.3.4 Superficial Tests

Superficial Rockwell hardness tests are performed to reduce the depth of indentation, and the minor and major loads are reduced. A 3-kg minor load and 15-, 30- and 45-kg major loads are applied depending upon the requirement of the specimen (Table 5.5).

Table 5.5 *Superficial Rockwell Hardness Scales*

Scale Symbol	Indenter	Major Loads (kg)
15N	Diamond	15
30N		30
45N		45
15T	1/16" ball	15
30T		30
45T		45
15W	1/8" ball	15
30W		30
45W		45

Example 5.4 60 HR 30 W indicates a superficial hardness of 60 in 30 W scale.

Solution:

Superficial tests are performed on thin samples. The specimen thickness should be at least 10 times the depth of indentation.

5.3.5 Microhardness Tests

To determine microhardness, i.e. hardness around a very small area, two hardness techniques are used: Knoop and Vicker's. For each test, a very small diamond indenter having pyramidal geometry is forced into the surface of the specimen under a very small load up to 1000 g. The resulting impression is observed under a microscope and the measurement of diagonal of impression is converted into hardness number.

Example 5.5 A 10-mm diameter Brinell ball produced an indentation of diameter 1.62 mm in a steel alloy when a load of 500 kg is used. Compute BHN.

Solution:

$$BHN = \frac{P \text{ in kg}}{\frac{\pi D}{2}\left[D - \sqrt{D^2 - d^2}\right]}$$

where

$$P = 500 \text{ kg}$$
$$D = 10 \text{ mm}$$
$$A = 1.62 \text{ mm}$$

$$BHN = \frac{500}{\frac{\pi \times 10}{2}\left[10 - \sqrt{10^2 - 1.62^2}\right]} = \frac{500}{15.708\left[10 - 9.8679\right]}$$

$$= \frac{500}{15.708 \times 0.132} = \frac{500}{2.075}$$

$$= 241$$

5.4 FRACTURE

Fracture is the breaking of a solid body into two or more parts under the action of applied stress. There are two stages of fracture: crack initiation and crack propagation, which leads to final fracture. There are two types of fractures: ductile fracture and brittle fracture. There is appreciable plastic deformation in ductile fracture, while brittle fracture is characterized by rapid rate of crack propagation without any gross deformation. It is similar to cleavage in ionic crystals. The tendency for brittle fracture is increased by (1) decreasing temperature, (2) increasing strain rate and (3) triaxial stress conditions (usually produced by notch, cuts and discontinuity). Brittle fracture occurs without any warning and is disastrous, therefore must be prevented.

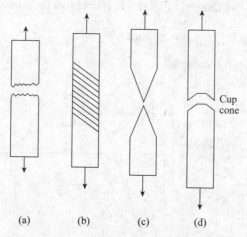

Cup
cone

(a)   (b)   (c)   (d)

Figure 5.7 *(a)–(d) Types of Tensile Fractures*

A brittle fracture is characterized by the separation of normal to tensile stress, without any evidence of deformation, as shown in Figure 5.7(a). Brittle fractures have been observed in BCC and HCP metals.

The ductile fractures can take several forms as shown in Figure 5.7(a)–(c). Figure 5.7(b) shows the ductile fracture in a single crystal due to successive slip; crystal separates by shear.

Polycrystalline materials that are highly ductile as gold or lead are drawn to a point in tensile loading as shown in Figure 5.7(c). In moderately ductile materials as mild steel, plastic deformation produces a necked region. Fracture begins at the centre of the specimen and then extends by a shear separation by making cup and cone type fracture [Figure 5.7(d)].

On the basis of behaviour of the metals, fractures are classified as follows:

1. Shear fracture—as a result of extensive slip on active slip planes.
2. Cleavage-type fracture is controlled by tensile stress acting normal to the crystallographic cleavage plane.
3. Fibrous fracture surface—caused by shear cleavage fracture, appears bright and granular. Generally, the fractured surfaces consist of a mixture of fibrous and granular fractures.
4. Fractures in polycrystalline samples are either transgranular (crack propagation through grain boundaries) or intergranular (crack propagates along the grain boundaries).
5. Ductile fracture exhibits a considerable degree of deformation.

Brittle fracture is arbitrary and depends on a situation. However, there is very little strain in brittle fracture. Most of the metals and alloys are ductile. The ceramics are notably brittle, while polymers exhibit both types of fractures, i.e. ductile and brittle.

5.4.1 Theoretical Cohesive Strength

The strength due to cohesive forces between the atoms, curve shown, is a resultant of attractive and repulsive forces between the atoms.

As the tensile force on the sample is increased further, the repulsive force continues to decrease. A point is reached where the repulsive force is negligible and the attractive force is also decreasing because of the increased separation of atoms. This corresponds to a maximum in the curve, and equals to theoretical cohesive strength σ_{max} as shown in Figure 5.8. If cohesive force curve is taken as sinusoidal,

$$\sigma = \sigma_{max} \sin \frac{2\pi x}{\lambda} \tag{5.4}$$

where σ_{max} = theoretical cohesive strength

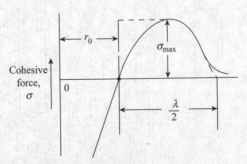

Figure 5.8 *Cohesive Strength*

$$\text{Work done} = \int_{r_0}^{\frac{\lambda}{2}+r_0} \sigma_{max} \sin \frac{2\pi x}{\lambda} \, dx = \frac{\lambda \sigma_{max}}{\pi} \tag{5.5}$$

If

$$\frac{\lambda \sigma_{max}}{\pi} = 2\gamma \tag{5.6}$$

$$\sigma_{max} = \frac{2\pi\gamma}{\lambda} \tag{5.7}$$

Stress, $\sigma = \frac{E_x}{r_0}$, Hooke's law,

$$\tag{5.8}$$

$$\frac{d\sigma}{dx} = r_{max} \frac{2\pi}{\lambda} \cos \frac{2\pi x}{\lambda} \tag{5.9}$$

$2\pi x/\lambda$ is very small, therefore,

$$\cos \frac{2\pi x}{\lambda} \approx 1$$

$$\frac{d\sigma}{dx} = \sigma_{max} \frac{2\pi}{\lambda} \tag{5.10}$$

From Eq. (5.8)

$$\frac{d\sigma}{dx} = \frac{E}{r_0} \tag{5.11}$$

From Eqs (5.10) and (5.11),

$$\sigma_{max} \frac{2\pi}{\lambda} = \frac{E}{r_0}$$

$$\sigma_{max} = \frac{E}{r_0} \times \frac{\lambda}{2\pi}$$

But,

$$\frac{\lambda}{2\pi} = \frac{\gamma}{\sigma_{max}} \tag{5.12}$$

or,

$$\sigma_{max} = \frac{E}{r_0} \times \frac{\gamma}{\sigma_{max}}$$

$$\sigma_{max} = \sqrt{\frac{E\gamma}{r_0}}$$

The theoretical cohesive strength is 10–1000 times greater than the observed values of fracture strength of the metals. Only dislocation-free metal whiskers approach this theoretical cohesive strength.

5.5 FRACTURE MECHANICS

The fracture mechanics provides quantification of the relationship among material properties, stress level, presence of crack (or flaw) and crack propagation mechanism and stress concentration.

The fracture strength of a solid material is a function of cohesive strength. For a brittle material, the theoretical cohesive strength is approximately $0.1E$, where E is the Young's modulus. But the

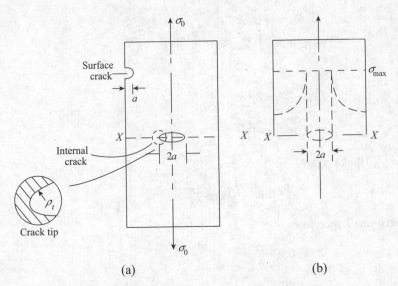

Figure 5.9 *(a) Crack Tip (b) Stress Distribution*

experimental values of bulk materials lie between 10 and 1000 times below this theoretical value, because of microscopic flaws and cracks in the solid materials.

In 1920, A.A. Griffith proposed that the discrepancy between the theoretical and the observed fracture strength can be explained by the presence of very small microscopic flaws and cracks that always exist under normal conditions at the surface unit within the interior of the material. These flaws are detrimental to the fracture strength because an applied stress may be amplified or concentrated at the tip, which depends upon crack initiation and geometry. This phenomenon is shown in Figure 5.9(b) by the distributions across a section containing an internal crack.

The magnitude of localized stress σ_{max} diminishes with distance away from the crack tip, and the stress becomes σ_0, equal to the applied load, in the cross-sectional area. Due to their ability to amplify an applied stress in their vicinity, these flaws are sometimes called 'stress raisers'.

It is assumed that the crack is of an elliptical shape and is oriented perpendicular to the applied stress; the maximum stress at the crack tip is equal to

$$\sigma_{max} = \sigma_0 \left[1 + 2 \left(\frac{a}{\rho_t} \right)^{\frac{1}{2}} \right]$$

where σ_0 is the amplitude of nominal stress, a is the length of surface crack and ρ_t is the radius of curvature at the crack tip.

For a relatively long crack with a small tip radius of curvature, the factor $(a/\rho_t)^{1/2}$ is very large in comparison to 1, therefore, under these circumstances.

$$\sigma_{max} = \sigma_0 \, 2\sqrt{\frac{a}{\rho_t}}$$

or

$$\frac{\sigma_{max}}{\sigma_0} = 2 \left(\frac{a}{\rho_t} \right)^{\frac{1}{2}} = \text{stress concentration factor } K_t$$

Moreover, stress magnification is not restricted to the microscopic internal flaws. It may occur at macroscopic internal discontinuities (e.g. voids), at sharp corners and at notches in large components.

Example 5.6 The fracture strength of glass sample is 42 MN/m². Estimate the Griffiths crack length in this sample assuming that $E = 60,000$ MN/m² and $\gamma = 0.21$ J/m².

Solution:

Fracture strength,

$$\sigma_f = \left(\frac{2E\gamma}{\pi c}\right)^{\frac{1}{2}}$$

where c = crack length

$$E = 60,000 \times 10^6 \text{ N/m}^2$$

$$\gamma = 0.21 \text{ J/m}^2$$

$$\sigma_f = 42 \text{ MN/m}^2$$

Putting in the equation above

$$42 \times 10^6 = \left[\frac{2 \times 6 \times 10^{10} \times 0.21}{\pi \times c}\right]^{\frac{1}{2}}$$

or squaring both the sides

$$1764 \times 10^{12} = \frac{2.52 \times 10^{10}}{\pi \times c}$$

$$c = \frac{0.80214}{1764 \times 10^2}$$

$$= 4.55 \times 10^{-6} \text{ m}$$

$$= 4.55 \ \mu\text{m}$$

Example 5.7 Determine the cohesive strength of a silica fibre, if $E = 96$ GPa, $\gamma_s = 1.03$ J/m² and $r_0 = 1.61$ Å

Solution:

Maximum cohesive strength,

$$\sigma_{max} = \sqrt{\frac{E\gamma_s}{r_0}}$$

$$= \sqrt{\frac{96 \times 10^9 \times 1.03}{r_0}}$$

$$r_0 = 1.61 \text{ Å} = 1.61 \times 10^{-8} \text{ m}$$

$$\sigma_{max} = \sqrt{\frac{96 \times 10^9 \times 1.03}{1.61 \times 10^{-8}}} = 2478 \times 10^6 \text{ N/m}^2$$

$$= 2478 \text{ N/mm}^2$$

The effect of stress raisers is more pronounced in brittle materials than in ductile materials. For a ductile material, the plastic deformation start when the maximum stress exceeds the yield strength of the material, which leads to a uniform distribution of stress in the vicinity of stress raiser, and to the development of a maximum stress concentration factor less than the theoretical value. But yielding and stress distribution do not occur around the flaws and discontinuities in brittle materials, obviously, therefore the theoretical value of stress concentration factor will result.

Griffiths has proposed that all brittle materials contain a population of small cracks and flaws that have a variety of shapes, sizes and orientations. Fracture will occur when on the application of tensile stress, the theoretical cohesive strength of the material is exceeded at the tip of one of the flaws, leading to the formation of a crack that rapidly propagates. If no flaws are present, the fracture strength is equal to cohesive strength. Very small and virtually defect-free metallic and ceramic whiskers have been grown with fracture strengths that approach the theoretical cohesive strength.

5.5.1 Griffith Theory of Brittle Fracture

During crack propagation, elastic strain energy is released. Some of the energy is stored in the material as it is elastically deformed. Further, during crack extension process, new free surfaces are created at the faces of a crack, which give rise to an increase in the surface energy of the system.

Griffith developed a criterion of crack propagation of an elliptical crack, by using an energy balance of two energies. He showed that the critical stress σ_c required for crack propagation in a brittle material is given by

$$\sigma_c = \left(\frac{2E\gamma_s}{\pi a}\right)^{\frac{1}{2}}$$

where E is the Young's modulus of the material, γ_s is the specific surface energy and a is half of the length of internal crack.

This expression does not take into account the crack tip radius ρ_t. However, it is assumed that this radius is sufficiently sharp (of interatomic spacing) so as to raise the local stress at the tip, much above the cohesive strength of the material.

Above equation applies only to perfectly brittle materials like glass, in which there is no plastic deformation. Most metals and many polymers do experience some plastic deformation during fracture, resulting in the increase in surface energy, γ_s and the term is replaced by $\gamma_s + \gamma_p$; surface energy + plastic deformation energy at critical stress,

$$\sigma_c = \sqrt{\frac{2E(\gamma_s + \gamma_p)}{\pi a}}$$

For highly ductile material, where $\gamma_p \gg \gamma_s$,

critical stress
$$\sigma_c = \sqrt{\frac{2E(\gamma_p)}{\pi a}}$$

5.5.2 Stress Analysis of Cracks

Let us study the stress distribution in the vicinity of the tip of an advancing crack. There are three fundamental modes of crack: (1) opening tensile mode, (2) sliding or shear mode and (3) tearing mode as shown in Figure 5.10(a)–(c).

In these three modes, a load can operate on a crack and each will reflect a different crack surface displacement. Mode I is encountered most frequently, therefore, only this mode will be discussed.

Mode I

Stresses acting on an element of material as shown in Figure 5.11, obtained from the theory of elasticity are

$$\sigma_x = \frac{K}{\sqrt{2\pi r}} \times f_x(\theta)$$

$$\sigma_y = \frac{K}{\sqrt{2\pi r}} \times f_y(\theta)$$

$$\tau_{xy} = \frac{K}{\sqrt{2\pi r}} \times f_{xy}(\theta)$$

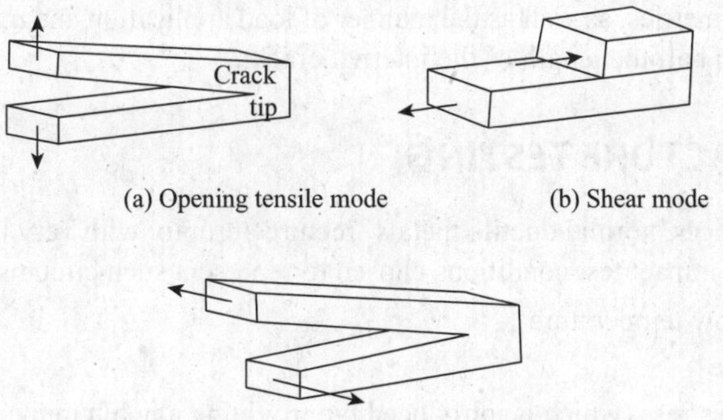

Crack tip
(a) Opening tensile mode
(b) Shear mode
(c) Tearing mode

Figure 5.10 *(a) Mode I (b) Mode II (c) Mode III Cracks*

If we take a thin plate, $\sigma_z = 0$ under plane stress condition. For a thick plate, $\sigma_z = \nu(\sigma_x + \sigma_y)$ under plane strain conditions, where ν is the Poisson's ratio.

y
γ
θ
x
z
σz
σy
τxy
τyx
σx
σx
σz
σy

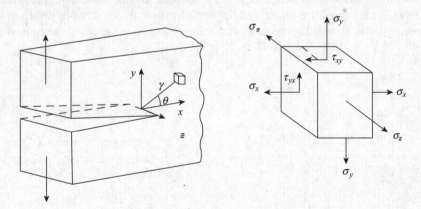

Figure 5.11 *Stresses on an Element*

Again, with the help of the theory of elasticity, the following functions are obtained:

$$f_x(\theta) = \cos\frac{\theta}{2}\left(1 - \sin\frac{\theta}{2}\sin\frac{3\theta}{2}\right)$$

$$f_y(\theta) = \cos\frac{\theta}{2}\left(1 + \sin\frac{\theta}{2}\sin\frac{3\theta}{2}\right)$$

$$f_{xy}(\theta) = \sin\frac{\theta}{2}\cos\frac{\theta}{2}\cos\frac{3\theta}{2}$$

The parameter K is termed as stress intensity factor—a convenient factor for stress distribution around a flaw.

$$\text{SIF, } K = \gamma, \sigma\sqrt{\pi a}$$

where γ is a dimensional parameter. Unit of K is MPa$\sqrt{m}$. Y is a function that depends on both crack and specimen sizes and geometries, as well as the manner of load application and a is the length of a surface crack, which is equal to half the length of the internal crack.

5.6 IMPACT FRACTURE TESTING

Under some circumstances, normal ductile metals fracture abruptly with very little plastic deformation (a brittle fracture). The impact test conditions chosen to represent such circumstances are as follows:

1. Deformation at low temperature
2. At high strain rate
3. A triaxial state of stress (which is introduced by providing a notch in the sample)

Two standardized tests—The Charpy and Izod tests, are used to measure the impact energy, i.e. notch toughness test. These notched bar impact tests are used to determine the tendency of a ductile material to behave in a brittle manner. The specimen is forced to bend and fracture at a strain rate of the order of 10^3 mm/mm/s. The Izod specimen contains a V-notch near one end. The specimen is clamped vertically at one end as a cantilever beam and is struck with a pendulum at the other end. The notch is subjected to tensile stress and the plastic constraint at the notch produces a triaxial state of stress in specimen. The relative values of three principal stresses depend on the dimensions of specimen and details of the notch. So, it is important to use standard specimens. The value of transverse stress at the root of the notch

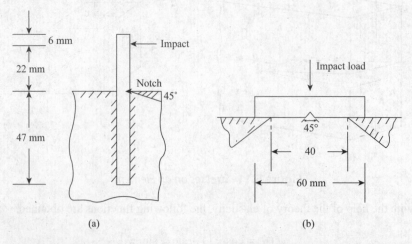

Figure 5.12 *(a) Izod Impact Test Sample (b) Charpy Impact Test Specimen*

depends on the width of the bar and the notch radius. Figure 5.12(a) shows an Izod impact test sample. Figure 5.12(b) shows a Charpy impact test specimen.

The response of a specimen to the impact test is usually measured by the impact energy absorbed in fracturing the specimen (in Nm). It is also important to examine the fracture surface to determine whether it is fibrous (shear failure) or granular (cleavage fracture).

The notched bar impact test is most meaningful when conducted over a range of temperatures so that the temperature at which the ductile-to-brittle transition takes place can be determined.

5.6.1 Transition

Figure 5.13 shows that the impact energy absorbed decreases with decreasing temperature, but in most of the cases decrease in energy does not occur abruptly at a particular temperature. So, it becomes difficult to determine accurately the transition temperature. In selecting a material from the consideration of notch toughness, transition temperature is an important factor.

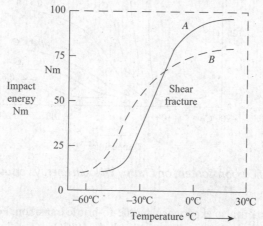

Figure 5.13 *Transition Temperature Curves*

Steel A shows higher notch toughness at room temperature, yet its transition temperature is higher than that of steel B. The material with the lowest transition temperature is to be preferred.

Because the transition temperature is not sharply defined, it is important to understand the criteria adopted for this definition. In general, criteria for determining the transition temperature are based on a transition in energy absorbed. The change in appearance of fracture or transition in ductility is measured by contraction at the root of the notch, e.g.

Ductile fractured surface—fibrous and dull
Brittle fracture surface—a granular (shiny) texture (or cleavage type)

For many alloys, there is a range of temperature, over which the ductile-to-brittle transition occurs. The structures constructed from alloys that exhibit ductile-to-brittle behaviour should be used only at room temperature or above the transition temperature to avoid brittle and catastrophic failure.

All metals and alloys do not display a ductile to brittle transition. *Metals with an FCC structure remain ductile even at very low temperatures* (including aluminium- and copper-based alloys).

The alloys with BCC and HCP structures experience this transition. For these materials, the transition temperature is sensitive to both alloy composition and microstructure.

For example, decreasing the average grain size of steels results in a lowering of the transition temperature. Hence, grain refining strengthens and toughens the steel. In contrast, increasing the carbon content increases the strength of the steel, but raises Charpy V-Notch (CVN) impact energy transition of steels (Figure 5.14).

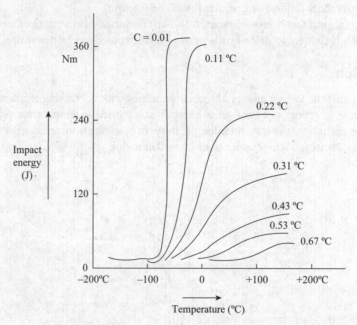

Figure 5.14 *Influence of Carbon Content on Charpy V-Notch Energy Versus Temperature for Steels*

Most ceramics and polymers also experience ductile-to-brittle transition. For organic materials, transition occurs only at elevated temperatures, generally above 100°C.

Cold working by itself will increase the transition temperature, but strain ageing results in a greater increase around 15°C.

5.7 TEMPER EMBRITTLEMENT

There is a loss of notch toughness of plain carbon steels when exposed to temperatures above 370°C, but below the temperature there is formation of austenite. Alloy steels are especially susceptible to embrittlement when they are tempered in the region of 425–600°C and slowly cooled through this temperature range. This is more important for heavy sections, which cannot be cooled rapidly enough to suppress embrittlement.

Temper embrittlement can be completely eliminated from an embrittled steel by heating it into the austenite region and cooling rapidly through the embrittling temperature range. It is generally hypothesized that the temper embrittlement is due to the segregation of impurities to the grain boundaries.

Molybdenum is the only alloying element, which decreases the susceptibility to temper embrittlement. Tempering at a higher temperature for a short time may be better than a long-time tempering at a lower temperature.

5.8 HYDROGEN EMBRITTLEMENT

Many metals are severely embrittled by very small amount of hydrogen, as low as 0.0001 per cent by weight. Both BCC and HCP crystals are most susceptible to hydrogen embrittlement, but FCC metals are generally not susceptible. Hydrogen may be introduced during melting and solidification or may be picked up during heat treatment, acid pickling, electroplating or welding. The formation of hair line cracks, or flakes, in large ingots or forgings during cooling or room temperature ageing is attributed to the presence of hydrogen.

Hydrogen embrittlement is increased by slow strain rates. A common method of studying hydrogen embrittlement is to charge notched tensile specimens with known amounts of hydrogen and load at different stress levels and observe the time to failure. A typical delayed fracture curve is shown in Figure 5.15.

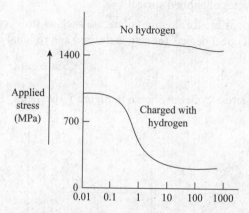

Figure 5.15 *Time of Fracture Versus Delayed Fracture Curve*

Note that the notched tensile strength of a charged specimen is much lower than the strength of a hydrogen-free specimen.

Hydrogen is present in solution as monatomic hydrogen. It diffuses very rapidly at the interstitial sites at temperature above the room temperature, because it is very small in size. Hydrogen atom precipitates as molecular hydrogen in voids, microcracks and regions of high dislocation density. As hydrogen builds up into the voids, the pressure also builds up and produces fracture.

5.9 FATIGUE

Fatigue is a form of failure that occurs in machine components and structures, which are subjected to dynamic and fluctuating loads, for example, bridges, air craft structure and turbine blades. Under repetitive stress reversals, it is possible for the failure to occur at a stress level much lower than the tensile or yield strength under a static load. Fatigue type of failure occurs under a long duration of repeated stress cycles.

Fatigue is the single largest cause of failure and it amounts to about 90 per cent of all metallic failures. Polymers and ceramics (except glass) are also prone to this type of failure. This failure is catastrophic, occurs suddenly without any warning.

Fatigue failure is like a brittle failure with very little plastic deformation. The stages of fatigue failure are: (1) crack initiation, (2) crack propagation and (iii) sudden fracture. Ordinarily, the fractured surface is perpendicular to the direction of the applied stress.

A fatigue failure can usually be recognized from the appearance of fractured surface, showing a smooth region due to rubbing action as the crack propagates through the section, and a rough region, where the member has failed in a ductile manner when the cross section is no longer able to carry the load. Progress of the fracture is indicated by a series of beach marks progressing inward from the point of crack initiation. Fatigue failure initiates from a point of stress concentration such as sharp corner or notch or at a metallurgical stress concentration as an inclusion.

The three basic factors necessary for fatigue failure are as follows:

1. Maximum tensile stress of sufficiently high value
2. Enough variation of applied stress
3. A large number of cycles of applied stress

Many other factors responsible for fatigue failure are such as stress concentration, corrosion, temperature, over load, metallurgical defects (as slag inclusion) and residual stresses.

5.9.1 Stress Cycles

There are various types of stress cycles as shown in Figure 5.16(a)–(c).

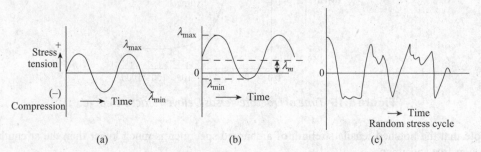

Figure 5.16 *Types of Stress Cycles*

The applied stress may be axial (tension–compression), flexural (bending) or torsional shear (twisting). In general, three different types of fluctuating stress–time modes are shown.

1. Sinusoidal variation of stress with mean stress, $\sigma_m = 0$

$$\frac{\sigma_{max} + \sigma_{min}}{2} = 0$$

Stress range,

$$\sigma_r = \sigma_{max} - \sigma_{min}$$

Stress amplitude,

$$\sigma_a = \frac{\sigma_{max} - \sigma_{min}}{2}$$

Stress ratio,

$$R = \frac{\sigma_{max}}{\sigma_{min}}$$

It is a completely reversed cycle.

2. Illustrates a repeated stress cycle, in which σ_{max} and σ_{min} are not equal.
3. Shows a complicated stress cycle that may be encountered in a part such as aircraft wing, which is subjected to periodic unpredictable overloads due to gusts.

A stress cycle in which stress is completely reversed from positive maximum to negative minimum, with mean stress $\sigma_m = 0$ produces the worst type of fatigue failure. This type of stress cycle occurs in rotating bending or rotating twisting (shafts) components.

5.9.2 *S–N* Curve

The fatigue properties of materials are determined from laboratory simulation tests. In a rotating bending apparatus, commonly used for fatigue test, compressive and tensile stresses are induced in the specimen as it is simultaneously bent and rotated. Tests are also conducted using an alternating uniaxial tension and compression stress cycle. A series of tests are preformed by subjecting a specimen to the stress cycling, keeping the magnitude of maximum stress of the order of $0.6\ \sigma_{ut}$. The number of cycles to complete failure is noted from the counter provided on the testing machine. This procedure is repeated on other specimens at gradually decreasing maximum stress amplitude till the test at a stress level on which the specimen does not fail for any number of cycles. Data are plotted as stress versus log N scale (N is the number of cycles to failure) for each of the specimens.

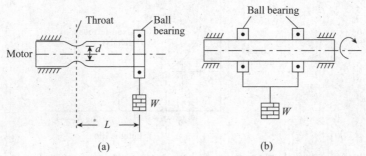

Figure 5.17 *(a) Cantilever-type Specimen (b) Rotating Bending Beam Specimen*

Two distinct types of *S–N* curves are observed. These plots indicate that the higher the amplitude of stress, smaller will be the number of cycles, and the material is capable of sustaining before failure. The following are the two types of curves:

1. For some ferrous (iron base) and titanium base alloys, *S–N* curve becomes horizontal at higher values of N. This limiting stress level is called 'fatigue limit'.

   Figure 5.17(a) and (b) shows two types of rotating bending-type fatigue testing machines. Dead load W is applied through bearings on the rotating specimens. In the second case [Figure 5.17(b)], bending moment remains constant over the gauge length of the specimen and the specimen may fail any where at any section along the gauge length. In the first case, bending moment varies linearly; specimen fails at the throat of diameter d, where bending moment is WL.

   The fatigue limit is sometimes called the 'endurance limit'. The fatigue limit represents the largest value of fluctuating stress that will not cause fracture for essentially an infinite number of cycles (Figure 5.18).

   For many steels, the fatigue limit ranges between 35 and 60 per cent of the tensile strength.

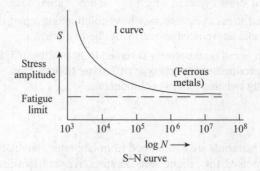

Figure 5.18 *Fatigue Limit S–N Curve*

2. Most non-ferrous alloys (of aluminium, copper and magnesium) do not have a fatigue limit. The *S–N* curve continues its downward trend at increasing values of *N* (Figure 5.19). For these materials, fatigue response is specified as 'fatigue strength', which is defined as the stress level at which *failure will occur for some specified number of cycles*. Another important parameter is fatigue life, N_f, which is the number of cycles to cause failure at a specified stress level.

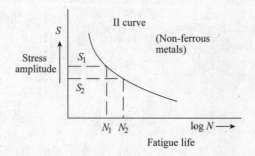

Figure 5.19 *Stress Amplitude Versus Fatigue Life Curve*

Unfortunately, there always exists a considerable scatter in a fatigue test data, i.e. variation in the measured *N* values, for a number of specimens tested at the same stress level *S*. This leads to a number of design uncertainties when fatigue life or fatigue limit is being considered.

Scatter in results is due to a number of factors, which are as follows:

1. Fabrication and surface preparations
2. Metallurgical variable, i.e. random distribution of defects as cracks, blow holes and notches
3. Alignment of specimen
4. Mean stress
5. Test frequency

Several statistical techniques have been used to specify fatigue life or fatigue limit in terms of probabilities. However, values are taken for 90 per cent survivals. [At a particular stress, a number of specimens, e.g. 10, are tested. *N* is that value of number of cycles that 90 per cent of total specimens (9 out of 10) tested have survived.]

The fatigue behaviour can be classified into two domains:

1. High loads, producing not only elastic, but also plastic strain and fatigue lives are 10^6–10^5 cycles, known as 'low cycle fatigue'.
2. For lower stress levels, wherein the deformation is totally elastic, longer fatigue lives result, i.e. 10^6–10^8 cycles.

5.9.3 Crack Initiation and Propagation

Fatigue has certain features in common with plastic flow and fracture under static load deformation in fatigue.

1. A metal deforms under cyclic strain by a slip on some atomic planes and in some crystallographic directions as in unidirectional strain.
2. In unidirectional deformation, slip is usually widespread throughout the grains, but in fatigue some grains show slip lines, while others give no evidence of slip.
3. Slip lines are formed during the first few thousand cycles of stress.
4. Successive cycles produce additional slip bands, but the number of silp bands is not directly proportional to the number of cycles of stress.
5. In many metals, increase in visible slip reaches a saturation value, resulting in distorted regions of heavy slip.
6. Cracks form in the regions of heavy distortion.

A study of crack formation in fatigue is made by interrupting the fatigue test to remove the deformed surface by electropolishing. Several slip bands will be visible and other slip lines are polished away. Such slip bands have been observed after only 5 per cent of the total life of the sample. *These persistent slip bands are nucleation of fatigue cracks* and they open up into wide cracks on application of small tensile strains.

Once formed, the fatigue cracks tend to propagate initially along the slip planes; later on take a direction normal to the maximum applied tensile stress. The fatigue crack propagation is ordinarily transgranular.

In fatigue, there is formation of ridges and grooves where fatigue cracks initiate. Moreover, cross slip is needed for the formation of these ridges and grooves (called intrusion and extrusions).

In brief, the process of fatigue crack is often divided into three stages:

1. *Primary stage:* In primary stage, stress level is above the static yield stress, and widespread bulk deformation occurs until the metal strain harden to a point where it can withstand the applied stress. The first stage lasts for about 10^3–10^4 cycles.
2. *Secondary stage:* It comprises the major part of fatigue life of a specimen. It extends from wide-spread strain hardening to the formation of visible crack. A crack is initiated, so the process of fatigue failure is characterized by three distinct steps:
   (a) Crack initiation —a small crack (on submicroscopic scale) forms at some point of high-stress concentration.
   (b) Crack propagation—incremental advancement of crack at each stress cycle.
   (c) Final fracture, which occurs suddenly when the advancing crack reaches a critical size.

Fatigue life,
$$N_f = N_i + N_p$$

= Number of cycles required for crack initiation + number of cycles for crack propagation

At low stress levels (high cycle fatigue), large fraction of fatigue life is utilized in crack initiation—with increasing stress level, N_i (the number of cycles required for crack initiation) decreases and cracks form more rapidly.

Cracks for fatigue failure generally initiate on the surface of the component at some point of stress concentration. Crack nucleation sites include surface scratches, sharp fillets, keyways, threads, dents and similar sites. In addition, the cyclic loading can produce microscopic surface discontinuities resulting from dislocation slip steps, which may also act as stress raisers.

Once a stable crack is nucleated, it propagates initially at a slow rate and in polycrystalline metals, along the crystallographic planes of high shear stress, sometimes referred to as 'stage I propagation'. This stage may constitute a large or small fraction of the total fatigue life N_f, depending on the stress level and geometry of the test specimen, i.e.:

3. High stress and presence of notches favour short-lived stage I.

In polycrystalline metals, cracks normally extend through several grains during this propagation and the fatigue surface formed during stage I has a flat and featureless appearance.

(a) In the second stage of propagation, crack extension rate increases and there may be change in the direction of propagation to a crack which is roughly perpendicular to the direction of the applied stress.

During this stage, crack growth proceeds by a repetitive plastic (deformation) blunting and sharpening (strain hardening) process at the crack tip.

At the beginning of the stress cycle (zero or maximum compressive load) the crack tip has the shape of a sharp double notch. When the tensile stress is applied (cycle of stress), localized deformation occurs at each of these tip notches along the slip planes that are oriented at 45° angle relative to the plane of the crack. With increased crack ordering, the tip advances by continued shear deformations and assumption

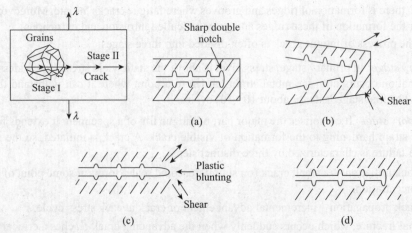

Figure 5.20 *Crack Growth Stages*

of a blunted configuration. During compressions, the directions of shear deformation at the crack tip are reverted until at the end of the cycle, and a new sharp double notch tip is formed. Thus, the crack tip has advanced a one-notch distance during the course of complete stress cycle. This process is repeated with each subsequent cycle until some critical crack dimensions are achieved, which precipitate the final fracture step and the catastrophic failure also occurs (Figure 5.20).

The region of a fracture surface that formed during stage II propagation is characterized by two types of markings: (1) beach marks and (2) striations. Both these features indicate the position of crack tip at some point in time and appear as concentric ridges and expand away from the crack initiation sites frequently in a circular or semicircular pattern.

Striatories are of microscopic size and beach marks are of macroscopic size. Final rapid failure may be either ductile or brittle. There is evidence of plastic deformation in ductile fracture and the absence of plastic deformation in the brittle failure.

5.9.4 Factors Affecting Fatigue Behaviour

Following are the major factors affecting fatigue behaviour:

Stress Concentration Factor

Fatigue strength is seriously reduced by the presence of stress raiser such as notch or hole. Actual machine components invariably contain stress raisers like fillets, keyways, screw threads, press fits and holes and fatigue cracks in structural parts usually start at such geometrical irregularities. Moreover, the stress concentrations can also arise from surface roughness, porosity, inclusions, local overheating in grinding and decarburizations.

$$K_t = \text{theoretical stress concentraion factor}$$

$$= \frac{\text{maximum stress}}{\text{nominal stress}}$$

$$K_f = \text{fatigue strength reduction factor or fatigue notch factor}$$

$$= \frac{\text{fatigue limit of unnotched specimens}}{\text{fatigue limit of notched specimens}}$$

$$= \frac{\text{fatigue strength of unnotched specimens}}{\text{fatigue strength of notched specimens}}$$

Materials, which do not exhibit fatigue limit
K_f is usually less than K_t.
Notch sensitivity index,

$$q = \frac{K_f - 1}{K_t - 1},$$

where

K_f = notch fatigue factor
K_t = theoretical stress concentration factor
$Q = 0$, if the material does not experience any reduction in fatigue strength
$Q = 1$, when notch has its full theoretical effect

Q is not a true material constant because it varies with the severity and type of notch, size of the specimen and type of loading. The notch sensitivity increases with section size and tensile strength.

Size Effect

Fatigue tests are performed on small samples, but fatigue life is to be predicted for large machine members, therefore, there is a necessity of size factor. Experience has shown that in most cases, a size effect exists, i.e. the fatigue strengths of a large member is lower than that of a small specimen and only a few fatigue machines can accommodate specimens having a wide range of cross sections. For example, wings of aeroplane are tested under fatigue loading.

Experiments support the idea that a size effect in fatigue is due to the existence of a stress gradient. Actual failures in large size parts are directly attributable and it is usually impossible to duplicate the same stress concentration and stress gradient in a small-sized laboratory specimen.

Surface Effects

Practically all fatigue failures start at the surface. The fatigue properties are very sensitive to surface conditions. The surface factors are divided into three categories:

1. Surface roughness or stress raisers at the surface
2. Changes in fatigue strength of the surface of the metal
3. Changes in residual stress condition of the surface

Smoothly polished specimens, in which fine scratches are oriented parallel to the direction of the principal tensile stress give the highest values in fatigue tests.

Decarburization of the surface of heat-treated steel is detrimental to fatigue performance. Marked improvements in fatigue properties can result from the formation of harder and stronger surface on steel parts by carburizing and nitriding. Electroplating of the surface generally decreases the fatigue limit of the steel.

The formation of a favourable compressive residual–stress pattern at the surface is the most effective method of increasing fatigue performance. Commercial methods of introducing favourable compressive residual stresses in the surface are by surface rolling with contoured rollers and by shot peening. Surface rolling is adapted for large parts, such as fillets of crankshafts and bearing surface of rail road axles. Shot peening consists of projecting fine steel or cast iron shots against the surface at a high velocity.

Corrosion Fatigue

The simultaneous action of cyclic stress and chemical attack is termed as 'corrosion fatigue'. The corrosive attack produces pitting of the metal surfaces. The pits act as notches and produce reduction in fatigue strength. However, when corrosive attack occurs simultaneously with fatigue loading, fatigue properties are badly reduced. When corrosion and fatigue occur simultaneously, the chemical attack greatly accelerates the rate of crack propagation in fatigue.

Fretting

Fretting is the surface damage, which results when two surfaces in contact experience slight periodic relative motion. It is frequently found on the surface of a shaft with a press-fitted hub or bearing.

Surface pitting and deterioration occur along with oxide debris. Fatigue cracks start often in the damaged area. Fretting is caused by mechanical and chemical effects. The metal is removed from the surface either by a grinding action or by the alternate welding and tearing away of the high spots. The removed particles are oxidized and become abrasive powder, which continues the destructive process.

There is no complete method of preventing fretting. Solid lubricants such as MoS are most successful for maintaining a lubricant film between the two surfaces.

Effect of Mean Stress

Most of the fatigue data have been determined for conditions of completely reversed stress cycle, with $\sigma_m = 0$. But in engineering applications, one may find stress situation where $\sigma_m \neq 0$.

Fatigue tests are performed by applying a series of stress cycles with decreasing maximum stress and adjusting the minimum stress in each case so that it is a constant fraction of the maximum stress. Note that as the mean stress becomes more positive, the allowable alternating stress decreases (Figure 5.21).

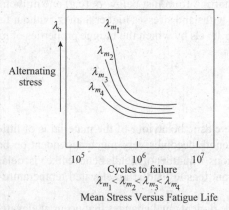

Figure 5.21 *Mean Stress Data*

An alternative method of presenting mean stress data is shown in Figure 5.21, which is known as Hough–Soderberg diagram. The alternating stress is plotted against the mean stress. A straight-line relationship follows the suggestion of Goodman while the parabolic curve was proposed by Gerber. Test data for ductile metals generally fall closer to the parabolic curve. However, because of the scatter in the results and the fact that the tests and notched specimens fall closer to the Goodman line, the linear relationship is usually preferred in the engineering design.

$$\sigma_a = \sigma_e \left[1 - \left(\frac{\sigma_m}{\sigma_u} \right)^x \right]$$

shows relationship between alternating stress and mean stress, where σ_e is the fatigue limit, for completely reversed stress, σ_m is the mean stress, σ_u is the ultimate tensile stress, σ_0 is the yield strength and σ_a is the stress amplitude. For Goodman line $x = 1$ and for Gerber parabola $x = 2$.

Figure 5.22 is obtained for alternating axial or bending stresses with static tension or compression or alternating torsion with static torsion.

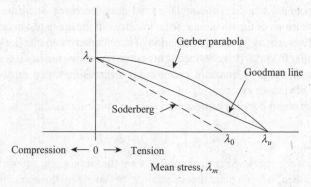

Figure 5.22 *Goodman Diagram*

5.9.5 Understressing

In some materials, which have well-defined fatigue limit (σ_e), it has been observed that the application of stress cycles at stresses below σ_e strengthens the material. If these cycles are applied to a material in a series of increasing stress starting from just below σ_e (e.g. one million cycle at each stress level), the materials have been found to withstand stresses higher than σ_e without failure. This process of repeated cycling at successively higher levels by which the fatigue properties of materials are improved is called understressing.

5.10 CREEP

At room temperature test, the elastic behaviour of the material is of little practical significance. But at elevated temperature, the strength becomes very much dependent on both strain rate and the time of exposure. Under these conditions, a number of metals behave like viscoelastic materials in many respects. A metal subjected to a constant tensile load at an elevated temperature creeps and undergoes a time-dependent increase in length.

The creep test measures the dimensional changes that occur at elevated temperature exposure, while stress rupture test measures the effect of temperature on long-time, load-bearing properties.

5.10.1 Creep Curve

The time-dependent *deformation* of a material at constant stress is called creep. The simplest type of creep is a viscous flow.

To determine the engineering creep curve of a metal, a constant load is applied to a tensile specimen maintained at constant temperature, and the stress in the specimen is noted as a function of time. The elapsed time of such tests may extend to several months.

Curve A is the idealized type of creep curve. The slope of the curve in the secondary creep is called creep rate $\dot{\epsilon}$. When there is initial instantaneous strain ϵ_0, the creep rate decreases with time, then gradually reaches a steady state in which the creep rate changes little with time, finally the creep rate increases rapidly with time until the specimen fractures. The degree to which the three stages [i.e. primary, secondary and tertiary as shown in (Figure 5.23)] are readily distinguishable depends upon the magnitude of the applied stress and the temperature of the test.

In an engineering creep test, the load is maintained constant throughout the tests, so when the specimen elongates, the cross-sectional area decreases and the axial stress increases. There are methods of compensating the change in dimensions of the specimen, so as to carry out the creep test under constant stress. When constant stress creep tests are made, there is no region of accelerated creep rate (i.e. tertiary creep, stage III) and a creep curve similar to curve B is obtained. This curve represents the basic creep curve of a metal.

The first component, stage I, transient creep has a decreasing creep rate with time. Next is the constant creep rate, i.e. viscous creep.

Andrade found that creep curve is represented by an empirical relation

$$L = L_0 \left(1 + \beta t^{\frac{1}{3}}\right) \exp kt,$$

where L is the length of the specimen at time t and β, k are the empirically determined constants and L_0 is the length of the specimen, when instantaneous strain ϵ_0 produced by the application of load has ceased.

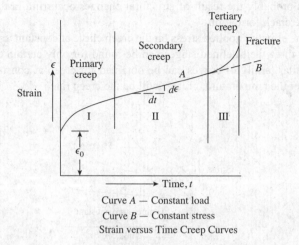

Curve *A* — Constant load
Curve *B* — Constant stress
Strain versus Time Creep Curves

Figure 5.23 *Creep Curves*

1. Transient creep represented by a constant β, when $k = 0$, yields a creep rate, which vanishes with long time

$$L = L_0 \left(1 + \beta t^{\frac{1}{3}} \right)$$

Strain rate

$$\epsilon = \frac{dL}{dt} = \frac{1}{3} L_0 \beta t^{-\frac{2}{3}}$$

2. If $\beta = 0$

$$\frac{L}{L_0} = \exp kt$$

$$\frac{dL}{dt} = kL_0 \exp kt = kL$$

$$k = \frac{1}{L} \frac{dL}{dt}$$

The exponent k represents an extension per unit length, which proceeds at a constant rate. This represents the 'viscous creep' phenomenon. Actually, k represents quasi-viscous flow because the rate of change of length is not proportional to stress. Sometimes, transient creep is referred to a β flow, a viscous creep (steady state).

Strain represented by ε_0 occurs instantaneously on the application of load. Even though the applied stress is below the yield stress, all the instantaneous strains are not elastic. Most of these strains are instantaneously recovered upon release of the load (elastic), yet part is recoverable with time (inelastic) and the rest is non-recoverable (plastic).

The first stage of creep, known as primary creep, represents a region of decreasing creep rate, and the creep resistance of the material increases by virtue of its own deformation.

For low temperature and stresses, creep of lead at room temperature and primary creep is the predominant creep process. The second stage of creep, known as secondary creep, is a period of nearly constant creep rate, resulting from a balance between the processes of strain hardening (due to increased strain) and recovery (due to thermal softening) referred to a steady state creep.

The tertiary creep is probably the result of structural changes occurring in the metal, such as void formation and extensive crack formation.

Figure 5.24 shows the effect of applied stress on the creep curve at constant temperature. This shows that a creep curve with three well-defined stages can be found for only certain combinations of stress and temperature. A similar family of curves can be obtained for creep at constant stress for different temperatures. The higher the temperature, greater will be the creep rate.

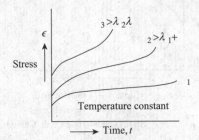

Figure 5.24 *Effects of Stress on Creep*

The minimum creep rate is the most important parameter for the design of components operating at high temperature and high stress conditions. The following are two standards:

1. Stress to produce a creep rate of 0.0001 per cent/h or 1 per cent /10,0000 h—used for jet engine alloys
2. Stress for a creep rate of 0.0001 per cent /h or 1 per cent/10,0000 h—used for steam turbine blades

5.10.2 Stress Rupture Test

Stress rupture test, though similar to creep test, is carried out upto the failure of the material. Higher loads are used in stress rupture test than in creep test, so creep rates are higher. Generally, creep test is performed at low stresses so as to avoid tertiary creep. Creep tests are frequently conducted for periods of 2000 h and often up to 14,000 h. In creep test, total strain is often less than 0.5 per cent, but in stress rupture test, *total strain may be up to 50 per cent*. Simple strain-measuring devices such as dial gauges can be used for this purpose. The higher stresses and creep rates in stress rupture test cause structural changes in the metals at shorter times, and stress rupture test can be completed in 1000 h. It is particularly used to determine high-temperature creep strength of new alloys for jet engine applications.

The basic information obtained from the stress rupture test is the time to cause failure at a given stress under constant temperature. The elongation and reduction in the area at fracture are also determined. If stress is plotted against the rupture time on a log–log scale, a straight line is usually obtained as shown in Figure 5.25. The changes in the slope of the stress rupture line are due to structural changes occurring in the metals, such as transgranular to intergranular fracture, oxidation, recrystallization and grain growth.

The principal deformation processes at elevated temperatures are slip, subgrain boundaries and grain boundary sliding. High-temperature deformation is characterized by extreme inhomogeneity. A number of secondary processes have been observed in metals at elevated temperatures, such as multiple slip, formation of coarse slip bands, fold formation at grain boundaries and grain boundary migration.

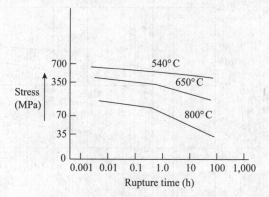

Figure 5.25 *Rupture Time Hours*

5.10.3 Low-temperature Creep

Creep is possible only because the obstacles to deformation can be overcome by the combined action of thermal fluctuation and stress. Diffusion-controlled processes are important mainly at temperature greater than $0.5\ T_m$, where T_m is the melting point. At low temperature, the recovery processes are not dependent on diffusion. High-temperature creep is mainly the steady state or viscous creep when temperature is $0.5\ T_m$. Below this temperature, the primary or transient creep dominates. Cotrell has suggested that

$$\epsilon = AT^{-n'}$$

where A and n' are empirical constants.

If $n' = 0$, creep rate is constant.

$$\epsilon = \alpha\ Ln(t)$$

where α is a constant. Logarithmic creep law found at low temperature $n' = 2/3$.
It becomes Adrode's equation for transient creep if

$$\epsilon = \beta t^{\frac{1}{3}}$$

A logarithmic creep occurs at low temperatures and low stresses, where recovery cannot occur.

5.10.4 Engineering Creep Data

A common method of presenting creep data is to plot log of stress against log of minimum creep rate and straight lines will be frequently obtained for lower temperature, but discontinuities due to structural instabilities will often occur at higher temperatures. Values of minimum creep rate lower than 0.001 or 0.01 per cent/h are generally determined by standard creep test, while higher values of minimum creep rate are frequently determined for a stress rupture test (Figure 5.26).

Creep strength is defined as the stress at a given temperature that produces a minimum creep rate of a certain amount, generally 0.0001 per cent/h or 0.001 per cent/h.

Rupture strength refers to the stress at a given temperature to produce a life to rupture of a certain amount, usually 100, 1000 or 10, 000 h.

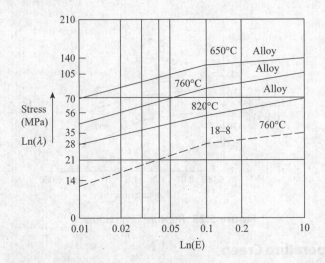

Figure 5.26 *Log–Log Plot of Stress Versus Minimum Creep Rate*

5.10.5 Creep-resistant Alloys

The ferritic alloys were developed first to meet the increased temperature requirements in steam power plants. These are essentially carbon steels, with increased chromium and molybdenum to form complex carbides, which resist softening. Molybdenum is particularly effective in increasing creep resistance of steel, but their use is limited to 550°C. Then austenitic stainless steels are used up to a temperature of 650°C.

The superalloys for jet engine applications are nickel- or cobalt-based austenitic alloys. Superalloys are multiphase alloys that attain their strength from a dispersion of second-phase particles. In cobalt base alloys and in certain complex (Ni–Cu–Cr–Fe) alloys second-phase particles are complex metal carbides. Molybdenum, tungsten and columbium are added to these alloys to form stable complex carbides.

Nickel-based superalloys may be strengthened by the addition of small amounts of aluminium or titanium. A new class of dispersion-strengthened high-temperature alloys are developed in which thermally stable second-phase particles as Al_2O_3, S_1O_2 and ZrO_2 are introduced into a metal matrix.

The following are some of the common creep-resistant alloys:

1. Ferritic steels 1.25 Cr, Mo alloy

   C = 0.10, Cr = 1.25, Mo = 0.5, Rest is Fe

2. Austenitic steels 16–25–6

   C = 0.10, Cr = 16.0, Ni = 25, Mo = 6, Rest is Fe

3. Nickel-based alloys

   In conol C = 0.004, Cr = 15.5, Ni = 76, Rest is Fe

   Nimonic 90 C 0.08, Cr 20, Ni 58, Co 16, Fe 0.5, Ti 2.3, Ne 1.4

4. Cobalt-based alloys

   Vitallium (HS 21)

   C 0.25, Cr 27.0, Ni 3, Mo 5, Co 62, Fe 1.0

5.11 STRESS RELAXATION

Stress relaxation under creep conditions refers to the decrease in stress at constant deformation. When stress relaxation occurs, the stress required to maintain constant total deformation decreases as a function of time. Consider a specimen under tensile stress, such that the total strain at elevated temperature where creep can occur is

$$\epsilon = \epsilon_e + \epsilon_p = \frac{\sigma}{E} + \epsilon_p,$$

where ϵ is the total strain, ϵ_e is the elastic strain, ϵ_p plastic (creep strain), E is the Young's modulus and σ is the tensile stress.

For the total strain to remain constant as the metal creeps, it is necessary for the elastic strain to decrease.

$$\epsilon_e = \epsilon - \epsilon_p \text{ (continuously increasing as creep progresses)}$$

This means that the *stress required to maintain the total strain decreases with time as creep increases.*

The relaxation of stress in bolted joints and press-fitted assemblies may lead to loose joints and leakage. Therefore, stress relaxation tests are generally made on bolted components for high-temperature service.

Figure 5.27 shows the type of curves, which are obtained, i.e. stress versus time. The initial rate of decrease in stress is high, but it levels off because the stress level is decreased and the transient creep decreases with time. These types of curves can be used to estimate the time required to relieve residual stress by thermal treatments.

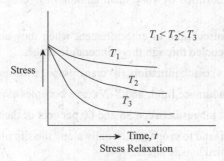

Figure 5.27 *Stress Versus Time*

KEYPOINTS TO REMEMBER

❑ Yield strength is the load corresponding to a small specified plastic deformation divided by original area of cross section of the specimen.

❑ There are practical difficulties in the measurement of elastic limit, so offset strength is noted as 0.002 strain, known as proof stress.

❑ Area under the elastic curve gives resilience.

❑ Spring steel has higher yield point strength.

❑ True stress, $\sigma_T = \sigma(1 + \epsilon)$, where σ and ϵ are engineering stress and engineering strain, respectively.

❑ True strain, $\epsilon_T = \ln(1 + \epsilon)$, where ϵ is the engineering strain.

❑ Hardness is a measure of material resistance to plastic deformation.

❑ Ultimate tensile strength, $\sigma_{ut} = 3.5 \times BHN$, in MPa.

❑ Rockwell hardness test is the most widely accepted test, because of its speed of measurement, freedom from personal error, small size of indentation and it utilizes depth of indent as a measure of hardness.

❑ Superficial hardness tests are performed on thin samples as razor blades.

❑ There are three types of fractures: (a) shear fracture due to extensive slip on active slip planes, (b) fibrous fractured surface caused by shear cleavage and (c) ductile fracture exhibiting considerable plastic deformation.

❑ Theoretical cohesive strength between two atoms

$$\sigma_{max} = \sigma_0 \left[1 + 2 \left(\frac{a}{\rho_t} \right)^{\frac{1}{2}} \right]$$

where σ_0 is the nominal stress, a is the length of surface crack and ρ_t is the crack tip radius.

❑ Three types of fracture modes are: (a) tensile mode, (b) sliding or shear mode and (c) tearing mode; but tensile mode is most common.

❑ Impact test conditions are: (a) deformation at low temperature, (b) high strain rate and (c) triaxial stresses.

❑ Structures constructed from alloys that exhibit ductile-to-brittle behaviour should be used only at room temperature or above the transition temperature.

❑ Many metals are severely embrittled by very small amount of hydrogen, as low as 0.0001 per cent by weight.

❑ Alloy steels are especially susceptible to embrittlement when they are tempered in the region of 425–600°C and then slowly cooled through this temperature range.

❑ Steps of fatigue failure are: (a) crack initiation, (b) crack propagation and (c) sudden fracture.

❑ Fatigue limit is also called endurance limit, and S–N curve becomes asymptotic at this stress.

❑ For many steels, fatigue limit ranges between 35 and 60 per cent of their tensile strength.

❑ Once initiated, fatigue cracks tend to propagate initially along the slip planes, later on take a direction normal to the maximum applied tensile stress.

❑ Practically, all fatigue failures start at the surface, and the surface is strengthened by carburizing, surface rolling and shot peening.

❑ Simultaneous action of cyclic stresses and chemical attack is known as corrosion fatigue.

❑ Three stages of creep curve are: (a) primary or transient stage, (b) secondary or viscous creep and (c) tertiary stage.

❑ Creep test measures the dimensional changes that occur at elevated temperature exposure.

❑ Stress rupture test measures the effect of temperature on long-time load-bearing properties.

❑ Tertiary creep is the result of structural changes such as void formation and extensive crack formation occurring in the metals.

❑ Inconel, Nimonic and Vitalliium alloys are creep resistant.

❑ During stress relaxation, the stress required to maintain constant total deformation decreases as a function of time, and elastic strain decreases as plastic strain increases with time.

MULTIPLE CHOICE QUESTIONS

1. Presence of hydrogen in a steel causes
   (a) Improvement in weldability
   (b) Embrittlement
   (c) Corrosion resistance
   (d) None of these

	A	B	C	D
(a)	1	2	3	4
(b)	1	3	2	4
(c)	3	1	2	4
(d)	4	1	2	3

2. Which one of the following microconstituents has maximum hardness?
   (a) Austenite   (c) Cementite
   (b) Pearlite   (d) Sorbite

3. Which one of the following deformations is time dependent?
   (a) Elastic deformation
   (b) Elastomeric deformation
   (c) Plastic deformation
   (d) Inelastic deformation

4. Brinell hardness test is inaccurate if hardness number is greater than
   (a) 250   (c) 450
   (b) 350   (d) 500

5. Which one of the following materials has lowest hardness on the Moh's scale?
   (a) Talc   (c) Lead
   (b) Steels   (d) Silicon carbide

6. Creep phenomenon is most pronounced in which of the following components?
   (a) Industrial belts
   (b) Gas turbine blades
   (c) Nuclear reactors
   (d) All the above

7. Match List I (hardness test) and List II (scale range)

List I	List II
(A) Mohs' hardness test	1. 1–10
(B) Brinell's hardness test	2. 1–450
(C) Rockwall Hardness test	3. 1–100
(D) Vicker's Hardness test	4. 1–1000

8. Which portion of the creep curve provides the information on steady state creep rate?
   (a) Primary stage   (c) Tertiary stage
   (b) Secondary stage   (d) All the above

9. Which one of the following has maximum value of yield point strength?
   (a) Medium-carbon steel
   (b) High-carbon spring steel
   (c) Copper
   (d) Mid steel

10. What is the ratio of true stress/engineering stress?
    (a) $1 + \epsilon$ (c) $\dfrac{1}{1-\epsilon}$
    (b) $1 - \epsilon$ (d) None of these
    where ϵ is the engineering strain.

11. What is the ratio of ultimate strength of a metal in MPa and Brinell hardness number?
    (a) 50.0   (c) 3.5
    (b) 5.0   (d) None of these

12. If E is the Young's modulus, γ is the surface energy, r_0 is the equilibrium distance between the atoms and σ is the cohesive strength, then what is γ surface energy?
    (a) $\sigma^2 r_0/E$ (c) $\sigma^2 E/r_0$
    (b) $\sigma r_0^2/E$ (d) None of these

13. What is the purpose of notch in an impact test sample?
    (a) To produce a triaxial state of stress
    (b) To produce high strain rate
    (c) To produce high plastic deformation
    (d) All the above

14. Characteristic shape of ductile fractional surface is
    (a) Granular
    (b) Fibrous and dull
    (c) Intergranular and shinning
    (d) None of these

15. Which one of the following is the correct statement?
    (A) Molybdenum decreases the susceptibility of temper embrittlement in steel.
    (B) BCC and HCP are most susceptible to hydrogen embrittlement.
    (C) Hydrogen embrittlement is decreased by slow strain rates.

    (a) A and B   (c) C only
    (b) B and C   (d) All the above

16. Ninety per cent of the failure of engineering components in service happens by the process of
    (a) Creep   (c) Fatigue
    (b) Shock loads (d) None of these

17. Which component is worst affected by fatigue loading?

    (a) Gas turbine blade
    (b) Wings of an aircraft
    (c) Wire rope moving on a sheave to lift a load
    (d) All the above

18. Which of the following processes does not improve fatigue strength of a component?
    (a) Nitriding
    (b) Case carburizing
    (c) Electroplating
    (d) Shot peening

19. In cobalt base alloys, what alloying element is used to form stable complex carbides?
    (a) Tungsten
    (b) Columbium
    (c) Molybdenum
    (d) All the above

20. What is the percentage of nickel in composition of Nimonic 90 alloy (a creep-resistant alloy)
    (a) 1.25   (c) 58
    (b) 25   (d) 76

Answers

1. (b)   2. (c)   3. (d)   4. (d)   5. (a)   6. (d)   7. (a)   8. (b)   9. (b)   10. (a)
11. (c) 12. (a) 13. (a) 14. (b) 15. (a) 16. (c) 17. (d) 18. (c) 19. (d) 20. (d)

REVIEW QUESTIONS

1. Explain the following:
   (a) Engineering stress, true stress
   (b) Engineering strain, true strain
   (c) Offset strength

2. Why the Young's modulus of carbon steel decreases with temperature? Draw a curve showing the variations of Young's modulus with temperature.

3. Differentiate between resilience and toughness.

4. How do you define the property of hardness? Which hardness test is most acceptable by the industry and why?

5. Explain three scales, A, B and C of Rockwell hardness test.

6. What is microhardness? Why loads on indentors are reduced in this microhardness test?

7. Derive expression for theoretical cohesive strength between two atoms.

8. What is the effect of crack tip radius on stress concentration factor?

9. What are the three modes of fracture? Which is most common in service?

10. Explain the behaviour of steels with respect to ductile-to-brittle transition temperature.

11. Explain the difference between temper embrittlement and hydrogen embrittlement.

12. What are the three stages of fatigue failure? Explain.

13. Explain the process of crack initiation and crack propagation in fatigue.

14. Explain notch sensitivity index in fatigue.

15. By what processes the surface is improved for fatigue resistance?

16. Explain the process of fretting? How is it reduced?

17. Differentiate between the following:
    Transient creep and viscous creep

18. What are creep strength and creep rupture strength?

19. What are superalloys used as creep-resistant materials?

20. Describe the reason for stress relaxation in bolted members?

PRACTICE PROBLEMS

1. An aluminium alloy specimen of 12.5 mm diameter and 50 mm gauge length was tested under tension. During the first part of the test, following readings were observed.

Load in KN	0	7.357	9.810	12.262	14.715	17.167	19.62
Extension (mm)	0	0.0327	0.0450	0.0568	0.0756	0.120	0.216

Plot the load extension curve and determine the following values:
   (a) Young's modulus of elasticity
   (b) Limit of proportionality
   (c) 0.1 per cent proof stress

Ans. [90.853 kN/mm^2; 99.94 N/mm^2, 146.95 N/mm^2]

2. Compute the strain-hardening exponent n for an alloy with $\sigma_T = 415$ MPa, $\epsilon_T = 0.10$, $K = 1035$ MPa.

Ans. [$n = 0.4$]

3. What will be the diameter of indentation to yield a BHN of 450, when a 500 kg load is used. Ball diameter is 10 mm.

Ans. [1.187 mm]

4. A sodium silicate glass has no surface defects as etching has removed them, but inside cracks vary from 2 to 5 μm. Calculate the surface energy of glass, if fracture strength is 100 MPa. Young's modulus $E = 70$ GPa.

Ans. $\begin{bmatrix} \gamma = 0.45 \text{ J/m}^2 \\ \gamma = 1.12 \text{ J/m}^2 \end{bmatrix}$

5. A specimen of an aluminium alloy, which is 12 mm in diameter was tested in tension. The linear and lateral strains measured with the help of strain gauges were as follows:

P (kN)	3.924	7.848	11.772	15.696	19.62	23.54	22.89	26.16	27.795	29.43	30.298	31.65	31.88	32.29
$\epsilon_1 \times 10^{-4}$ Linear	3.43	6.92	11.03	13.9	17.2	20.7	24.10	27.34	35.3	43.0	49.0	56.5	69.5	86.0
$\epsilon_2 \times 10^{-4}$ Lateral Strain	1.08	2.17	3.22	4.35	5.41	6.50	7.54	8.57	–	–	–	–	–	–

Plot graphs: (i) P versus ϵ_1

(ii) ϵ_1 versus ϵ_2

Determine   (a) Young's modulus   (b) Poisson's ratio   (c) 0.1 per cent proof stress

6. For a material with a true stress–strain curve of the form $\sigma_T = K\epsilon_T^n$, show that the ratio of yield strength to the tensile strength is a direct function of the strain-hardening exponent n.

7. The variation of percentage elongation with gauge length has been found empirically to follow relationship $X = b + c\sqrt{A}/L_0$, where b and c are constants. The following data were obtained for a steel sample of diameter 28 mm.

L_0	100 mm	250 mm
X	30.6	25.7

Determine constants b and c.

Ans. [$b = 0.224$, $c = 0.33$]

8. Following true stresses produce corresponding true plastic strains for a brass alloy

True stress (MPa)	True strain
345	0.10
346	0.20

What true stress is necessary to produce a true plastic strain of 0.25?

Ans. [440 MPa]

9. A relatively large plate of glass is subjected to a tensile stress of 40 MPa. If the specific surface energy and E for the glass are 0.37 J/m² and 69 GPa, respectively, determine the maximum length of a surface flaw that is possible without fracture.

Ans. [8.2 µm]

10. A brittle material has the following properties:

$$E = 102 \text{ GPa}$$

$$\gamma_s = 1.0 \text{ J/m}^2$$

$$r_0 = 0.3 \text{ nm}$$

$$C = 10^4 \, r_0$$

What is the fracture stress for this material?

Ans. [92.2 MPa]

A relatively large plane of diffusion placed on a metal sheet of 10 kHz. If the specific charge and for the sizes are 0.5 μm.
phase need there, possible wire estimation.

6

DIFFUSION

6.1 INTRODUCTION

Diffusion is defined as a natural tendency of the molecules to flow from higher concentration to lower concentration. Impurity diffusion is the process by which impurity particles move from a region of high concentration near the surface of a crystal to the region of low concentration within the crystal. Diffusion is the net action of matter (atoms or molecules) in the form of heat, momentum or light, whose purpose is to minimize concentration gradient.

Diffusion of various impurities into selected regions of a semiconductor allows to fabricate complex electronic circuits in a single semiconductor crystal. A beam of impurity ions is accelerated to kinetic energy level of 50 keV or more and then directed to the surface of a semiconductor. The high-energy impurity ions enter the crystal and cause to rest at some average depth from the surface. This ion implantation can be controlled to introduce specific number of impurity atoms in a specific region of a crystal.

Atomic diffusion is a process whereby thermally activated random hopping of atoms in a solid results in the net transport of atoms. Helium atoms inside a balloon can diffuse through the wall of the balloon and escape resulting in the deflation of the balloon slowly. There is high concentration of helium atoms near the wall of the balloon and less concentration outside the balloon. The rate of transport is governed by the diffusivity and concentration gradient.

The atoms and molecules change their positions under the influence of thermal energy, stress gradient, electric and magnetic field gradient and concentration gradient. Thermal energy derived from their atomic vibrations is responsible for the atomic diffusion.

This chapter discusses the concept of the diffusion process, various types of diffusion mechanisms, laws of diffusion and special-purpose surface treatments.

6.2 DIFFUSION COUPLE

Natural tendency of the molecules to flow from higher concentration to lower concentration is called 'diffusion'. In diffusion, there is transfer of mass on microscopic scale from a gas, liquid or solid phase within a specific solid. The transfer of the material takes place by atomic motion and the atoms move due to thermal vibrations.

Therefore, diffusion is a temperature-dependent process. The atomic movement is fast in gases, slow in liquids and very slow in solids. In other words, diffusion is time dependent also. Process of diffusion can be best explained by a diffusion couple, e.g. of two metals A and B. Two containers of two metals A and B are joined together by removing the barrier between them [Figure 6.1(a)].

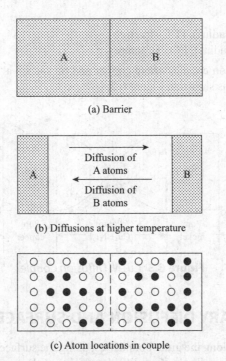

(a) Barrier

(b) Diffusions at higher temperature

(c) Atom locations in couple

Figure 6.1 *Diffusion Couple of Two Metals*

This couple is heated for an extended period at a higher temperature, but certainly lower than the melting points of A and B, and then cooled to room temperature. It is observed that atoms A have migrated into atoms B and atoms B have migrated into atoms A. There is a net flow of atoms from higher concentration to lower concentration regions.

This type of diffusion is known as interdiffusion or impurity diffusion. In Figure 6.1, clear circles represent atom A and dark circles represent atom B.

In the case of pure metals, the positions of all exchanging atoms are of the same type. This diffusion is called self-diffusion (Figure 6.2).

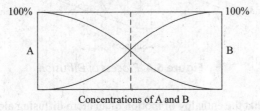

Concentrations of A and B

Figure 6.2 *Self-diffusion*

A reader can think of the following diffusion couples:

1. Copper and nickel

   Cu 0.128 nm (atomic radius), FCC structure
   Ni 0.125 nm (atomic radius), FCC structure

2. Gold and silver

   Au 0.133 nm (atomic radius), FCC structure
   Ag 0.144 nm (atomic radius), FCC structure

Consider a Cu–Ni diffusion couple, where copper and nickel are at two extremities of the couple, separated by alloyed region as shown in Figure 6.3.

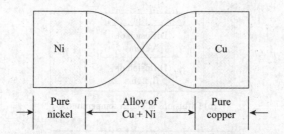

Figure 6.3 *Cu–Ni Diffusion Couple*

6.3 GRAIN BOUNDARY DIFFUSION AND SURFACE DIFFUSION

Process of diffusion occurs along the grain boundaries, along the surface of a solid and *in the lattices of a polycrystalline solid.* This is called surface diffusion (Figure 6.4).

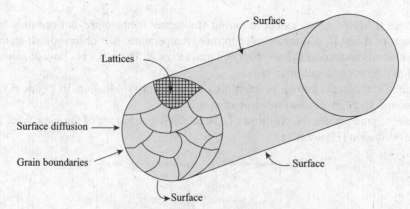

Figure 6.4 *Process of Diffusion*

It has been observed that the enthalpy of motion of an atom diffusing along the surface of a crystal is much less than the enthalpy of the atom diffusing within the surface. In a single-crystal material, grain boundary region is closely packed; but grain boundary regions are loosely packed in a polycrystalline material, because grain boundaries are of irregular shape and distorted. Therefore, diffusion rate is more in polycrystalline material. *Diffusion along the edge dislocation* is known as 'pipe diffusion'.

Consider Arrhenius equations

$$\phi = A \exp\left(-\frac{E_d}{RT}\right)$$

where E_d is the activation energy and the rate of diffusion process ϕ varies qualitatively as follows:

$$E_{d-dislocation} > E_{d-lattice} > E_{d-grain\ boundary} > E_{d-surface}$$

or

$$\phi_{dislocation} < \phi_{lattice} < \phi_{grain\ boundary} < \phi_{surface}$$

In grain boundary diffusion, the diffusion rate may be as high as 10^6 times the diffusion rate in a bulk crystal.

6.4 TYPES OF DIFFUSION

There are two types of diffusion: (1) Vacancy diffusion or substitutional diffusion and (2) Interstitial diffusion.

6.4.1 Vacancy Diffusion

Vacancy diffusion necessitates the presence of vacancies. In a crystal, significant concentrations of vacancies may exist at higher temperatures. Diffusing atom goes to the position of vacancy in one direction and correspondingly a vacancy is created at the site of diffusing atom in the opposite direction. The activation energy for diffusing atom is provided by thermal vibrations of the atoms. Due to rise in temperature, the amplitude of thermal vibrations increases and the diffusion rate also increases. As diffusion continues, there is counterflow of atoms and vacancies. This is a very important mechanism for diffusion in FCC, BCC and HCP crystals.

In case of alloys, there must exist solid solubility of one type in another type of atom. This diffusion process is dependent on solid solubility rules of Home Rothery, which are as follows:

1. The difference in diameter of two atoms should not be greater than 15 per cent.
2. Two elements should have same crystal structure.
3. Electronegativity of two elements should nearly be the same.
4. Two atoms should have the same valency.

Vacancy diffusion is illustrated in Figure 6.5(a) and (b). A vacancy exists at site A and atom B at site B moves to fill the vacancy at site A. Because of this movement of atom from B to A, a vacancy is created at site B, and consequently there is movement of atoms from A to B.

6.4.2 Interstitial Diffusions

In between large atoms or ions if there are smaller atoms or ions of other element at interstitial sites, the smaller atoms move from one interstitial site to another. No vacancies are required for this mechanism, as there are more interstitial sites available, and interstitial diffusion occurs more easily than vacancy diffusion. Smaller interstitial atoms move faster and can diffuse faster than vacancy diffusions.

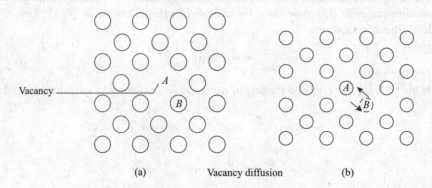

(a)   Vacancy diffusion   (b)

Figure 6.5   *Vacancy Diffusion*

In many ceramics with ionic bonding, the structure can be considered as close packed of anions with cations in the interstitial sites. In such materials, smaller cations often diffuse much faster than larger anions.

Diffusion of carbon atoms in BCC, α iron and FCC, γ irons are examples of interstitial diffusions. Small atoms of hydrogen, oxygen and nitrogen can diffuse very easily in many metallic crystals. Figure 6.6(a) and (b) shows the interstitial diffusions of atoms A to site B.

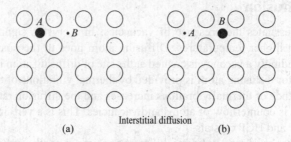

                        Interstitial diffusion
(a)   (b)

Figure 6.6   *Interstitial Diffusion*

6.5 FACTORS AFFECTING DIFFUSION

Basically, there are two factors that influence the diffusion process: (1) diffusing species, i.e. guest atoms, their size and structure and (2) temperature. The magnitude of diffusion coefficient indicates the rate at which the atoms diffuse. The diffusion atoms and host atoms influence the diffusion coefficient. Table 6.1 gives the values of constant D_0 and diffusions rate D (at 500°C) for various diffusing species and host atoms.

One can notice from the figures of diffusion rate in Table 6.1 that the interstitial diffusion rate is more than self-diffusion rate. For Example, take the self-diffusion of Fe in α-Fe; diffusion rate at 500°C is 3.0 $\times 10^{-21}$, but the interstitial diffusion of smaller carbon atoms is higher and iron atoms at 500°C is much larger, i.e. 2.4×10^{-12}.

The reader can find the atomic radius of Cu, Al, Ni and Zn and observe that Cu–Al, Zn–Cu and Cu–Ni are substitutional diffusions.

Table 6.1 *Diffusion Data for Various Diffusing Species and Host Atoms*

Diffusion Species	Host Metal	D_0 (m²/s) Constant	Activation Energy kJ/mol	Activation Energy eV/atom	D at 500°C
Self-diffusions					
Fe	α–Fe	2.8×10^{-4}	251	2.60	3.0×10^{-21}
Cu	Cu	7.8×10^{-5}	211	2.18	4.2×10^{-19}
Al	Al	2.3×10^{-4}	144	1.49	4.2×10^{-14}
Interstitial diffusion					
C	γ–Fe	5.0×10^{-5}	284	2.94	–
C	α–Fe	6.2×10^{-7}	80	0.83	2.4×10^{-12}
Substitutional diffusion (alloys)					
Cu	Al	6.5×10^{-5}	136	1.41	4.1×10^{-14}
Zn	Cu	2.4×10^{-5}	189	1.96	4.0×10^{-18}
Cu	Ni	2.7×10^{-5}	256	2.65	1.3×10^{-22}

Temperature: Rate of any process is a function of temperature as given by $\phi = Ae^{(-Ea/RT)}$, where ϕ is the rate of process, E_a is the activation energy, A is the pre-exponent constant, R is the gas constant and T is the absolute temperature. Similarly, we can make equations for rate of diffusion process.

$$D = D_0 \exp(-E_d/RT) \tag{6.1}$$

where D is the diffusion rate, D_0 is the pre-exponent constant, E_d is the activation energy in diffusion, R is the gas constant and T is the absolute temperature in K.

The activation energy may be thought of as that energy required to produce the motion for diffusion of 1 mol of atoms. A large activation energy results is a relatively small diffusion coefficient, D.

Taking natural log of Eq. (6.1), we get

$$\text{In}D = \text{In}D_0 - \frac{E_d}{RT} \tag{6.2}$$

Since D_0, Q_d and R are all constants, Eq. (6.2) is equation of a straight line

$$y = mx + c$$

where y and x are analogous to variables in D and $1/T$; intercept $C = \text{In}D_0$

$$\text{Slope } m = -\frac{E_d}{R}$$

Example 6.1 Pre-exponential constant for diffusion of copper into aluminium is 6.5×10^{-5} (m²/s). If the activation energy is 6.41 eV/atoms what is the diffusion rate at 600°C.

Solution:

$$D_0 = 6.5 \times 10^{-5} \text{ (m}^2/\text{s)}$$

$$T = 600 \times 273 = 873 \text{ K}$$

$$E_d = 1.41 \text{ eV/atom}$$

$$R = 8.02 \times 10^{-5} \text{ eV/atom} - \text{K}$$

$$D = D_0 e\left(-\frac{E_d}{RT}\right)$$

$$= 6.5 \times 10^{-5} \left(\frac{m^2}{s}\right) e\left(-\frac{1.41 eV}{atom} \times \frac{atom \cdot K}{8.62 \times 10^{-5} \times 873 \ K}\right)$$

$$= 6.5 \times 10^{-5} \ e \ (-18.737) \ m^2/s$$

$$= \frac{6.5 \times 10^{-5}}{137206.8} \ m^2/s$$

$$= 4.737 \times 10^{-10} \ m^2/s$$

Example 6.2   For the diffusion of carbon in FCC irons, the activation energy is 148 kJ/mol and an initial temperature is 900 K. Find the temperature that will increase the diffusion coefficient by a factor of 10. Given gas constant $R = 8.31$ J/mol.K.

Solution:

Activation energy,

$$E_d = 148 \ kJ/mol$$

$$R = 8.31 \ J/mol. \ K$$

Temperature,

$$T = 900 \ K$$

Diffusion rate,

$$D = D_0 \exp\left(-\frac{E_d}{RT}\right)$$

So

$$D_1 = D_0 \exp\left(-\frac{E_d}{R \times 900}\right)$$

$$D_2 = D_0 \exp\left(-\frac{E_d}{R \times T_2}\right)$$

But

$$D_2 = 10 \ D_1$$

So

$$D_0 \exp\left(-\frac{E_d}{RT_2}\right) = 10 \times D_0 \exp\left(-\frac{E_d}{R \times 900}\right)$$

or

$$10 = \exp\left[\frac{E_d}{R}\left(\frac{1}{900} - \frac{1}{T_2}\right)\right]$$

or

$$2.3026 = \frac{E_d}{R}\left(\frac{1}{900} - \frac{1}{T_2}\right)$$

Putting the values of E_d and R

$$2.3026 = \frac{148 \times 1000}{8.31}\left(\frac{1}{900} - \frac{1}{T_2}\right)$$

$$1.293 \times 10^{-4} = \frac{1}{900} - \frac{1}{T_2}$$

$$T_2 = 1018 \ K$$

6.6 LAWS OF DIFFUSION

Fick has given two laws of diffusion. Fick's first law of diffusion is about the steady state diffusion process and the second law describes the non-steady state diffusion process.

Diffusion is a time-and temperature-dependent phenomenon. It gives the rate of mass transfer through a solid material. If we take temperature constant, then on macroscopic scale, the rate of mass transfer of an element within another is a function of time. If the rate of mass transfer is constant, then it is said to be steady state diffusion. Mass transfer in terms of mass in kilograms per unit area and per unit second or in terms of number of atoms per unit area per unit second is known as 'diffusion flux', its units are kg/m^2-s or atoms/m^2-s. Consider the diffusion of a gas with concentration C_1 on one side of a thin plate of concentration and C_2 on the other side of the plate as shown in Figure 6.7.

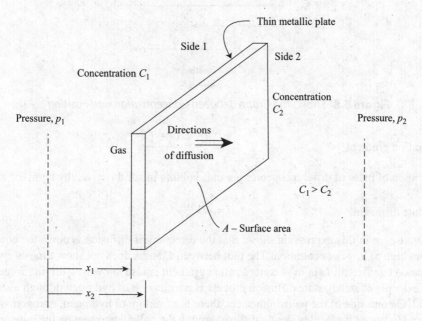

Figure 6.7 *Gas Diffusion Through a Thin Metallic Plate*

Concentration $C_1 > C_2$; gas passing through the plate with thickness $x_2 - x_1$ and surface area A is shown. If the pressures p_1 on one side and p_2 on the other side are maintained constant, then concentrations will remain constant.

Diffusion flux,
$$J = \frac{M}{A \times \text{time}(t)} = \frac{\text{mass of gas}}{\text{surface area of plate} \times \text{time}}$$

If taking very small values of $M \to dM$ and $t \to dt$, then diffusion flux, $J = \frac{1}{A}\frac{dM}{dt}$, units are kg/m^2-s or atoms/m^2-s

If diffusion flux, J does not change with time, then it is a steady state diffusion, for example, diffusion of carbonaceous gas into a thin iron plate (Figure 6.8).

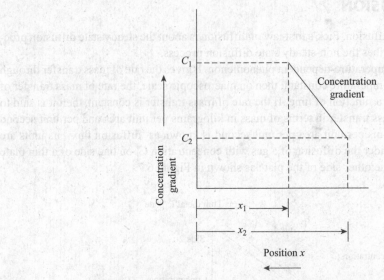

Figure 6.8 *Shows the Graph Between Concentration and Position*

Concentration gradient $= \dfrac{dC}{dx} = \dfrac{C_1 - C_2}{x_1 - x_2}$

Concentration of mass of different species per unit volume in solid is given by kg/m³ or atoms/m³.

Steady state diffusion, $\qquad\qquad\qquad J = -D\dfrac{dC}{dx}$

The negative sign in this expression shows that the direction of diffusion is down the concentration gradient from high to low concentration. The plot between C and x does not show time as a variable.

The diffusion coefficient, D in m²/s concentration gradient is also known as 'driving force'.

Another example of steady state diffusion process is purification of hydrogen through a sheet of palladium metal. On one side of the palladium sheet, there is a mixture of hydrogen, nitrogen, oxygen and water vapour. Hydrogen molecules slowly diffuse through the palladium sheet on the other side, which is maintained at low hydrogen pressure.

Example 6.3 During a corrosion resistance process, outward flux of copper atoms from aluminium is 10^{21} m²/s, while concentration of copper at room temperature is 2×10^{12}/m³ on one side of aluminium. If the concentration of copper on the other side of aluminium is 5×10^6/m³ and aluminium sheet is 3.2 mm thick, determine the diffusivity and concentration gradient.

Solution:

Diffusion flux,

$$J = -D\dfrac{dM}{dx}$$

$$J = 10^{21} \, \text{m}^2/\text{s}$$

$$dM = 2 \times 10^{12} - 5 \times 10^6$$

$$= (2 \times 10^6 - 5) \times 10^6 \, \text{atom/m}^3$$

$$dx = 3.2mm = 0.0032m$$

$$10^{21}m^2/s = -D \frac{(2 \times 10^6 - 5) \times 10^6}{0.0032}$$

Diffusion coefficient

$$= + \frac{10^{15} \times .0032}{(2 \times 10^6 - 5)}$$

$$= 1.6 \times 10^6 \text{ m}^2/s$$

Concentration gradient,

$$\frac{dC}{dx} = \frac{2 \times 10^{12} - 5 \times 10^6}{0.0032}$$

$$= \frac{(2 \times 10^6 - 5) \times 10^6}{0.0032} \text{ atoms/m}^2$$

$$= 625000 \times 10^9 \text{ atoms/m}^2$$

$$= 6.25 \times 10^{14} \text{ atoms/m}^2$$

6.7 FICK'S SECOND LAW

Fick's second flaw deals with the non-steady state diffusion, i.e. when diffusion rate is dependent on both time and position. As diffusion proceeds through the thickness of a solid material, concentration changes with time and the diffusing atoms accumulate on one side of the plate and move out from the other side of the plate (Figure 6.9).

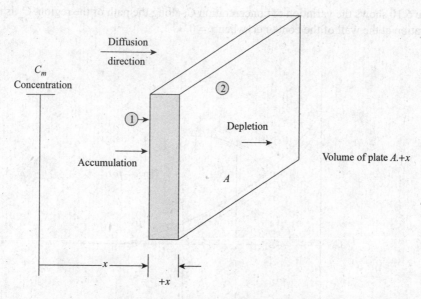

Figure 6.9 *Non-steady State Diffusion*

The number of atoms accumulating on surface (1) are not the same as the number of atoms depleting out from surface (2) of the plate. Difference between outgoing flux and incoming flux in the solid is equal to the

Flux entering the region $= J_x$ (6.3)

Flux leaving the flux, $\qquad J_x + \Delta x = +Jx + \left(\dfrac{\partial J}{\partial x}\right)\Delta x$ (6.4)

Difference in flux, $\qquad J_x + \Delta x - J_x = \left(\dfrac{\partial J}{\partial x}\right)\Delta x$ (6.5)

Rate of accumulation—rate of depletion of atoms in the volume through the area A

$$A\Delta x = \dfrac{\partial C}{\partial t}A\Delta x$$

So $\qquad\qquad\qquad \left(\dfrac{\partial J}{\partial x}\right)A\Delta x = \dfrac{\partial C}{\partial t}A\Delta x$ (6.6)

or $\qquad\qquad\qquad \dfrac{\partial C}{\partial t} = \dfrac{\partial J}{\partial x}$

But $\qquad\qquad\qquad J = D\left(\dfrac{\partial C}{\partial x}\right)$

$$\dfrac{\partial C}{\partial t} = D\dfrac{\partial}{\partial x}\left(\dfrac{\partial C}{\partial x}\right)$$

or $\qquad\qquad\qquad \dfrac{\partial C}{\partial t} = D\dfrac{\partial^2 C}{\partial x^2}$ (6.7)

Figure 6.10 shows the variation of concentration C, along the path of the region. C_m is the maximum concentration at the wall of the container, when $x = 0$.

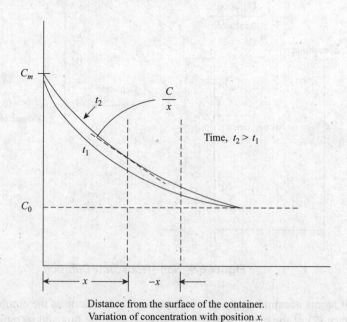

Distance from the surface of the container.
Variation of concentration with position x.

Figure 6.10 *Variation of Concentration with Position*

Initially, the concentration of diffusing atoms (or solute) is C_0, which is uniform throughout the material. The maximum concentration at the wall of the container is C_m. Concentration C_m is maintained constant throughout the diffusion process.

Considering Eq. (6.7) again

$$\frac{\partial C}{\partial t} = D \frac{\partial^2 C}{\partial x^2}$$

where diffusion coefficient D is independent of concentration C, and is dependent on x only. This is Fick's second law of diffusion. The solution of this equation is

$$C(x, t) = A - B \, erf\left(\frac{x}{2\sqrt{Dt}}\right) \tag{6.8}$$

where erf is a special function called error function and A and B are constants. The error function $erf(Z)$ is defined as

$$erf(Z) = \frac{2}{\pi} \int_0^z e^{-n_x^2} \, dx$$

where x is a variable, which gets eliminated when the limits of integral are substituted. The constants A and B are obtained by fixing the initial conditions.

Initial concentration, $C(x, 0) = C_0$, at time $t = 0$. Concentration at the end, $C(0, t) = C_m$, maximum concentration at the origin maintained constant throughout the diffusion process.

The values of error function for various values of argument Z are given in Table 6.2.

Table 6.2 *Arguments and Error Functions*

Z	Erf(Z)	Z	Erf(Z)
0	0	1.2	0.9103
0.025	0.0282	1.4	0.9523
0.050	0.0564	1.6	0.9763
0.10	0.1125	1.8	0.9891
0.20	0.2227	2.0	0.9953
0.30	0.3286	2.2	0.9981
0.40	0.4284	2.4	0.9993
0.50	0.5205	2.6	0.9999
0.60	0.6039	∞ (infinity)	1.0000
0.70	0.6778		
0.8	0.7421		
0.9	0.7970		
1.0	0.8427		

Using the initial conditions

$$C(x, 0) = C_0 = A - B \qquad \text{taking } x = \infty, \text{ infinity [because } erf(\infty) = 1]$$

$$C(0, t) = C_m = A, \qquad\qquad\qquad\qquad [\text{because } erf(0) = 0]$$

From these two equations

$$B = C_m - C_0$$

$$A = C_m$$

Equation (6.8) for time- and position-dependent concentration can be written as

$$c(x, t) = C_m - (C_m - C_0) \, erf\left(\frac{x}{2\sqrt{Dt}}\right)$$

$$= C_m + (C_m - C_0) - (C_m - C_0) - (C_m - C_0) \, erf\left(\frac{x}{2\sqrt{Dt}}\right)$$

$$= C_0 + (C_m - C_0)\left[1 - erf\left(\frac{x}{2\sqrt{Dt}}\right)\right]$$

or

$$\frac{C(x, t) - C_0'}{C_m - C_0} = 1 - erf\left(\frac{x}{2\sqrt{Dt}}\right) \tag{6.9}$$

From this equation, the concentration of solute atoms in the solid along the thickness Δx can be determined.

For the diffusion to take place under the concentration gradient, the diffusing atoms require minimum energy level to overcome the barrier due to the potential, which binds them to the crystal lattice. The diffusion coefficient D is dependent on temperature; therefore, the diffusion process must be carried out at high temperatures.

$$D = D_0 \, erf\left(-\frac{E_d}{RT}\right)$$

D_0 = pre-exponent factor.

An increase in temperature increases the amplitude and frequency of vibrations of atoms within the crystal lattice, therefore, the temperature increases the base energy level of the material, so that energy barrier is easily overcome. D_0 can be thought of as a frequency factor. The frequency factor D_0 and the activation energy E_d are constant for each diffusion couple.

Example 6.4 A piece of steel having 0.12 per cent carbon is carburized at 900°C for 600 minutes. Draw a graph showing carbon concentration in the case after 10-h carbonizing operation. At 900°C, it is γ iron with FCC structure.

Solution:

From the table

$$D_0 = 2.3 \times 10^{-5} \text{ m}^2/\text{s}$$
$$= 0.23 \text{ cm}^2/\text{s}$$

Temperature, 900°C $\quad = 1173° \text{ K}$

$$E_d = 148 \text{ KJ/mol}$$

$$R = 8.314 \text{ J/mol.K}$$

$$C_m = 1.6 \text{ (let us assume), maximum concentration}$$

Diffusion constant

$$D = D_0 \, erf\left(-\frac{E_d}{RT}\right)$$

$$= 0.23 \times erf\left(-\frac{148 \times 1000}{8.314 \times 1173}\right)$$

$$= \frac{0.23}{3897321}$$

$$= 5.90 \times 10^{-18} \text{ cm}^2/\text{s}$$

Now

$$C(x) = C_m + (C_0 - C_m)\, erf\left(\frac{x}{2\sqrt{Dt}}\right)$$

$$C(x) = 1.6 + (0.12 - 1.6)\,erf\left(\frac{x}{2\sqrt{5.90 \times 10^{-8} \times 36,000}}\right)$$

$$= 1.6 - 1.48\, erf\left(\frac{x \times 10^4}{2 \times 460.86}\right)$$

$$= 1.6 - 1.48\, erf\,(10.84x)$$

The concentrations at different values of x are given in Table 6.3.

Table 6.3 *Concentrations at Different Values of x*

X (cm)	10.84 x	Erf (Z)	1.48 erf (Z)	C(x)
0	0	0	0	1.6
0.1	1.084	0.871092	1.289	0.311
0.2	2.168	0.09976	1.476	0.123
0.3	3.252	0.9959	1.48	0.12

Figure 6.11 shows the variation of carbon concentration in the case of steel having 0.12 per cent carbon.

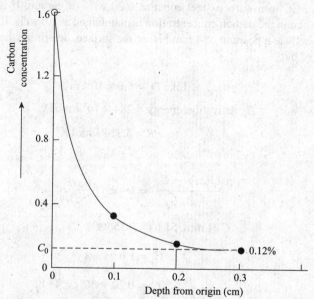

Figure 6.11 *Carbon Concentration in Steel with Respect to Depth*

6.8 DEPTH OF CASE CARBURIZATION

The surfaces of steel components are hardened by diffusing carbon atoms into them. Components like gears, cams, balls and roller bearings are surface hardened to improve their performance and to reduce wear and tear by case carburizing. Carbon-rich solid, liquid or gaseous matter as solid coke, liquid petroleum or a gas is used for this purpose. Carbon atoms diffuse into the surface of the steel components at elevated temperatures. In such cases, the depth of carburized case is defined as that 'depth at' which a carbon concentration is an average of minimum (C_0) and maximum (C_m) concentrations.

$$C(x_p) = \frac{C_m + C_0}{2}$$

So

$$C(x_p, t) = C_m + (C_0 - C_m) \, erf\left(\frac{x}{2\sqrt{Dt}}\right)$$

Note that $erf(0.5) = 0.5205 \approx 0.5$

Therefore,

$$C(x_p, t) = C_m + (C_0 - C_m) \times \frac{1}{2} \approx \frac{C_0 + C_m}{2}$$

6.9 IMPURITY DIFFUSION

Silicon wafers of 100 μm thickness are diffused with impurity atoms so as to change their electrical conductivity. Silicon wafers are obtained from single crystals of silicon grown in the laboratory and the impurities are like arsenic, gallium and phosphorus. Silicon wafers are exposed to the vapours of certain impurity atoms at a temperature nearly 1100°C in a quartz tube furnace. The depth of penetration of impurity atoms into silicon wafers is only a few microns.

Example 6.5   An FCC iron–carbon steel contains 0.20 wt% of carbon. It is carburized at higher temperature $(T°C)$, wherein the carbon concentration is maintained at 1.0 wt%. If after 51 h, the carbon concentration is 0.35 wt% at a position of 4 mm before the surface, determine the temperature at which the process was carried out.

Take $D_0 = 5.0 \times 10^{-5}$ m^2/s

E_a, activation energy = 284×10^3 J/mol

$R = 8.314$ J/mol.K

Solution:

$$\frac{C(x, t) - C_0}{C_m - C_0} = 1 - erf\left(\frac{x}{2\sqrt{Dt}}\right) \tag{6.10}$$

or $C(4 \text{ mm}, 51 \text{ h}) = 0.35$ wt%

$$C_m = 1.0 \text{ wt\%}$$

$$C_0 = 0.20 \text{ wt\%}, \, t = 48 \text{ h}$$

Putting the values in Eq. (6.10)

$$\frac{0.35 - 0.1}{1 - 0.1} = 1 - erf\left(\frac{4 \times 10^{-13}}{2\sqrt{D} \times 51 \times 3600}\right)$$

$$erf\left(\frac{4 \times 10^{-13}}{2\sqrt{D} \times \sqrt{51} \times 3600}\right) = 1 - 0.27777 = 0.72222$$

or

$$\text{Argument } (z) = 0.75 + \frac{.7421 - .7222}{.7112}$$

$$= .75 + .028 = 0.778$$

So

$$\frac{4 \times 10^{-13}}{2\sqrt{D} \times 428.486} = 0.778$$

$$\sqrt{D} = \frac{4 \times 10^{-3}}{2 \times 428.486 \times 0.778}$$

$$= 6 \times 10^{-3} \times 10^{-3} = 6 \times 10^{-6}$$

$$D = 36 \times 10^{-12}$$

$$= 3.6 \times 10^{-11}$$

Now

$$D = D_0 \, erf - \left(\frac{E_d}{RT}\right)$$

$$\frac{3.6 \times 10^{-11}}{5 \times 10^{-5}} = erf - \left(\frac{284 \times 1000}{8.314 \times T}\right) = 0.72 \times 10^{-6}$$

$$erf\left(+\frac{34159.2}{T}\right) = 1.389 \times 10^6$$

$$= 1389000$$

or

$$\frac{34159.2}{T} = 14.144$$

$$T = \frac{34159.2}{14.144} = 2224 \text{ K}$$

$$= 1951°C$$

Example 6.6 Phosphorus is diffused into a thick wafer of silicon with no previous presence of phosphorus in it at a temperature of 1100°C. If the surface concentration of phosphorus is 1×10^{18} atom/cm^3 and its concentration at 1 cm is 4×10^{16} atoms/cm^3, how long must be the diffusion time?

If $D = 3.0 \times 10^{-13}$ cm^2/s for phosphorus in Si at 1100°C, what depth in microns would the phosphorus concentration be 4×10^{16} atoms/cm^3, if the diffusivity of phosphorus is 4.0×10^{-13} cm^2/s.

Solution:

$$D_{1100°C} = 3.0 \times 10^{-13} \text{ cm}^2/\text{s} = 3.0 \times 10^{-17} \text{ m}^2/\text{s}$$

$$C_m = 1 \times 10^{18} \text{ atom/cm}^3$$

$$C_0 = 4 \times 10^{16} \text{ atom/cm}^3$$

$$\frac{C_m - C_x}{C_m - 10} = erf\left(\frac{1 \times 10^{-6}}{2\sqrt{3.0 \times 10^{-17} \times t}}\right)$$

where t is time in s.

$$\frac{10^{18} - 4 \times 10^{16}}{10^{18} - 0} = erf\left(\frac{1 \times 10^3}{54\sqrt{t}}\right) = erf\left(\frac{91.287}{\sqrt{t}}\right)$$

$$0.96 = erf\left(\frac{91.287}{\sqrt{t}}\right)$$

Argument (2) = 0.96

$$= 1.4 + \frac{.9661 - 196}{.9661 - .9523} \times 0.1$$

$$= 1.4 + \frac{6.1 \times 10^{-4}}{.0138}$$

$$= 1.4 + .044$$

$$= 1.444$$

So

$$z = 1.444 = \frac{91.287}{\sqrt{t}}$$

Time,

$$t = 5771 \text{ s}$$

$$= 96.18 \text{ min}$$

Let us determine the depth x, for diffusivity of

$$4 \times 10^{-13} \text{ cm}^2/\text{s} = 4 \times 10^{-17} \text{ m}^2/\text{s}$$

$$\frac{10^{18} - 4 \times 10^{16}}{10^{18} - 0} = erf\left(\frac{x}{2\sqrt{4 \times 10^{-17} \times 5771}}\right)$$

$$0.96 = erf\left(\frac{x \times 10^8}{2 \times 48.046}\right)$$

$$= erf\left(\frac{x \times 10^6 \times 1.04}{1}\right)$$

Argument (z) = 1.444

So

$$x \times 10^6 \times 1.04 = 1.444$$

$$x = 1.386 \times 10^{-6} \text{ m}$$

$$= 1.386 \text{ μm}$$

6.10 DIFFUSION-CONTROLLED APPLICATIONS

The following are various diffusion-controlled processes:

1. Sintering
2. Case carburization
3. Decarburization
4. Doping of semiconductors
5. Conducting ceramics
6. Annealing and normalizing
7. Optical fibres coating
8. Turbine blade coating
9. Moisture absorption

6.10.1 Sintering

Sintering is defined as particle coalescence of powdered aggregate by diffusion that is accomplished by firing at an elevated temperature.

During firing, the formed piece shrinks and experiences a reduction of porosity and the mechanical integrity gets improved. Powder particles coalesce into a more dense mass. Initially in sintering, necks are formed along the contact regions as shown in Figure 6.12. Grain boundaries are formed within each neck.

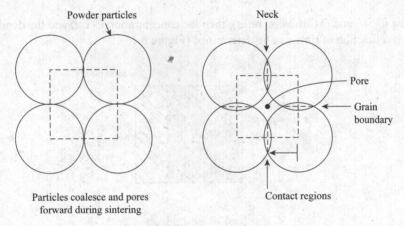

Figure 6.12 *Sintering*

The driving force for sintering is the reduction in total particle surface area; the surface energies are greater in magnitude than grain boundary energies. Sintering is carried out below the melting temperature, so a liquid phase is normally not present. Mass transport necessary to affect the changes shown in Figure 6.12 is achieved by atomic diffusion from bulk particles to neck particles with hot pressing, while the powder pressing and heat treatment are performed simultaneously.

The relation between neck radius r and time t is

$$r = Ct^m$$

where r is the radius of the neck, C is the coefficient of proportionality depending upon temperature, size and surface energy and m is the index of mass transportation.

Grinding wheels and bushes are made by sintering process.

6.10.2 Case Carburization

Many steel components are surface hardened by increasing the carbon percentage in case near the surface by a process called 'carburization'. Surface hardness is important for wear resistance as in the case of gears, wheels, cams, ball and rollers, so that their fatigue life is enhanced.

Carbon atoms from solid coke, liquid petroleum or gaseous methane atmosphere diffuse into steel at elevated temperature.

The initial condition for carbon concentration is

$$C(x, 0) = C_s, \quad \text{when } x > 0.$$
$$C(0, t) = C_m$$
$$C_s = C_1 - C_2 \; erf(\infty)$$
$$C_s = C_1 - C_2 \; \text{as } erf(\infty) = 1$$
$$C_m = C_1 - C_2 \; erf(0)$$
$$C_m = C_1$$
$$C_s = C_m - C_2 = C_m - C_2$$
$$C_2 = C_m - C_s$$

If we know C_m, C_s and D (diffusion rates), then the concentration $C(x, t)$ and the depth x of carbon penetration as a function of time can be determined (Figure 6.13).

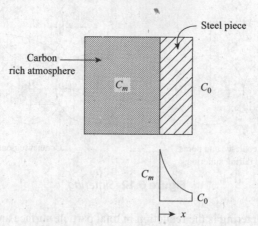

Figure 6.13 *Carbon Penetration*

Low-carbon steels (with $C < 0.15$ per cent) are used for improving wear resistance and fatigue life. The diffusion of carbon is carried out at 850–950°C. The depth of carburized surface can be up to 1 mm.

6.10.3 Decarburization of Steel

Decarburization is opposite to carburization. In this process, carbon content from the surface of the steel is reduced by keeping the steel in an oxidizing atmosphere, and the surrounding oxygen combines with carbon to form CO or CO_2 on the surface. The surface layer becomes soft and the fatigue resistance of the surface is decreased. Therefore, decarburization should be done in non-protective atmosphere such as air.

The extent of decarburization and hence of thickness of decarburized layer can be determined by the following equation

$$C(x, t) = C_1 - C_2 \, erf\left(\frac{x}{2\sqrt{D.t}}\right)$$

where x is the case depth, C_1 and C_2 are the concentrations determined by boundary conditions on concentration, D is the diffusion coefficient and t is the time in s.

If a steel with a relatively high carbon content (>1 per cent) is heated in a furnace that has a carbon-free atmosphere (air), carbon will tend to diffuse out of the steel.

6.10.4 Doping of Semiconductors

Extrinsic semiconductors (both n and p type) are produced from materials that are initially of extremely high purity, commonly having total impurity contents of the order of 10^{-7} wt%. Controlled concentration of specific donors or acceptors is then intentionally added, using various techniques. This process is known as 'doping'.

In one process, the surface of silicon wafers is exposed to the vapour of an appropriate impurity at a temperature above 1100°C in a quartz tube furnace. The part of the surface not to be exposed to the impurity diffusion must be masked off so that the impurities diffuse into the portion selected by the designer for conductivity change.

In another technique, p-type silicon wafer is coated with phosphorus and heated to permit the phosphorus to diffuse into the silicon.

6.10.5 Conducting Ceramics

Generally, the polycrystalline ceramics are good insulators due to strong covalent and ionic bonds. Yet, many ceramics can conduct electricity and some are super conductors. Diffusion of ions, electrons or holes plays an important role in the electrical conductivity of many conducting ceramics. Zirconia (ZrO_2), indium tin oxide (ITO) and lithium cobalt oxide ($LiCoO_2$) are few examples of ionically conductive materials that are used in lithium-ion batteries. The application of the conduction ceramics are oxygen sensors in cars, touchscreen displays, fuel cells and batteries.

6.10.6 Annealing and Normalizing

Annealing is a heat treatment process in which a material is exposed to an elevated temperature for an extended time period and then slowly cooled. The purpose of annealing is to relieve stresses and to increase ductility and toughness. In annealing, time must be long enough to allow for any necessary transformation reactions. In annealing, diffusional processes are normally involved.

Normalizing is accomplished by heating at about 55–85°C above the upper critical temperature of the steel, which is dependent on the composition of the steel. After sufficient time is allowed for the steel to completely transform to austenite, the treatment is terminated by cooling in air. Normalizing is a faster process than annealing.

6.10.7 Optical Fibres Coating

Optical fibres made from silica (SiO_2) are coated with polymeric materials to prevent diffusion of water molecules into the optical fibres. Fibre components include the core, cladding and coating. The signal passes through the core, whereas the surrounding cladding constrains the light rays to travel within the core and outer coating protects the core and cladding from damage due to abrasion and external pressures and from water molecules outside the fibres.

6.10.8 Turbine Blade Coating

In an aircraft engine, nickel-based super alloys are used in turbine blades. The blades are coated with zirconia (ZrO_2), a ceramic coating to protect the alloy from high temperatures and thus to act as thermal barrier coating. The diffusion of oxygen through these ceramic coatings and subsequent oxidation of the underlying alloy play a major role in improving the life of a turbine blade, which is subjected to cyclic loading.

6.10.9 Moisture Absorption

Absorption of moisture by non-metallic solids such as plastics, ceramics, rubber and polymeric composites is of major concern to material scientists. These solids absorb liquid and vapours by the process of diffusion. The moisture concentration at surfaces is denoted as C_m (Figure 6.14).

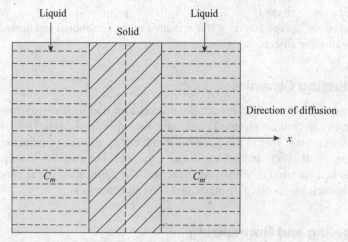

Figure 6.14 *Moisture Absorption*

The solid plate under consideration may also be exposed to different ambient conditions of vapour, in place of liquid. Ambient relative humidity is given by the expression

$$C_m = a(\text{RH})^b \text{ per cent}$$

where a and b are the empirical constants depending on the materials. Values of a lie between 0.5 and 2. Values of b lie between 0 and 1 for various materials.

6.11 KIRKENDAL EFFECT

In a binary alloy (as Cu + Ni alloy) the rates at which both constituents (i.e. Cu and Ni atoms) diffuse may not be equal. The constituent with lower melting point diffuses much faster than the other (i.e. copper having lower melting point will diffuse faster than nickel atoms).

Two or more adjacent atoms jump past each other or exchange their positions as shown in Figure 6.15, i.e. three atoms exchange their positions with each other or four atoms exchange their positions with each other. Two atoms or four atoms (Zenner ring) interchange their positions. Different patterns of interchange are shown in Figure 6.15. This diffusion mechanism involves severe local distortion due to displacement of atoms surrounding the jumping pairs. Much more energy is required in this case for atom jumping.

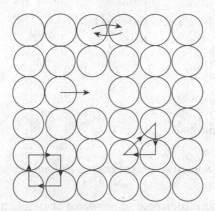

Figure 6.15 *Diffusing by Exchanging Positions*

Mr. Kirkendal used a couple of α-brass/copper and showed that zinc atoms diffused out of brass into copper more rapidly than copper atoms diffused into brass. The concept of exchange is very important in metal cladding, sintering and so on.

KEYPOINTS TO REMEMBER

❑ A natural tendency of the molecules or atoms to flow from higher concentration to lower concentration is called diffusion.

❑ Diffusion is a time- and temperature-dependent process.

❑ In a diffusion couple, the type of diffusion is interdiffusion or impurity diffusion.

❑ Diffusion rate ϕ

$$\phi_{dislocation} < \phi_{lattice} < \phi_{grass\ boundary} < \phi_{surface}$$

❑ In a vacancy diffusion, diffusing atom goes to vacancy site and vacancy atom goes to the site of diffusing atom.

❑ In interstitial diffusion, smaller atoms move from one interstitial site to another, for example, diffusion of carbon atoms in α-Fe and γ-Fe.

❑ Diffusion rate, $D = D_0 \exp(-E_d/RT)$, where D_0 is the pre-exponent constant, E_d is the activation energy, R is the gas constant and T is the temperature in K.

❑ Steady state diffusion

The concentration gradient is independent of time, but dependent on position.

❑ The concentration gradient is known as driving force.

❑ Fick's second law of diffusion

The diffusion rate is dependent on both time and position

Concentration, $\qquad C(x, t) = A - B \, erf \, C(x, t) = A - B \, erf \dfrac{x}{2\sqrt{Dt}}$

$\qquad$ A, B $\qquad$ are constants

$\qquad$ x $\qquad$ position

$\qquad$ D $\qquad$ diffusion rate

$\qquad$ t $\qquad$ time

❑ In depth of case carbonization

$$C(x_p, t) = \frac{C_0 + C_m}{2}$$

Where C_0 average concentration and

C_m maximum concentration

❑ Silicon wafers are exposed to impurity atoms of arsenic, gallium or phosphorus to change the electrical conductivity.

❑ Sintering is defined as particle coalescence of powdered aggregate by diffusion, accomplished by firing at elevated temperature.

❑ Case carburization, the concentration of carbon in steel

$$C_s = C_1 - C_2 \, erf(\alpha) \text{ infinity}$$

where $C_1 = C_m$ = concentration at $x = 0$

$$C_2 = C_m - C_s$$

❑ Diffusion of ions, electrons or holes plays an important role in the electrical conductivity of many conducting polymers, such as zirconia, indium tin oxide and lithium cobalt oxide.

❑ Optical fibres are coated with a polymeric material, which protects the core and cladding from damage and moisture absorption.

❑ Turbine blades are coated with zirconia so that the fatigue life of turbine blade is improved.

Moisture, $C_m = a(\text{RH})^b$ per cent

where a and b are constants and RH is the ambient relative humidity.

MULTIPLE CHOICE QUESTIONS

1. Lattice diffusion is caused by
   (a) Grain boundaries
   (b) Screw dislocations
   (c) Point imperfections
   (d) None of these

2. Diffusion along an edge dislocation is termed as
   (a) Self-diffusion
   (b) Vacancy diffusion
   (c) Pipe diffusion
   (d) None of these

3. The value of $erf(6)$ is equal to
   (a) 1   (c) +0.6
   (b) −0.6   (d) ∞ (infinity)

4. Diffusion couple is the name given to
   (a) A system of two materials, with a common interface in which one material diffuses into the other
   (b) Couple developed by diffusion forces
   (c) A couple of atom diffusing together
   (d) None of these

5. Coefficient of diffusion increases with
   (a) Flow of flux under steady state conditions
   (b) Increase in temperature
   (c) Higher melting point for increased diffusion coefficient
   (d) None of these

6. Diffusivity is lower for solids with
   (a) Coarse grain size
   (b) Lower melting point
   (c) Low packing factor
   (d) None of these

7. Diffusion in doping is more sensitive to
   (a) Time   (c) Wafer thickness
   (b) Temperature   (d) None of these

8. When diffusion is not activated, temperature dependence of diffusivity is
   (a) Proportional to T
   (b) Uniform
   (c) Zero
   (d) None of these

9. What is the type of diffusion of copper in nickel?
   (a) Self-diffusion
   (b) Substitutional diffusion
   (c) Interstitial diffusion
   (d) None of these

10. What is gas constant R?
    (a) 8.11 J/mol.K
    (b) 8.31 J/mol.K
    (c) 83.1 J/mol.K
    (d) None of these

11. Silicon wafers used as semiconductors are generally made of what thickness?
    (a) 1.0 mm   (c) 0.01 mm
    (b) 0.1 mm   (d) 0.001 mm

12. Coating of which material is provided on turbine blades?
    (a) Zirconia   (c) Alumina
    (b) Silica   (d) None of these

Answers

1. (c)   2. (c)   3. (a)   4. (a)   5. (b)   6. (a)   7. (b)   8. (c)   9. (b)   10. (b)
11. (b)   12. (a)

REVIEW QUESTIONS

1. What is diffusion couple, explain. Take the case of silver/gold couple.

2. Differentiate between grain boundary diffusion, lattice diffusion and surface diffusion.

3. What are different types of diffusion processes?

4. Explain the effect of diffusing species (guest atoms) and temperature on diffusion rate.

5. Explain steady state diffusion process. Give a few applications of the type of diffusion.

6. Explain Fick's second law of diffusion. Derive expression for concentration $C(x, t)$.

7. What is the difference between case carburization and impurity diffusion?

8. Explain the processes of sintering and decarburization.

9. What do you understand by optical fibres coating and turbine blade coating?

10. What are conducting ceramics?

11. Explain doping process of semiconductors.

12. What is interchange diffusion? Explain with the help of a neat sketch.

PRACTICE PROBLEMS

1. If diffusion rate of zinc into copper at 500°C is 4.2×10^{-18} (m²/s), find D_0, pre-exponential constant. Given activation energy $E_d = 189$ kJ/mol.

   Ans. [2.57×10^{-5} m²/s]

2. Pre-exponential constant, D_0 for diffusion of copper in nickel is 2.7×10^{-5} (m²/s). If activation energy is 2.65 eV/atom, what is the diffusion rate at 550°C. Given $R = 8.62 \times 10^{-5}$ eV/atom-K.

   Ans. [1.84×10^{-21} (m²/s)]

3. For the diffusion of zinc in copper, the activation energy is 189 kJ/mol and the initial temperature is 200°C. Find the temperature that will increase the diffusion coefficient by a factor of 20. Given gas constant $R = 8.31$ J/mol.K.

   Ans. [231°C]

4. A plate of iron is exposed to a carburizing atmosphere on one side and carbon-deficient atmosphere on the other side at 750°C. If the condition of steady state is achieved, calculate the diffusion flux of carbon through the plate if the concentration of carbon at position 6 and 10 mm ($x_1 = 6$ mm, $x_2 = 10$ mm) beneath the carbonizing surface are 1.25 and 0.75 kg/m³, respectively. Assume a diffusion coefficient of 2.8×10^{-11} m²/s at this temperature.

   Ans. [3.5×10^{-9} kg/m²-s]

5. The diffusivity of zinc in copper is 4×10^{-18} m²/s at 500°C and 5×10^{-13} m²/s at 1000°C. Calculate the values of D_0 (pre-exponent constant) and E_d for this diffusion couple. $R = 8.314$ J/mol.K.

   Ans. [42.2×10^{-6} m²/s, 192. kJ/mol]

6. In a steel, the initial carbon percentage is 0.25 per cent by weight. It is to be treated at 950°C. If the concentration of carbon at the surface is suddenly brought to and maintained at 1.2 wt%, how long will it take to achieve a carbon content of 0.80 wt% at the position of 0.5 mm below the surface. Assume that $D = 1.6 \times 10^{-11}$ m^2/s for carbon in iron and that the steel piece is semi-infinite.

Ans. [7.1 h]

7. A BCC iron–carbon steel containing initially 0.15 wt% carbon is carbonized at an elevated temperature and in an atmosphere where the surface carbon concentration is maintained at 1.2 wt%. If after 50 h the concentration of carbon is 0.35 per cent at a position 5 mm below the surface, determine the temperature at which the treatment was carried out?

$$D_0 = 2.8 \times 10^{-4}\,\text{m}^2/\text{s}$$
$$E_d = 251\,\text{kJ/mol}$$
$$R = 8314\,\text{J/mol.K}$$

Ans. [1653.5° C]

8. Boron is diffused into a slice of pure silicon at 1100°C for 2 h. What is the depth below the surface at which the concentration is 10^{17} atoms/cm^3, if the surface concentration is 10^{18} atoms/cm^3. Diffusion coefficient of boron into silicon is 4.2×10^{-13} cm^2/s.

Ans. [1.31 μm]

7 PHASE DIAGRAMS

7.1 INTRODUCTION

Phase diagrams are important for a metallurgist, as they provide relationship between phases in a system as a function of temperature, pressure and composition. The development of microstructures of an alloy of a particular composition at different temperatures is clearly depicted by a phase diagram. These diagrams also provide information on melting, casting and recrystallization of alloys. If more than two components are present in a system, the phase diagram becomes extremely complicated and it is difficult to represent various phases. Practically, the variation in pressure is not considered and for all phase diagrams studied in this chapter, the pressure is taken as 1 atm.

This chapter describes the solid solution of two elements, which are completely soluble in each other at any composition such as Cu–Ni and Au–Ag system, the development of microstructures in such systems at various compositions and temperatures, binary eutectic systems and development of microstructures in binary eutectic system and equilibrium diagrams with intermediate reactions as eutectoid and peritectic reactions.

In addition, a detailed study is made of iron-carbon system, explaining various types of steels, allotropic transformations, eutectic and eutectoid compositions and the development of microstructures at various stages.

7.2 PHASES

A phase is defined as a homogeneous part of a system that has uniform physical and chemical properties. A homogeneous mixture of water and sugar is a single phase at ordinary temperatures and on macroscopic scale, but on atomic scale there are two phases of water and sugar molecules. For phase diagrams in this chapter, a sugar solution in water is considered a single phase.

Every pure metal is considered to be a phase. If more than one phase is present in a given system, each will have its own distinct properties. For example, in a mixture of oil and water, droplets float on water, so there are two phases of oil and water. A boundary separating the two phases will exist and across this boundary there are discontinuous and abrupt changes in physical and chemical properties.

Sometimes, a single-phase system is known as 'homogeneous phase'. Systems composed of two or more phases are termed as mixtures or 'heterogeneous systems'. Ordinarily, phases interact in such a way that the properties of a combination of multiphase system are different from the properties of individual phases. A crystal with a definite lattice structure is also a phase. When a liquid solidifies, there is a change of phase from liquid to solid (during solidification). During the allotropic transformation, phase change takes place as on heating ferrite-α iron with BCC structure to austenite-γ iron with FCC structure, as there is a change in crystal structure.

A solid solution of an alloy with the component atoms mixed at the unit cell level constitutes a single phase. The microstructure in metal alloys is characterized by the number of phases present, their proportions and the manner in which they are distributed. The microstructure of an alloy mainly depends upon: (1) alloying elements, (2) concentration of the alloying elements and (3) heat treatment of the alloy. For example, pearlitic structure in a steel consists of alternate layers of ferrite and cementite (cementite layers are thin and ferrite layers are thick).

The following are some important definitions:

1. Components in a multiphase system are metals, which form alloys such as Cu–Zn alloy and Ni–Cu solid solution alloy.

2. Solute atoms are guest atoms, which are solidly soluble in solvent atoms, i.e. host atoms. For example, carbon as solute atom takes interstitial positions in iron atoms. In 80 Ni 20 Cu alloy, copper atoms are solute (guest) and nickel atoms (host) are solvent atoms.

3. Systems is:

   (a) Specific body of materials under consideration.
   (b) Series of possible alloys consisting of same components, as in Cu–Zn alloy.
   (c) Different percentages of zinc in copper produce different types of brasses.
   (d) *Solid solution:* Solute atoms occupy either the substitutional or interstitial position in the solvent lattice.
   (e) *Solubility limit:* Maximum concentration of solute atoms that may dissolve in solvent to form a solid solution.
   (f) For example, sugar and water $(C_{12}H_{22}O_{11} + H_2O)$. The solubility limit of sugar in water depends upon the temperature of water.
   (g) *Phase equilibrium:* Equilibrium is described in terms of free energy, which is a function of internal energy of the system.

      A system is at equilibrium if its free energy is minimum under specified conditions of temperature, pressure and composition.

      If the state of equilibrium is not reached because the rate of approach to equilibrium is extremely slow, such a system is said to be in a non-equilibrium or meta-stable state.

   (h) *Equilibrium phase diagrams or constitutional diagrams:* Equilibrium phase diagrams represent the relationships among the temperature, composition and relative quantities of phases at equilibrium.

7.3 SOLIDIFICATION OF METAL IN AN INGOT MOULD

When the molten metal is poured into the ingot mould, it comes into contact with the cold mould walls, and chilled grains are nucleated all along the boundary of the mould. These nuclei are heterogeneously produced. Further, growth takes place along the surface of the nuclei and columnar grains (i.e. they are created perpendicular to the surface of the wall). Heat from the molten metal is extracted through the mould wall and layer of chilled grains. During the growth of columnar grains, the liquid metal in the interior continuously gets cooled and its temperature at one stage comes below the melting point or freezing point. At this stage, homogeneous nucleation takes place throughout the molten metal and the nuclei grow equally in all directions *producing equiaxed grains*. At the completion of solidification of molten metal, one may observe a depression in the centre of ingot at the top, and this shrinkage cavity is known as 'pipe' as shown in Figure 7.1. Shrinkage is due to the fact that specific volume of liquid metal is more than the specific volume of solid metal.

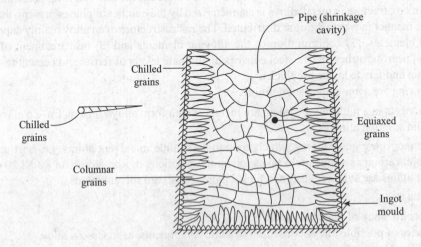

Figure 7.1 *Ingot Structure*

When the molten metal solidifies, there exists an interface between the liquid and the solid phases; the liquid phase at higher temperature and the solid phase at temperature below the melting point.

The temperature gradient from solid to liquid is positive as shown below. The temperature at the interface is more than the temperature of the solid, and the columnar crystals grow in the solid phase.

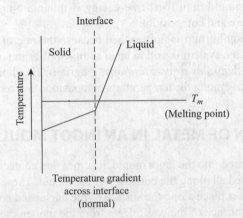

But under certain conditions, inverse temperature gradient is set up in the liquid phase as shown below.

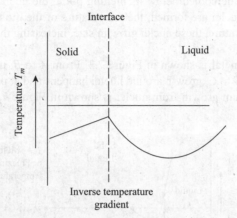

Due to inverse temperature gradient, the temperature at the interface is more than the temperature of the solid as well as that of the liquid metal. So, growth is taking place under cooled state. The crystals grow faster in some preferential directions than in other directions; this type of growth is known as *dendritic growth* as shown in Figure 7.2.

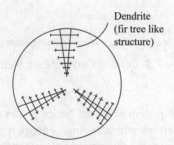

Figure 7.2 *Dendrites Formation*

7.3.1 Dendritic Growth

Heat energy is required to change a solid into a liquid at a particular temperature, which is known as 'latent heat'. Similarly, when hot metal changes into a solid at a particular temperature, the energy has to be removed (while the temperature remains constant), which is also called latent heat.

The latent heat released warms up the liquid in front of the growing crystal face, which stops or slows down the growth in that direction and the crystal grows in other direction in which the liquid is coolest, i.e. in a perpendicular direction, resulting in the development of spikes.

In alloys or metals containing impurities, the inverse temperature gradient is generally set up and solidification takes place in dendritic form.

7.3.2 Solidification of a Pure Metal

The molten metal is cooling down in a crucible and is allowed to cool to room temperature. When the molten metal gets slightly undercooled below its melting point, the nuclei appear too random at various sites. As soon as these nuclei are formed, the temperature of the molten metal rises to its melting point. At this constant temperature, these nuclei grow in size, increasing the solid content of the molten metal.

Cooling curve of a pure metal is shown in Figure 7.3. From A to B, undercooling takes place and nucleation starts at B. From B to C, growth around nuclei happens and at point C all the liquid is solidified at freezing point T_m. Grain growth from nuclei is shown in Figure 7.4. The grain boundaries are shown by dark lines.

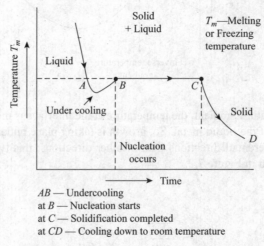

AB — Undercooling
at B — Nucleation starts
at C — Solidification completed
at CD — Cooling down to room temperature

Figure 7.3 *Cooling Curve of Pure Metal*

At the grain boundaries, the regular pattern of crystal lattice breaks down. The grain boundaries consist of atoms in a non-equilibrium position, which are high-energy regions of instability. The region of grain boundary disorder is about 20 times the thickness of atomic diameters.

Grains exist in three forms in solid polycrystalline material as: (1) dendrites, (2) equiaxed grains and (c) elongated grains. The elongated grains are formed by cold working of equiaxed grains as shown in Figure 7.5. Metal-forming processes such a drawing, rolling and extrusion produce elongated grains.

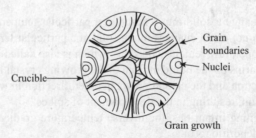

Figure 7.4 *Grain Growth*

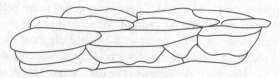

Figure 7.5 *Elongated Grains*

7.4 TYPES OF PHASE DIAGRAMS

There are three types of phase diagrams:

1. Binary—involves two elements; the behaviour depends upon the solubility of the elements
2. Ternary—three elements
3. Multiphase—many elements

In a binary system, there is a eutectic system, soluble components and partially soluble components. In a eutectic system (or a mechanical mixture), the two elements are completely soluble in liquid state, but are insoluble in the solid state. Although there are no metals, which are soluble in solid state, yet for practical purposes, the alloys with very low solubility of components are considered as mixture.

1. A eutectic structure is defined as a two-phase microstructure resulting from solidification of a liquid having eutectic composition. The phases exist as lamellae that alternate with one another. At the eutectic temperature, one liquid phase gets converted into two solid phases. The composition of the eutectic alloy is a fixed composition. Eutectic means 'easily melted'. For example, copper and silver make a eutectic mixture of 71.9 wt% Ag + 28.1 wt% Cu.

   Eutectic reactions

$$\text{Liquid} \underset{\text{heating}}{\overset{\text{cooling}}{\rightleftharpoons}} [(\text{solid } A + \text{solid } B)], \text{ a eutectic mixture}$$

2. *Soluble components:* Two elements are completely soluble in both liquid and solid states, yet no chemical compound is formed. A solid solution is obtained for any composition of two elements as 60 per cent A + 40 per cent B or 70 per cent A + 30 per cent B. Two elements are completely soluble in liquid state above the liquidus line and are completely soluble in solid state below the solidus line. The behaviour of the system is studied with the help of distinct liquidus and solidus lines. For example, a solid solution of copper and nickel.

3. *Partially soluble components:* Two elements are completely soluble in liquid state and partially soluble in solid state, but no chemical compound is formed. There are two types of phase diagrams for these partially soluble components.

   (a) With a eutectic point
   (b) With a peritectic point

In a peritectic reaction, upon cooling a solid and a liquid phase transform isothermally and reversibly to a solid having a different composition.

7.5 BINARY AMORPHOUS ALLOYS

An alloy composed of two elements such as copper–nickel, iron–carbon, silver–gold and copper–zinc are binary amorphous systems because its composition may range from 0 wt% of copper + 100 wt% of

nickel to 100 wt% of copper + 0 wt% of nickel. Copper and nickel make solid solution as their structure is the same, i.e. FCC structure and atomic radii of copper and nickel are 0.128 nm and 0.125 nm,
respectively. Three different phase regions appear in the phase diagram, i.e. α solid phase; L liquid
phase and $(\alpha + L)$ phase. Liquid is a homogeneous solution of both copper and nickel. α Phase is a solid
solution of copper and nickel. Melting point of copper is 1085°C and that of nickel is 1455°C.

At temperatures below 1085°C, copper and nickel are mutually soluble in each other in the solid
state for all compositions, since they make a solid solution as explained above. As there is complete
solid solubility and liquid solubility of two components (Cu + Ni), the system is termed as isomorphous
binary system. Figure 7.6 shows the phase diagram for Cu–Ni binary system. ACB is the liquidus line,
ADB is the solidus line, melting point of copper is 1085°C and Nickel is 1455°C.

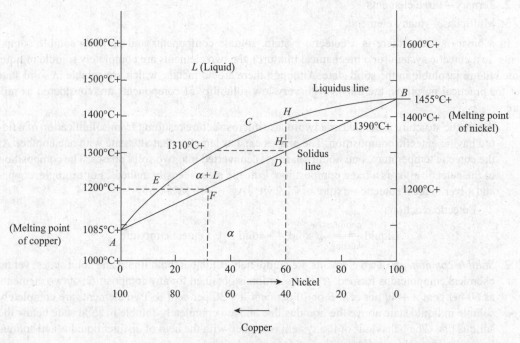

Figure 7.6 *Copper and Nickel Phase Diagram*

Liquidus and solidus lines intersect at the two composition extremities as shown in Figure 7.6, i.e. at
A and B. As the mixture of copper and nickel is heated, copper remains solid until it melts at 1085°C.
Increasing the temperature further, copper is in liquid form but nickel remains solid, so at any other
temperature, e.g. at 1200°C at point E along the line EF, there is liquid of copper and nickel, at F, there
is solid of composition Ni 32 wt%, Cu 68 wt% and in between E and F there is α phase + liquid phase L.
As the temperature is increased further, at 1455°C, i.e. at melting point of nickel, there is complete
liquid phase L.

For any composition, the melting phenomenon occurs over the range of temperatures between solidus and liquidus lines. Let us take an example of 60 wt% Ni + 40 wt% Cu; melting begins at 1310°C,
and the amount of liquid phase continuously increases with temperature until about 1390°C at which
the alloy is completely liquid.

Interpretation of phase diagram:

From the phase diagram, three following informations can be obtained:

1. Phases that are present
2. Composition of the phases
3. Percentage or fraction of each phase

A portion of phase diagram is enlarged in Figure 7.7.

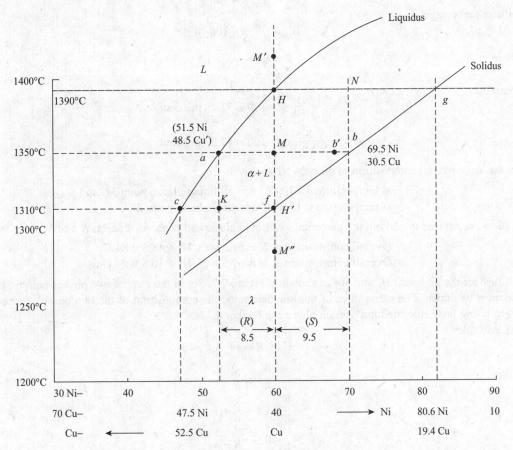

Figure 7.7 Cu + Ni Phase Diagram

Locate the temperature—composition point on the diagram point by M, temperature 1350°C, composition 60 Ni, 40 Cu. Two phases are present at point M, i.e. liquid phase L and α phase. A tie line is drawn across the two phase regions at temperature 1350°C. The intersections of the tie lines and phase boundaries (liquidus and solidus) are noted.

At 'a', liquid phase, C_L, 51.5 wt% Ni + 48.5 wt% Cu
At 'b', solid phase, C_α, 69.5 wt% Ni + 30.5 wt% Cu
At 'a', there is only liquid phase and at 'b' there is only α phase (solid).

In these two phase regions lever rule may be applied.

7.5.1 Lever Rule

1. The overall composition is located along tie line, at point M (60 wt% Ni, 40 wt% Cu).
2. Fraction of one phase is noted by taking the length of line Mb, overall composition to phase boundary (solidus) for the other phase and dividing by total tie line.

Liquid percentage,

$$W_L = \frac{S}{R+S} \times 100$$

α Phase percentage,

$$W_\alpha = \frac{R}{R+S} \times 100$$

where

$$R = 8.5$$
$$S = 9.5$$

Therefore,

$$W_L = \frac{9.5}{9.5 + 8.5} \times 100 = 52.78 \text{ per cent}$$

$$W_\alpha = \frac{8.5}{9.5 + 8.5} \times 100 = 47.22 \text{ per cent}$$

For the same overall composition of 60 wt% Ni + 40 wt% Cu,

at temperature > 1390°C, it is all liquid phase, point M' and
at temperature < 1310°C it is all α phase, point M''.

Readers are advised to find out the percentage of liquid phase and α phase at points K and N.

Overall composition at K is 51.5 wt% Ni + 48.5 wt% Cu
Overall composition at N is 69.5 wt% Ni + 30.5 wt% Cu

Consider the tie lines cH' and Hg as shown in Figure 7.7. So, in the case of two phases present, tie line must be drawn. The extremities of the line determine the composition of the two phases, respectively. Using lever rule, fraction of each phase can be found.

Lever rule

$$W_L R = W_\alpha S$$

$$\frac{W_L}{W_\alpha} = \frac{S}{R}$$

$$\frac{W_L}{W_\alpha} + 1 = \frac{S}{R} + 1$$

$$\frac{W_L + W_\alpha}{W_\alpha} = \frac{R+S}{R}$$

$$\frac{W_\alpha}{W_L + W_\alpha} = \frac{R}{R+S}, \text{ fraction of a phase}$$

$$W_\alpha \, \alpha \, R$$

$$W_L \, \alpha \, S$$

Many a times it is desired to have volume fraction in place of mass fraction, then

$$V_\alpha = \frac{V_\alpha}{V_\alpha + V_L} = \frac{W_\alpha / \rho_\alpha}{\dfrac{W_\alpha}{\rho_\alpha} - \dfrac{W_L}{\rho_L}}$$

where ρ_α and ρ_L are densities of respective phases, i.e. α and L phases in this case.

7.6 DEVELOPMENT OF MICROSTRUCTURE IN BINARY AMORPHOUS ALLOY

To study the development of microstructure, as the molten metal of alloy cools down to room temperature, let us refer to Figure 7.7. Consider the composition of 60 wt% Ni + 40 wt% Cu, shown by line M' H MHM''. At point M', temperature > 1390°C, it is all liquid of composition 60/40, Ni /Cu. Under the microscope, the structure is as shown in Figure 7.8(a). Consider the point M, a combination of two

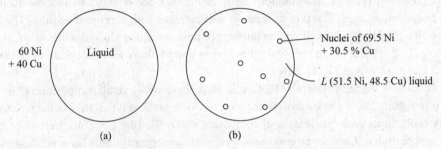

60 Ni + 40 Cu · Liquid

Nuclei of 69.5 Ni + 30.5 % Cu

L (51.5 Ni, 48.5 Cu) liquid

(a)   (b)

Figure 7.8 *(a); (b) Nuclei Formation*

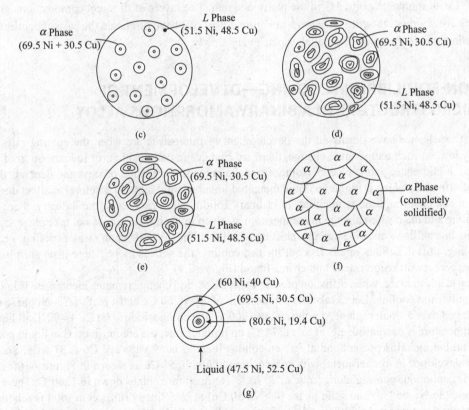

α Phase (69.5 Ni + 30.5 Cu)

L Phase (51.5 Ni, 48.5 Cu)

(c)

α Phase (69.5 Ni, 30.5 Cu)

L Phase (51.5 Ni, 48.5 Cu)

(d)

α Phase (69.5 Ni, 30.5 Cu)

L Phase (51.5 Ni, 48.5 Cu)

(e)

α Phase (completely solidified)

(f)

(60 Ni, 40 Cu)

(69.5 Ni, 30.5 Cu)

(80.6 Ni, 19.4 Cu)

Liquid (47.5 Ni, 52.5 Cu)

(g)

Figure 7.8 *(c); (d); (e); (f); (g) Grain Growth*

phases $L + \alpha$. Along the tie line $a\ b$, at the point 'a', there is a composition of 51.5 per cent Ni and 48.5 per cent Cu. Nucleation has just started as shown in 7.8(b) of composition 69.5 Ni, 30.5 Cu. At the point M, there is liquid, L, phase of 51.5 per cent Ni + 48.5 per cent Cu and a solid α phase of 69.5 per cent Ni + 30.5 per cent Cu, as shown in Figure 7.8(c), and the temperature is 1350°C. The overall composition at M is 60 Ni, 40 Cu.

At the point b' (very near to point 'b'), there is small percentage of liquid phase of composition (51.5 Ni, 30.5 Cu) as shown in Figure 7.8(d). With continued cooling, both composition and relative amounts of each of the phases will change. The composition of the liquid, L and α phases will follow the liquidus and solidus lines, respectively. Fraction of α phase will increase with continued cooling. The overall alloy composition (60 Ni, 40 Cu) will remain unchanged during cooling along the line $M'\ H\ M\ H'M''$. At a point very close to point H' on the solidus line, say at point f, there will be α phase of composition (47.5 N, 52.5 Cu) as shown in Figure 7.8(e).

At point M'', below the temperature 1310°C, it is all α phase with overall composition of 60 Ni, 40 Cu as shown in Figure 7.8(f). Let us analyse the structure of a grain at point M''. As the molten metal continuously cools, inner core (nucleus) is of composition 80.6 Ni, 19.4 Cu. Thus, portion of Ni goes on reducing and portion of Cu goes on maximizing till at the outer most liquid layer is of composition 47.5 Ni, 52.5 Cu. When the last layer of liquid solidifies, the overall composition of solid phase will be 60 Ni, 40 Cu as shown, at point M'' in the phase diagram. The layers of different compositions growing successively around the core are shown in Figure 7.8(g). We have discussed the case of equilibrium solidification, where the solidification takes place very slowly.

7.7 NON-EQUILIBRIUM COOLING—DEVELOPMENT OF MICROSTRUCTURE IN A BINARY AMORPHOUS ALLOY

In the last article, we have discussed the development of microstructure when the cooling rates are extremely low. At each temperature change, there are changes in composition (or redistribution of two phases, i.e. liquid phase and α phase). Compositional change is a diffusion process and depends upon the rate of diffusion, which is higher in liquid metal but lower in solid metal. Therefore, to affect desired changes in composition, time is required. In ordinary solidification process in the industry, there is a rapid cooling and the desired change in composition as given by solidus line does not take place, rather the solidus line shifts to one side and this shifting of solidus line depends upon rate of cooling, i.e. for slow cooling, shift in solidus line is less but for fast cooling, the shift is more. There is no shift in liquidus line, because diffusion rate is higher in a liquid (Figure 7.9).

Cooling at a faster rate, when diffusion process for composition change remains incomplete is known as non-equilibrium cooling. Let us take the composition of 40 Ni, 60 Cu and a part of Cu–Ni phase diagram enlarged over a small region. At point 'a', at 1300°C, the composition is 60 Cu + 40 Ni, all liquid. As the temperature is decreased, e.g. at 'b' (1274°C) on liquidus line, the composition is in liquid phase, 40 per cent, but nickel is present and at 'g', on solidus line, Ni is 49 wt% and Cu is 51 wt%. So, the nuclei are developed in mother metal with composition of 49 Ni, 51 Cu as shown in Figure 7.10(a).

There is continuous cooling along 'a, b, c, d'. At 'c', temperature comes down to 1260°C. There are liquid phase (35 Ni, 65 Cu) and solid phase (44 Ni, 50 Cu) at 'h'. Since diffusion in solid is relatively low, the α phase formed at 'g' (49 Ni, 51 Cu) has not changed to 44 Ni, 56 Cu as per solidus curve of

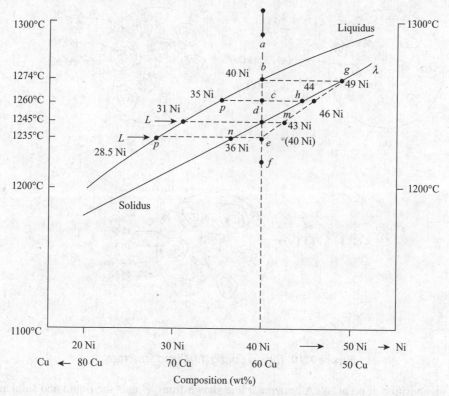

Figure 7.9 *Liquidus and Solidus Curves*

equilibrium cooling, but change has taken place to some weighted average, e.g. 49 Ni changed to 46 Ni per cent, therefore, solidus line is shifted from '*gh*' to '*gl*' (as shown in the Figure 7.10), say the temperature is decreased further to 1245°C, at '*d*' in solidus, α phase should be of composition 40 Ni, 60 Cu, but due to delay in diffusion, change in nickel percentage has taken place to 43 Ni only. So, point '*d*' is shifted to '*m*' and solidus '*g h d*' is shifted to '*g l m*'.

As the cooling continues and the temperature decreases continuously, the diffusion rate in solid also decreases continuously. The displaced solidus line, if extended further, may meet the vertical line of 40

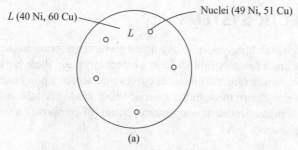

(a)

Figure 7.10 *(a) Nuclei Growth*

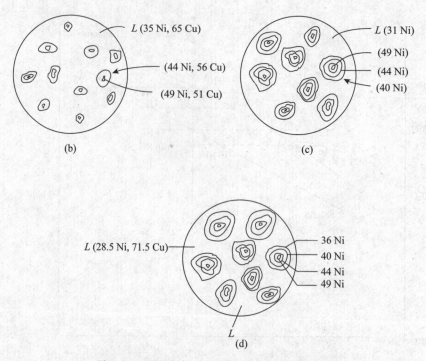

Figure 7.10 *(b); (c) Coring (d) Cored Structure*

Ni/60 Cu composition at point 'e'. A horizontal line shown from 'e' cuts the liquid and solid at points 'n' and 'p' as shown. At 'n', composition is 36 Ni, 64 Cu and liquid (28.5 Ni, 71.5 Cu) α phase at 'n' is of composition 36 Ni, 64 Cu and grows surrounding the microstructure as shown in Figure 7.10(d).

Figure 7.10 shows that the distribution of two elements (Cu + Ni) within the grains is non-uniform. This phenomenon is termed as 'segregation', and the concentration gradients are established across the grains. The centre of each grain is rich in high melting element (as Ni in Cu + Ni system) and the concentration of low melting elements (Cu in this case) increases with position from inner region to grain boundary. This type of structure is called 'cored structure'. Coring may be carried out at a temperature below the solidus point for a particular composition of alloy. During the heat treatment, atomic diffusion produces homogeneous grains with regard to composition.

7.8 BINARY EUTECTIC SYSTEMS

In a eutectic reaction, 'in which upon cooling, one liquid phase transforms isothermally and reversibly into two solid phases that are intimately mixed' so in a eutectic system, there are three phases: α, β and L (liquid) phase. In the phase diagram, two liquidus curves intersect at a point called *eutectic point*, at a particular temperature. A line drawn through the eutectic line gives the 'isotherm line'. As the temperature decreases below the eutectic isotherm temperature, liquid (of composition given by eutectic point) solidifies into two solid phases α + β.

$$ac = R = 18 - 5 = 13$$
$$cb = S = 40 - 18 = 22$$

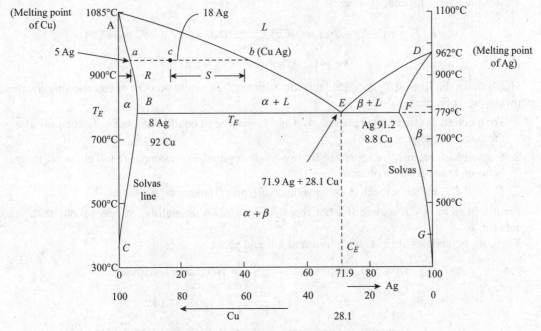

Figure 7.11 *Eutectic System of Copper and Silver*

Consider the example of a copper–silver eutectic system; melting point of copper is 1085°C and silver is 962°C. Make a eutectic system at composition of 71.9 wt% Ag + 28.1 wt% Cu, at temperature of 779°C as shown in Figure 7.11. Both silver and copper have FCC structure. In the phase diagram, *AED* is the liquidus curve in two parts *AE* and *ED* meeting at eutectic point *E* and *B E F* is the isotherm line at 779°C. α Phase consists of maximum 8 per cent Ag and rest copper and β phase consists of maximum 8.8 per cent copper and rest silver as shown in the diagram. *ABC* is the solidus curve in α region and *DFG* in β region. In the α region, silver is the solute and copper is the solvent and in the β region copper is the solute and silver is the solvent in solid solution of copper and silver. α and β are solid solutions, which are formed at the extreme ends of liquidus curve. Solid solubility between α and (α + β), i.e. *BC* is termed as solvas line. Boundary *AB* is known as solidus line. Similarly for β phase, *FG* is solvas line and *DF* is solidus line. The horizontal isotherm line *BEF* is also called solidus line. Isotherm line *BEF* represents the lowest temperature at which a liquid phase may exist for a Cu–Ag alloy at equilibrium. Solidus line *BEF* shows that the melting point of copper is reduced by the addition of silver. Similarly, the melting point of silver is reduced by the addition of copper.

Point '*E*' is also called an invariant point, i.e. a fixed point with no degree of freedom. Temperature and percentages of two elements are also fixed. An important reaction occurs for an alloy of composition C_E (Figure 7.11) as it passes through temperature T_E.

$$L_{(C_E)} \underset{\text{heating}}{\overset{\text{cooling}}{\rightleftharpoons}} \alpha(C_{aE}) + \beta(C_{bE})$$

Upon cooling, a liquid phase is transformed into two solid phases, i.e. α and β phases, at the temperature T_E. But, upon heating, exactly opposite reactions take place. The word 'eutectic' means easily melted. C_E and T_E represent eutectic composition and temperature.

Eutectic reactions for copper–silver

$$L \text{ (71.9 wt\% Ag + 28.1 wt\%Cu)} \underset{\text{heating}}{\overset{\text{cooling}}{\rightleftarrows}} \text{ (8.0 wt\% Ag + 92 wt\% Cu)}$$
$$+ \text{ (91.2 wt\% Ag + 88 wt\% Cu)}$$

Horizontal solid lines at T_E is called 'eutectic isotherm'. The solid product of eutectic solidification is always two solid phases.

1. For a eutectic system, three phases, α, β and L, may be in equilibrium, but only at points along the eutectic isotherm.
2. Single-phase regions are separated by two-phase regions. For example $\alpha + \beta$ phase is situated between α and β single phases.
3. $C_{\alpha E}$ and $C_{\beta E}$ are the respective compositions of α and β phases at 'E'.

Point 'e' lies in $\alpha + L$ region. If a horizontal line is drawn through 'c', it cuts solidus at 'a' and liquidus at 'b'.

There are two phases at C: α solid phase and L liquid phase.

$$\text{wt\% of liquid phase, } C_L = \frac{R}{R+S} \times 100 \text{ (using lever rule)}$$

$$= \frac{13}{13+22} \times 100 = 37.14$$

$$\text{wt\% of solid phase, } C_\alpha = \frac{S}{R+S} \times 100 = \frac{22}{22+13} \times 100 = 62.86$$

7.8.1 Lead–Tin Eutectic System

In the lead–tin binary eutectic system, the invariant point is located at 61.9 wt% Sn + 38.1 wt% Pb at 183°C. Maximum percent of Sn in α region is 18.3 per cent and maximum percentage of lead in β region is 2.2 per cent. In α phase, tin is the solute and lead is the solvent, while in β region, lead is the solute and tin is the solvent. So, α phase is rich in lead and β phase is rich in tin (Figure 7.12).

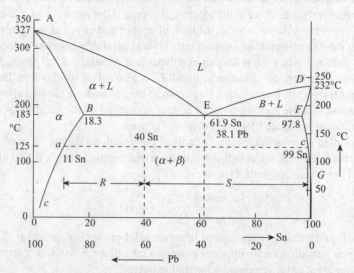

Figure 7.12 *Lead–Tin Eutectic System*

Let us consider 60/40 Sn/Pb system used as a solder, a low-melting point alloy having nearly eutectic composition. An alloy of this composition is completely molten at 185°C. Solder is most commonly used in joining connections in electrical circuits.

Let us find out the fraction of phases present at point 'b' (40 Sn, 60 Pb) in the phase diagram, the temperature is 125°C. Draw a horizontal line from 'b', intersecting solvas BC at 'c' and solvas FG at 'C' (Figure 7.12).

In percentage

at 'a' is 11 wt%

at 'b' it is 40 wt%

at 'c' it is 99 wt%

The dimensions

$$R = 40 - 11 = 29$$
$$S = 99 - 40 = 59$$

Using lever rule,

$$\text{Fraction of } \alpha \text{ phase, } C_\alpha = \frac{S}{R+S} = \frac{59}{59+29} = \frac{59}{88} = 0.67$$

$$\text{Fraction of } \beta \text{ Phase, } C_\beta = \frac{R}{R+S} = \frac{29}{59+29} = \frac{29}{88} = 0.33$$

7.9 DEVELOPMENT OF MICROSTRUCTURE IN EUTECTIC ALLOYS

Let us consider tin–lead eutectic system as shown in Figure 7.13 with solidus AB, solvas line BC, liquidus AE and isotherm eutectic line BE. Eutectic point lies at 'E'. Let us study the development of

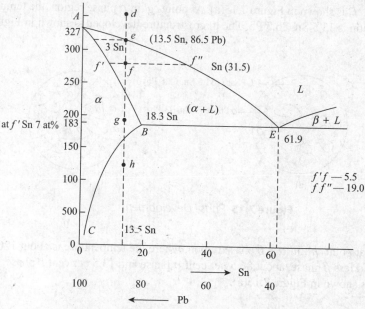

Figure 7.13 *Tin–Lead Eutectic Alloy*

microstructure as the alloy cools down from molten state to solid state. Take the composition as shown by line '*d e f g h*', with Sn 13.5 wt% and Pb 86.5 wt%. At point '*d*', where the temperature is more than 327°C, there is only liquid phase as shown in Figure 7.14(a). Alloy is continuously cooling, say at point '*e*', on liquidus *AE*, liquid phase (13.5 Sn, 86.5 Pb). The nuclei of composition (Sn 3, Pb 97) have been developed in molten metal.

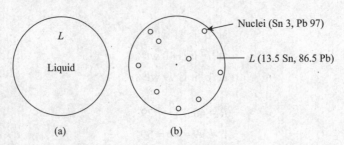

Figure 7.14 (a); (b) Nuclei Formation

Now, the temperature is further reduced and the point in phase diagram is '*f*', i.e. in $\alpha + L$ region. Draw a tie line '*f' f f'''* through the point '*f*'. Using the lever rule,

$$\alpha \text{ phase fraction } C_\alpha = \frac{19.0}{19.0 + 5.5} = 0.78$$

$$L \text{ phase fraction, } C_L = \frac{5.5}{19.0 + 5.5} = 0.22$$

Microstructure at '*f*' is shown in Figure 7.15(a). At point '*g*' in α phase region, the temperature is about 185°C, composition is 13.5 Sn, 86.5 Pb. The microstructure developed is shown in Figure 7.15(b).

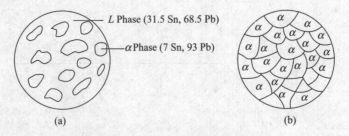

Figure 7.15 Phase Development

Now, we are at point '*h*', in $\alpha + \beta$ phase region, where the temperature is about 120°C, and there is more α phase and less β phase, about 86.5 per cent α phase and 13.5 per cent β phase. The microstructure developed is shown in Figure 7.16(a).

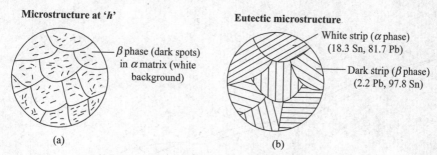

Figure 7.16 *Eutectic Structure*

7.9.1 Eutectic Microstructure

The process of redistribution of lead and tin occurs by diffusion in the liquid just ahead of eutectic liquid interface. At eutectic isotherm 183°C, the liquid transforms into two α and β phases. This transformation can be represented by the reaction.

$$L\,(61.9\ \text{wt\% Sn} + 38.1\ \text{wt\% Pb}) \underset{\text{heating}}{\overset{\text{cooling}}{\rightleftharpoons}} \alpha\,(18.3\ \text{wt\% Sn} + 81.7\ \text{wt\% Pb})$$

$$+\ \beta\,(97.8\ \text{wt\% Sn} + 2.2\ \text{wt\% Pb})$$

The redistribution is accomplished by atomic diffusion. The microstructure of solid that results from the transformation consists of alternate layers of (also called lamellae) α and β phases that form simultaneously during the transformation—eutectic structure is shown in Figure 7.16(b).

7.10 EQUILIBRIUM DIAGRAMS HAVING INTERMEDIATE PHASES OR COMPOUNDS

We have studied about binary phase diagram of alloys of Cu–Ni, Au–Ag and so on, which are completely soluble in each other in solid state and there are only two phases. Then, we have learnt about binary eutectic systems of two elements as Cu–Ag and Sn–Pb, in which there are three phases and making an alloy of eutectic composition at a fixed temperature. For other alloy systems, intermediate solid solutions (or intermediate phases) may be found at other than two composition extremities (as α and β solid solutions in Sn–Pb and Cu–Ag alloys). Such is the case with Cu–Zn system. Copper has FCC structure, but zinc has HCP structure.

In the case of Cu–Zn alloys, there are six different solutions. Two terminal solutions α and η as shown in Figure 7.17. Four intermediate solutions, i.e. β, γ, δ and ε are also shown in Figure 7.17. There is one β' phase as shown, which is termed as ordered solid solution in which copper and zinc atoms are situated in a specific and ordered arrangement within each unit cell. Some phase boundaries near

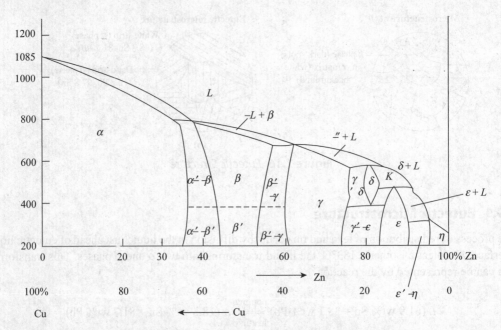

Figure 7.17 *Equilibrium Diagrams of Compounds*

the bottom of the phase diagram are dashed lines to indicate that their positions have not been exactly determined. Reason of this uncertain boundary is that at low temperature, diffusion rates are very low and longer time is required for the achievement of equilibrium. Only single- and two-phase regions are found in the diagram.

Commercial brasses are copper-rich brasses, 70 wt% Cu + 30 wt% Zn (i.e. α phase alloy as shown in Figure 7.17). For some other systems, discrete intermediate compounds (instead of solid solution) may be found and these compounds have distinct chemical formula as Mg_2Pb (19 wt% Mg + 81 wt% Pb) in Mg–Pb system. This compound can exist by itself only at this precise composition.

7.11 EUTECTOID OR PERITECTIC REACTIONS

In addition to the eutectic, in which three different phases are involved, some other invariant points are also found in some alloys. A eutectoid reaction is defined as 'a reaction in which upon cooling, *one solid phase* transforms isothermally and reversibly into two new solid phases, which are intimately mixed'. In a peritectic reaction, upon cooling, *a solid and a liquid phase* transform isothermally and reversibly into a solid phase having a different composition'.

Considering a silver–platinum system, in which melting point of platinum is 1772°C and that of silver is 962°C. The difference in melting points of platinum and silver is more than 800°C, and when the alloy of platinum–silver cools down, various solid phases, two phase regions and liquid phases are formed.

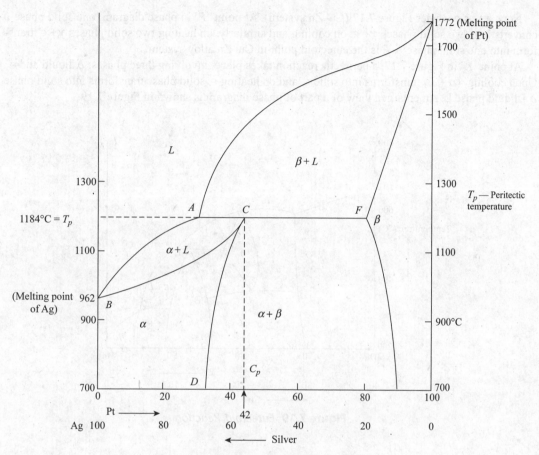

Figure 7.18 *Peritectic Reaction*

Horizontal tie line ACF indicates the peritectic temperature T_p, equal to 1184°C. The composition at the point 'C' is called peritectic composition. At this point, the solid + liquid phase ($\beta + L$) transforms into a single solid phase α on cooling and vice versa. At this point 'C', degree of freedom is zero. This is called peritectic reaction (Figure 7.18).

$$(\beta + L) \underset{\text{heating}}{\overset{\text{cooling}}{\rightleftharpoons}} \alpha \text{ phase}$$

7.11.1 Eutectoid Phase Diagram

Such phase diagrams involve transformation of two solid phases into a different solid phase on cooling and vice versa. Contrary to peritectic reaction, in which $\beta + L$ (solid + liquid) phases change to another solid phase α, here solid–solid phase changes to another solid phase, which is given by

$$\gamma + \epsilon \text{ solid phase} \underset{\text{heating}}{\overset{\text{cooling}}{\rightleftharpoons}} \delta \text{ solid phase}$$

Now, let us consider Figure 7.17 (Cu–Zn system). At point 'P' in phase diagram, one solid phase δ converts into two solid phases $\gamma + \in$ on cooling and similarly, on heating two solid phases $\gamma + \in$ transform into one solid phase δ. P is the eutectoid point in Cu–Zn alloy system.

At point 'K' in Figure 7.17, a peritectic reaction takes place, involving three phases: δ, liquid and $\in$. Upon cooling, $(\alpha + L)$ transforms into solid $\in$ and on heating $\in$ solid phase transforms into solid phase $\delta +$ liquid phase L. An enlarged view of a part of phase diagram is shown in Figure 7.19.

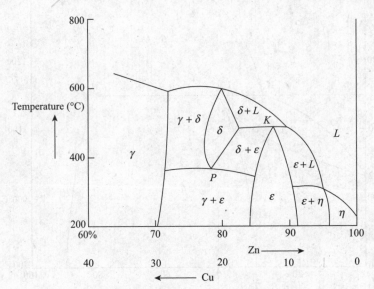

Figure 7.19 *Eutectoid Reaction*

Peritectic
At point 'K' in Figure 7.19, a peritectic reaction takes place, involving three phases: δ, L and $\in$.

$$(\delta + L) \underset{\text{heating}}{\overset{\text{cooling}}{\rightleftharpoons}} \in \text{ solid phase}$$

(Peritectic reaction)

Eutectoid Reaction
Eutectoid reaction takes place at point 'P' in Figure 7.19. One solid phase δ upon cooling, transforms into two solid phases $\gamma + \in$.

$$\text{One solid } \delta \underset{\text{heating}}{\overset{\text{cooling}}{\rightleftharpoons}} \gamma + \in \text{ two solid phases}$$

(Eutectoid reaction)

A common example of eutectoid reaction is the transformation of γ iron into α (ferrite) + cementite at 780°C.

7.12 GIBB'S PHASE RULE

The conditions of phase equilibrium are given by laws of thermodynamics. Mr Gibb, a physicist, has proposed a rule which demonstrates the criterion of number of phases that can co-exist within an equilibrium system. The rule is stated as follows:

$$P + F = C + N$$

where P is the number of phases present and F is the number of degrees of freedom.

That is, the number of externally controlled variables such as temperature, pressure and composition, which must be specified to define the system completely is equal to number of such variables, which can be changed independently without altering the number of phases that co-exist at the equilibrium.

C is the number of components in this system and N is the number of non-compositional variables.

1. Taking Cu–Ni system, a binary system, presented by composition and temperature,

   $N = 1$, taking pressure = 1 atm; there is only one variable, i.e. temperature.
   $C = 2$, number of components, i.e. Cu + Ni

So, $\qquad\qquad\qquad\qquad\qquad P + F = 2 + 1 = 3$

or degree of freedom, $\qquad\qquad\qquad F = 3 - P$

$$= 3 - \text{number of phases}$$

If $\qquad\qquad\qquad\qquad\qquad P = 1, \text{number of phase}$

Degree of freedom, $\qquad\qquad\qquad F = 3 - 1 = 2$

This means that to completely describe the properties of (Cu–Ni system) alloy that exists within one of these phase fields, one has to specify two parameters:

    (a) Composition along horizontal axis.
    (b) Temperature along vertical axis, so that the position of the alloy is located in the phase diagram.

2. In case, two phases exist, for $\alpha +$ liquid phase, $\beta +$ liquid phase and $\alpha + \beta = $ (solid phases).

Degree of freedom, $\qquad\qquad\qquad\qquad F = 3 - P = 3 - 2 = 1$

In this case, it is necessary to specify either the temperature or the composition of one of the phases to completely define the system.

Figure 7.20 shows the copper–silver phase diagram with melting point of copper 1085°C, melting point of silver 960°C, eutectic isotherm at 780°C and eutectic at a composition of 71.9 wt% Ag + 28.1 wt% Cu.

Consider a tie line at temperature T_1, as shown in the $\alpha +$ liquid (L) phase region, where C_α and α_L are given by two extremities of the tie line. In the region where two phases co-exist, i.e. $\alpha + L$, $\beta + L$ and $\alpha + B$ (both solid phases).

Degree of freedom, $\qquad\qquad\qquad\qquad F = 3 - P = 3 - 2 = 1$, single degree

For any composition $C_\alpha + L$, along the tie line, temperature is T_1.

Degree of freedom, $\qquad\qquad\qquad\qquad F = 3 - P = 3 - 2 = 1$

That is, the composition, which can be obtained from the horizontal axis.

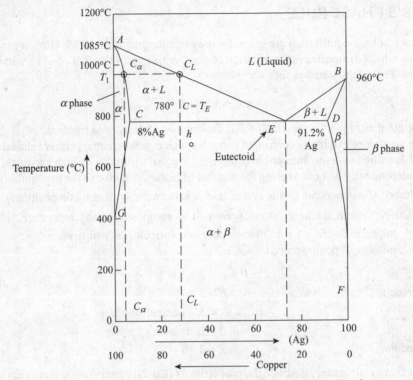

Figure 7.20 *Copper–Silver Phase Diagram*

At eutectic isotherm *CED*, a unique horizontal isotherm line at 780°C, all the three phases α, β and $\alpha + \beta$ will be in equilibrium. For any alloy having composition along the length of the isotherm, i.e. composition between 8 wt% Ag + 92 wt% Cu and 91.2 wt% Ag + 8.8 wt% Cu, degree of freedom is zero, because

$$F = 3 - P$$
$$= 3 - 3 \text{ (number of phases)}$$
$$F = 0$$

7.13 IRON CARBON SYSTEM

7.13.1 Phases Fe and Fe₃C

A study of the composition and structure of all steels and cast irons starts with the iron–carbon equilibrium diagram. Many of the basic features of the system influence the behaviour of the steels. The iron–carbon diagram provides a basic knowledge about plain carbon steels and alloy steels.

Normal equilibrium diagram actually presents the metastable equilibrium between iron and iron carbide (cementite, but cementite is metastable). The true equilibrium is between iron and graphite. Although graphite occurs freely in cast irons (2–4 wt% C), it is usually difficult to obtain this equilibrium phase in steels (with 0.03–1.5 wt% C). Therefore, the metastable equilibrium between iron and iron carbide is considered, because it is relevant to the behaviour of most of the steels.

The much larger phase field of γ-iron (austenite) compared with that of α-iron (ferrite) shows that the solubility of carbon in γ-iron is much more with a maximum value of 2 wt% at 1148°C. This high solubility of carbon in γ-iron is of utmost importance in heat treatment, when solution treatment in γ region followed by rapid quenching to room temperature allows a supersaturated solid solution of carbon in iron to be formed.

The α-iron phase (ferrite) is severely restricted with a maximum carbon solubility of 0.02 wt% at 727°C, so over the carbon range used in steels, from 0.05 to 1.5 wt%, α-iron is normally associated with iron carbide (cementite) in one form or the other. Similarly, the δ phase field is very much restricted between 1394°C and 1538°C and disappears completely when the carbon content reaches 0.5 wt%.

Figure 7.21 shows the iron–carbon equilibrium diagram—pure iron when heated experiences two changes in crystal structure before it melts.

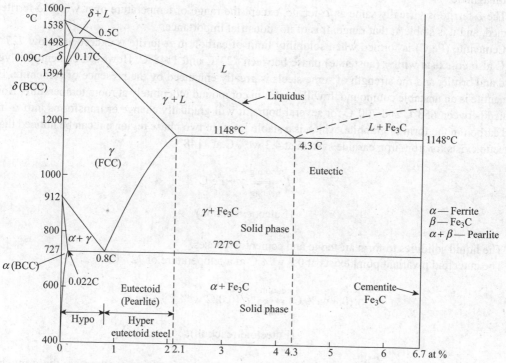

Figure 7.21 *Iron–Carbon Equilibrium Diagram*

At room temperature, α-iron BCC crystal structure, ferrite experiences a polymorphic transformation into FCC (austenite) at 912°C. This austenite (γ-iron) persists up to 1394°C at which FCC austenite reverts to a BCC phase known as δ phase, i.e. δ-ferrite.

The horizontal composition axis extends only up to 7.7 wt% C. At this concentration, an intermediate compound Fe_3C (iron carbide) or cementite is formed.

This iron–carbon diagram can be divided into two parts:

1. Iron-rich part C, 0–6.7 wt%
2. 6.7–100 wt% C (graphite) not shown

For practical purposes, all steels and cast irons have carbon content less than 6.7 wt%. In reality, it is an Fe–Fe$_3$C system, where 6.7 wt% C compounds to 100 wt% Fe$_3$C.

Carbon is an interstitial impurity in iron as it forms a solid solution with each of α, γ and δ, i.e. ferrite, austenite and δ-ferrite.

In BCC ferrite, only small concentration of carbon is soluble. The maximum solubility is 0.022 wt% at 727°C and at room temperature it is much less than 0.022 per cent. The shape and size of BCC interstitial position is such that there is limited solubility of carbon in iron atoms, which makes it difficult to accommodate carbon atoms.

The austenite or γ phase, when alloyed with carbon is not stable below 727°C. The maximum solubility of carbon in austenite is 2.1 wt% at 1148°C. This solubility is about 100 times the maximum solubility in BCC ferrite, because FCC interstitial positions are much larger. Moreover, austenite is non-magnetic.

The δ-ferrite is virtually same as α-ferrite, except the range of temperature over which δ-ferrite is formed, and it is stable at that range. It is of no industrial importance.

Cementite (Fe$_3$C) is formed when solubility limit of carbon in α-ferrite is exceeded below 727°C. Fe$_3$C also co-exists with γ (austenite) phase between 727°C and 1148°C. However, cementite is very hard and brittle, and the strength of some steels is greatly enhanced by the presence of cementite. But cementite is an unstable compound. It will remain in compound indefinitely at room temperature. But if heated between 650°C and 700°C for several hours, it will gradually change or transforms into α-iron and carbon in the form of graphite, which is a stable form. In two phase regions, it can be noticed that a eutectic exists for iron–iron carbide system at 4.3 wt% C at 1148°C.

$$L \underset{\text{heating}}{\overset{\text{cooling}}{\rightleftharpoons}} \gamma + Fe_3C$$

(Eutectic reaction)

The liquid solidifies to form austenite and cementite phases.

The eutectoid invariant point exists at 0.8 wt% C at a temperature of 727°C.

$$\gamma \, (0.8 \text{ wt\% C}) \underset{\text{heating}}{\overset{\text{cooling}}{\rightleftharpoons}} \alpha \, (0.022 \text{ wt\% C}) + Fe_3C$$

(Eutectoid reaction)

Upon cooling, the γ phase is transformed into α-iron and cementite. Ferrous alloys are those in which iron is the prime component, yet carbon and other alloying elements may be present. These are classified as follows:

1. Iron—0.008 wt% C, ferrite phase at room temperature, more or less a pure form of iron.
2. Steels—0.008–2.1 wt% C, microstructure of steels consists of both α phase and Fe$_3$C phase in practice, carbon percentage rarely exceeds 1 per cent.
3. Cast irons— 2.1–6.7 wt% C.

But commercial cast irons normally contain up to 4.0 wt% C. At the eutectoid point (0.8 wt% C, 727°C) γ-austenite is transformed into two solid phases: α-ferrite and cementite. A combination of ferrite and cementite in the form of alternate layers of ferrite and cementite is known as *pearlite*.

At the eutectic point (4.3 wt% C, 1148°C temperature) molten metal solidifies and forms a ledeburite structure. Ledeburite is a phase mixture of austenite and cementite. Steels with 0–0.8 wt% carbon are termed as hypo-eutectoid steels and with 0.8–2.1 wt% carbon are termed as hyper-eutectoid steels.

Example 7.1 Calculate the theoretical change in volume, when an FCC structure is transformed into a BCC structure in pure iron. Assume hard sphere atomic model. There is no change in the radius of atom before and after the transformation.

Solution:

Say lattice parameter of FCC structure = a_1

$\sqrt{2}a_1 = 4R$ where R is radius of atom

$R = 0.353a_1$ or $a_1 = 2.828R$

$a_1^3 = (2.828R)^3 = 22.617 \times R^3$

In FCC structure, there are four atoms per unit cell volume per atom

$V_1 = \dfrac{22.617}{4} R^3 = 5.654R^3$

BCC structure, lattice parameter = a_2 say

$\sqrt{3}a_2 = 4R$

$a_2 = 2.309R$

$a_2^3 = 12.31R^3$

There are only two atoms per unit lattice of BCC structure

V_2, volume per atom $= \dfrac{12.31}{2} R^3$

$= 6.155R^3$

Change in volume $= 6.155R^3 - 5.654R^3$

$= 0.501R^3$

Percentage change in volume $= \dfrac{0.501R^3}{5.654R^3} \times 100$

$= 8.8 \%$

7.14 MICROSTRUCTURAL DEVELOPMENTS

7.14.1 Iron–Carbon Alloys

Let us consider a very slow cooling of steel alloys, in which equilibrium is maintained. An alloy of eutectoid composition (0.8 wt% C), as it is cooled from a temperature within the γ (austenite) region, e.g. at 850°C, point 'a' contains entirely γ phase (austenite) (Figure 7.22). Microstructure at 'a' will contain grains of γ phase, as shown in Figure 7.23(a).

As the alloy cools down, no changes in microstructure occurs until temperature 727°C. Let us take temperature below 727°C, e.g. 700°C, at this temperature γ iron transforms into two solid phases: α (ferrite) + β (cementite). The microstructure at 'b' consists of alternate layers of the phases, i.e. α and Fe_3C, that are formed simultaneously during transformation. Thickness of the layer of ferrite is eight

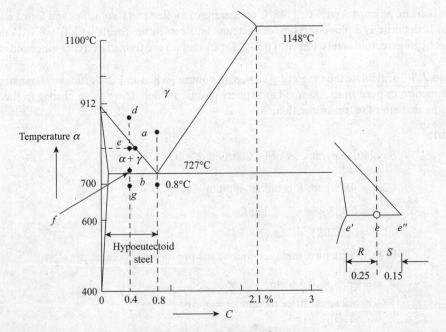

Figure 7.22 *Phase–transformation*

times the thickness of cementite layer as shown in Figure 7.23(b). *The thick light layers are of ferrite and thin dark layers are of cementite.* Microstructure at '*b*' is a pearlite structure (as it has the appearance of mother pearls when viewed under a microscope).

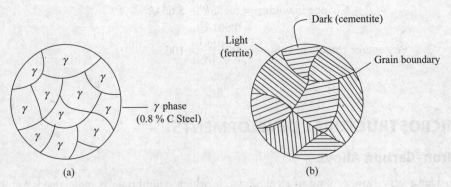

Figure 7.23 *Pearlite Structure*

The mechanical properties of pearlite (like strength and ductility) are the intermediate properties of ferrite and cementite. So, during phase transformation ($\gamma \rightarrow \alpha + \beta$), there is a redistribution of carbon by diffusion.

Hypoeutectoid Alloys

Plain carbon steels in which carbon percentage is less than 0.8 wt% are called *hypoeutectoid steels.* Consider a composition of 0.4 C steel; as the steel is cooling down from molten state, e.g. at temperature 900°C, there is γ(austenite) region. Microstructure at point 'd' (0.4 per cent C, 900°C) will be all γ (austenite) as shown in Figure 7.24(a).

As the steel is cooling down, take a point 'e' in $\alpha + \gamma$ region along the grain boundaries of γ iron. α Phase grows as shown in Figure 7.24(b). The fraction of α phase can be found by lever's rule, along the tie line e'' e e'.

$$C_\alpha = \frac{S}{R+S} = \frac{0.15}{0.15+0.25} = 0.375$$

At the point 'f', very near to 727°C, just above the eutectoid point but still in $\alpha + \gamma$ region, an increased fraction of α phase will be produced, depending upon tie line at 'f'. Phase will be distributed along the grain boundaries of γ grains as shown in Figure 7.24(c).

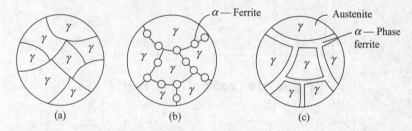

(a)   (b)   (c)

Figure 7.24 *(a) Austenite Microstructure at d (b) $\alpha + \gamma$ at e (c) Microstructure at f*

As the temperature is lowered below 727°C, just below eutectoid, e.g. at 700°C, point 'g', the γ phase will transfer into pearlite. Ferrite phase will remain along the grain boundaries, but γ phase in grains will be transformed into pearlite, i.e. alternate layers of α and cementite as shown in Figure 7.25.

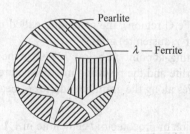

Figure 7.25 *Microstructure at g*

7.14.2 Hypereutectoid Steels

Consider a steel of carbon percentage more than 0.8 wt%. Take line 'hij' at 1.2 wt% C as shown in Figure 7.26. Steel having more than 0.8 wt% C (more than that at a eutectoid point) is termed as hypereutectoid steel. For example, at point 'h', temperature is 900°C and the region is γ region austenite. At point 'h', it is all austenite as shown in Figure 7.27(a).

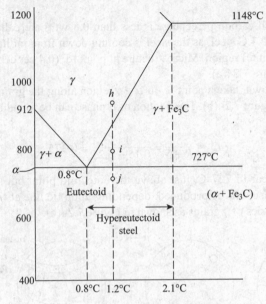

Figure 7.26 *Cooling of 1.2% C Steel*

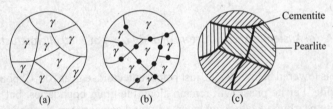

Figure 7.27 *Development of Microstructure of 0.12% C Steel*

At point '*i*' (which lies in $\gamma + Fe_3C$ region), the cementite called *proeutectoid cementite* begins to grow along the grain boundaries of γ (austenite) grains.

As the steel is continuously cooling, at point '*j*', below 727°C, in the region of $\alpha + Fe_3C$, the austenite composition is converted into pearlite and the resulting microstructure contains pearlite and proeutectoid cementite, i.e. the cementite lies along the grain boundaries of pearlite grains.

Example 7.2 What is the fraction of proeutectoid cementite in 1.4 per cent C steel.

Solution:

Eutectoid is made at 0.8 per cent C, in iron–iron carbide diagram

$$\text{Proeutectoid cementite} = \frac{1.4 - 0.8}{6.67 - 0.8}$$

$$= 0.1022$$

Example 7.3 Calculate the fraction of proeutectoid ferrite, eutectoid ferrite and total ferrite in 0.18 per cent steel.

Solution:

Note that eutectoid reaction takes place at 0.8 per cent carbon

$$\text{Proeutectoid ferrite} = \frac{0.8 - 0.18}{0.8 - 0.025} = 0.8$$

$$\text{Eutectoid ferrite (in 6.67 per cent steel)} = \frac{6.67 - 0.8}{6.67 - 0.025} = \frac{5.87}{6.645} = 0.883$$

Eutectoid in 0.18 per cent C steel $= 1 - 0.8 = 0.2$

Eutectoid ferrite in 0.18 per cent C steel $= 0.883 \times 0.2 = 0.177$

Total ferrite $= 0.8 + 0.177 = 0.977$

KEY POINTS TO REMEMBER

❑ A phase is a homogeneous part of a system (alloy) that has uniform physical and chemical properties.

❑ A single phase system is known as homogeneous phase.

❑ Systems containing more than one phase are termed as mixtures or heterogeneous systems.

❑ During allotropic transformation, phase changes takes place with change in crystal structure.

❑ In a solid solution, the solute atoms occupy either the substitutional or interstitial positions in solvent atoms.

❑ Equilibrium phase diagrams represent the relationship among temperature, composition and relative fractions of phases at equilibrium.

❑ During solidification of metal into ingot mould, first of all, chilled grains grow along the boundaries of mould walls, and finally equiaxed grains inside the ingot.

❑ Due to inverse temperature gradient, dendritic growth takes place.

❑ In the case of solidification of pure metal, grain growth takes place around the nuclei and there is no dendritic growth.

❑ There are three types of phase diagrams: binary, ternary and multiphase diagrams.

❑ Cu–Ni and Au–Ag are solid solutions with 100 per cent solubility in each other. Phase diagrams have one solidus and one liquidus lines. Lever rule gives the fraction of phases at a particular temperature and composition. There are only two phases: liquid and solid. A cored structure is produced in this type of binary system. In cored structure, the centre of each grain is rich in high melting element (as Ni in Cu + Ni system) and concentration of low melting element (Cu in Cu + Ni system) increases with position from the inner region to the grain boundary.

❑ In a eutectic reaction, a liquid phase transforms isothermally and reversibly into two solid phases that are intimately mixed. $L \rightleftharpoons \alpha + \beta$

❑ Ag–Cu and Pb–Sn make eutectic reactions.

❑ In eutectic microstructure, each grain has alternate layers of two phases, α and β.

❑ Eutectoid reaction—one solid phase transforms isothermally and reversibly into two solid phases (a diffusion-dependent reaction).

❑ Peritectic reaction—solid + liquid phases of alloy transform into a new solid phase of different composition.

$$(\delta + L) \rightleftharpoons \in (\text{peritectic reaction in brass})$$

❑ Gibb's phase rule $P + F = C + N$, where P is the number of phases present, F is the degrees of freedom, C is the number of components in the system and N is the number of non-compositional variables.

❑ Iron–carbon system

Allotropic transformation α (BCC) $\rightarrow \gamma$ (FCC) $\rightarrow \delta$ (BCC) as temperature is increased

❑ Maximum solubility of carbon in α (BCC) is 0.022 wt%.

❑ Maximum solubility of carbon in γ(FCC) iron is 2.1 per cent. This is due to FCC structure, which can accommodate carbon atoms in interstitial positions.

❑ Fe_3C is meta-stable.

❑ Fe_3C—heating at 650–700°C for several hours— gradually transforms into α-iron and graphite.

❑ Hypoeutectoid steel 0.8 wt% C, hypereutectoid steel 0.8–2.1 wt% C.

❑ At eutectoid point, 0.8 wt% C and 727°C, γ (austenite) is transformed into pearlite (alternate layers of ferrite and cementite).

❑ At 4.3 wt% C and 1148°C, eutectic liquid iron solidifies into austenite + cementite.

❑ Commercial cast iron contains 2.1–4.0 wt% graphite.

MULTIPLE CHOICE QUESTIONS

1. A molten metal is poured into an ingot mould. The type of the grains produced at the walls of the mould are
   - (a) Equiaxed grains
   - (b) Chilled grains
   - (c) Columnar grains
   - (d) None of these

2. Dendritic growth when the molten metal is solidified is due to
   - (a) Inverse temperature gradient
   - (b) Undercooling at interface
   - (c) Rapid cooling
   - (d) None of these

3. Which one of the following combination of elements gives eutectic reaction?
   - (a) Gold–silver
   - (b) Copper–nickel
   - (c) Copper–silver
   - (d) Copper–zinc

4. What is the type of transformation in peritectic reaction?
   - (a) One solid phase transforms into two solid phases
   - (b) One solid + one liquid phase transform into one solid phase
   - (c) One liquid phase transforms into two solid phases
   - (d) None of these

5. In commercial brasses, made of Cu/Zn alloy, what is the maximum percentage of zinc?

   (a) 20 wt%   (c) 40 wt%

   (b) 30 wt%   (d) 45 wt%

6. In platinum–silver phase diagram, what type of solution is obtained at 18 wt% Ag + 0.82 wt% Pt?

   (a) Peritectic   (c) Solid solution

   (b) Eutectic   (d) None of these

7. What is the degree of freedom of lead–tin eutectic composition?

   (a) 0   (c) 2

   (b) 1   (d) None of these

8. What is the degree of freedom of Cu–Ni alloy in liquid state?

   (a) 0   (c) 2

   (b) 1   (d) 3

9. In a pearlitic structure, ratio of thickness of ferrite layer to thickness of cementite layer is

   (a) 4   (c) 1

   (b) 2   (d) None of these

10. What is the type of microstructure of 0.4 wt% C steel at 900°C?

   (a) Austenitic

   (b) Pearlite

   (c) Austenite grains and ferrite on grains boundaries

   (d) None of these

11. In hypereutectoid steel, $C = 1.2$ wt%, temperature is 800°C, what is the type of the microstructure?

   (a) All austenite

   (b) Pearlitic grains and cementite along the grain boundaries

   (c) Austenitic grains with cementite growth on the grain boundaries

   (d) None of these

12. What is the maximum solubility of carbon in iron at room temperature?

   (a) 0.02 wt%

   (b) 0.8 wt%

   (c) 2.1 wt%

   (d) None of these

Answers

1. (b)   2. (a)   3. (c)   4. (b)   5. (b)   6. (c)   7. (a)   8. (c)

9. (d)   10. (a)   11. (c)   12. (d)

REVIEW QUESTIONS

1. What are homogeneous and heterogeneous systems?

2. Describe the following:

   Solid solution, solute, solvent and solubility limit.

3. When a molten metal is poured into an ingot mould, explain how equiaxed grains are produced in the central zone.

4. Explain the difference between a cooling curve of a metal containing impurities and that of a pure metal.

5. What are the different types of phase diagrams?

6. Take gold–silver phase diagram and draw liquidus and solidus curves. Draw a vertical line at 50–50 composition and draw microstructure at points where the vertical line intersects the liquidus and solidus curves.

7. With the help of an example in silver–copper phase diagram, explain the lever rule.

8. What is a cored structure in Cu–Ni alloy? Explain with the help of an alloy 40 Cu/60 Ni.

9. What is the composition of solder used in making joints in an electrical circuit?

10. Consider an alloy of 13.5 Sn/86.5 Pb. Draw microstructures at 200°C and 100°C.

11. Explain the following
    (a) Eutectic   (b) Peritectic   (c) Eutectoid reactions
    Give one example of each.

12 Explain the Gibb's phase rule.

13. Differentiate among the mechanical properties of ferrite, austenite and cementite.

14. What is the type of structure produced with 4.3 wt% C iron solidified at eutectic temperature of 1148°C?

15. Draw the microstructure of 0.8 wt% C steel at eutectoid temperature of 727°C.

PRACTICE PROBLEMS

1. What is the fraction of proeutectoid cementite in (a) 0.7 per cent C steel and (b) 1.2 per cent C steel.

    Ans. [(a) Zero (b) 0.068]

2. Consider a point at 0.3 wt% carbon and temperature 800°C. Determine the fractions of α and γ phases

    Ans. $[C_\alpha = 0.58 \ C_\gamma = 0.42]$

3. Find the atomic per cent of carbon in a mild steel containing 0.2 wt% C.

    Ans. [0.93]

PHASE TRANSFORMATIONS

8.1 INTRODUCTION

A metal with desirable mechanical properties can be developed with the help of phase transformation, i.e. controlling the microstructure of the metal with the help of controlled rate of cooling during the phase transformation. The mechanical properties of a metal very much depend upon the grain size refinement, solid solution strengthening and strain hardening. For example, by phase transformation of 0.8 wt% C steel, the strength of this steel can be modified from 600 to 2000 MPa.

Many a times, the rate of cooling is more than the rate of phase transformation, causing delay in transformation and metastable states are formed, because equilibrium microstructures are seldom developed due to this delay. Therefore, the effect of time (or rate) on phase transformation will be discussed in this chapter.

This chapter also discusses kinetics of solid state reaction, pearlitic, bainite and martensitic transformations of steels. In addition, we will study various properties of ingot solidification and different types of steels produced by ingot solidification in a mould. The processes of precipitation hardening and age hardening along with their effects on the mechanical properties will also be discussed. In the end, we will discuss continuous cooling transformation (CCT) diagram.

8.2 SOLIDIFICATION OF METAL IN INGOT MOULD

In Chapter 7, we have already discussed about the solidification of a molten metal: (1) with impurity and (2) without any impurity, i.e. pure metal and studied about chill grains, columnar grains, equiaxed grains, inverse cooling, dendritic growth in impure metal and cored structure in a pure metal.

In this chapter, we will discuss about various defects in the cast metal and the removal of these defects, which are as follows:

8.2.1 Cavities

When a layer of solid metal is formed around the ingot walls, contractions occur resulting in a fall in the level of liquid. Successive layers of solid forms are also accompanied by a fall in the liquid level. The fall in the level increases as the material solidifies, resulting in a central cavity at the top (as shown in Figure 8.1).

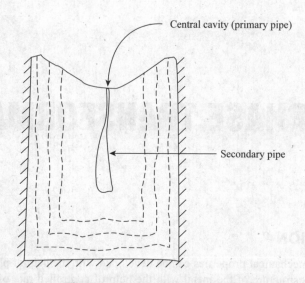

Figure 8.1 *Cavity in Ingot Casting*

There is a conical shape of the liquid, because some liquid metal still remains after the solidification of the top of the ingot, and further solidification of metal gives rise to a secondary pipe as shown in the Figure 8.1. If the wider side of the ingot is put at the top, the secondary pipe can be avoided. The centrifugal casting of the ingot will eliminate the central cavity also.

8.2.2 Gas Holes

Gases dissolved in molten metal during melting are evolved during solidification. Hydrogen is a common source of gas unsoundness, for example, the distributions of fine pin holes in aluminium alloys. The gas may enter the melt from hydrated corrosion products and oils on the surface of the raw material from the atmosphere, damp flux, crucibles, sand moulds, furnace and so on.

Dry nitrogen does not give rise to blowholes and the bubbling of nitrogen through most metals tends to get rid of other gases by reducing the partial pressure of the dissolved gas in the melt.

In steels, carbon monoxide is formed by the reduction of oxides by carbon. In killed steels, the oxides are reduced to a negligible quantity by deoxidation by adding metals such as aluminium, ferrosilicon and ferromanganese. The soluble ferrous oxide originally present is replaced by insoluble oxides, which move to the slag before carbon is added. (In killed steels, oxygen bubbles in the molten steel are killed.)

The bulk of low-carbon steels (C = 0.2 wt%) for sheets and nails is only partially deoxidized. When this partial deoxidation is properly controlled, a thick rim of exceptionally pure metal solidifies. The central core is rich in impurities which are uniformly distributed. This type of steel is called 'rimming steel'. A typical macrostructure of rimming steel is shown in Figure 8.2. Due to its ductile properties, rimmed steel is used for deep drawing and pressing.

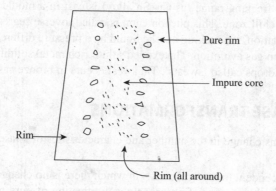

Figure 8.2 *Rimming Steel*

A semi-killed or balanced steel is made by adding more aluminium to the ingot in the rimming steel so that the gas holes just balance the shrinkage. Stabilized steels are sometimes made by completely deoxidizing the molten core with the addition of 0.03 wt% of aluminium after the rim has formed.

The upper part of the ingot containing the exposed pipe in killed steels has been rejected, which decreases the casting yield to 80 per cent.

8.2.3 Segregation

The molten metal contains soluble impurities such as sulphur, phosphorus and soluble alloying elements together with insoluble impurities or slag particles in suspension. The first crystals to be separated from the liquid metal contain less impurity than that is indicated by average composition of the alloys. Elements like S, P, C, Mn and Si lower the freezing point and are collect in the last portions to solidify. This *separation of various substances* with different places in the ingot is called segregation.

Interdendritic Segregation
Under non-equilibrium cooling, coring takes place and solute atoms get segregated in the volume of the liquid that solidifies last. The liquid that solidifies last lies in the spaces between the dendritic arms. This type of segregation is known as microsegregation and can be removed by homogenization. In this process, casting is heated for a prolonged time at a high temperature, and diffusion occurs on the solid state, which reduces microsegregation. Interstitial element as C in steels becomes fully homogenized, but substitutional elements diffuse much more slowly. Therefore, only partial homogenization takes place.

Directional Solidification
During the growth of dendrites, when the dendrites of the neighbouring grains grow in the same direction, columnar grains are resulted. The direction of columnar growth is always in the preferred dendritic directions, i.e. <1 1 0> directions of a cubic crystal. The growth of dendritic structure takes place in preferential directions, e.g. material with unidirectional solidification in highly stressed components, as turbine blade, if the direction of growth is along the length of the turbine blade.

Macrosegregation is caused by the physical movement of liquid and solid. A liquid flows as a result of thermal contraction, solidification shrinkage and density differences. Solid crystals either float or settle down depending upon their density, for example, graphite floats in hypereutectic cast irons. However, heavier crystallites settle down.

When an ingot of wide freezing range (as Cu–Sn alloy) is cast in a mould, a solute-rich region is obtained in the vicinity of chill zone. This phenomenon is called inverse segregation. Another form of inverse segregation is exudation, i.e. sucking out the liquid by a pressure difference created by the pressure build up in metal due to gas evolution. The exuded solute-rich metal solidifies on the surface of the metal in the form of small drops called 'sweats'. Tin sweat occurs in bronze casting.

8.3 TYPES OF PHASE TRANSFORMATIONS

Phase transformation means change in the number and characteristics of phases. There are three types of phase transformations:

1. Simple diffusion-dependent transformations—in which there is no change in the composition of phases present and in the number of phases, e.g. solidification of pure metals, allotropic transformation of metals (as α, γ, δ transformation for Fe), nucleus, growth and grain boundaries in pure metals.
2. Diffusion-dependent transformation—in which there are changes in phase composition and layers in the number of phases such as (a) eutectoid reaction, in which one solid phase transforms into two solid phases with different properties and (b) eutectic reaction, in which one liquid phase transforms into two solid phases at eutectic temperature and eutectic composition.
3. Diffusion-less transformation—in which a metastable phase is present, e.g. quenching of steel from recrystallization temperature produces martensite (metastable) structure in steels.

8.4 NUCLEATION AND GROWTH KINETICS

During solidification of a molten metal, a few atoms combine to form a fine particle called nucleus, and more atoms from liquid metal join the nucleus and grows. A number of nuclei are developed in a molten metal, and these nuclei grow and become grains. The grains impinge on one another to form grain boundaries, as shown in Figure 8.3.

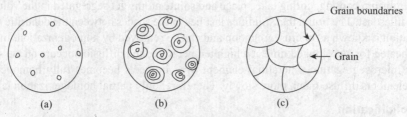

(a)   (b)   (c)

Figure 8.3 *(a) Nuclei (b) Growth Around Nuclei*
(c) Grains and Grain Boundaries

Nucleation can be homogeneous and heterogeneous. In homogeneous type, the probability of occurrence of nucleation at any given site is identical to the probability at any other site in the parent metal. In homogeneous nucleation, energy required to create interface between the nucleus and the liquid is equal to the energy released by the volume of condensing phase; surface energy is always positive and energy released by the volume of condensing phase is negative.

Severe supercooling is necessary for homogenous nucleation. A nucleus formed spontaneously in the melt by random atomic motion will be a cluster of a few atoms, and extreme supercooling is necessary to grow spontaneously. The temperature at which homogeneous nucleation occurs is always below the equilibrium freezing point because it is necessary to overcome the surface tension forces that impede nucleus growth. The energy tending to produce a nucleus is the difference in free energy per unit volume between the liquid and the solid phases.

In a heterogeneous process, the probability of nucleation occurring at certain preferred sites in the parent metal is different from the probability at other sites. If water is boiled, bubbles generate only from the bottom of the pot (a particular location). This is called heterogeneous nucleation.

In actual practice, before homogeneous nucleation starts, drops of liquid formed on any foreign matter serve as nucleation catalyst, for example, walls of container, dust particles, grain boundaries, stacking faults and dislocations.

8.4.1 Kinetics of Solid State Reaction

Most of the solid-state transformations are not spontaneous but are time dependent, and these transformations involve the formation of at least one new phase, with composition and crystal structure different from the parent metal. In these transformations, some atomic rearrangement through diffusion (a time-dependent process) are required. However, obstacles impede the course of reaction. Moreover, a second impediment to the formation of a new phase is the increase in energy associated with the phase boundaries, which lie between the parent metal and the product phases.

Phase transformations proceeds in three stages:

1. *First stage:* Formation of nuclei of a new phase, which are capable of growing. Favourable sites for nucleation are imperfection sites, especially the grain boundaries.

2. *Second stage:* Growth in which the nuclei increase in size, therefore some volume of the parent metal disappears.

3. *Third stage:* The transformations reach completion, if growth of the new phase particles is allowed to proceed until the equilibrium fraction is reached.

The time dependence of transformation fraction is termed as kinetics. The fraction of reaction that has occurred is measured as a function of time, while the temperature is maintained constant. The data of fraction of transformed material versus log of time are plotted, and an S-shaped curve represents the kinetic behaviour of the most solid-state reactions, as shown in Figure 8.4.

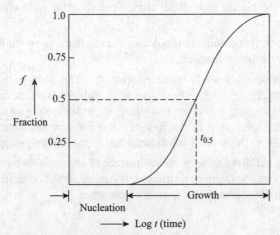

Figure 8.4 *Kinetic Behavior of Reaction*

$$f = 1 - \exp(-kt^n) \tag{8.1}$$

where k and n are time-dependent constants and t is time. Eq. (8.1) is known as Arrami's equation.

By convention, the rate of transformation, r is taken as the reciprocal of time required for the transformation to proceed half way to completion, i.e. $t_{0.5}$ or

Rate, $\qquad\qquad\qquad\qquad\qquad\qquad r = \dfrac{1}{t_{0.5}}$

Temperature is a major variable in a phase transformation process and should be controlled, because it has profound influences on the diffusion rate, i.e. on the kinetics of phase transformation—on the rate of transformation.

Rate, $\qquad\qquad\qquad\qquad\qquad\qquad r = A \exp\left(-\dfrac{Q}{RT}\right) \tag{8.2}$

where R is the gas constant, T is the absolute temperature, Q is the activation energy for a particular reaction and A is a temperature-independent constant. Such processes are known as thermally activated processes.

8.5 MULTIPHASE TRANSFORMATIONS

Phase transformations in metal alloys are obtained by varying temperature, composition and the external pressure. But the temperature changes by means of heat treatment are most conveniently utilized to induce phase transformation. On the phase diagram, it corresponds to crossing a phase boundary on the composition, i.e. temperature as an alloy of given composition is heated or cooled.

During phase transformations, an alloy proceeds towards an equilibrium state, which is characterized by the phase diagram in terms of product phases, i.e. their compositions and relative fraction. Most phase transformations require some finite time to go to the completion and the rate of transformation is often important in the relationship between the heat treatment and the development of microstructure. But phase diagrams do not give any indication about the time required to achieve equilibrium.

The rate of transformation to equilibrium for solid solution is very slow and true equilibrium structures are rarely achieved. The equilibrium conditions are maintained only if heating or cooling is carried out at extremely slow and highly impractical rates. Therefore, the following factors are important for maintaining equilibrium:

1. For processes other than equilibrium cooling, transformations are shifted to lower temperatures than indicated by the phase diagram.

2. For heating, the shifting is towards higher temperature. This phenomenon is termed as supercooling or superheating, respectively. The degree of each depends on the rate of temperature change; the more rapid the cooling or heating, the greater the supercooling or superheating. For example, for normal cooling rates used in the industry, the iron–carbon eutectoid reaction is typically displaced by 10–20°C below the equilibrium transformation temperature.

For many alloys, the preferred state or microstructure is a metastable one, i.e. intermediate between initial and equilibrium state. Sometimes a structure is desired, which is far from equilibrium state, then the influence of time on phase transformations is investigated.

8.6 PEARLITIC TRANSFORMATION

Considering the isothermal transformation of austenite (γ iron) into pearlite at 727°C, the eutectoid reaction is

$$\gamma\,(0.8 \text{ wt\% C}) \underset{\text{heating}}{\overset{\text{cooling}}{\rightleftharpoons}} \alpha \text{ iron (0.022 wt\% C)} + \text{Fe}_3\text{C (6.7 wt\% C)}$$

Upon cooling, the austenite having an intermediate carbon concentration of 0.8 wt% transforms to a ferrite phase (0.022 wt% C) and cementite with much higher carbon concentration.

Temperature plays a vital role in the rate of transformation of austenite into pearlite. Curves between the fraction of pearlite transformed versus time (at a particular temperature maintained during the course of reaction) are plotted for various temperatures. Let us consider the temperatures as given below.

T (°C)	ΔT (temperature fall from 727°C)
675	52
650	77
600	127

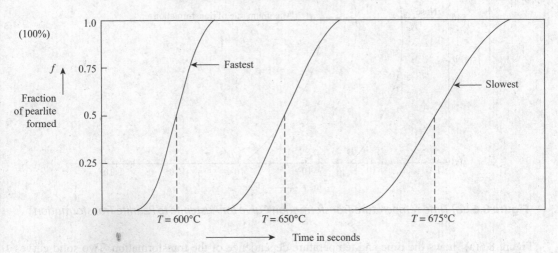

Figure 8.5 *Pearlite Fraction of f Versus Time t at Constant Temperature Curve*

Below greater is ΔT, the fall in temperature during cooling, faster is the rate of transformation, i.e. slope of curve f/time along f fraction goes on increasing as ΔT increases as shown in Figure 8.5.

As ΔT increases, the time for nucleation of pearlite and to complete transformation decreases. For each curve, the data are collected after rapidly cooling a specimen composed of 100 per cent austenite at temperature indicated, the time to start nucleation, time for 50 per cent transformation and time for 100 per cent transformation of austenite into pearlite. The data are plotted with temperature of transformation on y-axis and the time to initiate nucleation, for 50 per cent transformation and for 100 per cent transformation on x-axis as shown in Figure 8.6. The time is plotted on log t.

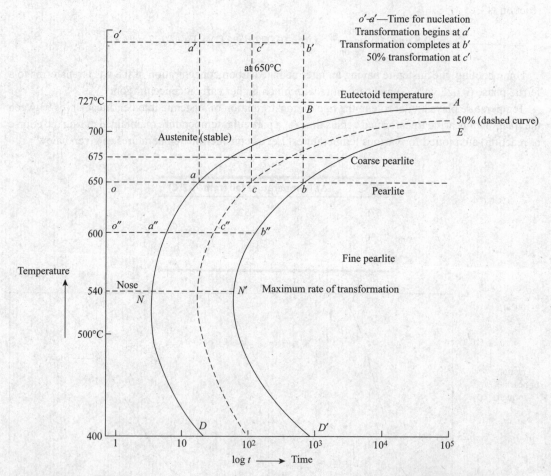

Figure 8.6 *(a) Time-temperature Transformation Curve for Austenite to Pearlite Transformation*

Figure 8.6(a) shows the time and temperature dependence of the transformation. Two solid curves are plotted: *ABaND* represents the time required at each temperature for the initiation or start of the transformation (austenite to pearlite) and *EbN'D'* represents the completion of transformation. The dashed curve represents 50 per cent of the transformation completion. These curves are generated from a series of plots of fraction of transformation versus log t (time in seconds) over a range of temperatures. The line $a'c'b'$ represents the time to initiate, time for 50 per cent completion and time for 100 per cent completion at 650°C. Similarly, for the temperature of 600°C,

$o''a''$—time for initiation

$o''c''$—time for 50 per cent completion

$o''b''$—time for 100 per cent completion

At 600°C, the structure at a'', c'' and b'' are shown in Figure 8.6(b).

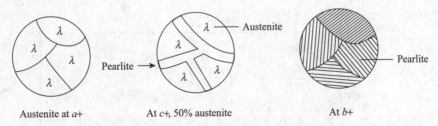

Austenite at $a+$ At $c+$, 50% austenite   At $b+$

Figure 8.6 *(b) Austenite to Pearlite Transformation*

The transformation rate increases with decreasing temperature (or increasing ΔT from eutectoid temperature) such that at 540°C, only about 3 s is required for the reaction to go to 50 per cent completion.

At 540°C (cooling from 727°C), the transformation rate is controlled by the rate of pearlite nucleation and the nucleation rate decreases with increasing temperature (or decreasing ΔT). This behaviour can be explained by the activation energy.

$$r = A \exp\left(-\frac{Q}{RT}\right)$$

where r is the rate, Q is the activation energy and T is the absolute temperature, R is gas constant.

The graph shown in Figure 8.6(a) is valid only for the iron–carbon alloy of eutectoid composition (0.8 wt% C).

Conditions of constant temperature are termed as isothermal—or the isothermal transformation diagram sometimes called T–T–T, i.e. time-temperature transformation. The thickness ratio of ferrite and cementite layers in pearlite is approximately 8.

8.6.1 Coarse Pearlite

At temperatures just below the eutectoid, relatively thick layers of both α-ferrite and Fe_3C phases are produced—a microstructure called 'coarse pearlite'. At these temperatures, the diffusion rates are relatively high, such that during transformation carbon atoms can diffuse relatively long distances, resulting in the formation of thick layers.

8.6.2 Fine Pearlite

With decreasing temperature, the carbon diffusion rate decreases, and the layers become progressively thinner. The thin-layered structure produced in the vicinity of 540°C is termed as 'fine pearlite'.

8.7 BAINITE STRUCTURE

The ferrite and cementite layers are expected to become thinner and thinner as the isothermal transformation temperature is lowered below 540°C (at which the fine pearlites are formed) as shown below.

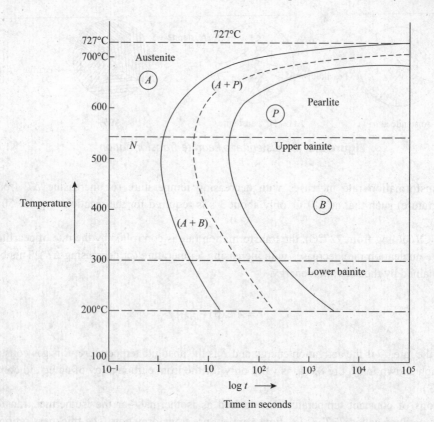

At temperatures below 540°C, other microconstituents are formed, i.e. upper bainite and lower bainite. Between 540°C and 300°C, bainite formation takes place as series of parallel lathes (thin narrow strips) or needles of ferrite, which are separated by elongated particles of cementite phase. This is known as upper bainite. The phase that surrounds the bainite is martensite, as shown in Figure 8.7.

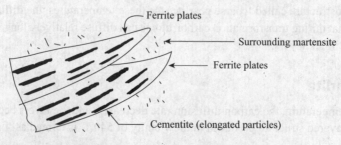

Figure 8.7 *Upper Bainite Structure*

At lower temperatures, between 200°C and 300°C, lower bainite is the transformation product of austenite. In this microstructure, ferrite phase exists as thin plates (instead of strips) and narrow cementite particles (as very fine rods or blades) are formed within the ferrite plate.

Note that the cementite particles within the bainite plate are very small as shown in Figure 8.8.

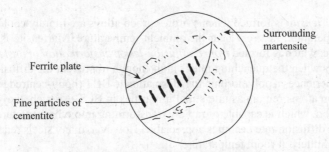

Figure 8.8 *Lower Bainite Structure*

Time-temperature dependence of bainite transformation can also be presented on isothermal transformation diagram.

These are C-shaped curves with nose at point N where the rate of transformation is maximum. Salient features of this curve are as follows:

1. Pearlite is formed above the nose.
2. Bainite is formed below the nose.
3. Coarse pearlite below 720–650°C.
4. Fine pearlite below 650–540°C.
5. Upper bainite microstructure at 540–300°C.
6. Lower bainite microstructure below 300°C.

It should be noted that the pearlite and bainite transformations are competitive to each other. Once a portion of an iron–carbon alloy has transformed to pearlite or bainite, the transformation to other microconstituents is not possible without reheating the alloy to form austenitic structure again.

8.7.1 Spheroidite

If a steel with pearlitic or bainite microstructure is heated and left at a temperature below the eutectoid point for a sufficiently long period of time, e.g. for 18–24 h at 700°C, another microstructure is formed, called 'spheroidite', where Fe$_3$C (cementite) phase is formed in the shape of sphere-like particles embedded in a continuous matrix of α-ferrite phase as shown in Figure 8.9.

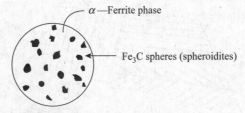

Figure 8.9 *Spheroidites Structure*

This transformation is the result of additional carbon diffusion with no change in composition or relative amounts of ferrite and cementite phases.

8.8 MARTENSITIC TRANSFORMATION

Microstructure of *martensite* is formed when γ-iron–carbon alloys are rapidly cooled (or quenched) to a relatively low temperature, i.e. very near the ambient temperature. Martensite is a non-equilibrium single-phase structure, which is formed *from a diffusion-less transformation of austenite.* So martensite transformation occurs when the quenching rate is high enough to prevent the diffusion of carbon.

FCC austenite experiences a polymorphic transformation to BCT (body-centred tetragonal structure) martensite. All carbon atoms remain as interstitial impurities in BCT. As such, they constitute a super-saturated solid solution, which is capable of rapidly transforming into other structures if heated to temperature at which the diffusion rate becomes appreciable. However, many steels retain their martensites structure almost indefinitely at room temperature.

Martensitic transformations are time independent because martensite grains nucleate and grow at a very fast rate, i.e. with the velocity of sound within the austenite matrix. A BCT structure is shown in Figure 8.10.

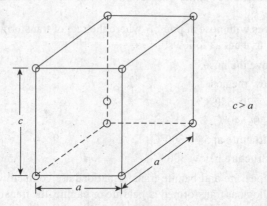

Figure 8.10 *BCT Structure*

Two clearly different martensite microstructures are found in iron–carbon alloys, which are as follows:

1. When C < 0.6 wt%

Martensitic grains are formed as thin plate-like blades of grass, forming side by side. These plates are grouped into larger structural entities called blocks as shown in Figure 8.11.

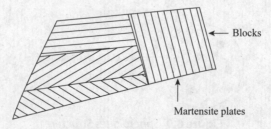

Figure 8.11 *Martensitic Grains*

2. C > 0.6 wt%

Needle-like martensite is formed in these alloys. Martensite grains in the shape of needles in the matrix of austenite are shown in Figure 8.12.

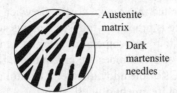

Figure 8.12 *Martensite Needles in Autenite Matrix*

8.9 FORMATION OF AUSTENITE

While heating the pearlite slightly above AC_1, equilibrium temperature, austenite is formed as free energy of pearlite is more than that of austenite. The cementite gets dissolved and ferrite disappears on heating, and austenite nuclei are formed and growth takes place. This transformation is of diffusion type, which is dependent on the movement of carbon atoms over long distances. The higher the temperature, greater is the rate of carbon diffusion. Due to diffusion, austenite composition is equalized throughout the crystals.

8.9.1 Grain Size of Austenite

Various physical and mechanical properties of steel depend on the grain size of austenite. In selecting the rate at which steel is to be heated, the effect of austenite grain growth on increase in temperature should be taken into consideration. The changes in the size of the austenite grains have the following effects:

1. If grains are fine, there is improvement in the strength of the steel after heat treatment, and also in the machinability and machining finish.
2. If grains are coarse, creep strength is improved.
3. Quenching cracks and distortion are reduced in fine grains.
4. During fabrication of the steel, fine-grain steel may be heated to higher temperature without appreciable coarsening of grains.

8.9.2 Grain Size Measurement

American Society for Testing of Materials (ASTM) has standardized grain size index, which is widely used in determining the size of austenite grains in steels.

Number of grains,

$$n = 2^N - 1$$

where n is the number of grains per square millimetre as seen under microscope with 100 magnification and N is the ASTM grain size number.

Planimeter can be used on photomicrograph, indicating the number of grains per square millimetre in a drawn area of a circle.

$$N = 1\text{–}5 \text{ for coarse grains}$$
$$= 6\text{–}8 \text{ for fine grains}$$

8.10 PRECIPITATION AND AGE HARDENING

In a terminal solid solution (as α and β are solid solutions at the ends in a binary eutectic alloy), the solubility of solute in solvent decreases with decreasing temperature. On cooling, such an alloy may become supersaturated or just saturated in terms of solute. So when the excess solute is rejected in the form of precipitates, a driving force is produced. Industrial alloys such as Cu–Al and Cu–Be undergo precipitation while they are cooled to room temperature. During tempering of a quenched steel or ageing of a rapidly cooled low-carbon steel, carbides are precipitated. If the precipitates are fine particles, they add to the strength and hardness of the alloy. A careful control of precipitation process in such alloys is an important step during heat treatment of these alloys.

Consider an alloy of composition C_α as shown in Figure 8.13 in hypothetical phase diagram of a binary eutectic system. T_E is the eutectic temperature. Consider the alloy is rapidly cooled to room temperature T_1, to the extent that any diffusion or the formation of β phase is prevented; so a non-equilibrium exists in which only α-phase solid solutions supersaturated with β atoms are present at temperature T_1. In this state the alloy is relatively soft and weak. Moreover, for most of the alloys diffusion rates at T_1 are extremely slow, and the single-phase α is retained for very long periods.

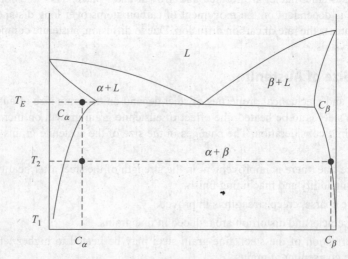

Figure 8.13 *Hypothetical Phase Diagram of Precipitation Hardenable Alloy of Composition C_α*

Now, the supersaturated α solid solution is heated to an intermediate temperature T_2 within the $\alpha + \beta$ phase region, at which temperature diffusion rates become significant. The β-precipitate phase begins to form as finely dispersed particles of composition C_β, and this process is sometimes termed as ageing.

After appropriate time for ageing, the alloy is cooled to room temperature and the character of these β particles and subsequently their hardness and strength of the alloy depend on precipitation temperature T_2 and ageing time at this temperature.

With increasing ageing time, the strength and hardness increase, reaching a maximum and finally diminish. This reduction in strength and hardness that occurs after long time periods is known as 'overageing'.

8.10.1 Precipitation in Al–4 wt% Cu Alloy (Duralumin)

Although the composition of Duralumin is Cu 4.0 per cent, Mg 0.5 per cent, Si 0.7 per cent, the rest is aluminium, yet it can be considered as binary alloy of Al–Cu.

The solubility of copper in aluminium decreases from 4 wt% at 500°C to less than 0.2 wt% at room temperature. If the Al–4 wt% Cu alloy is cooled slowly from 500°C, it becomes supersaturated and tends to form particles of β phase (CuAl$_2$)

$$\alpha_{supersaturated} \rightarrow \alpha_{saturated} + \beta_{tetragonal}$$

FCC   FCC   FCC

4 per cent Cu   0.2 per cent Cu   52 per cent Cu

During slow cooling, the precipitates that formed are coarse and do not produce any improvement in mechanical properties.

If the alloy is quenched to room temperature, no time is available for diffusion to occur to bring about compositional changes. After heating to higher temperatures, i.e. about 400°C, if the alloy is left at room temperature for a prolonged period, precipitation occurs. Due to limited diffusion rates at room temperature, the solute atoms move through very small distances, only by a few tens of interatomic distance, and hence *extremely fine precipitates are formed*. This process is called ageing.

8.11 CONTINUOUS COOLING TRANSFORMATION CURVE

Many heat treatment processes of steels involve continuous cooling of a specimen to room temperature. In continuous cooling, the time required for a reaction to begin and end is delayed. The isothermal curves (of *T-T-T*) are shifted for longer times and lower temperatures.

A plot containing such modified beginning and end reaction curves is termed as continuous cooling transformation (CCT) diagrams as shown in Figure 8.14 for iron–carbon alloys of eutectoid composition. Some control has to be maintained over the rate of temperature change depending upon the cooling environment.

Two cooling curves corresponding to slow cooling and moderately fast cooling rates are superimposed as shown in Figure 8.15 for a steel of eutectoid composition. Moreover, the Figure 8.15 shows the beginning (nucleation of pearlite) and completion curves (complete formation of pearlite). The transformation starts after a time period corresponding to interaction of the cooling curve for moderately rapid cooling with the beginning reaction at point 'c' and concludes upon crossing the completion transformation curve at 'c''. The microstructural product for moderately rapid cooling rate will be 'fine pearlite'. Similarly, for slow cooling, the transformation starts after a time period corresponding to the point of intersection of slow cooling curve and the beginning reaction curve, i.e. at point 'd' and concludes upon crossing the completion transformation curve at 'd''. The microstructural product of slow cooling rate is coarse pearlite.

Normally, bainite is not formed when any plain carbon steel is continuously cooled to room temperature. This is because all the austenite has been transformed to pearlite by the time bainite transformation has become possible. Therefore, the region representing austenite–pearlite transformation terminates just below the nose as shown by curve 'ab'.

For any cooling curve passing through 'ab', the transformation ceases at the point of intersection with continuous cooling. The unreacted austenite begins transforming to martensite upon crossing M (start) line at about 225°C.

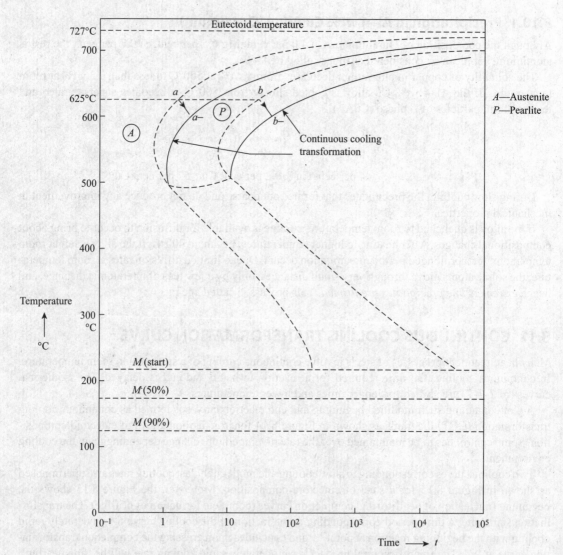

Figure 8.14 *Solid Line Curves are CCT Curves*

However, so for as martensitic transformation is concerned, M (start), M (50 per cent) and M (90 per cent) lines occur at identical temperatures for both isothermal and continuous cooling transformation diagrams.

For the continuous cooling of a steel alloy, there exists a critical quenching rate, which represents the minimum rate of quenching that will produce a total martensitic structure. The critical cooling curve (on the continuous transformation diagram) will just miss the nose (as shown in Figure 8.15) at which pearlitic transformation begins. Only martensite exists for quenching rates higher than the critical cooling rate. In addition, there are a range of cooling rates over which both pearlite and martensite are present. For a total pearlitic structure to grow, a low cooling rate is necessary.

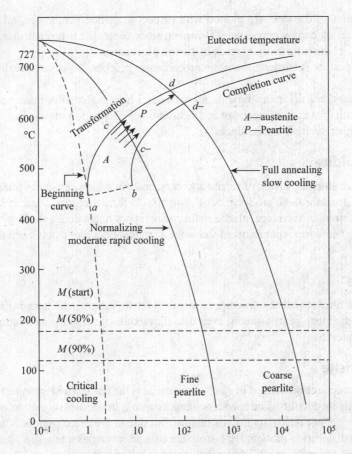

Figure 8.15 *Critical Cooling Curves*

The iron–carbon alloys containing 0.25 per cent C or less are not normally heat treated to form martensite, because the quenching rates too rapid to be practical are required.

The alloying elements that are particularly effective in rendering the heat-treatable steel are Cr, Ni, Mo, Mn, Si and W; however, there must be a formation of solid solution with austenite at the time of quenching.

8.12 MECHANICAL BEHAVIOUR OF IRON–CARBON ALLOYS

Let us discuss the mechanical behaviour of iron–carbon alloys having microstructure as pearlite, fine and coarse pearlite, spheroidite, bainite (upper and lower bainite) and martensite. The mechanical properties are highly dependent on the microstructure of iron–carbon alloy.

8.12.1 Pearlite

In pearlite, there are alternate strips (layers) of ferrite and cementite. Ferrite is soft but cementite is harder and more brittle than ferrite. Rather, cementite reinforces the ferrite. If ultimate strength, yield strength and hardness of the steel are plotted with respect to carbon percentage, all three parameters increase with increasing carbon percentage. However, since cementite is more brittle, the ductility and toughness of the steel decrease with increase in carbon percentage.

Moreover, fine pearlite is harder and stronger than coarse pearlite, but coarse pearlite is more ductile than fine pearlite.

For fine pearlite, there are more boundaries through which dislocation must pass during plastic deformation. So with greater reinforcement and restriction of dislocation motion in fine grains, pearlite accounts for its higher strength and hardness.

8.12.2 Spheroidite

In pearlite, there are alternate layers of ferrite and cementite, in which cementite reinforces the ferrite, but in spheroidite structure there are spheres of cementite in ferrite matrix. There is less boundary per unit volume in spheroidite; therefore, plastic deformation is not much constrained, giving rise to a soft and weak material. Moreover, spheroidized steels are extremely ductile, much more than either fine or coarse pearlite.

8.12.3 Bainite

Bainite steels have finer structure (structure contains α-ferrite matrix with cementite particles). They are harder and stronger than pearlite steels, even then they exhibit desirable combination of strength and ductility, i.e. toughness.

8.12.4 Martensite

Among the microstructures developed in steels, martensite is the hardest and strongest, yet most brittle, because of its negligible ductility. The hardness of martensite is dependent on carbon content. The properties of martensite are not due to its microstructure, but due to the effectiveness of interstitial carbon atoms in impeding dislocation motion. BCT structure of martensite has a few slip planes.

On quenching of austenite to BCT structure, there is net increase in volume because austenite is denser than martensite. If carbon content is greater than 0.5 wt%, then there are chances of quenching cracks.

8.12.5 Tempered Martensite

Martensite is hard and brittle, and because of its brittle behaviour it cannot be used for most engineering applications. Moreover, the internal stresses are developed in steel during the quenching process, which causes a weakening effect. To enhance the ductility and toughness of the material and to relieve internal stresses the steel is tempered.

Tempering is achieved by heating a martensitic steel to a temperature much below the eutectoid temperature of 727°C, for a specified period of time. Normally, tempering is carried out at temperatures between 250°C and 650°C, and internal stresses may be relieved at temperatures as low as 200°C. Tempering heat treatment is a diffusion process, and tempered martensite is formed as per following equation.

Martensite (single-phase BCT) —tempered martensite (α + Fe$_3$C),

where the single-phase BCT martensite, which is supersaturated with carbon transforms to tempered martensite composed of stable ferrite and cementite phases.

The microstructure of tempered martensite consists of extremely small and uniformly distributed cementite particles embedded in a ferrite matrix (Figure 8.16).

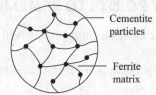

Figure 8.16 *Tempered Martensite Structure*

The tempered martensite is nearly as hard and strong as martensite, but its ductility is significantly enhanced thereby thoroughly increasing its toughness also.

The hard cementite phase reinforces the ferrite matrix along the boundaries and these boundaries act as barriers to dislocation motion during plastic deformation. The continuous ferrite phase is also very ductile and tough, which accounts for the improvement of these properties.

8.12.6 Temper Embrittlement

The tempering of some steels may result in a reduction of toughness as measured by impact tests, which is known as 'temper embrittleness'. The phenomenon occurs when the steel is tempered at a temperature above 525°C, followed by slow cooling to room temperature or when tempering is carried out between 375°C and 525°C.

Steel alloys that are susceptible to temper embrittlement have been found to contain significant concentrations of alloying elements like Mn, Ni and Cr, and in addition one or more of Sb, P, Ar and Sn as impurities in relatively low concentrations.

The presence of these alloying elements and impurities shifts the ductile-to-brittle transition temperature to significantly higher temperatures. Crack propagation in these embrittled materials is intergranular as in brittle materials.

Temper embrittlement can be avoided by the following processes:

1. Control of composition of alloy
2. Tempering above 575°C or below 375°C followed by quenching to room temperature

Table 8.1 shows approximate values of hardness, R_c (as Rockwell C scale) and tensile strength in MPa of various microconstituents.

Table 8.1 *Rockwell Hardness and Tensile Strength of Various Microconstituents*

Constituent	Hardness (R_c)	Tensile Strength (MPa)
Ferrite		
Cementite		
Spheroidite	15	450
Coarse pearlite	18	700
Fine pearlite	32	950
Bainite	45	1400
Martensite	63	—
Tempered martensite (at 250°C tempering)	63	1950

KEY POINTS TO REMEMBER

❑ Gases dissolved in molten metals during melting are evolved during solidification. Hydrogen is a common source of gas unsoundness.

❑ In an ingot, a thick rim of exceptionally pure metal solidifies, while the central core is rich in impurities.

❑ Stabilized steels are sometimes made by completely deoxidizing the molten core with the addition of 0.03 wt% of aluminium after the rim has been formed.

❑ Segregation: Molten metal contains soluble impurities like S, P and soluble alloying elements together with insoluble impurities as slag particles in suspension.

❑ Growth of dendritic structure takes place in preferential direction.

❑ Diffusion-dependent transformation, α, β, δ in Fe.

❑ During solidification, a few atoms combine to form fine particles called nuclei.

❑ The nuclei grow, become grains and grains impinge on one another to make grain boundaries.

❑ Fraction of transformation (austenite into pearlite) versus log of time plot represents the kinetic behaviour of most solid-state reactions.

❑ Transformation rate, $r = 1/t_{0.5}$, where $t_{0.5}$ is the time taken for 50 per cent transformation.

❑ The rate of transformation to equilibrium for solid solution is very slow and true equilibrium structures are rarely achieved.

❑ For other than equilibrium cooling, transformations are shifted to lower temperatures than indicated by the phase diagram—supercooling. For heating, shifting is towards higher temperature—superheating.

❑ In T–T–T of eutectoid steel, at 727–650°C: coarse pearlite, 650–540°C: fine pearlite, at nose: maximum rate of transformation (austenite into pearlite), 540–300°C: upper bainite and 300–200°C: lower bainite formation due to isothermal cooling.

❑ Spheroidate structure—Fe_3C sphere is α-ferrite phase.

❑ Martensitic transformations are time independent.

❑ Martensitic structure is BCT (body-centred tetragonal).

❑ C > 0.6 wt%, martensite structures contain martensitic needles in austenite matrix.

Number of grains, $n = 2^N - 1$, where n is the number of grains per square millimetre and N is the ASTM grain size number.

❑ During tempering of quenched steel or ageing of a rapidly cooled low-carbon steel, carbides are precipitated.

❑ Fine precipitates add to the strength and hardness of an alloy.

❑ Precipitation of Al–4 wt% Cu (Duralumin)

$$\alpha_{supersaturated} \rightarrow \alpha_{saturated} + \beta_{tetragonal}$$

FCC   FCC   FCC

4 per cent Cu   0.2 per cent Cu   52 per cent Cu

❑ Solubility of copper in aluminium decreases from 52 wt% at 500°C to less than 0.2 wt% at room temperature.

❑ In continuous cooling, the time required for a reaction to begin and end is delayed. The isothermal curves (*T-T-T*) are shifted for longer times and lower temperatures.

❑ By slow cooling (full annealing) of eutectoid composition steel, coarse pearlite is obtained.

❑ By moderate rapid cooling (normalizing) of eutectoid composition steel, fine pearlite is obtained.

❑ The critical cooling curve (CTT) will just miss the nose at which pearlitic transformation begins.

❑ Only martensite exists for quenching rates higher than the critical cooling rates.

❑ In steel, ultimate strength, yield strength and hardness increase with increasing carbon percentage.

❑ Spheroidized steels are extremely ductile.

❑ Bainitic steels contain α-ferrite matrix with cementite particles.

❑ Martensite is the hardest and strongest in steel, but most brittle. To reduce brittleness, tempering is done.

❑ Tempered martensite contains α-ferrite matrix with cementite particles on the grain boundaries of ferrite grains.

MULTIPLE CHOICE QUESTIONS

1. Stabilized steels are made by adding 0.03 wt% of which metal, after the rim has been formed.
   (a) Silicon
   (b) Aluminium
   (c) Copper
   (d) None of these

2. In making killed steels, oxides are reduced to a minimum by the addition of deoxidizers. Which of the following is not used as a deoxidizer?
   (a) Aluminium
   (b) Ferrosilicon
   (c) Ferromanganese
   (d) Sulphur

3. Quenching of steel from a recrystallization temperature produces which microstructure?
   (a) Austenite
   (b) Cementite
   (c) Martensite
   (d) None of these

4. Which one is a correct statement.
   (A) Severe supercooling is necessary for homogeneous nucleation.
   (B) Nucleus forms spontaneously in the melt by random atomic motion by a cluster of a few atoms.
   (C) Foreign matter in melt serves as nucleation catalyst.
   (a) A and B
   (b) B and C
   (c) A, B and C
   (d) None of the above

5. Fine grain sizes are obtained by
   (a) Very slow cooling
   (b) Decreasing nucleation rate
   (c) Fast cooling
   (d) None of these

6. Hardness of martensite in a steel is a function of
   (a) Carbon content
   (b) Cooling rate
   (c) Nose location
   (d) None of these

7. Martensitic transformations are
   (a) Diffusion-less
   (b) Yield a hard and brittle product
   (c) Yield two products of transformation
   (d) None of these

8. Ratio of c/a in martensitic structure depends on the concentration of
   (a) Phosphorous
   (c) Nickel
   (b) Carbon
   (d) None of these

9. During overageing, hardness
   (a) Decreases
   (b) Remains unaffected
   (c) Increases
   (d) None of these

10. What is the carbon percentage in cementite?
    (a) 0.022 wt%
    (c) 6.67 wt%
    (b) 0.8 wt%
    (d) None of these

11. At 600°C, C = 0.8 wt% in steel, what is its microstructure?
    (a) Austenite
    (b) Austenite + Pearlite
    (c) Pearlite
    (d) None of these

12. Fine pearlite is formed (when cooling a eutectoid steel)
    (a) At a temperature just below the eutectoid
    (b) At a temperature close to 540°C
    (c) At a temperature about 675°C
    (d) None of these

13. Pearlite is transformed into spheroidite by
    (a) Heating the eutectoid steel at a temperature below eutectoid for sufficiently long period
    (b) Moderately cooling the eutectoid steel
    (c) By fast cooling the eutectoid steel
    (d) None of these

14. If C > 0.6 wt%, martensitic structure contains
    (a) Martensitic needles in α-ferrite matrix
    (b) Martensitic needles in γ-austenite matrix
    (c) Blocks of thin plates of martensites
    (d) None of these

15. Fine-grained structure is
    (a) Stronger than coarse-grained structure
    (b) Good in creep resistance
    (c) ASTM grain size numbers are 1–4
    (d) None of these

16. During precipitation
    (a) Coarse grains precipitate
    (b) Extremely fine precipitates are formed
    (c) Diffusion rates are fast
    (d) None of these

17. In T-T-T curve, at what temperature 90 per cent martensite is formed from eutectoid steel?
    (a) 225°C
    (c) 125°C
    (b) 175°C
    (d) None of these

Answers

1. (b)   2. (d)   3. (c)   4. (c)   5. (c)   6. (a)   7. (a), (b)   8. (b)
9. (a)   10. (c)   11. (c)   12. (b)   13. (a)   14. (b)   15. (a)   16. (b)   17. (c)

REVIEW QUESTIONS

1. Describe the formation of cavities, gas holes and segregation in a steel ingot.

2. What are killed, semikilled, rimmed and stabilized steels, explain?

3. What are the different types of phase transformation processes? Explain with one example of each.

4. Explain the stages of nuclei, growth and grain boundaries in a hot metal during solidification.

5. What do you understand by varieties of phase transformation? What do you mean by rate?

6. In a non-equilibrium condition what do you mean by supercooling and superheating?

7. Make a *T-T-T* curve for 0.8 wt% eutectoid steel. Mark the areas of coarse pearlite, fine pearlite, upper bainite and lower bainite.

8. Consider eutectoid steel during cooling from eutectoid temperature and show microstructures at beginning, 50 per cent transformation and complete transformation.

9. Explain what are upper bainite and lower bainite structures? Show these microstructures.

10. Explain how spheroidite structure is obtained and make a sketch of spheroidite structure.

11. Describe the properties of a martensitic structure with sketches of different martensites.

12. What is the importance of grain size? How is it measured?

13. What is precipitation hardening? Explain with the help of Al–Cu (Duralumin).

14. What is ageing process? Describe?

15. Explain the salient features of CCT.

16. Explain the difference among slow cooling, moderate rapid cooling and critical cooling.

17. Explain the mechanical properties of pearlite, spheroidite and bainite microstructured steels.

18. What is tempered martensite? What are its advantages over martensite?

19. What is the driving force for the formation of spheroidite?

20. Compare strength and hardness of following microconstituents: coarse pearlite, bainite and martensite.

PRACTICE PROBLEMS

1. Prove that the thickness of ferrite layer is eight times the thickness of cementite layer in a pearlitic structure.

2. Show that carbon percentage in cementite is 6.7 per cent.

3. Draw microstructures of spheroidite and tempered martensite. Draw comparisons between them.

4. Take a 0.6 wt% steel and show microstructures when it is cooled from a temperature of 800°C.

5. Make a copy of the *T-T-T* diagram of iron–carbon alloy of eutectoid composition. Label on this diagram the temperature path to produce (a) 100 per cent coarse pearlite, (b) 100 per cent tempered martensite, (c) 50 per cent coarse pearlite and (d) 50 per cent bainite.

6. Some alloys obey Arrami's equation, and the value of $n = 2.5$ in the exponent. If at some temperature, fraction recrystallized is 0.4 after 200 min, determine the rate of recrystallization at this temperature

Ans. [$r = 4.42 + 10^{-3}$/min]

7. Following are the data for fraction crystallized-time for recrystallization at 800°C of previously deformed steel. Assume that the kinetics of the process obey Arrami relationship. Determine the fraction recrystallized after a total time of 22.8 min.

Fraction (f)	Time (min)
0.20	13.1
0.70	29.1

Ans. [$f = 0.51$]

HEAT TREATMENT OF STEELS

9.1 INTRODUCTION

Heat treatment of steels is as important as its production for the development of desired mechanical, electrical and chemical properties, and the commercial alloys are invariably heat treated. Steel is heated to a specified temperature and then cooled at a controlled rate for the improvement of mechanical properties of the steel such has hardness, strength and ductility of the material. The heat treatment processes are carried out for specific industrial purposes: (a) to relieve internal stresses in the steel, which have crept in the steel due to mechanical deformation, (b) to improve machinability for easy machining of the steel products, (c) to improve tensile strength and tensile Young's modulus, (d) to get desired hardness by quenching process so as to increase wear resistance of the material, (e) to improve toughness of the material as by tempering after quench hardening process, (f) to produce desired changes in the microstructure as austenite is converted into pearlite at the Eutectoid temperature of the steel, (g) to improve surface hardness by selective hardening processes so that wear and tear of the surface of a component is reduced and (h) to refine grain size of the steel again for better mechanical properties.

By heat treatment, remarkable improvement in the properties is obtained by spheroidizing. The cementite in steel is converted into spheres of cementite, decreasing the brittleness of the material and by annealing the dislocation density of the steel is drastically reduced and steel becomes soft and ductile.

This chapter discusses various processes of annealing, hardening and tempering. The surface treatments as induction hardening, flame hardening, carburizing and nitriding also will be briefly discussed.

9.2 HEAT TREATMENT PROCESSES

The heat treatment processes can be broadly classified as follows:

1. Annealing
2. Surface hardening
3. Spheroidizing
4. Normalizing
5. Hardening
6. Tempering

In the process of annealing, the steel is exposed to an elevated temperature and soaked at this temperature for some time and then very slowly cooled so as to relieve stresses, to increase ductility and toughness and to produce desired microstructure.

In hardening process, the steel is heated to an austenizing temperature and then quenched in water or oil to get desired hardness by the production of martensitic structure in it. However, at the same time, steel becomes brittle. To reduce brittleness and to improve internal toughness, the steel is tempered after quenching process. The hardness is marginally reduced, but toughness is greatly improved.

The strength and hardness of some metal alloys may be enhanced by the formation of very small uniformly dispersed particles to second phase within the original phase matrix. This is accomplished by heat treatment process of 'precipitation hardening'.

In many applications, to improve wear resistance only the outer case of the component (i.e. surface of the component) needs to be hardened as in the case of surface of gears, rollers and screws. The main surface hardness techniques are flame hardening, induction hardening, laser and electron beam (*EB*) hardening.

Normalizing is used to refine the grains and to produce uniform and desirable grain size distribution, as fine-grained steels are tougher than coarse-grained steels. Normalizing is accomplished by heating the steel at approximately 55–85°C above the upper critical temperature of specific steel. Then, sufficient time is allowed for the alloy to completely transform into austenite, and the component is cooled in air.

Medium- and high-carbon steels with coarse pearlite structure are spheroidized. The process consists of heating the alloy at temperature just below 700°C in the pearlite region, and the temperature is maintained for 15–25 h, so that cementite coalesces to form spheroid particles. By this process, the steel becomes soft and *brittleness is removed*.

9.3 TEMPERATURE RANGES OF VARIOUS HEAT TREATMENT PROCESSES

There are three stable phases of carbon in iron:

1. Carbon as solid solution in BCC iron, a soft, ductile and magnetic material.
2. Carbon as solid solution in FCC iron, soft, moderately strong and non-magnetic.
3. Carbon as a component with iron, i.e. Fe_3C (cementite), which is hard and brittle.

These are the three principal stable phases present in the steels. The microstructures of steels at room temperature range from ferrite to all pearlite or to pearlite plus free cementite. Phase diagrams are used only for slow heating and slow cooling, especially to determine the temperature for hardening and softening, under equilibrium conditions.

Basic requirements of hardening carbon steels are as follows:

1. Heating to the austenizing temperature.
2. Sufficient carbon content.
3. A rapid quench to prevent the formation of equilibrium products.

However, the steels that are heat treated by different methods will have different microstructures.

9.3.1 Critical Temperatures

The structural changes occur at critical points A_1, A_2 and A_3, where $A_1 = 727$°C, $A_2 = 770$°C and $A_3 = 912$°C in iron–carbon phase diagram. Following allotropic changes occur in iron at the critical temperatures.

At $A_3 = 912°C$, α (BCC) iron transforms into γ(FCC) structure. At 1410°C, γ(FCC) iron transforms into δ(BCC) iron structures (not shown in Figures 9.1 and 9.2).

At $A_2 = 770°C$, α iron that is magnetic becomes non-magnetic and γ (FCC) structure is non-magnetic (Figure 9.1).

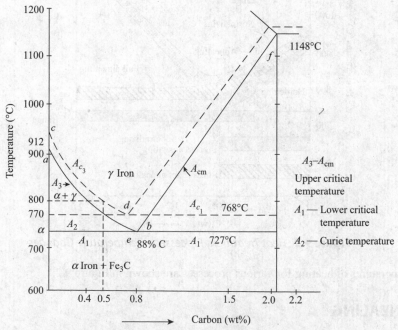

Figure 9.1 *Lower and Upper Critical Temperatures*

The horizontal line at eutectoid temperature (727°C) is termed as A_1, as lower critical temperature, below which under equilibrium conditions all austenite is transformed into pearlite (i.e. cementite plus ferrite phases) for both hypoeutectoid and hypereutectoid steels.

Phase boundaries shown by A_3 and A_{cm} (line ef) of represent the upper critical temperature lines for hypoeutectoid and hypereutectoid steels, respectively.

Iron–carbon diagram is plotted for equilibrium cooling or heating, i.e. cooling or heating is done at a very slow rate. But in the industry, for any treatment process, heating is not done at a very slow rate, but the steel is heated at moderately high rate, i.e. under non-equilibrium conditions and the steel is slightly superheated to achieve the desired effect. For example, for any hardening process, steel is heated to the austenizing temperature, i.e. A_3 boundary line ab for hypoeutectoid steel and A_{cm} boundary for hypereutectoid steel, and when heating is done at a faster rate, steel is heated above A_3 temperature by about 40–45°C. Considering steel with 0.5 per cent carbon, temperature A_3 is 760°C, while heating is done up to A_{c_3} line ab, which is about 800°C. Point A_{c_3} during heating is called decalescence point and also known as chauffage (a French word meaning heating). Similarly, students may find out A_3 and A_{c_3} temperature for 0.6 per cent carbon steel, i.e. 750°C and 780°C, respectively from the curves A_3 and A_{c_3}.

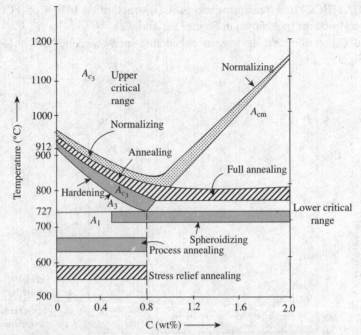

Figure 9.2 *Heat Treatment Processes—Temperature Changes*

The temperatures of heating for various processes are shown in Figure 9.2.

9.4 ANNEALING

Steels are softened to improve their machinability for steel mill shaping operations. They are softened either by tempering after quench hardening to improve toughness or by annealing to allow rework or welding operations.

Annealing consists of heating the steel to its austenizing temperature (A_{c_3}) and then cooling at a slow rate so as to prevent the formation of hardened structure. For moderately slow cooling at the rate of 50–55°C/h, cooling is done in packed sand and lime. For very slow cooling, after the steel is soaked at annealing temperature, the furnace is switched off and the cooling of steel components takes place in furnace itself.

Slow cooling amounts to cooling under equilibrium conditions, and after annealing, the structure contains (1) ferrite and pearlite in hypoeutectoid steels and (2) pearlite and cementite in case of hypereutectoid steels.

Annealing achieves the following objectives:

1. The structural changes of hard materials to a comfortable structure of ferrite and pearlite
2. Diffusion of carbon atoms from metastable martensite to austenite
3. Structure transforms to all austenite

There are two types of annealing processes: Full annealing and partial annealing (or process annealing). In full annealing, steel is heated upto A_{c_3} (austenizing temperature) and then slowly cooled. But in process annealing, steel is heated to a point below austenite transition temperature (727°C) of the annealing temperature range of 600–650°C, where recrystallization annealing takes place and when *annealing temperature range is below 600°C, then it is called stress relieving*. The cold-worked ferrite recrystallizes during this annealing. During recrystallization, the deformed grains are reoriented to increase plasticity and to remove internal stresses. Stress relief anneal is a subcritical treatment given to hypoeutectoid steels up to 0.3 per cent C steel. The recovery processes occur without recrystallization. The residual stresses due to cold working, forming or machining operations are removed by stress relief process. Distortion and warpage may result if residual stresses are not removed.

Table 9.1 shows approximate annealing temperatures for various plain carbon steels.

Table 9.1 *Annealing Temperatures*

Steel	Carbon Percentage	Annealing Temperature (°C)
Dead steel	0.1	900 ± 25
Mild steel	0.2–0.35	870 ± 25
Medium carbon steel	0.35–0.60	830 ± 25
Medium carbon steel	0.6–0.80	800 ± 25
High carbon steel	0.8–1.50	760 ± 20

Hypereutectoid steels have to undergo full annealing after hot working operations as hot rolling, in which austenite decomposes into pearlite and cementite. Other annealing processes are (a) spheroidize annealing and (b) diffusion annealing.

9.4.1 Spheroidize Annealing

Medium- and high-carbon steels contain coarse pearlite. These steels are difficult to machine and to deform plastically. These steels are heat treated (annealed) to develop spheroidite structure of Fe_3C (cementite) embedded in a matrix of α phase (ferrite) of iron. These steels are heated below the lower critical temperature (A_1) at about 600°C, soaked at this temperature for about 18–24 h and then slowly cooled at 600°C. This process is costly and time-consuming. The microstructure of spheroidized steel is shown in Figure 9.3. During the annealing process, Fe_3C coalesces to form the spheroid particles.

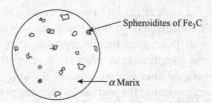

Figure 9.3 *Spheroidite*

Steels containing pearlitic microstructure have greater strength and hardness than steels with spheroidite. In spheroidite, there is less boundary area per unit volume and plastic deformation of such steels becomes easier, giving rise to a weak and soft material. In fact, all steels having spheroidite microstructures are softest and weakest.

9.4.2 Diffusion Annealing

Diffusion annealing is used in the case of heavy castings, for the removal of heterogeneity in the composition. The austenite grains are homogenized when heated above the upper critical (A_{c_3}) point. But the process of diffusion annealing is followed by full annealing to obtain fine-grained structure in castings.

9.5 NORMALIZING

Normalizing is done on steels for grain refinement and improvement in mechanical properties. Hardness and strength of steels obtained after normalizing process are higher than those obtained by annealing process. It is a final heat treatment process done on products, which have been subjected to relatively higher stresses. Normalizing temperatures are higher than annealing and hardening temperatures of steels. For hypoeutectoid steels, normalizing temperature is above A_{c_3} and for hypereutectoid steels, normalizing temperature lies between A_{c_1} and A_{cm}. Steels are held at normalizing temperature for a short duration and then cooled in still air (called air quenching). For high-carbon steels, heating between A_{c_1} and A_{cm} helps to break-down the network structure of proeutectoid cementite around the austentic grain boundaries and air cooling is fast enough to prevent the reformation of cementite along the grain boundaries. In medium-carbon steels, normalizing produces microstructures consisting of ferrite and pearlite.

Normalizing is done on cast or forged products. This is essential to eliminate dendritic structure developed during casting process and removing internal stresses developed during forging.

The process of normalizing is suggested for manufacturing operations such as hot rolling and forging, which are carried out on steels in austenitic range, but at much higher temperatures. This is useful in refining coarse-grained structure in castings and removing internal stresses in forgings. Microstructure of hot-rolled products is approximately the same as of normalized steel.

9.6 HARDENING

A heat treatment process that produces a microstructure, which is predominantly a martensite is known as hardening. Steel is heated to 30–50°C above A_{c_3}, temperature for hypoeutectoid steels and 30–50°C above A_{c_1}, temperature for hypereutectoid steels, holding for sometime at that temperature and then quenching in water, oil or salt bath in the hardening process. On quenching, carbon is trapped in the crystal structure to make martensite. On heating, in hypoeutectoid steel, austenite is converted into ferrite and pearlite and in hypereutecoid steel, a considerable part of cementite is retained. Cooling the steels at a rate greater than the critical cooling rate supercools the austenite to martensitic structure, which is very brittle and is in a stressed condition, due to uneven cooling. During quenching, the outer surface of the component cools faster than the inner region, as a result tensile stresses are developed on the surface of steel part and compressive stresses are developed in the inner region of the steel part. So, residual stresses are developed after heating process and at the same time ductility is reduced and brittleness is greatly increased rendering the part useless for any practical use; therefore, brittleness and residual stresses are reduced by a subsequent process called *tempering*.

Hardening process is carried out on cutting tools, machine parts, alloy steels, high-carbon steels and high-speed steels to produce desired hardness for cutting operation or for wear resistance.

During the hardening process, eutectoid composition of steel decomposes into α ferrite and cementite, while austenite decomposes into pearlite, bainite and martensite microstructures. Steels with low carbon percentage do not respond to hardening process, therefore, minimum 0.5 per cent carbon must be present in the steel for the production of martensitic structure.

Following factors must be considered for effective hardening of the steels:

1. Carbon percentage in steel
2. Heating rate and time of heating
3. Quenching medium and quenching rate
4. Size of the machine part
5. Surface conditions

As discussed earlier, there should be minimum 0.5 per cent carbon in the steel for the production of martensitic structure due to entrapment of carbon atoms in the crystal structure.

Heating rate should be optimum to get the desired effect. If the heating rate is too high, there will be high temperature gradient set up between the outer surface and the inner region, and internal residual stresses may develop in steel. The exact heating rate depends upon the heat production capacity of the furnace and the range of heating and thermal conductivities of the metal. By preheating the work, the heating rate can be reduced. Therefore, to achieve desired results, the articles to be hardened are heated to a required temperature, then hold at that temperature until the entire volume of article attains the same temperature. Lower the heating temperature, larger will be the soaking time. Heating in salt baths may be conducted more rapidly than heating in box furnaces.

Quenching media can be water, oil, salt bath, air blast or inert gas cooling. Water quenching is more severe, followed by oil, molten salt bath and gas quenching. Cooling rate due to water quenching can be further increased by (a) 10 per cent sodium hydroxide mixed in water, which increases the cooling rate twice that of room temperature and (b) adding salt to water (brine solution) with violent agitation, which improves the quenching rate further.

Depending upon the requirement, the cooling rate can be decreased by the following: (a) water-soluble oils or polymers are added to slow down the water quenching rate and (b) inert gas quenching further lowers the cooling rate.

Slower the quenching rate, lesser will be the quench warping in steel, but the desired hardness is not obtained. Therefore, to get desired hardness, appropriate quenching media have to be selected. However, automatic quenching equipments are also available.

The effect of size on the hardening process is equally important. Small parts are more easily hardened than the larger parts, because of the higher quenching rates. To achieve good effect of hardening process, following guidelines should be taken into account:

1. Long or cylindrical parts must be immersed in water or other quenching media along the axis, i.e. the axis is to be kept normal to the surface of bath.
2. Thin section must be immersed along the edge.
3. Recess in the part, if any, should be kept upward while immersing the part in bath.
4. Heavy sections can be held stationary as quenching bath and liquid are agitated.

The surfaces of the articles must be cleaned thoroughly before the start of heat treatment process, by hot water, wire brush and sand blasting to remove any surface impurities, because the impurities decrease the hardening effect.

During quenching of thick cross sections, cracks are formed on the surface of the machine parts and when these sections are quenched, they warp due to plastic deformation. Both warping and cracking are undesirable, as presence of crack reduces the fatigue life of a machine component. To avoid formation of cracks, the part to be hardened must be soaked at the hardening temperature so that the temperature from surface to inner region is the same and no thermal gradient exists.

It is important to note that the residual stresses are produced (1) from steep temperature gradient and (2) due to lack of simultaneous transformation throughout the cross section. If the cooling rates are lower, the temperature gradient is less and transformation occurs more or less simultaneously throughout the section. Then, negligible residual stresses are developed. Addition of some alloying elements in steels increases their hardenability, and permits slower cooling rates for the development of required hardness. However, soaking of steel at hardening temperature to eliminate temperature gradient is of utmost importance.

9.7 HARDENABILITY

There are several definitions of hardenability. The easiest one is that 'the ease with which a steel will transform to hardened structure on quenching is called *hardenability*' The second definition says that it is the 'ability of a steel to harden (by forming martensite) throughout its cross section without having to resort to drastic quenching'. As per the third definition, 'hardenability is a qualitative measure of the rate at which hardness drops off with distance into the interior of a specimen as a result of diminished martensite content. In other words, a steel alloy has hardenability of 1 if martensite is formed not only on the surface, but also to a large degree throughout the entire interior. For a steel which is hardenable, a letter '*H*' is added to its designation. That is, the steel can be hardened to provide more strength and wear resistance. The materials, which have a lower critical cooling rate have higher hardenability and the materials, which have a higher critical cooling rate have lower hardenability.

When a steel piece is water quenched, if the cooling rate at the core of the piece is more than the critical cooling rate, then whole cross section of the piece will transform into martensitic structure. But, if the cooling rate is less than the critical cooling rate, then the work is hardened up to a certain depth from the surface towards the core, the outer surface is transformed into martensite but the core contains martensite plus troostite structure and the middle layers with less percentage of troostite and more percentage of martenstie as shown in Figure 9.4. Steels alloyed with elements like Mg, Cr, Mo and B have

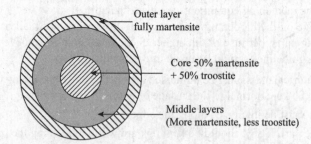

Figure 9.4 *Cooling Rate Less than Critical Cooling Rate*

lower critical cooling rate, but addition of cobalt raises the critical cooling rate. Grain size also affects the hardenability of steels. Larger grain size increases the hardenability or the depth of hardened layer and can be increased by two times by controlling the grain size.

A steel, which is highly hardenable will retain larger hardness values for a relatively longer distances from the outer surface.

9.7.1 End Quench Test

Jominy bar test is most commonly used to determine the depth to which a piece is hardened by water quenching. The factors that affect the hardenability, i.e. size, shape of the specimen, quenching media and method of cooling are maintained constant during the test.

A specimen of cylindrical size of 12.7 mm diameter and 100 mm long, with a collar at one end is held in a fixture as shown in Figure 9.5.

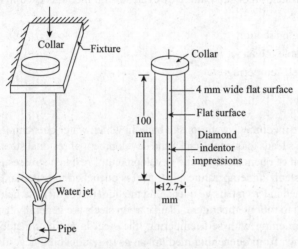

Figure 9.5 *Jominy End Quench Test*

The specimen is austenized for a prescribed time period in a furnace, then it is taken out of the furnace and held in a fixture as shown in Figure 9.5. Lower end of the specimen is quenched by a set of water, at specific flow rate and at room temperature. Cooling rate is maximum at the quenched end. After the specimen is cooled to room temperature, it is taken out from fixture and a flat surface of 4 mm wide and 0.4 mm deep is ground on the surface as shown in Figure 9.5. Rockwell hardness *C* test is performed on the flat surface at regular interval of 1.6 mm from quench end up to 38 mm and then at an interval of 3.2 mm up to the end. Rockwell hardness *C* readings are plotted along the length of the specimen as shown in Figure 9.6.

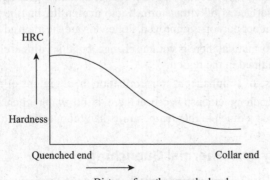

Figure 9.6 *Jominy Bar Quench Test*

Figure 9.6 shows that the maximum hardness is obtained at quenched end, because quenched end cools most rapidly and 100 per cent martensite is formed. At the collar end, the microstructure of steel contains martensite and troostite. So hardness is less.

9.8 HARDENING METHODS

We have discussed only one method so far, i.e. heating the steel up to more than austenizing temperature and then quenching in water, oil or salt bath. However, several methods used in hardening can be listed as follows:

1. Quenching in single medium
2. Quenching in double media
3. Hardening with self-tempering
4. Martempering
5. Austempering

Quenching in a single medium as water or salt bath, in which water quenching is most severe but produces maximum hardness leads to quench cracks and development of residual stresses in quench-hardened steel. To avoid formation of quench cracks and development of residual stresses, steel is cooled down in two media; from the austenizing temperature (A_{c_3}), steel is quenched in water and quickly removed from water. Then, it is quenched in less intensive quenching medium (oil or air) and held in the medium till it is completely cooled down to room temperature. Plain carbon steels are generally hardened by this process.

In the process of hardening with self-tempering, the steel is not completely cooled in quenching media, but it is withdrawn from quenching medium so as to retain some heat in the component, *which is used for self-tempering*. Outer surface of the steel is hardened due to quenching, but the inner core is tempered due to retained heat; the toughness of the core is greatly improved, but outer surface is hard for wear resistance. This technique is commonly used for hardening of hammers, punches and chisels made of high-carbon steels. This is specially followed in induction hardening process.

Martempering is also known as *stepped quenching*. In this process, steel is first heated to a hardening temperature, then it is quenched in salt bath, the temperature of which is maintained constant slightly above the point where martensite starts forming (say at about 300–350°C). Article is held in hot salt bath until it reaches the temperature of the salt bath for sufficient time. Now, the article is removed from salt bath and cooled in air. During this second step of cooling, austenite gets transformed into martensite. In this process, the outer surface is fully transformed into martensite, but the inner region retains some austenite, i.e. toughness of inner portion is improved. Following are the main advantages of martempering:

1. During martensitic formation, there is volume change, but this volume change is reduced because some austenite is retained in the region.
2. Less warping because of simultaneous transformation in all regions of the article.
3. Less danger of quenching cracks, because there is no water quenching; there is salt bath quenching, which is at a much higher temperature than room temperature.

9.8.1 Austempering or Isothermal Quenching

The article is heated to a hardening temperature (i.e. austenizing temperature) and then cooled in salt bath maintained at about 500°C, where bainitic transformation takes place and the article is held in salt bath for a longer period so that austenite is completely transformed into bainite. After removal of the article from salt bath, it is water quenched to room temperature to *achieve martensite formation*. Special features of austempered steel are as follows:

1. Hardness is maintained (52 HRC for 0.95 per cent C steel).
2. Toughness of steel is increased.
3. Quench cracks are eliminated.
4. Warping distortion is minimized.
5. Uniform microstructure is obtained.

However, the process is uneconomical because of *long duration cooling in salt bath* during bainite formation. The components of aircraft engines are austempered.

9.9 TEMPERING

After quench hardening, steel becomes brittle. Moreover, quench cracks are developed and residual stresses due to warping are induced in steel. To remove all these defects, hardening is always followed by tempering.

Tempering is a subcritical heat treatment process used to improve the toughness of the hardened steels. Tempering temperatures are less than the lower critical temperature, but proper tempering temperature depends on the composition of steels and mechanical properties desired. Figure 9.7 shows the variation of impact strength and hardness on the variation of tempering temperature.

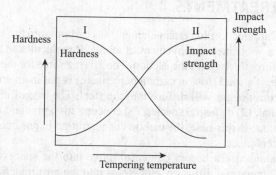

Figure 9.7 *Variation of Hardness and Impact Strength with Tempering Temperature*

In the tempering process, the article is heated in a furnace to a desired temperature—soaked for 2 h and slowly cooled in air. During tempering, following microstructural changes take place:

1. At low tempering temperature, a fine transition carbide (Fe_3C) is distributed parallel to the martensite platelets.
2. During tempering, some austenite is retained, which is transferred to cementite and ferrite.
3. At higher temperatures, transition carbide transforms to equilibrium carbide Fe_3C (spheroids) as in the case of spheroidizing process.

If the tempering is performed above 300°C, the residual stresses are completely removed. There are generally three tempering temperature ranges as follows:

1. *Low tempering temperature:* 200°C, microstructure retains hard martensite—generally, core-hardened articles are tempered at this range.

2. *Medium tempering temperature:* 175–275°C, troostite microstructure is obtained possessing high Young's modulus *E*—coil and leaf springs with high elastic limits are tempered at this range.

3. *High tempering temperatures:* 275–375°C—sorbitic microstructure is obtained and the internal stresses are fully relieved.

4. More than 400°C tempering temperature—martensite is converted into spheroids of cementite at 700°C, spheroidizing takes place.

Reader may note that a shock-resisting steel should possess adequate toughness, which is provided by the tempering process after hardening.

9.10 SUBZERO TREATMENT OF STEEL

During the hardening process in medium-carbon steels and low-alloy steels, 100 per cent austenite is converted into martensite, but in high-carbon steels and high alloy steels, some austenite is retained after the hardening process, as 100 per cent transformation to martensite does not take place. This retained austenite reduces hardness and strength of the steel and causes dimensional instability in steels. For complete conversion of retained austenite into martensite, the hardened article is subjected to subzero treatment, i.e. the article is quenched in a bath with temperature of −30 to −120°C, and is held in the bath for 2 h. The retained austenite is also converted into martensite. Steels used for high speed tools, measuring tools, carburized gears and machine parts of alloy steels are subjected to subzero heat treatment.

9.11 DIFFUSION TREATMENTS

Diffusion treatment can be applied to add certain elements (as carbon) into the surface that will make the surface hard. Diffusion is a spontaneous movement of atoms or molecules in a substance that tends to make the composition uniform throughout the section. The driving force for the diffusion is a concentration gradient. For example, if a steel (low in carbon percentage) is put in an atmosphere of carbon-rich gas as CO, then carbon from the gas will diffuse into the steel. The rate of diffusion process depends upon (1) nature of host metal, (2) diffusion species, (3) concentration gradient and (4) temperature. The concentration gradient means, in this case, the carbon concentration in gas outside the steel and carbon concentration inside the steel piece.

Extremely small solute atoms (carbon in this case) move into the spaces between the host atoms (iron atoms of steel)—i.e. interstitial diffusion. Big atoms into the host material find their way into the vacancy sites—a substitutional diffusion. For the diffusion to take place, the host metal must have a low concentration of diffusing species and there should be sufficient concentration of diffusing species on the surface of the host metal.

Diffusion processes for hardening steels, by carbon diffusion, usually require higher temperatures. Suitable temperature for carbon diffusion in steel is between 840°C and 950°C, and for nitrogen, it is 480–560°C.

Following diffusion processes are generally employed for hardening of steels:

1. Carburizing
2. Case Depth
3. Nitriding
4. Carbonitriding
5. Cyaniding

9.11.1 Carburizing

If a piece of low-carbon steel (say 0.2 per cent C steel) is placed in a carbon-saturated atmosphere at an elevated temperature, the carbon atoms will diffuse (penetrate) into the steel. Charcoal and Barium Carbonate promote the formation of CO_2 gas. In pack carburizing, the part to be carburized is packed in a steel chamber, so that it is completely surrounded by granules of charcoal. The charcoal is treated with Barium Carbonate ($BaCO_3$), which promotes the formation of CO_2. This gas, in turn, reacts with excess carbon in charcoal to produce CO. The carbon monoxide reacts with low-carbon steel surface to form atomic carbon, which diffuses into the steel. The carburized depth can be 1–1.25 mm. Gas carburizing can also be done with any carbonaceous gas, but natural gas, propane gas or any generated gas.

Salt or liquid carburizing is performed in internally or externally heated molten salt pots, e.g. salt in NaCN. All the carburizing processes (pack, gas and salt) require quenching from the carburizing temperature to a lower temperature. The parts are then tempered to desired hardness.

9.11.2 Case Depth

A small sample of steel, which is to be carburized is filled with a notch. Then, it is carburized. After carburizing and hardening, the sample is cut at the notch and the cut surface of hardened zone is tested for hardness HRC. Hardness measurements are made at regular spacing as shown in Figure 9.8. Until the point at which hardness falls below 50 HRC is the effective case depth, as shown in Figure 9.8.

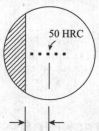

Figure 9.8 *Effective Case Depth*

The application of carburizing is limited to low-carbon and low-alloy steels. This process is not used on stainless steels or on cast irons.

9.11.3 Nitriding

Nitrogen in monoatomic form is diffused into the surface of the steel, and very hard nitrides of iron or nitrogen alloy compounds are formed. The resulting nitride case is much harder than carburized case. Subcritical temperatures are used and hardness is achieved without quenching. Hardening is performed in a nitrogen atmosphere that prevents scaling and discolouration.

Source of nitrogen used in diffusion process is ammonia and the nitriding temperature is 500–575°C.

$$\text{Chemical reaction, } 2NH_3 \xrightarrow[\text{Heating}]{} 2N + 3H_2$$

Nitrogen is diffused into the steel and hydrogen is exhausted. After nitriding, the parts may be slowly cooled in a retort.

Nitrided surfaces have different characteristics than other surface-hardened steels. Nitridied case is categorized into three zones:

1. White layer, which is brittle and prone to spalling.
2. A hard nitride layer.
3. A diffusion zone of decreasing hardness.

The white layer has detrimental effect on the fatigue life of nitrided parts, so it is removed from the nitrided parts.

Nitrogen diffusion and formation of hard nitrides can be enhanced by the presence of elements such as Al, Cr, Mo, V and W in the steel. The most common nitrided steels are Mo–Cr steels, i.e. nitralloys. The addition of 1 per cent aluminium greatly enhances the formation of hard nitrides.

9.11.4 Carbonitriding

In this process, both carbon and nitrogen are diffused into the steel surface. The process is performed in a gaseous atmosphere in a furnace using propane gas and a small fraction of ammonia. Propane provides carbon and ammonia provides hardness of the order of 60–65 HRC, which can be obtained by carbonitriding. Low-carbon-and low steels carbon alloy steels are carbonitrided. For the reduction of brittleness, carbonitrided parts are tempered. Case depth of 0.2–0.25 mm is obtained on plain carbon steels.

9.11.5 Cyaniding

Source of diffusion element is a molten salt bath, a cyanide salt such as NACN (sodium cyanide) maintained at a temperature range of 760–860°C. Heating in salt bath is followed by water quenching. Case depth of the order of 0.25–0.75 mm can be achieved. Processing time is only about 15 min. Only low-carbon steels are cyanided.

9.12 SURFACE HARDENING TECHNIQUES

In these techniques, only the selected area of a surface is heated to the austenizing temperature and the quenching is applied to that selected area. For example, if the blade of a knife is to be hardened, then only the blade area is heated to austenizing temperature and then quenched. Following are the techniques of surface hardening:

1. Flame hardening
2. Induction hardening
3. Laser hardening
4. Electron beam hardening

9.12.1 Flame Hardening

This process is generally performed on low alloy or plain carbon steel with low hardenability, e.g. 0.4 per cent C steel. A combustible gas flame is the source of heat for austenizing the steel, and after heating,

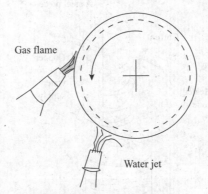

Figure 9.9 *Flame Hardening*

the part is moved and the transformation to martensitic structure is obtained by rapid water quenching as shown in Figure 9.9. Quenching is almost instantaneous. Heating gas is oxyacetylene or propane. Depth of flame-hardened zone is about 0.7–0.8 mm. Plain carbon steels with 0.4–0.95 per cent carbon and low-alloy steels are flame hardened.

Steels with high hardenability have a greater tendency to crack during flame hardening. Yet, the cracking tendency can be reduced by preheating the part to a temperature of about 150–175°C before hardening and by using oil or water-soluble polymer and water quench.

Cast steels of similar compositions as of plain carbon steels can also be flame hardened. Cast irons have low hardenability because of graphite content and they can also be flame hardened. Flame-hardened parts must be tempered before use. For example, gears, wheels, sheaves and cast iron bushings are flame hardened.

9.12.2 Induction Hardening

In induction hardening, an electric current is induced in the work piece to produce heating effect. Every electric conductor has a surrounding magnetic field, when current flows through it. If a coil of wire is made and an electrical conductor is put inside the coil, then electric current inside the coil will induce current flow in the core conductor through the magnetic flux lines produced by the outer coil. *Net effect is heating of the wire.* If an ac is used in the system, the induced current in the core is also ac. The resistance to current flow causes rapid heating of the core material. Now, in place of wire, if a steel round piece is placed inside the induction coil, induced current will heat the steel piece and can be heated to its austenizing temperature and if after heating, the steel piece is dropped in water bath, quenching will occur. Coils are made generally of soft copper tube (filled with running water to prevent heating) (Figure 9.10).

Heating time in induction hardening is much less than heating time in flame hardening. But depth of hardening is less; it is only about 0.25 mm. Small parts are easily flame hardened. After induction hardening, tempering of the hardened part must be done.

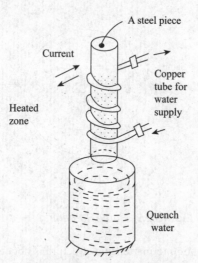

Figure 9.10 *Induction Hardening*

9.12.3 Surface Hardening by Laser and Electron Beams

Like flame hardening, these processes also produce local hardening of surfaces. These processes are extremely fast and energy efficient, produce hardness more than that obtained by extremely rapid quench and speed of hardening surface is as high as 1 m/min. By these processes, only the plain carbon steels and low-alloy steels are hardened. But the local area to be hardened is very small, i.e. 5–10 mm² in case of electron beam hardening and up to 100 mm² in case of laser hardening because laser hardening is not done in vacuum as in the case of electron beam (EB) hardening. In these processes, the specific temperature of the spot to be hardened is raised to the critical temperature required for hardening, and the mass of the material provides self-quenching. The depth of hardening depends on the mass and composition of the part and energy density; but the depth of hardening of 1–2 mm is easily obtained.

But these processes are extremely costly, yet are extremely fast. Use of these processes is limited to carbon steels and oil-hardened tool steels.

9.13 SPECIAL PURPOSE HEAT TREATMENTS

Detailed discussion on special heat treatment processes is beyond the scope of this book; however, the following processes are briefly described:

1. Ferritic nitrocarbonizing
2. Cementation
3. Boronizing
4. Metalliding
5. Toyota diffusion
6. Vacuum carburizing
7. Salt nitriding

9.13.1 Ferritic Nitrocarbonizing

A steel with ferritic structure is diffused with carbon and nitrogen from a gas mixture of ammonia and hydrocarbon gas, at a temperature of 570–670°C and a processing time of 3 h. Heating is accomplished by contact with heated fluidized alumina particles. By this process, low-carbon steel parts are skin hardened.

9.13.2 Cementation

Introduction of one or more elements into the surface of the metal by high-temperature diffusion is called 'cementation'.

Chromium is driven into the surface of the steel from a chromium-rich gas at a temperature of 1100°C, which is called 'chromizing'. If chromizing is performed on low-carbon steel, the surface of steel can acquire corrosion-resistant properties, and acts as ferritic stainless steel. If high-carbon steel is chromized, then carbon combines with chromium to form hard carbides and performs as hard wear-resistant surface. Case depth of the order of 0.05–0.15 mm can be obtained by cementation.

9.13.3 Boronizing

It is a pack cementation process. From boron-rich gases, boron is diffused into the surface of the steel. Boronizing can be performed on low-carbon, high-carbon and alloy steels. But the process is mostly used on low-carbon steels, because it produces extremely hard and wear-resistant surface with hardness more than 70 HRC on low-cost steels.

9.13.4 Metalliding

It is a pack cementation process and species of elements such as aluminium, silicon and beryllium are diffused into the surface by a special electroplating process. In this process, elements are electroplated on a metal in a molten salt bath. Bath temperature and plating rate are controlled in such a manner that plating rate is equal to the diffusion rate of the species into the metal surface. There is no production of coating on metal, but surface of the metal has a concentration of species like beryllium, boron and aluminium. The process is extremely difficult and costly, and is used in special applications such as high-temperature oxidation.

9.13.5 Toyota Diffusion

Toyota diffusion process was developed in Japan in 1968. This process produces a thin hard case of carbide compounds by diffusion of refractory metals into a substrate containing carbon. Diffusion species can be borax ($Na_2B_4O_7$) at a temperature of 800–1000°C. Tools like dies and cutting devices may benefit from a very hard skin on a hardened tool material substrate.

Titanium carbide coating is applied by pack cementation or chemical vapour deposition, and the treatment is done at higher temperatures. Coating is very thin, i.e. .025 mm, which is not sufficient to allow grinding for removing process distortion. Essentially, this treatment is done on annealed substrates.

9.13.6 Vacuum Carburizing

The parts to be carburized are heated to carburizing temperature in a retort-type vacuum furnace. A controlled amount of pure natural gas is introduced into the furnace so as to provide a source of carbon for diffusion. In this process, we get scale-free parts and the carburizing cycle time is also much less than in ordinary carburizing process. However there is a disadvantage of high cost of the equipment.

9.13.7 Salt Nitriding

Salt nitriding is usually performed in proprietary salts (trade names of process are Tuffriding and Melonite).

Tuffriding produces a nitride case on most ferrous metals, which is free from white layer that is common in gas nitriding. The alloys that are difficult to gas nitriding generally respond to this process. Process is useful for thin nitride cases on tool steels with improved scuffing resistance.

Melonite process eliminates the environmental problems, which exist in cyanide salts. In this process, parts are preheated to about 575°C in a furnace with neutral atmosphere. Then, the parts are transferred to the nitriding salt bath, where soaking time is reduced because of preheating. Then, there is salt quench at about 370°C, and finally oil or air quench at room temperature. Salt quench removes cyanide salt remaining on the parts after removal from nitriding salt. This process produces a black surface that has a property of rust resistance.

KEY POINTS TO REMEMBER

❑ In annealing, steel is heated up to austenizing temperature (above the upper critical temperature), soaked at that temperature and then cooled in a furnace (for very slow cooling). Annealing increases the toughness of the steel.

❑ In hardening, steel is heated at austenizing temperature (above the upper critical temperature), soaked at this temperature and then water quenched to achieve martensitic structure for high hardness.

❑ In normalizing, steel is heated at austenizing temperature (much above the upper critical temperature—more than the temperature used for annealing and hardening), soaked at that temperature and then air cooled. Internal stresses are removed by normalizing.

❑ Medium- and high-carbon steels with coarse pearlitic structures are spheroidized. Steel or alloy is heated just below 700°C, temperature is maintained for 15–25 h. Steel becomes soft.

❑ Basic requirements for hardening of steels.
  • Sufficient carbon content.
  • Heating to austenizing temperature.
  • Rapid quenching to prevent formation of equilibrium products; only martensite is formed.

❑ Objective of annealing.
  • Structural changes of hard materials into soft ferrite and pearlite.
  • Diffusion of carbon atoms from metastable martensite to austenite.
  • Structure transforms to all austenite.
  • Stress relief annealing is a subcritical treatment given to hypoeutectoid steels.
  • Annealing temperature decreases as the carbon percentage in the steel increases.

❑ During spheroidizing, Fe_3C coalesces to form spheroids. The material becomes weak and soft.

❑ Normalizing is done on cast or forged parts to remove internal stresses.

❑ Cooling rate of water quenching during hardening can be further increased by the following:
  • Mixing sodium hydroxide in water
  • Adding salt to water (brine solution)

❑ Ability of a steel to harden by forming martensite throughout the section is called 'hardenability'.

❏ During hardening, water surface becomes fully martensitic, but the core contains mixture of martensite and troostite.

❏ Jominy bar end quench is used to determine the depth to which a piece is hardened by water quenching.

❏ In hardening with self-tempering, steel is completely cooled in quenching, but withdrawn from quenching medium to retain some heat and the core of the parts gests toughened.

❏ In martempering, steel is heated up to austenizing temperature but cooled by quenching in salt bath maintained at 300–350°C and cooling in air.

❏ In austempering, steel is heated up to austenizing temperature, cooled in salt bath (at 500°C) for bainitic transformation and then water quenched.

❏ Tempering is a subcritical heat treatment process used to improve toughness of steel. Tempering temperature depends on the composition of steel and the mechanical properties desired.

❏ To convert retained austenite into martensite in hardened steel, subzero treatment (−30 to −150°C) is given to steel.

❏ Carburizing, nitriding, carbonitriding and cyaniding are diffusion treatments for improving hardness of low-carbon steels.

❏ In carburizing, a mixture of charcoal and barium carbonate, in nitriding, ammonia gas, in carbonitriding, a mixture of propane gas and ammonia and in cyaniding, salt bath of sodium cyanide are used.

❏ In surface hardening techniques, selected area of surface is heated to austenizing temperature and then water quenched.

❏ Laser and electron beams are used to provide heat at localized spot in the material, so that temperature of spot is raised to austenizing temperature.

MULTIPLE CHOICE QUESTIONS

1. For which process, a steel part is heated to the maximum temperature?
   - (a) Full annealing
   - (b) Process annealing
   - (c) Normalizing
   - (d) Hardening

2. Purpose of normalizing is
   - (a) To improve strength
   - (b) To increase hardness
   - (c) To remove internal stresses
   - (d) To improve toughness

3. What are the correct statements for annealing?
   - (A) Diffusion of carbon atoms from metastable martensite to austenite
   - (B) To improve surface hardness
   - (C) Structure changes to all austenite
   - (D) To obtain all pearlitic structures
   - (a) A only
   - (b) A and B only
   - (c) A and C only
   - (d) B and C only

4. Spheroidizing process is carried out at
   - (a) 780°C
   - (b) 680°C
   - (c) 550°C
   - (d) None of these

5. Microstructure of hot-rolled bar is approximately the same as of
   - (a) Normalized steel
   - (b) Annealed steel
   - (c) Surface-hardened steel
   - (d) None of these

6. Cooling rate of water quenching can be decreased by
   - (a) Addition of 10 per cent sodium hydroxide in water
   - (b) Adding salt to water
   - (c) Adding water-soluble polymers in water
   - (d) None of these

7. What is the hardenability of steel, if martensite is formed not only at the surface, but also throughout the interior region?
   - (a) 1.0
   - (b) 0.9
   - (c) 0.5
   - (d) None of these

8. Quenching (during hardening) in water produces
   - (a) Quench cracks
   - (b) Austenized surface
   - (c) Distortion
   - (d) None of these

9. What is tempering temperature range for spring (coil and leaf)?
   - (a) 200°C
   - (b) 175–275°C
   - (c) 275–375°C
   - (d) Above 400°C

10. By what process maximum hardness is obtained for a steel part?
   - (a) Carburizing
   - (b) Nitriding
   - (c) Cyaniding
   - (d) Same hardness in all processes

11. What is the depth of hardened layer by flame hardening of a steel wheel?
   - (a) 0.15 mm
   - (b) 0.35 mm
   - (c) 0.8 mm
   - (d) 1.2 mm

12. How much hardness can be obtained by boronizing?
   - (a) 80 HRC
   - (b) 70 HRC
   - (c) 52 HRC
   - (d) 46 HRC

Answers

1. (c)	2. (c) and (d)	3. (c)	4. (b)	5. (a)	6. (c)
7. (a)	8. (a) and (c)	9. (b)	10. (b)	11. (c)	12. (b)

REVIEW QUESTIONS

1. What do you mean by annealing? Enumerate various annealing processes. Differentiate between full annealing and process annealing.

2. Describe the following annealing process:
   (i). Recrystallization annealing
   (ii). Spheroidize annealing
   (iii). Diffusion annealing

3. Describe the importance of annealing temperature on variation of carbon percentage in steels. Why the annealing temperature decreases as carbon percentage in steel decreases?

4. Write a short note on normalizing process.

5. What is hardening of steels? What factors are taken into account while deciding hardening of steels?

6. What are the different quenching media? What is the effect of quenching media on the mechanical properties of hardened steel?

7. What is hardenability? What do you mean by hardenability equal to 1? Explain the effect of grain size on hardenability of a steel.

8. Explain the Jominy bar test on hardenability. How hardness of quenched part varies with respect to the distance from the quenched end.

9. Explain the difference between self-tempering hardening and hardening in double quench media.

10. Explain the austempering and martempering heat treatment processes. What is the basic difference between the two processes?

11. Why tempering is essential after hardening process? Describe the effect of tempering temperatures on the microstructure of tempered steels.

12. What is the necessity of subzero treatment of steel?

13. Describe the carburizing process. What is the difference among pack, gas and salt carburizing.

14. What are nitriding and carbonitriding processes? How nitriding is enhanced?

15. Describe the flame hardening process? What are its applications?

16. What are laser hardening and electron beam hardening processes? What are their applications?

17. What are cementative, boronizing and metalliding processes?

18. What is Toyota diffusion? What are its applications?

19. Explain Tuffriding and Melonite processes of salt nitriding.

METALS AND ALLOYS

10.1 INTRODUCTION

From the beginning of civilization, man is in the search of newer and newer materials. Gold, silver and copper are known to the man from the Stone Age, when the ancient people used to kill their prey with the help of stone weapons. Iron is being used for more than last 8000 years, when the iron tools were chipped from the pieces of meteorites containing metallic iron. Initially, iron was used in forged form, and then the iron casting was established.

There are two types of alloys: Ferrous alloys and non-ferrous alloys. In ferrous alloys, iron is the prime constituent and for the improvement of its mechanical and physical properties, various elements as Ni, Cr, Mn and W are added. There are different types of plain carbon steels depending upon the carbon percentage and the majority of the materials used in engineering industry are plain carbon steels. Depending upon the specific requirement, alloy steels are developed for high-temperature or cryogenic applications, corrosion resistance and cutting tools steels. Superalloys have been developed for use in aerospace applications, where engine components suffer from high temperature for long duration.

In non-ferrous alloys, prime constituent is not iron but other elements like Cu, Ni, Ti, Al, Mg and so on. For example, there are copper-base and nickel-base alloys. Applications and properties of important non-ferrous alloys will be discussed in this chapter. Then, there are wrought and cast alloys, as well as heat-treatable and non-heat-treatable alloys, which are also discussed in this chapter.

Discussion on various types of manufacturing and fabrication techniques as rolling, forging, extrusion, drawing, casting and welding are beyond the scope of this chapter.

10.2 TYPES OF FERROUS ALLOYS

In ferrous alloys, iron is the prime constituent; as in plain carbon steels, carbon varies from 0 to 1.4 per cent and the rest is iron. Ferrous alloys are produced in much larger quantities than any other metal alloys. The majority of engineering components are made from ferrous alloys as plain carbon steels, cast irons and alloy steels. There are three main factors for the use of ferrous alloys: (1) iron ore exists in abundance in the Earth's crest, (2) extraction of iron from ores and manufacture of steel and cast irons are economical and (3) iron alloys are extremely versatile and can be made as per the requirements of mechanical and physical properties.

However, ferrous alloys are susceptible to corrosion and oxidation. For the protection from corrosion, alloying elements such as chromium and nickel are added to produce stainless steels. Special-purpose steels are developed for specific requirements like (1) high-temperature application, (2) cryogenic temperature applications, (3) application in measuring instruments and steel with minimum coefficient of thermal expansion and (4) high-speed cutting tools.

10.3 PLAIN CARBON STEELS

About 90 per cent of the total steel production is of plain carbon steels used in various forms and various applications in the form of wires, wire products, tubular products, sheets, strips, cast and forged parts and cutting tools.

Plain carbon steels are divided into various categories as follows:

1. Low-carbon steel (C < 0.25 per cent)
2. Medium-carbon steel (C0.25–0.60 per cent)
3. High-carbon steel (C > 0.60 per cent)
4. Hypoeutectoid steel (C < 0.80 per cent)
5. Eutectoid steel (C = 0.80 per cent)
6. Hypereutectoid steel (C > 0.8 per cent)

10.3.1 Types of Steels

Based on the degree of deoxidation, steels are classified as killed, semikilled and rimmed steels. Killed steels are those, which had been strongly deoxidized and there is no gas evolution during solidification. Steel with about 0.25 per cent carbon are treated with silicon or aluminium (when deoxidized, no bubbling of oxygen gas in the molten metal). The degree of deoxidation is lower in semikilled steel. A wide range of these steels is used in general-purpose structural applications.

Rimmed steels (outer rim of the ingot) are those, which either have not been deoxidized or have been partially deoxidized. Rimmed steels, being low in carbon and silicon content can be heated for rolling into sheets, thin plates, strips and tubes.

Based on the method of fabrication, steels are classified as wrought steels and cast steels. Wrought steels are shaped by plastic deformation and cast steels can be cast in moulds.

Effects of Minor Elements on Behaviour of Steels

Manganese is often added as a deoxidant. It combines with sulphur forming MnS. The presence of manganese ensures production of sound steel free from blow holes. It increases the strength and toughness of the steel.

Silicon in the form of ferrosilicon is used as a deoxidant. It opposes the formation of iron oxide (FeO), which is detrimental to the properties of the steel. Sulphur is present either as MnS or FeS. Steel with iron sulphide has poor mechanical properties. But MnS is less harmful. During rolling or forging of steel, iron sulphide gets cracked or teared.

Like sulphur, phosphorus also is an undesirable impurity. It is present as iron phosphide (Fe_3P), and due to this steel develops cracks during mechanical working.

Copper and tin are usually present in the steel due to the use of steel scrap. Copper > 0.4 per cent improves resistance of steel against corrosion.

Hydrogen has the highest rate of diffusion in steels and results in hydrogen embrittlement, which can be minimized by annealing steel at 600–650°C.

Nitrogen is absorbed from the atmosphere in molten metal, resulting in the formation of 'Luder's bands' during plastic deformation.

Oxygen content in the steel is controlled by deoxidation. Oxygen present in the form of non-metallic oxides, inclusions of iron, manganese, silicon and aluminium break up the continuity of the structure and imparts directional properties.

Effect of Carbon Content

With the increase in carbon content, tensile strength and hardness increase linearly, but ductility decreases rapidly. Steel with C = 1.3 per cent is very brittle.

10.3.2 Specifications of Steels

A large number of steels with different compositions, properties and applications exist. Hence, specifications for designating the steels have become essential. As per Indian Standards, steels are designated as per chemical composition and mechanical properties.

1. Fe is used to indicate steel based on minimum tensile strength.
   For example, Fe 400 steel having minimum $\sigma_{ut} = 400$ MPa.
2. Fe E is used to indicate steel designation based on minimum yield strength.
   For example, Fe E 250 steel having minimum yield strength $\sigma_{yp} = 250$ MPa.

'Q' stands for quality of the steel
   Q1: non-ageing quality
   Q2: flake-free steel
   Q3: given size controlled
   Q4: inclusion-controlled steel
   Q5: steel with guaranteed homogeneity

For example, Fe 450 Q4 indexing-controlled steel with minimum $\sigma_{ut} = 450$ MPa.
Similarly,

W: (W_1, W_2) weldability
B: (0, 2, 4) resistance to brittle fracture
V: notch Charpy impact strength
W: (S_1–S_7) surface condition of steel
D: (1–3) formability
F: (1–13) surface finish
T: treatment of steel
T1: shot peened
T2: hard drawn
T3: normalized

T5: annealed

T7: solution treated

T8: solution treated and aged

T13: case hardened

T14: hardened and tempered

H: elevated temperature-guaranteed properties

L: low temperature-guaranteed properties

C: stands for carbon percentage (multiplied by 100)

T: tool steel

C or T is followed by a number representing average manganese content multiplied by ten.

For example, 95 T 15, carbon tool steel having average carbon content of 0.95 per cent and manganese content of 1.5 per cent.

10.3.3 Low and Medium Alloy Steels with 10 Per cent Alloy Content

Descriptions of these steels are as follows:

1. A number indicating 100 times the average percentage of carbon.
2. Chemical symbol of alloying element.
3. Average percentage of alloying element multiplied by a factor, given in Table 10.1.

   (The chemical symbols and percentages in designation in the order of decreasing content).
4. Mn for manganese, if Mn > 1 per cent.

Multiplying factor for Indian designations of alloy steels are given in Table 10.1.

Table 10.1 *Multiplying Factor for Alloy Steels*

Chemical Symbol of Alloying Element	Multiplying Factor
Co, Cr, Mn, Ni, Si, W	4
Al, Be, Cu, Mo, Nb, Pb, Ta, Ti, Zr	10
P, S, N	100

For example, 40 Ni 8 Cr 4 Mo 2, low alloy steel with 0.40 per cent carbon, 2 per cent nickel, 1 per cent chromium and 0.2 per cent molybdenum.

High-alloy steels (with more than 10 per cent of alloy content): The designation of these steels starts with alphabet X after which is put number, i.e. 100 times of average carbon content, and next symbols for alloying elements and percentage of alloying element rounded off to nearest integer. Symbols indicating specific characteristics such as weldability and quality are placed in the last.

For example, X T 7o W 18 Cr 4 V 1, high alloy tool steel, with 0.70 carbon, 18 per cent tungsten, 4 per cent chromium and 1 per cent vanadium

Different applications of steels are as follows:

1. Low-carbon steels (C < 0.25 per cent)

   These steels are unresponsive to heat treatment for the purpose of forming martensitic structure. These are strengthened by cold working. The microstructure consists of ferrite and pearlite. These are ductile, tough, machinable and weldable.

The applications are automobile body components, structural shapes (e.g. channel and axle) sheets. Strength, σ_{ut} = 400–450 MPa, σ_{yp} = 270 MPa, and elongation is 25 per cent.

2. Medium-carbon steels (C 0.25–0.60)

These can be heat treated by austenizing, quenching and then tempering to improve mechanical properties. They have tempered martensitic structure. Addition of Cr, Ni and Mo improves the capacity of these steels to be heat treated. The applications are railway wheels, tracks, gears, crank shafts and other machine parts for high strength; wear resistance and high toughness structural components are made from this steel.

3. High-carbon steels (C 0.6–1.4 per cent)

Hardest and strongest, but least ductile steels, always used in hardened and tempered conditions. These are wear resistant and can provide sharp cutting edge. The tools and die steels are high-carbon alloys with Cr, V, W and Mo as alloying elements, which form hard carbides as $Cr_{23}C_6$, V_4C_3, WC. Composition of typical tool steels are given in Table 10.2.

Table 10.2 *Composition of Typical Tool Steels*

C	Cr	Ni	Mo	W	V	Typical Applications
1.0	5.15	0.3 Max	1.15	–	0.35	Punches, embossing dies, drills
1.5	12	0.3 Max	0.95	–	1.10 max	Cutlery, drawing dies
0.95	0.5	0.3 Max	–	0.5	0.30	Shear blades, cutting tools

4. High-strength low-alloy steels (HSLA)

These are plain, low-carbon steels with alloying elements Cu, V, Ni and Mo (total 10 per cent) and possess high strengths.

Some compositions of these steels are as follows:

(a) C 0.28, Mn 1.35, Si 0.3, Cu 0.2, bolted riveted structures

(b) C 0.22, Mn 1.35, Si 0.3, V 0.08, Ni 0.2, Nb 0.03, structures used at low ambient temperatures

(c) C 0.18, Mn 1.6, Si 0.6, V 0.1, Al 0.2, railway cars

Oil-quenched and tempered plain carbon steels are used for crankshafts, bolts, chisels, hammers, knives and hacksaw blade with σ_{ut} = 600–1200 MPa and σ_{yp} = 400–800 MPa, and elongation is 10–30 per cent.

10.4 ALLOY STEELS

Plain carbon steels find limited applications for some specific purposes. Carbon steels when alloyed with elements are referred to as alloy steels. Alloying elements improve the properties of plain carbon steels such as (1) corrosion resistance, (2) wear resistance, (3) toughness, (4) strength, (5) magnetic and (6) electrical properties.

Table 10.3 gives the effects of alloying elements and specific applications.

Table 10.3 *Alloying Elements in Steels*

Alloying Elements	Effects	Specific Applications
Aluminium	Strong deoxidizer, refines grains	Nitroalloy steel
Boron	Improves hardenability	
Chromium	Stabilizes ferrite, forms hard carbides, increases strength, wear resistance and hardness	Stainless steels, ball-bearing steels, spring steels
Cobalt	Retains hardness at elevated temperatures, checks grain growth	High-temperature steels
Copper	Causes precipitation hardening when exceeds 0.3 per cent, improves strength	Steels with corrosion resistance
Manganese	Stabilizes carbides, increases strength, eliminates bad effects of sulphur, stabilizes austenite	Hadfield steels
Molybdenum	Strong carbide former, imparts high temperature strength, improves creep resistance	High-speed steels, creep-resistant steels
Nickel	Acts as graphitizer, stabilizes austenite, improves fatigue strength	Low-temperature steels, stainless steels
Niobium	Forms stable carbides, enhances high temperature strength and creep resistance	Creep-resistant steels
Silicon	Stabilizes ferrite, promotes graphitization	Spring steels, transformer steels
Titanium	Forms hard and stable carbides, raises creep strength	Creep-resistant steels
Tungsten	Forms carbides, raises strength and hardness, increases wear resistance, increases hot strength	High-speed steels, wear-resistant steels
Vanadium	Forms carbides and nitrides, refines grains, increases hardness	Wear-resistant steels, high-speed steels

10.4.1 Miscellaneous Alloy Steels

Alloy steels are classified into various categories depending upon various parameters as follows:

1. Amount of alloying elements
2. Principal alloying elements
3. Application of steels
4. Microstructure of steels

In general, (a) low alloy steel containing 0–5 per cent total alloying elements, medium alloy steel containing 5–10 per cent total alloying elements and high alloy steels having more than 10 per cent total alloying elements; (b) depending upon principal alloying elements, such as nickel steels, nickel–chromium steels, nickel–chrome–molybdenum steels and so on; (c) as per applications such as spring steels, bearing steels, creep-resistant steels and high-speed steels; and (d) as per the microstructure such as pearlite, ferrite, martensitic steel and so on.

Chromium Steels

Chromium is added to the steels to improve hardness and strength.
Cr percentage:

0.6–1.0	structural steels
1–2.0	ball bearings

4–6	air-hardenable steels
12–14	valve steels, tool steels, heat-resistant steels
16–18	stainless, corrosion-resistant steels

Manganese Steels

Manganese:

1.65–2.00	structural steels, rails, gears, axles, connecting rods, crankshafts, bolts, nuts
2–10	no commercial utility
11–14	excellent abrasion resistance, Hadfield steel

Molybdenum Steels

Low carbon (0.1–0.2 C) and molybdenum up to 0.7 per cent are used for case carburizing steels, shafts, transmission gears, bearings and axles.

Nickel Steels

Nickel:

1. Low-carbon, low-nickel steels (3–5 per cent) are preferred for case carburizing.
2. Medium-carbon, low-nickel steels for heavy-duty applications.
3. High carbon content in nickel steels is not preferred.
4. High-nickel steels (12–13 per cent) are used for low-temperature applications.

Silicon Steels

Silicon steels usually have better elastic, electrical and magnetic properties. A steel with 0.5 per cent C and 3–4 per cent Si is known as *electrical steel*, which is used for cores of electrical motors, generators and transformers. Steel with 1–2 per cent Si is known as *dynamo steel*.

Nickel–chromium Steels

These are the most extensively used alloy steels. Low-carbon grades (0.1–0.15 C), Ni (2–5) and Cu (0.5–2) are widely used for case carburizing.

Medium-carbon grades (0.3–0.4 C), Ni (2–5) and Cr (0.5–2) as structural steels for heavy-duty applications. High nickel–chromium steels make stainless steels.

Nickel–chromium–molybdenum Steels

Ni–Cr steels suffer from temper embrittlement. Molybdenum (0.3–0.6 per cent) eliminates temper embrittlement. The applications are axle shafts, bolts, heavy-duty engine, connecting rod and high-temperature bolts and nuts.

Nickel–chrome–vanadium Steels

Vanadium is used in combination with Ni and Cr. It improves strength, hardness and fatigue strength. Vanadium (0–2 per cent) is used in structural steels.

Chromium–molybdenum Steels

These steels have good mechanical properties. Chromium content varies from 0.4 to 15 per cent and molybdenum content varies from 0.2 to 4 per cent. These steels have good resistance to corrosion.

Chromium–vanadium Steels

Addition of vanadium to chromium steels enhances hardness, strength, ductility and toughness. These steels are fine grained and can be successfully used under heavy static or dynamic loading. Chromium content is 0.4–1.5 per cent, and Vanadium varies 0.1–0.2 per cent.

Silicon–manganese Steels

Steels with about 2 per cent silicon, 1 per cent manganese and 0.5–0.7 per cent carbon are of great commercial importance. These steels are used for leaf springs, coiled springs, chisels and punches.

10.4.2 Applications of Alloy Steels

The following are the application-wise alloy steels:

Spring Steels

Steels possessing high elastic limit, toughness and fatigue strength are suitable for making springs. A typical composition of spring steel is C 0.55–0.65, Si 0.1–0.35, Mn 0.7–1.0, Cr 0.4–0.6, Ni 0.4–0.7, Mo 0.15–0.25, rest Fe.

Ball Bearings

Steels suitable for making ball bearings must have high surface hardness to resist wear, tough case to withstand shocks and good fatigue strength.

Composition of E51100 steel: C 0.95–1.00, Cr 0.9–1.20, Si 0.2–0.35, Mn 0.25–0.45, maximum S&P 0.025. Minimum hardness of hardened and tempered ball-bearing steel should not be less than 62 HRC.

HSLA (High-strength, Low-alloy Steels)

The mechanical treatment of these steels is carried out in such a manner that the desired mechanical properties are obtained. These steels are not strengthened by heat treatment.

Dual-phase Steels

Microstructures of these steels consists of mainly hard martensite embedded in a soft ferrite matrix; therefore, named as dual-phase steel. Strength is 650 MPa and elongation is 28 per cent.

Low-temperature Steels

Steels, which are capable of retaining good toughness at low temperature as well as at normal temperatures are well suited for applications at low temperatures. Nickel is very effective in decreasing the ductile-to-brittle temperature of iron. Low-carbon grades of nickel steels are most frequently used in low-temperature applications.

Valve Steels

Valve steels should possess very good resistance against oxidation, corrosion by gases and wear resistance. Composition of a typical valve steel is C 0.2–0.3 per cent, Si 1–2.5 per cent, Mn 1.0 per cent, Cr 17 per cent, Ni 6–12 per cent, rest Fe, having austenitic structure.

Hadfield Steels

It is the only high-manganese steel of commercial importance. It contains C 1.1–1.4 and Mn 11–14, possesses toughness and excellent wear resistance to deformation. Important applications of Hadfield steel are jaw crusher plates, nuts and bolts, dredging equipment and chain for tanks. σ_{ut} = 780–980 MPa, maximum BHN is 180–220.

Maraging Steels

Maraging steels are well known for their high yield to tensile strength ratio, excellent fracture toughness and resistance to hydrogen embrittlement.

Composition is C (< 0.03 per cent), Ni 25, Co 7–10, Mo 3–5, Ti 1.75, Al 0.2, beryllium, niobium and tungsten in small percentages. These are used in aircraft under carriage parts, portable bridges and booster motor in missiles, σ_{ut} = 1800 MPa.

Tool Steels

Steels for making cutting, shearing and forming tools. A large number of steels, plain carbon steels to high-alloy steels, are used as tool steels.

High-strength Steels

Steels having strength > 1500 MPa are called high-strength steels.

Weathering Steels

Low-carbon grades of low-alloy steels, in which copper and phosphorus increase the resistance against atmospheric corrosion. Composition of a weathering steel is C 0.1, Mn 0.35, Si 0.5, P 0.10, Cu 0.90, Ni 0.4, Cr 0.8, rest Fe.

Triple-alloy Steels

Steels having three alloying elements, Ni, Cr and Mo, are called *triple-alloy steels*. Ni 5, Cr 2 and Mo 0.7 per cent, used in gudgeon pins, gears, shafts, levers and cam shafts.

Rail Steel

A good combination of strength and ductility along with high resistance to impact and fatigue are required in rail steels. Composition is C 0.4–0.6 and Mn 1.5.

Heat-resisting Steels

Low-alloy, heat-resisting steels are used for steam pipe lines, super heaters and fittings operating at 500–600°C. Other applications are jet engines, rockets, gas turbines and boilers. Pearlitic heat-resisting steel composition is C 0.1–0.2, Mo 0.7–0.9, Cr 0.3–0.5 and V 0.3–0.4.

Martensitic heat-resisting, low-alloy steel has composition as C 0.1–0.2, Mo 0.45–0.65, Cr 2.5–3.5, V 0.25–0.35, rest Fe.

Ultra-high-strength Steels

Steels with yield strength > 1500 MPa are known as ultra-high-strength steel. These steels have a particular composition like C 0.09, Mn 1.0, Si 1.0, Cr 16–18, Ni 0.5–7.5 + Fe.

Cryogenic Steels

Steels that can be put to use at very low temperatures, approaching the temperatures of liquid hydrogen or liquid helium, are termed as cryogenic steels, which contain 0.3–0.5 per cent C and 25–28 per cent Ni.

High-speed Steels

These steels are used for manufacturing cutting tools, which can be operated at high speeds. These are high-carbon, high-alloy steels containing W, Cr, V and Mo as alloying elements. A tungsten-based high-speed steel contains 18–20 per cent W, 4 per cent Cr and 1–2 per cent V.

Invar Steel

The composition is Ni 36 and Fe 64. Coefficient of linear thermal expansion is very small and is used for precision-measuring instruments and survey-measuring tapes.

Elinvar Steel

The composition is Ni 32 and Fe 68. Low α (coefficient of linear thermal expansion) and is used for springs in watches and instruments.

10.5 STAINLESS STEELS

Stainless steels are highly resistant to corrosion and rusting in a variety of environments, especially the ambient environment. To provide corrosion resistance, minimum percentage of chromium added is 11, which can be enhanced by the addition of nickel and molybdenum. Depending upon the phase constituents of microstructures, stainless steels are classified into three categories:

1. Ferritic
2. Austenitic
3. Martensitic

Martensitic stainless steels are capable of being heat treated. In austenitic stainless steels, austenite phase is extended to room temperature due to the presence of nickel, a austenite stabilizer. Ferritic stainless steels are composed of α-ferrite iron. Austenitic and ferritic stainless steels are hardened and strengthened by cold working because they are not heat treatable.

Austenitic stainless steels are the most corrosion-resistant steels because of high chromium concentration. These are non-magnetic, produced in large quantities and used in domestic appliances. Both ferritic and martensitic stainless steels are magnetic.

10.5.1 Applications

Applications of stainless steel are as follows:

1. Ferritic stainless steels are used in automobile exhaust components, tanks for agricultural spray, valves and combustion chamber.
2. Austenitic stainless steels are used in chemical food processing, equipments, cryogenic vessels and domestic appliances.
3. Martensitic stainless steels are used in rifle barrels, cutlery, jet engine parts, surgical tools and bearings.

Some stainless steels are frequently used at elevated temperatures and in severe environments because they resist oxidation and maintain strength at high temperature up to 1000°C. Applications of such steels are gas turbines, high-temperature steam boilers, furnaces, aircraft, missiles and nuclear power-generating units. In these ultra-high-strength stainless steels, strengthening is accomplished by precipitation hardening. The composition of a typical steel is C 0.09, Cr 17, Ni 7, Al 1, Mn 1, rest Fe.

10.6 CAST IRONS

Grey cast iron is mainly used due to its (a) low cost and ease of machining, (b) low melting temperature (1140–1200°C), (c) ability to take good casting impression, (d) wear resistance, (e) high damping capacity and (f) a reasonable tensile strength of 100–300 MPa, but very high compressive strength of 550 MPa.

Different types of cast iron vary from grey iron (which is machinable) to white cast iron (which is not easily machinable). However, white cast iron can be annealed to give malleable cast iron. The new high-strength irons are formed by alloying or by special melting or casting methods to complete steels. Cast irons can be broadly classified as in Figure 10.1.

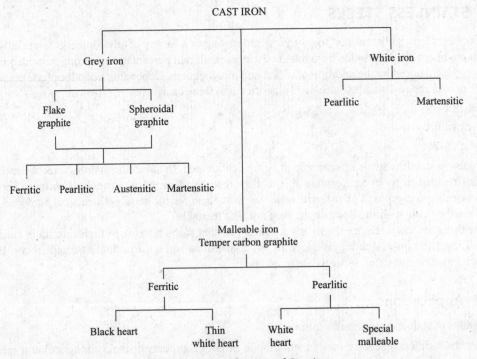

Figure 10.1 *Classification of Cast Iron*

While carbon in steels exists in the form of Fe_3C, in cast iron, it exists in two forms: (1) stable graphite form and (2) unstable cementite as combined carbon.

Graphite is very soft, occupies large space and hence counteracts shrinkage, while cementite is hard. The factors mainly influencing the character of carbon are: (1) rate of cooling, (2) chemical composition and (3) presence of nuclei of graphite and other substances.

10.6.1 Rate of Cooling

A high rate of cooling tends to prevent the formation of graphite. Slowly cooled sections will be grey and the rapidly cooled materials will be chilled.

10.6.2 Effect of Chemical Compositions

The main effects of chemical compositions are as follows:

1. Carbon lowers the melting point of the metal and produces more graphite, so it favours a soft, weak iron.
2. Silicon slightly strengthens the ferrite, but raises the brittle transition temperature. Indirectly, it acts as a softener by increasing the tendency of the cementite to split up into graphite and ferrite.
3. Sulphur and manganese: Sulphur can exist in iron as FeS and MnS. Sulphur tends to stabilize the cementite, producing a harder iron.

4. Manganese when added between 1 and 2 parts of sulphur hardens the iron.

5. Phosphorus has a little effect on graphite to cementite ratio, but imparts the metal fluidity through production of low-melting constituent. In the production of sound castings of heavy section, phosphorus should be reduced to 0.3 per cent in order to avoid shrinkage porosity.

6. *Trace elements:* Hydrogen content of 0.003 per cent can greatly affect the soundness of castings and tends to coarsen the graphite. Nitrogen behaves as a carbide stabilizer.

10.6.3 Formation of Graphite

Carbon content in grey CI is 2.5–4 per cent and silicon content is 1–3 per cent. Graphite exists in the form of flakes, which are normally surrounded by α-ferrite or pearlite matrix. Because of graphite flakes, a fractured surface of grey CI takes a grey appearance, hence the name grey CI.

Grey CI can have different microstructures depending upon composition and type of heat treatment. For example, lowering the silicon content or increasing the cooling rate may prevent complete dissociation of cementite into ferrite and graphite. Under such circumstances, the microstructure of cast iron consists of graphite flakes embedded in a matrix of pearlite as shown in Figure 10.2 for moderate cooling of cast iron.

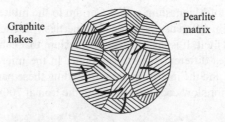

Graphite flakes

Pearlite matrix

Figure 10.2 *Moderate Cooling or Lowering Silicon Content*

For low silicon content (less than 0.1 per cent) and rapid cooling rates, most of the carbon exists as cementite instead of graphite. A *fractured surface of this appears white*, hence the name white cast iron. Microstructure contains pearlite and cementite as shown in Figure 10.3.

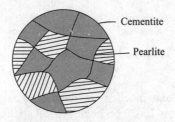

Cementite

Pearlite

Figure 10.3 *White Cast Iron*

If the cooling of cast iron is very slow, ferritic grey cast iron is obtained, and graphite flakes are along ferrite grains (Figure 10.4).

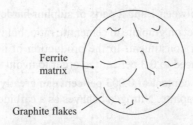

Figure 10.4 *Grey CI Slow Cooling*

Typical applications of grey CI are miscellaneous soft iron castings, in which tensile strength is not a primary consideration, for example, small cylinder blocks, cylinder heads, pistons, clutch plates, liners, transmission cases, ingot moulds and agricultural implements. Low strength and low ductility of grey CI are compensated by the attracting properties of high compressive strength, excellent machinability, good resistance to sliding wear, very good thermal conductivity and good vibration damping capacity.

Various grades of grey cast irons have been developed and a reader can refer to some standards to find an appropriate grade.

10.6.4 Ductile or Nodular Iron

Addition of a small amount of Magnesium and/or Cerium to the molten cast iron produces an entirely different microstructure with different mechanical properties. Magnesium removes any sulphur and oxygen present in the liquid melt. It is the residual magnesium that causes growth of spheroidal graphite. This inoculation provides different sites for graphite. In the microstructure, nodules or spherical particles of graphite appear, and the matrix phase surrounding these particles is (1) pearlite (for moderate cooling) and (2) ferrite (for slow cooling)—keeping the iron at 700°C for several hours as shown in Figures 10.5 and 10.6.

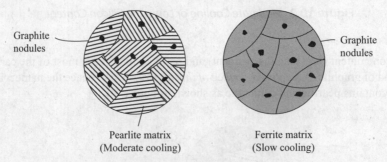

Figure 10.5 *Ductile Iron*

Nodular cast irons are stronger and much more ductile than grey CI. For ferrite ductile iron $\sigma_{ut} = 375$–475 MPa and the elongation is 10–20 per cent. Typical applications of nodular iron are valves, pump casings, crankshafts, gears and many automobile components.

10.6.5 Malleable Iron and White Cast Iron

For low silicon content (less than 1 per cent) in cast iron, on rapid cooling, most of the carbon exists as cementite (and is not converted into graphite + pearlite or ferrite). As a result, due to the presence of

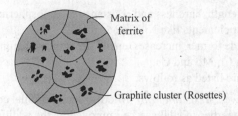

Figure 10.6 *Slow Cooling (Malleable Iron)*

large amounts of cementite, white iron is extremely hard and brittle and difficult to machine. It has hard wear-resistant surface, and its use is limited in such applications *as rollers in rolling mills* subjected to high compressive stresses.

By a heat treatment process, white iron is converted into a malleable iron. Heating white iron at temperatures between 800°C and 900°C for prolonged time period, and in a neutral atmosphere (to prevent oxidation) causes decomposition of cementite forming graphite, which exists in the form of clusters or rosettes surrounded by (1) ferrite matrix on slow cooling and (2) pearlite on fast cooling as shown in Figures 10.6 and 10.7.

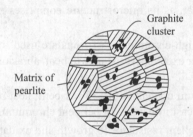

Figure 10.7 *Fast Cooling (Malleable Iron)*

10.6.6 High Strength Cast Irons

Modification of the microstructure and properties of cast iron can be brought about by the addition of alloying elements such as nickel, chromium, copper and molybdenum.

Nickel tends to produce grey iron in which it is less powerful than silicon. Therefore, in castings of widely varying sections, silicon can be slightly reduced and nickel can be added to prevent chilling in thin sections. Chromium by forming carbides acts in the opposite way to nickel, but it produces *grain refinement*. Molybdenum nodules the graphite and promotes a fine pearlite, but it is used preferably with nickel or chromium.

With the correct amounts of nickel and molybdenum correlated with the cooling rate of a particular casting, the pearlite change point can be suppressed and an acicular intermediate constituent (ferrite needles in austenite matrix) can be produced with high mechanical properties. *Acicular cast iron is very much tougher than any of the pearlite iron.*

Chromium (0.6 per cent) and molybdenum (0.6 per cent) irons are useful for engine liners, press sleeves, dies and so on, where wear resistance is important as in heavy sections.

Copper increases tensile strength, hardness and resistance to atmospheric and marine corrosion. It is used in combination with other elements like Ni, Cr, Mo and V.

Vanadium, a powerful carbide former, increases tensile strength and hardness of cast iron. It is usually added in combination with Ni, Cr, Mo and Cu.

Important alloy cast irons are listed as follows:

1. *Silal (A silicon-bearing wear-resistant iron):* Microstructure of Silal contains fine graphite flakes in ferrite matrix. The properties of silal can be improved by the addition of Cr, Mo, Cu and Ni.

2. *Nicrosilal:* Alloying Silal with nickel and chromium. Its microstructure consists of graphite in austenite matrix. A minimum of 18 per cent nickel is essential to stabilize austenitic matrix. It is preferred to Silal in terms of toughness, thermal shock resistance and resistance to scaling.

3. *High-silicon cast iron:* Contains 14–15 per cent silicon, exhibits excellent resistance to corrosion by acids, but is weak and brittle in nature. These irons exhibit good resistance to sulphuric acid, nitric acid and other organic acids, but not to hydrofluoric acid.

4. *Ni-resist cast irons:* A high-nickel cast iron (14–36 per cent Ni) gives rise to austenitic matrix. Microstructure of Ni-resist comprises graphite nodule flakes in austenitic matrix. Ni-resist cast irons have good resistance to corrosion and erosion, and are able to resist moderately high temperatures.

5. *Ni-hard cast irons:* Ni-hard cast irons are basically nickel–chromium cast irons possessing outstanding resistance to wear, as its microstructure comprises martensitic matrix with multitudes of refined carbides.

6. *High-chromium cast iron:* High-chromium cast irons are used for specific applications. These alloy white cast iron possesser excellent resistance to heat, abrasion or corrosion depending upon chromium percentage.

7. *Corrosion resistant:* Chromium content is 30–35 per cent; heat resistant: 15–18 per cent chromium and abrasion-resistant cast irons: 26–28 per cent chromium.

   These cast irons have excellent resistance to growth and oxidation.

8. *Mechanite cast iron:* A class of cast iron exhibiting good mechanical properties. In this, molten metal is treated with calcium silicide, which acts as a graphitizer producing fine graphite structures. Mechanite is basically a grey CI containing controlled graphite. It has 2.5–3 per cent of C, and is capable of retaining its strength up to 400°C and also exhibits good creep strength.

10.7 NON-FERROUS ALLOYS

Although ferrous alloys are produced abundantly and are used in large quantities, there are certain inherent disadvantages of using them: (1) high density, while for aerospace applications low density is the basic requirement, (2) low electrical conductivity, while in many electrical applications high electrical conductivity is of prime concern and (3) susceptibility to corrosion and in many applications in atmospheric environments, alloys with good corrosion resistance is the main requirement.

In non-ferrous alloys, the prime metal is non-ferrous such as copper, aluminium, nickel and zinc. Non-ferrous alloys are classified on the basis of this prime metal used such as copper-base, aluminium-base and nickel-base alloys. Under non-ferrous alloys, we will discuss cast and wrought alloys and heat-treatable and non-heat-treatable alloys. Superalloys used at high temperature and low duration and refractory metals, bearing metals will also be discussed.

10.8 COPPER AND ITS ALLOYS

Copper, a pinking red metal possesses the properties of high ductility, high malleability, excellent electrical and thermal conductivity and good corrosion resistance. Copper is available in wires, rods, tubes, thin sheets, strips and foils. The relative density of copper is 8.93 and the melting point is 1083°C with FCC structure.

Various forms of copper are (1) blister copper, (2) electrolytic copper, (3) electrolytic tough pitch copper and (4) oxygen-free high-conductivity (OFHC) copper.

Copper alloys can be classified into three categories: (1) brasses, (2) bronzes and (3) cupro nickels. In addition, depending upon the manufacturing method, there are wrought alloys and cast alloys.

Copper has a high strain-hardening coefficient. Brass is a copper-base alloy containing zinc as principal alloying element. Industrial brasses contain up to 45 per cent zinc. *Bronze* is the name given to represent a copper-base alloy with *tin as the alloying element*. Similarly, there are aluminium bronze, silicon bronze and manganese bronze. In cupro nickels, nickel is the main alloying element. Nickel confers upon copper its characteristic magnetic and electrical properties.

Zinc is soluble in copper up to 39 per cent. Therefore, less than 39 per cent of zinc forms a single-phase solid solution with copper, which is denoted by α. As zinc exceeds 39 per cent, a compound, CuZn having BCC structure is formed, which is denoted by β. Alloys with zinc between 39 and 45 per cent have microstructures consisting of both α and β phases.

In order to get enhanced properties, binary brasses (with α phase only) are alloyed with aluminium, iron, nickel, tin and silicon. Aluminium and silicon bronzes are famous for their excellent resistance to corrosion coupled with high strengths. Beryllium bronzes are capable of attaining highest strength among all copper-base alloys.

Table 10.4 enlists copper-base alloys along with their composition and applications.

10.9 ALUMINIUM AND ITS ALLOYS

Aluminium, a silvery white metal, widely used as an engineering metal next to steel has following properties. Specific gravity is 2.70, melting point is 660°C, and is the fourth best electrical conducting material.

Aluminium has a very good reflectivity and is used in search lights, television screens and reflectors. Strong affinity of aluminium to oxygen makes it a popular deoxidant, used in thermal welding (a mixture of granulated aluminium and mill scale reacts chemically to produce high heat energy). It has good ductility, malleability, formability and resistance to corrosion, but suffers from low strength and low hardness.

Alloying of aluminium with elements like Si, Cu, Mg, Mn and Zn increases its strength and hardness. Aluminium gets readily mixed up with other metals in liquid state, but solid solubility of various metals is limited only to a few per cent.

Copper as an alloying element enhances the elevated temperature properties and machinability of aluminium. Cast aluminium–copper alloys may have copper up to 12 per cent. Addition of copper improves fluidity, decreases surface tension of molten metal, refines grain structure and makes the alloy fine from hot shortness and porosity.

Silicon imparts very high fluidity and greatly reduces degree of solidification shrinkage, resulting in absence of hot shortness with lower degree of porosity. Magnesium increases strength and hardness by solid solution strengthening. Addition of manganese results in improved ductility, impact strength and decreased shrinkage.

Table 10.4 *Copper Base Alloys*

Nomenclature	Composition	Applications
Gilding metal	5 Zn, 95 Cu	Emblems, plaques, coins, medals, tokens, decorative items
Commercial bronze	10 Zn, 90 Cu	Marine hardware, costume, jewellery, lipstick cases, rivets, screws, forgings
Red brass	15 Zn, 85 Cu	Condenser, heat exchanger tubes, sockets, hardware, radiator cores
Cartridge brass	30 Zn, 70 Cu	Cartridge cases, head lamp reflectors, fasteners, springs, plumbing accessories
Admiralty brass	29 Zn, 1 Sn, 70 Cu	Condenser tubes, cold-worked marine parts, heat exchanger tubes
Yellow brass	35 Zn, 65 Cu	Automobile tanks, head-light reflector, fasteners, rivets, springs
Naval brass	38 Zn, 1 Sn, 61 Cu	Naval applications, welding rods, propeller shafts, nuts, piston rod, valve stems
Munz metal	40 Zn, 60 Cu	Condenser tubes, heads, architectural work, brazing rods, perforated metal
Gun metal (tin bronze)	10 Sn, 2 Zn, 88 Cu	Valves, fittings in corrosive environments
Delta brass	40 Zn, 3 Pb, 2 Fe, 55 Cu	Parts of mining industry, chemical plants, motor bushes
Manganin	13 Mn, 87 Cu	Resistors
Constantan	40 Ni, 60 Cu	Strain gage wire
Electrolytic tough pitch copper	Annealed 99.6 per cent Cu	Electrical wires, rivets, screening gaskets, pans, nails, rolling
Beryllium copper	1.9 Be, 0.2 Co, 97.9 Cu (precipitation hardened)	Springs, bellows, firing pins, bushings, valves, diaphragm
Phosphor bronze	5 Sn, 0.2 P, 94.8 Cu	Bellows, clutch discs, fuse, diaphragms, clips, springs, welding rods
Cupro-nickel	30 Ni, 70 Cu	Salt water piping, condenser, heat exchanger tubes
Leaded yellow brass	29 Zn, 3 Pb, 1 Sn, 67 Cu	Furniture, hardware, radiator fittings, light fixture, battery clamps
Aluminium bronze (imitation gold)	4 Fe, 11 Al, 85 Cu	Bearings, gears, worms, bushings, valve seats, pickling hooks
Manganese bronze	1.4 Zn, 1 Fe, 0.1 Sn, 39 Cu, 58.5 Mn	Marine engine pumps, ship propellers, gears, clutch discs, forgings, extruded shapes, shaft rods
German silver (Cu–Zn–Ni)	17–42 Zn 10–20 Ni	Looks like silver, silver-plated articles
Cunife	20 Ni, 20 Fe, 60 Cu	Permanent magnetic materials
Cunico	21 Ni, 29 Co, 50 Cu	Permanent magnetic materials

There are two types of aluminium alloys: wrought alloys and cast alloys. Aluminium alloys generally do not respond to heat treatment; these are strengthened by cold working.

Important alloying elements for wrought alloys are Cu, Mg and Mn for strengthening and for cast alloys, alloying elements are Cu, Mg and Si.

There are two types of wrought aluminium alloys:

1. Heat-treatable alloys—having inferior resistance to corrosion
2. Non-heat-treatable alloys

Non-heat-treatable wrought aluminium alloys are used in petrol and oil pipelines, welded tanks, rivets, partitions, ship hulls and masts and automobile parts.

The heat-treatable wrought alloys contain either copper (up to 4 per cent) or Si and Mg (up to 2 per cent). Such alloys are used extensively in applications, where tensile strength and other mechanical properties are of primary importance and moderate resistance to corrosion serves the purpose. Duralumin is the first commercially heat-treatable alloy, extensively used in aircraft industry for making frames, ribs, propeller blades, and in automobiles. Composition of duralumin is Cu 4, Mg 0.5, Si 0.7 and rest Al.

Cast alloys possess inferior mechanical properties than wrought alloys, but can be easily cast into complicated shapes. The maximum tensile strength values of commercial aluminium alloys in the as-cast condition for sand, permanent mould and die casting are above 180, 250 and 300 MPa, respectively. One important cast alloy is 'Y-alloy' with a composition of Cu 4, Mg 1.5, Ni 2, Fe 0.6 and rest Al and is used for casting of engine parts as aircraft wheels, crank cases, fly wheel, rear axle housing, aircraft pump parts and transmission cases.

Aluminium alloys rich in silicon (up to 12 per cent) are known as Silumins, which are used in cast state only in automotive and aircraft industries.

10.9.1 Aluminium–Lithium Alloys

These alloys are developed for aerospace industry, with properties of low density, high specific modulii, excellent fatigue strength and low temperature toughness properties. These alloys can be heat treated and cold worked; two such alloys are given in Table 10.5.

Table 10.5 *Some Aluminium–Lithium Alloys*

Composition	σ_{ut}	σ_{yp}	Percentage Elongation	Uses
2.7 Cu, 0.25 Mg, 2.25 Li, 0.12 Zn, + Al	455	355	5	Aircraft structures, cryogenic tank structure
1.3 Cu, 0.95 Mg, 2.0 Li, 0.1 Zr, + Al	465	360	–	Highly damage-tolerant aircraft structure parts

10.10 NICKEL BASE ALLOYS

Pure nickel has melting point of 1455°C, Young's modulus of 207 GPa, density of 7.05 g/cc and thermal coefficient of 15.1×10^{-6}/°C.

Nickel alloys have excellent properties. Ni–iron alloys (80–20, 50–50) have magnetic permeability, which makes them superior for magnetic shielding of electronic devices. Ni–Cr alloys (80 Ni, 20 Cr; 70 Ni, 30 Cr) are widely used as resistance heating elements. The properties of some nickel alloys are given in Table 10.6.

The important properties of nickel-base alloys are as follows:

1. Monel 400—resistance to sea water, sulphuric acid, hydrochloric acid and unusual resistance to deaerated hydrofluoric acid.
2. Ni–Cr–Mo alloy— exceptional resistance to pitting and stress–corrosion cracking.
3. Most nickel base alloys can be cold worked to higher strength.
4. Alloys containing chromium and boron have hardness of the order of 600 HB.

Table 10.6 *Properties of Some Nickel Alloys*

Alloy	Nominal Composition	Remarks
Pure nickel	99.0 Ni min	Resistant to strong caustics
Ni–Cu	63 Ni, 31 Cu, 2.5 Fe 2 Mn (Monel 400)	Resistant to neutral water, sea water and some acids
	60 Ni, 1 Fe, 29.5 Cu 2.7 Al (K-monel)	Age hardening grade of Monel 400
Ni–chrome	72 Ni, 15.5 Cr, 8 Fe (Inconel 600)	Resistant to oxidizing and reducing atmospheres at high temperature
	52.5 Ni, 19 Cr, 18.5 Fe, 3 Mo 5 Cu, Ta (Inconel 718)	Age hardenable, oxidation resistance at 980°C
	60 Ni, 16 Cr, 1 Mn, rest Fe (Ni–chrome)	Resistance for electric heating elements
	60 Ni, 20 Cr, 5 Fe, 1 Al, 3 Ti	Turbine/jet alloy
Ni–Cr–Fe	42 Ni, 21.5 Cr, 30 Fe, 3 Mo, 2.2 Cu (Incoloy 825)	Resistant to wide variety of chemicals
Ni–Mo	65 Ni, 28 Mo, 2 Fe (Hastealloy) B–2	Resistant to hydrochloric acid and other reducing acids
Ni–Cr–Mo	62 Ni, 16 Cr, 3 Fe, 16 Mo (Hastealloy C4)	Resistant to oxidizing and reducing acids, high temperature stability

10.11 MAGNESIUM AND ITS ALLOYS

Magnesium has low density of 1.74 g/cm^3, with HCP crystal structure, Young's modulus of 45 GPa and melting point of 651°C. At room temperature, magnesium and its alloys are difficult to deform. Most magnesium alloys are fabricated by casting or hot working.

Magnesium alloys, both wrought and cast, are heat treatable and non-heat treatable also. Aluminium, zinc, manganese and some rare earth metals are the major alloying elements. Alloys of magnesium are used in aircraft and missile applications.

Aluminium and zinc enhance the strength, and manganese increases corrosion resistance and refines the grains. Some elements such as Si, Sn, Zr and Th are usually added in minor amounts. Silicon improves casting properties. Tin renders ductility and cerium improves high temperature properties.

Table 10.7 *Wrought Magnesium Alloys*

Composition	Condition	Applications
3 Al, 1 Zn, 0.2 Mn + Mg	Extruded	Structures and tubing
3 Th, 0.6 Zr + Mg	Strain hardened	High strength components at 300°C
5.5 Zn, 0.45 Zr	Artificially aged	Forging for maximum strength in aircraft

Cast Magnesium Alloys

Composition	Applications
9 Al, 0.15 Mn, 0.7 Zn + Mg	Die casting parts of automobiles, electric devices
6 Al, 0.17 Mn + Mg	Automobile wheels
4.3 Al, 1.0 Si, 0.35 Mn + Mg	Die casting, good creep resistance

Wrought magnesium alloys are used as extruded bars, rods, sheets, plates and wires. Forgings are used for aircraft engine bearing caps, housings, rocker arm, doors, hinges, flaps and rudders.

Magnesium alloys have good castability and can be cast into intricate shapes with high dimensional accuracy and good surface finish. Sand casting, permanent mould casting and die casting techniques can also be employed. Table 10.7 gives composition, condition and applications of wrought and cast magnesium alloys.

A famous magnesium alloy is AZ 81, with 8 per cent Al and 1 per cent Zn. This alloy gives tough leak-tight castings, which are used for lightweight crank cases in some cars. The alloy can be used in pressure die casting by adding a small quantity of beryllium.

10.12 TITANIUM AND ITS ALLOYS

Titanium alloys are relatively new engineering materials with extraordinary properties: (1) high strength, 1400 MPa at room temperature, (2) easily forged and machined, (3) corrosion resistance, (4) immune to air, marine and variety of industrial environments, (5) high melting point of 1608°C, (6) low density of 4.5 g/cc and (7) good Young's modulus, $E = 107$ GPa. Pure titanium has an HCP structure at room temperature, which changes to BCC structure at temperature more than 885°C. Due to these properties, titanium alloys are widely used in aviation and rocket engineering, ship building and chemical processing.

Alloys of titanium with Al, Sn, Mn, Mo, V, Zr, Si, Cr or Fe are of great commercial use. There are α, $\alpha + \beta$ and β alloys of specific engineering importance. All these alloys are wrought and cast alloys.

Aluminium is the most important element in α alloys. It raises recrystallization temperature of titanium, so Ti–Al alloys have good high-temperature strength. An optimum combination of strength and ductility is obtained with a composition of 5 Al, 2.5 Sn, rest Ti, having good creep resistance. Non-heat-treatable α-alloys have better strength at elevated and cryogenic temperatures than at room temperature.

$\alpha + \beta$ Alloys have maximum strength and less susceptibility to hydrogen embrittlement than α-alloys. Wrought $\alpha + \beta$ alloys are available in the form of stampings, sheets and strips. High-strength fasteners, beams and some fittings for aerospace applications are fabricated from these alloys.

Titanium alloys of β type are developed by adding large amounts of alloying elements, i.e. more than 20 per cent. They are very expensive. A typical β alloy has a composition of 13 V, 11 Cr, 3 Al and 73 Ti, having special characteristics of high fluidity, pressure tightness, small solidification shrinkage, and not susceptible to hot cracking.

Some Ti alloys in annealed condition are given in Table 10.8.

Table 10.8 *Some Ti Alloys in Annealed Condition*

Composition	σ_{ut} (MPa)	Percentage Elongation	Applications
5 Al, 2.5 Sn + Ti	800	16	Gas turbine engine casings
8 Al, 1 Mo, 1 V + Ti	950	15	Jet engine components
6 Al, 4 V + Ti	950	14	Chemical processing equipment, air frame structure

10.13 ZINC

Zinc has an HCP structure, limited solid solubility with other elements, melting temperature of 370–480°C and specific gravity of 7.14. All zinc alloys are soft, and are usually used as cast or wrought.

Pure zinc and high-zinc alloys can be cold worked and drawn into wire and extended. Pure zinc alloys usually contain a fraction of a percent of Cu or Ti. Wrought zincs are used for jar covers, engraving plates, architectural panels and so on. A number of super plastic wrought zinc alloys contain 20–24 per cent aluminium strips and sheets of these alloys can be warm formed by vacuum forming. They have extremely high elongations (100 per cent+).

Because of their low melting point, zinc alloys can be easily cast in a variety of moulds as plaster, metal, graphite and even silicone rubber; they can be die cast also.

These alloys never behave elastically under any stress and they creep at all stress levels and at all temperatures, and there is no definite Young's modulus.

10.13.1 Die Castings

Zinc is alloyed with aluminium, copper, lead and cadmium, but their solubility in zinc is extremely low. The purpose of their addition is to improve strengthening or fabricability. Die casting operations are done at low temperature of 380°C.

Zinc die castings are frequently employed in design. They are inexpensive and have mechanical properties in many respects superior to those of plastics. A typical zinc alloy, AG 40A alloy (CuZinc), has 3 per cent Al, 5.5 per cent Cu, rest Zn, with σ_{ut} = 260 MPa, elongation is 10 per cent and BHN 82. This alloy possesses excellent retention of impact strength and good long-term stability.

10.13.2 Zinc Coatings

Pure zinc has a *corrosion rate of 2.5 µm/year* in normal urban atmosphere. Zinc coating have been used for many years to protect steel against atmospheric corrosion. Zinc is put on steel surface by hot dip galvanizing, electrode-position, diffusions coating, metal spraying and zinc-rich paints. A coating of zinc of 75-µm thickness may provide protection for as long as 30 years in non-industrial, non-coastal environments.

10.14 REFRACTORY METALS

High melting point (greater than 2000°C) is the primary requirement of a refractory metal and these are essentially heat-resistant metals. Four refractory metals, niobium, molybdenum, tantalum and tungsten, have BCC structure and display ductile to brittle transitions. Table 10.9 gives melting point and strength of these refractory metals.

Table 10.9 *Melting Point and Strength of Some Refractory Metals*

Metal	Melting Point (°C)	σ_{ut} (MPa)	
		at 25°C	1000°C
Niobium	2468	310	117
Molybdenum	2023	828	345
Tantalum	2996	345	186
Tungsten	3410	2064	455

Refractory metals and their alloys are heat resistant and are used in the construction of rockets, spaceships, nuclear reactors and various components operating at 1500–2000°C. High resistance against corrosion is the property of all refractory metals, and resists both acids and alkalis. Niobium can be used for nuclear engineering applications, because it possesses low neutrons—capture cross section.

Refractory metals are coated so as to protect against oxidation during service at elevated temperatures. In general, silicide or aluminide coatings are used, which protect oxidation up to 1650°C.

Tantalum is a popular choice in surgical implants because it is inert to body acids and tissues and is easily fabricated. Moreover, tantalum alloys are used in steam turbine blades, valves, nozzles, steels, agitators, containers and pipes in chemical industries. Composition of some tool materials are as follows:

1. Stellites—Co 40–50, Cr 25–30, W 15–30, C 2–4, used for rapid machining of hard metals
2. Cemented carbide—TaC 10 per cent, TiC 15 per cent + cobalt matrix
3. Throway tool ingots—Nb 50 per cent, Ti 30 per cent, W 20 per cent

10.15 SUPERALLOYS

Superlative combinations of properties by using refractory metals like Nb, Mo, W, Ta and Ti as alloying elements are used in high-temperature applications in aircraft turbine components for reasonable long period of operation. These alloys are generally nickel base, with trade names as follows:

1. Waspalloy
2. Astroloy
3. Nimonic
4. Inconel
5. Incoloy

Waspalloy is developed for high operating temperatures of 900°C. Composition of waspalloy is Cr 19, Co 13, Ti 3, Al 1.4, Zr 0.06, C 0.08, rest Ni.

Astrolloy contains Cr 15, Co 17, Ti 3.5, Al 4.0, Mo 5, Zr 0.04, C 0.02, B 0.02, rest Ni.

Nimonic contains Cr 14.5, Co 13.5, Ti 3.8, Al 5, Mo 3.3, Zr 0.04, C 0.15, B 0.01, operating temperature is 870°C, most commonly used.

Inconel contains Cr 15, Ti 2.4, Al 1.0, Nb 1.0, Ta 1.0, Fe 7.0, C 0.04, rest Ni, operating temperature is 820°C. Incoloy contains Co 15, Ti 1.4, Al 0.7, Mo 4.0, Nb 3.0, C 0.05, rest Ni.

10.16 BEARING METALS

In the case of journal bearings, a stationary (bush) bearing is widely used. Requisite properties of such a bearing are as follows:

1. Minimum friction between bearing and rotating journal (shaft).
2. Minimum wear of contacting surface of shaft and bearing.
3. Bearing should be able to withstand contacting pressure.
4. Bearing should have low melting point, so that it can soften and melt to prevent seizure.

Usually, a thin film of lubricating oil separates the surfaces of shaft and bearing. Soft and low-melting alloys for bearing can withstand relatively low pressures. Bimetal bearings use a strong bearing back with a thin layer of softer-bearing alloy, which is metallurgically bonded to strong backing material. So light load-bearing capacity of back-up material along with corrosion-resistant properties of weak bearing alloy make an excellent combination.

Generally, bearing alloy consists of a soft matrix in which hard particles are embedded. During operation, soft matrix wears off rapidly and hard particles stand out in relief. The lubricating oil is retained in between hard particles and matrix of bearing alloys (like leaded bronze).

Some of the bearing metals known as Babbits are listed in Table 10.10.

Table 10.10 *Bearing Alloys*

Alloy	Composition	Applications
Tin babbit	Sn 80, Sb 12, Cu 8	High-speed bearing bushes
Lead babbit	Pb 85, Sb 10, Sn 5	Railway wagon bearings
Silver bearing	Ag 95, Pb 4, Sn 1	Antifriction instrument bearings
Copper bearing (bronze)	Cu 80, Pb 10, Sn 10	Heavy-duty bearings
Nickel–Cadmium bearing	Ni 97, Cd 3	High-temperature bearings

10.17 AIRCRAFT MATERIALS

A few decades ago, mild steel was the only steel used in aircraft construction. Now a days, there are about 20 different kinds of steels regularly used in aircraft construction.

It is a common practice in aircraft construction to heat treat or case harden steel to obtain desirable properties. A galvanized steel wire is made from plain carbon steel. It is used as a locking wire on nuts and turnbuckles and for serving non-flexible cable splices. Plain carbon steels are also used for (1) aircraft nuts, (2) cold-drawn wires for the fabrication of aircraft tie rods and (3) high-carbon plain carbon steel for flat springs and coiled helical springs.

Nickel steels are used to produce bushings, trunnions for mounting machine parts, parts requiring wear-resistant surface combined with shock-resistant core, high-grade machine parts such as aircraft bolts, turnbuckle eyes and forks, and tie rod terminals.

Nickel–chrome steels possess exceedingly hard wear-resisting surface and a tough core. These are generally used in engine construction for gear pins, piston pins, cam rings, push rod ends and rollers, and in parts requiring high strength and good fatigue qualities and has a good creep resistance up to 550°C. Nickel–chrome steels with high strength of the order of 700 MPa are used for wrist pins, starter jaws, timing gears, rear axles and transmission gears for heavy-duty trucks.

Chrome–molybdenum steels (strength 900 MPa) are used for all welded assemblies, sheet fittings and landing gear axles, because of their excellent welding characteristics. To avoid welding cracks, parts made of this steel should be preheated before welding.

Nickel–chrome–molybdenum steels with excellent properties (of high strength and hardness) are used in forged parts as propeller shafts, crankshafts and other large forgings.

Chrome–vanadium steels are strong and tough and have high fatigue resistance. These are used for propeller hubs, welded steel propeller blades, engine bolts and nuts, coil springs and valve springs.

10.17.1 Special Steels

A few examples of special steels are as follows:

1. Silicon–chromium steel—all important springs.
2. Nitriding steel—used for bushings and gears requiring high surface hardness and wear resistance.

3. Austenite manganese steel (Hadfield steel)—has exceptionally high resistance to wear and abrasion, used for *tail skids and arresting hook toes*.

4. Fly Tuf (strength 1500–1800 MPa) is used in aircraft landing gear components, arresting hooks, catapult hooks and structural fittings.

10.17.2 Nickel Alloys

Following are few examples of nickel alloys:

1. Inconel is a nickel–chromium alloy (Ni 79.5 per cent, Cr 13 per cent, Fe 6.5 per cent, Mn 0.25, C 0.08 per cent, Cu 0.20, Si 0.25 per cent). It is a corrosion- and heat-resistant metal, used in exhaust collectors, heat exchangers, jet tail pipe and exhaust manifolds.

2. Monel is a high nickel–copper alloy possessing high strength and excellent resistance to corrosion. Monel has been used in the manufacture of air coolers, strainers and rivets for use with stainless steel.

3. K-monel (A non-ferrous alloy compound mainly of nickel, copper and aluminium) is used for instrument parts in the vicinity of compasses because of its non-magnetic properties. It has excellent corrosion resistance and is used for gears and chains for operating retractable landing gears in amphibian planes.

10.17.3 Copper and Its Alloys

Copper, brass and bronze have a limited use in aircraft constructions. These are mainly used in bearings and fuel tank oil lines. Copper wire is used in electrical system and copper–silicon bronze tubing considerably stronger than copper tubing is used in fuel, oil, water and air lines.

10.17.4 Wrought Aluminium Alloys

Except from fitting, carrying high concentrated loads or parts subjected to severe wear or special forms of corrosion require special alloy steels—today the general structure of the airplane is made of aluminium alloy. The ascendency of this material today is due to its lightweight, high strength, ease of fabrication and its availability in all standard forms. It is one third as heavy as steel and has a strength as high as 520 MPa.

Chemical composition of a typical aluminium alloy 2014 (cladding) is Mn 0.75, Mg 0.8–1.5, Cr 0.35, Cu 0.1, Si 0.35–1.00, Zn 0.2, rest Al. Its applications vary from formed cowling requiring a very ductile material to highly stressed wing beams requiring high strength. Depending upon the requirement, various alloying elements as copper, manganese, silicon, magnesium and zinc are added to aluminium.

The wrought alloys are manufactured in a number of different tempers. The temper designations are O, F, H or T, followed by a number, where

O: indicates annealed wrought material
F: as fabricated
H: strain hardened by cold work
T: heat-treatable alloys

Aluminium alloys can be extruded in aircraft construction channels, angles, T-sections, Z-section and many other structural slopes required.

Aluminium alloys may be forged to close limits to provide light, strong fittings or other structural parts. These forgings have a uniform structure and are free from blowholes, hard spots or cavities.

Electric spot and seam welding of aluminium alloys have been generally adopted for joining non-structural or semistructural parts.

Aluminium alloy rivets for structural parts can be grouped into two categories: (1) those requiring heat treatment just before riveting and (2) those that can be driven as received.

Aluminium alloy castings are frequently used in aircraft constructions. These can be cast by (1) sand casting, (2) permanent mould casting and (3) die casting. A typical aluminium alloy used for casting is A132 alloy, Cu 0.8, Fe 0.8, Si 12.0, Mg 1.0, Ni 2.5, rest Al.

10.17.5 Magnesium Alloys

Magnesium is commonly alloyed with aluminium, zinc and manganese to create usable structural materials. Magnesium alloys have SG = 1.8, as compared to 2.7 for aluminium. The lightweight and relatively high strength of magnesium alloys results in attractive strength to weight ratio for aircraft design. These are used in fairings, ducts, doors, brackets, bulkheads and partitions. These alloys are non-sparking and non-magnetic, which permit their use adjacent to magnetic compasses. A typical magnesium alloy AN 4–25 has a composition of Al 8.5, Mn 0.2, Zn 0.5 and rest Mg with σ_{ut} = 300 MPa, σ_{yp} = 180 MPa, elongation is 5 per cent and BHN 65. Magnesium alloys can be cast, forged and welded.

10.17.6 Plastics

Plexiglass, Lucite and Allite are used in aircraft enclosures, windows, windshields and lenses. The use of thermoplastic sheeting materials for cabin enclosures is universal.

10.17.7 Glass

Bullet-resistant laminated plate glass which is commonly used for windshields of military aircraft is composed of a number of varying thicknesses of plate glass.

Tempered glass is used for large windshields. It is produced by heating glass uniformly over entire surface to 700°C and then suddenly quenching it to room temperature. By this process, the outermost surface of the glass is placed under high compression and inside under tension. Tempered glass has a compressive to tensile strength of about 240 MPa.

10.17.8 Rubber

Various types of rubbers are used in oil and gasoline hose, tank linings, hydraulic accumulator, bags, gaskets, seals, carburettor, diaphragms, barrage balloons, life jackets, gas masks and paint spray hose.

=========================== **KEY POINTS TO REMEMBER** ===========================

❑ Low-carbon steel (C < 0.25 per cent), medium-carbon steel (C 0.25–0.60) and high-carbon steel (C > 0.6 per cent).

❑ In killed steel, oxygen is completely removed by using silicon or aluminium.

❑ Rimmed steels (outer rim of ingot) low in carbon and silicon content can be rolled into sheets, plates, strips and so on.

- ❑ Even very small percentage of hydrogen causes hydrogen embrittlement in steels.
- ❑ High-strength low-alloy (HSLA) steels are plain low-carbon steels with alloying elements like Cu, V, Ni, Mo and Cr, total less than 10 per cent.
- ❑ Oil-quenched and tempered plain high-carbon steels are used for crankshafts, bolts, chisels, hammers, knives, hacksaw blade and so on.
- ❑ Major alloying elements are Al, Cr, Co, Cu, Mn, Mo, Nb, Si, Ti, W and V.
  - • Manganese stabilizes carbides, increases strength and removes bad effects of sulphur.
  - • Nickel acts as graphitizer and stabilizes austenite.
  - • Niobium and titanium provide creep resistance at high temperature.
  - • Tungsten and vanadium form carbides, increase hardness and wear resistance, and are used in high-speed steels.
- ❑ Hadfield steel—used in jaw crusher plates and dredging equipment.
- ❑ Maraging steel, σ_{ut} = 1800 MPa, is used in aircraft under carriage, portable bridges and booster motor in missiles.
- ❑ Invar steel (64 Fe, 36 Ni) has a very low α, coefficient of linear thermal expansion.
- ❑ Ferritic stainless steel—used in automobile exhaust components, valves and combustion chamber.
- ❑ Austenitic stainless steel (non-magnetic) is used in chemical, food processing, cryogenic vessel and domestic appliances
- ❑ Martensitic stainless steel—used in rifle barrels, cutlery, jet engine parts and surgical tools.
- ❑ Grey cast iron (a) moderate cooling—pearlite matrix + graphite flakes, (b) slow cooling—ferrite + graphite flakes
- ❑ Cast iron on fast cooling—white cast iron (pearlite + cementite).
- ❑ Nodular cast iron (or ductile cast iron) by adding cerium or magnesium in molten cast iron.
- ❑ White cast iron on annealing (malleabilizing process)
  - (a) Graphite clusters in pearlite matrix on fast cooling
  - (b) Graphite clusters in ferrite matrix on slow cooling
- ❑ Oxygen-free high-conductivity copper (OFHC).
- ❑ Brass (Cu + Zn), bronzes (aluminium, silicon and phosphor bronzes).
- ❑ Aluminium–lithium alloys are used in aerospace industries due to their low density, high specific strength, excellent fatigue strength and low temperature toughness.
- ❑ Extraordinary properties of titanium alloys are (a) high strength, 1400 MPa at room temperature, (b) easily forged and machined, (c) corrosion resistance, (d) immune to marine and a variety of industrial environments, (e) high melting point and (f) low density.
- ❑ Zinc alloys never behave elastically under any stress at any temperature. They creep at all stress levels and temperatures.
- ❑ Niobium, molybdenum, tantalum and tungsten refractory metals have BCC structure.
- ❑ Superalloys—Waspalloy, Astrolloy, Nimonic, Inconel, Incoloy.
- ❑ Bearing alloys are tin babbit, lead babbit, silver, copper and Ni–Cd bearings.
- ❑ Nickel alloys, Monel, Inconel and K-monel are used in aircraft for various applications.

❑ Aluminium alloy castings are used in aircraft construction.

❑ Magnesium alloys due to lightweight and high specific strength are used in fairings, ducts, doors, brackets, bulk heads and partitions.

MULTIPLE CHOICE QUESTIONS

1. Plain carbon steel contains 1.1 per cent carbon. What is this type of steel?
   (a) Medium carbon steel
   (b) Hypoeutectoid steel
   (c) Hypereutectoid steel
   (d) None of these

2. Which one is a correct statement?
   (A) Silicon in the form of ferrosilicon is used as a deoxidizer.
   (B) Luder's bands are due to presence of nitrogen in mild steel.

   (a) Both (A) and (B)
   (b) Neither (A) nor (B)
   (c) Only A
   (d) Only B

3. In FeE 250 steel 250 stands for?
   (a) 250 MPa as yield strength
   (b) 250 MPa as ultimate strength
   (c) 2.5 per cent of alloying elements
   (d) None of these

4. Type of alloyed plain carbon steel used for drawing dies, punches and drills is
   (a) High-carbon steel
   (b) Medium-carbon steel
   (c) High-speed steel
   (d) None of these

5. Which one of the following alloying element provides creep resistance in steel?
   (a) Titanium   (c) Molybdenum
   (b) Niobium   (d) All of these

6. Steel used for the plates of stone jaw crushers

   (a) High-carbon steel
   (b) Martensitic stainless steel
   (c) Hadfield steel
   (d) Triple-alloy steel

7. Which stainless steel is used in cryogenic vessels?
   (a) Ferritic   (c) Martensitic
   (b) Austenitic   (d) None of these

8. Crankshafts and gears are made from
   (a) Grey cast iron
   (b) White cast iron
   (c) Nodular cast iron
   (d) None of these

9. Graphite clusters are observed in microstructure of which cast iron?
   (a) Grey cast iron
   (b) Nodular cast iron
   (c) White cast iron
   (d) Malleable cast iron

10. What is the commercial name of 60 Ni/40 Cu?
    (a) Yellow brass   (c) Delta brass
    (b) Constantan   (d) None of these

11. Alloy used in highly damage-tolerant aircraft structure parts is
    (a) Silumins   (c) Al–Li alloys
    (b) Duralumin   (d) None of these

12 What is the ultimate strength of a titanium alloy with composition Al 8, V 4, Ti 88
    (a) 500 MPa   (c) 950 MPa
    (b) 650 MPa   (d) None of these

13. Which tool is used for rapid machining of hard metals?
    - (a) Cemented carbide
    - (b) High-speed steel
    - (c) Stellites
    - (d) None of these

14. Which one of the following is not a super-alloy?

    - (a) Waspalloy
    - (b) Incoloy
    - (c) Nimonic
    - (d) Monel

15. What is the percentage of tin in lead–babbit?
    - (a) 10
    - (b) 5
    - (c) 8
    - (d) None of these

Answers

1.(c)   2. (a)   3. (a)   4. (a)   5. (d)   6. (c)   7. (b)   8. (c)
9.(d)   10. (b)   11. (c)   12. (c)   13. (c)   14. (d)   15. (b)

REVIEW QUESTIONS

1. Differentiate among low-, medium- and high-carbon steels. Give applications of each.

2. What are the differences among killed, semikilled and rimmed steels?

3. Discuss the effect of sulphur, phosphorus and hydrogen on the properties of steels.

4. Explain how low- and medium-alloy steels are designated as per Indian standards.

5. What are high-strength, low-alloy steels?

6. Discuss the effect of Mo, Ti, W and V as alloying elements or the mechanical properties of steels.

7. What are Ni–Cr–Mo steels? What are their applications?

8. Describe the following steels
   Maraging steel, weathering steel and triple-alloy steel

9. What is a stainless steel? What are ferritic, austenitic and martensitic stainless steels?

10. What is the effect of rate of cooling on microstructures of grey CI?

11. What is white iron? What are pearlite and martensitic white cast irons?

12. How nodular cast iron is obtained?

13. What are high-strength cast irons? What are Nicrosilal, Ni-resist and Ni-hard cast irons?

14. What are α and β phases in Cu/Zinc alloys?

15. Give applications of following copper-base alloys:
    Admirality brass, maganin, beryllium copper and muntz metal

16. What is the importance of Al–Li alloys?

17. What are wrought magnesium and cast magnesium alloys?

18. What are the applications of Ti-base alloys?

19. What are throway inserts? Where are they used?

20. What are superalloys?

21. Write a short note on bearing alloys.

22. What are the applications of wrought aluminium and cast aluminium alloys in aircraft structure?

11 ORGANIC MATERIALS

11.1 INTRODUCTION

Plastics are generally referred to as polymeric material. 'Poly' stands for many and 'mer' stands for parts, so polymer is an organic material with repeating molecular units (called mer) that can be formed into usable solid shapes by casting, sintering or melt processing. As ethylene consists of two carbon atoms and four hydrogen atoms and *polymer has n degree of polymerization*, the bonds on carbon atoms are unsaturated and these molecules can form covalent bonds with similar molecules to form a polymer chain.

Majority of the items of daily use such as skin, clothes, paper, hair and paint are made of organic polymers. Moreover, teeth muscle, glue, cling film, starch, crab cells and marmalade are all polymeric based. There are natural polymers like shellac, rosin, amber and rubber, and also synthetic polymers used as adhesives and lubricants in children's toys and aircraft parts. Paper is manufactured from cellulose of plants. Wood is composed of chains of cellulose molecules bonded together by another natural polymer called 'lignin'. Other natural polymers such as proteins, enzymes, starch and cellulose are important in biological processes in plants and physiological processes in animals.

The first synthetic moldable polymer was cellulose nitrate, and next phenolics were developed. Nylon replaced silks and vinyls replaced leathers. Then engineering polymers were developed with specific application. Vulcanization of rubber improved the durability of natural polymer rubber and greatly improved its strength. Polymers as polymethyl methacrylate find applications as photo-resist materials used in semiconductor manufacturing for use in high-performance microprocessor. Kevlar (aramid fibres) is a liquid crystal having excellent mechanical properties.

In this chapter, we will discuss natural and synthetic polymers, degree of polymerization, strengthening mechanism in polymers, thermoplastics and thermosetting plastics and special-purpose plastics.

11.2 TYPES OF ORGANIC MATERIALS

The materials in which carbon is the basic component are known as 'organic materials'. These are natural and synthetic organic materials, listed as in Table 11.1. Organic materials have strong covalent bonds.

Table 11.1 *Natural and Synthetic Organic Materials*

Natural Organic Materials	Synthetic Organic materials
1. Wood	1. Plastics
2. Biological fibres like jute and hemp	2. Oils
3. Rubber	3. Solvents
4. Coal	4. Adhesives
5. Petroleum products	5. Dyes
6. Food	6. Synthetic rubber
7. Cotton	7. Explosives
8. Flax	8. Lubricants

11.2.1 Monomers

A monomer is a small molecule, which on polymerization converts into a large molecule called a polymer, for example, ethylene, vinyl chloride and vinyl alcohol as shown in Figure 11.1.

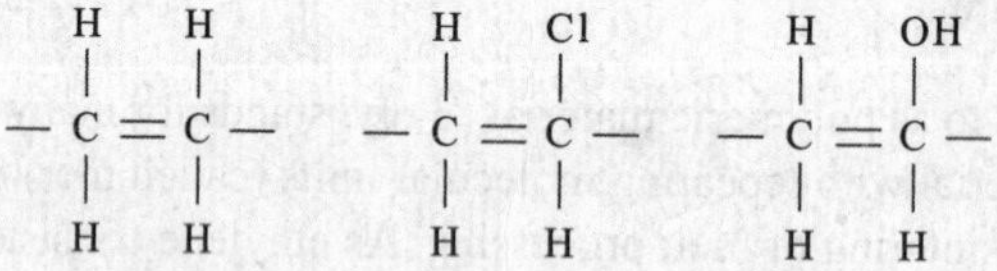

Ethylene　　Vinyl chloride　　Vinyl alcohol

Figure 11.1 *Some Monomers*

Polymers are composed of a large number of monomers, repeating in a long chain or network.

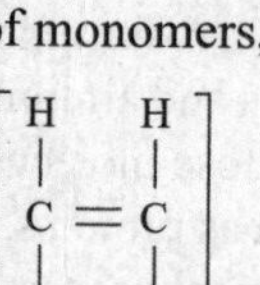

where n stands for degree of polymerization.
The structure of polyethylene chain is shown in Figure 11.2.

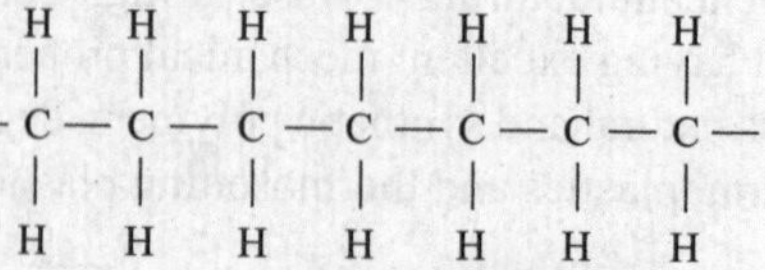

Polyethylene $(C_2H_4)_n$

Figure 11.2 *Polyethylene Chain*

There are natural polymers such as proteins, cellulose (in plants), shellac, lignin (in wood), hemp, silk, jute, starch, resin and so on. Besides there are a large number of synthetic polymers. A few commonly used synthetic polymers are polyethylene, polystyrene, polypropylene, nylon, polyvinyl chloride, plex-iglass (polymethyl methacrylate), polytetra fluoroethylene (PTFE) and orlon (polyacrylonitrile).

The molecular weight of a polymer is important in the determination of its properties. For example, a high-molecular-weight polyethylene has different properties than a low-molecular-weight polyethylene; low-molecular-weight synthetic oils have different properties than a high-molecular-weight oil.

11.3 TYPES OF POLYMERS

In polymer science, a single type of polymer molecule can be classified by one or more criteria, which may describe the arrangement of repeating subunits, chemical nature of repeating subunits and presence or absence of multifunctional junctions.

Depending upon the arrangement of monomers, polymers are classified as follows:

1. *Homopolymer*: Single monomer is repeated such as polyethylene or polymethyl methacrylate.
2. *Copolymer*: Two or more monomer species are repeated regularly or randomly such as in ethyl-vinyl acetate.

Depending upon the chemical nature of repeating monomers, polymers are classified as follows:

1. *Organic polymer*: Molecule is composed of organic-based monomers. Organic polymers with distinct biological functions are called biopolymers. Important biopolymers are polypeptides and proteins, and polysaccharides (starch, chitin and cellulose).
2. *Inorganic polymer*: Molecule is composed of inorganic repeating units. Silicones and polyphosphazenes are inorganic polymers.
3. *Polyelectrolyte*: Molecule is comprised of primarily ionizable repeating subunits. An 'ionomer' molecule is ionizable.

Depending upon the presence or absence of multifunctional junctions sites, polymers are classified as follows:

1. *Linear polymer*: One or more monomer species are arranged in a linear chain.
2. *Branched polymer*: This is comprised of a main chain with one or more substituent side chains or branches.
3. *Cross-linked polymers*: Adjacent linear chains are connected to each other by covalent bonds.
4. *Network polymers*: These are trifunctional mer units having three active covalent bonds forming a three-dimensional network.

Branched polymer molecules are further classified on the basis of branching arrangement as follows:

1. *Graft polymer*: Molecule is a branched polymer molecule in which one or more side chains are different from the main chain.
2. *Star polymer molecule*: A single branch point gives rise to multiple linear chains or arms. If the arms are identical, then the star polymer molecule is regular. If the adjacent arms are comprised of different repeating subunits, star polymer molecule is variegated.
3. *Comb polymer*: Molecule is comprised of a main chain with two or more three-way branch points and linear side chains.
4. *Brush polymer*: Molecule is comprised of a main chain with linear, unbranched side chains and where one or more of the branch points has four-way or more functionality.

11.4 DEGREE OF POLYMERIZATION

During polymerization process, large macromolecules are synthesized from smaller molecules resulting in chain lengths or molecular weights. Chain length of a polymer is the degree of polymerization n, which represents the average number of mer units in a chain.

Degree of polymerization,

$$n = \frac{M_n}{m}$$

where m is the molecular weight of a mer and M_n is the number of average molecular weight.

In terms of weight average n_w

$$M_w = m \times n_w$$

where M_w is the average molecular weights.

A lower value of n forms a light oil and higher value results into a solid plastic. Degree of polymerization of rubber to plastic ranges from 75 to 750.

Example 11.1 Determine the molecular weight of PTFE (Teflon) where $n = 100,000$

Solution:

Teflon monomer $CF_2 = CF_2$

$$m = 2C + 4F = 2 \times 12 + 4 \times 19 = 100$$

$$M_n = 100,000 \times 100 = 10^7$$

11.5 GEOMETRY OF POLYMERIC CHAINS

The bond angle varies with the type of atoms connected to the backbone atoms. Figure 11.3(a) and (b) shows bond angles between carbon atoms and ethylene monomers.

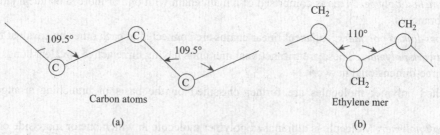

(a)   (b)

Figure 11.3 *Polymeric Chains–Bond Angles*

Single-chain bonds are capable of rotation and bending in three dimensions.

A third carbon atom may lie at any point on cone of revolution and still subtend an angle of 109.5° with the bond with other atoms.

Average end-to-end distance l_a in a freely rotating polymeric chain is determined by $l_a^2 = \lambda n r_0^2$, where λ is a constant, r_0 is the interatomic distance and n is the number of bonds as shown in Figure 11.4.

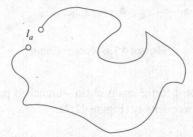

Figure 11.4 *Freely Rotating Polymeric Chain*

Polymers consist of large numbers of molecular chains, each of which may bond, coil and kink in the manner as shown in Figure 11.4. The length of the extended chain can be obtained from the generation of bonds or links (or mers) as shown in Figure 11.5.

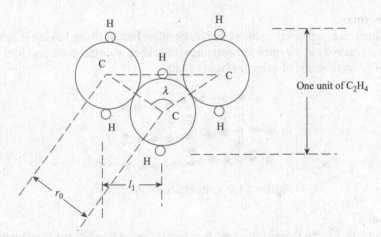

Figure 11.5 *Geometry of Extended Chain*

Length l of extended chain, $l = nr_0 \sin \theta/2$ as shown in Figure 11.5, where n is the number of bonds, r_0 is the interatomic distance between carbon atoms and θ is the bond angle.

11.5.1 Molecular Structure

The physical properties of a polymer not only depend on its molecular weight and shape, but also on differences in the structure of molecular chains. Different types of structures obtained are linear, branched, cross-linked and network in addition to many isomeric configurations.

Linear Polymers

The mer units are joined end to end in a single chain. Long chains are flexible. Polymers, which form linear chains are polyethylene, polyvinyl chloride, polystyrene, PMMA, nylon and fluorocarbons (Figure 11.6).

Figure 11.6 *Linear Chain*

Branched Chains

In this, side branches are connected to the main chain—branched polymer. Side branches lower the packing efficiency, resulting in lower density (Figure 11.7).

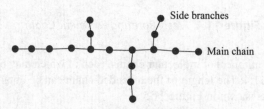

Figure 11.7 *Branched Polymer*

Cross-Linked Polymers

Adjacent linear chains are connected to each other by covalent bonds. Cross-linking is achieved by carrying out chemical reactions at elevated temperatures. In rubber, vulcanization provides cross-linking by the addition of additive atoms of sulphur (Figure 11.8).

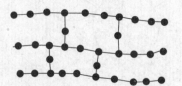

Figure 11.8 *Cross-linked Polymers*

Network Polymers

Trifunctional mer units, having three active covalent bonds form a three-dimensional network. Highly cross-linked polymer may be termed as network polymers. Epoxies and phenol formaldehyde belong to this group of polymers (Figure 11.9).

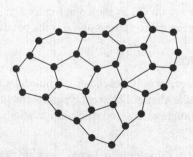

Figure 11.9 *Three-dimensional Network*

Polymers are not of strictly one distinctive type. A linear polymer may have branches and cross-linking.

11.6 MECHANISM OF POLYMERIZATION

In the formation of long-chain polymers, various monomers join the molecules together. They join each other only where the molecules are available at the ends of the chain. It is therefore necessary that the sites for polymerization reaction must exist in each monomer. These reactions may be bifunctional, trifunctional or tetrafunctional, if the available reaction sites are 2, 3 and 4, respectively.

Ethylene is bifunctional and it has two active bonds that covalently bind each other. It may also bind with two other units in forming a two-dimensional chain-like molecular structure. Phenol formaldehyde is trifunctional, and it has three active bonds from which a three-dimensional molecular network structure results as shown in Figure 11.10.

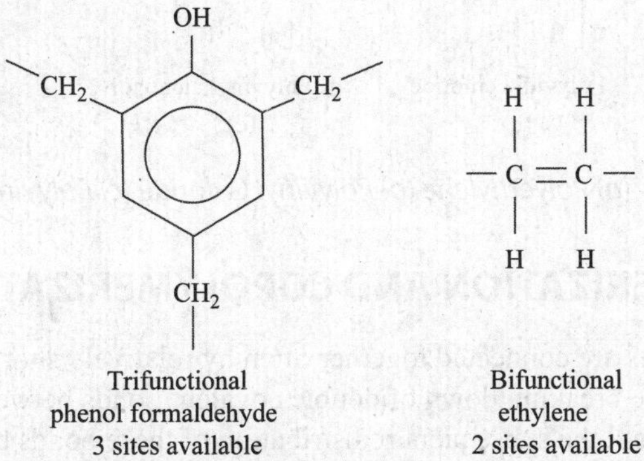

Figure 11.10 *Phenol Formaldehyde*

Trifunctional phenol formaldehyde 3 sites available

Bifunctional ethylene 2 sites available

There are two ways of attaching individual molecules to each other:

1. Molecules can physically link to each other like string beads on a string—addition polymerization.
2. A new molecule can be attached to another molecule by a chemical reaction—condensation polymerization.

In addition polymerization, the starting material is a monomer and the polymer resulting from polymerization has the same repeating units as the starting monomer. Addition polymerization is used in polyethylene, propylene, polyvinyl, chloride, polystyrene and so on.

In condensation polymerization, the repeating molecules in the polymer chain are different from the starting monomer. *Water is generally a by-product* of the chemical reaction, i.e. condensation. Some polymers like epoxies are formed by strong primary chemical bonds called cross-linking.

A catalyst of some form or an elevated temperature or pressure may be required to initiate both addition and condensation polymerizations. Length of polymeric chain can be controlled by processing parameters or by the type of the catalyst. To a designer, the molecular weight is important for finding out properties. For example, a high-molecular-weight polyethylene has different properties than a low-molecular-weight polyethylene; low-molecular-weight synthetic oils have different properties than a high-molecular-weight oil.

The physical structure of atoms in polyethylene is shown in Figure 11.11(a). Similarly, monomers of polyvinyl chloride and polyvinyl alcohol are given in Figure 11.11(b) and (c).

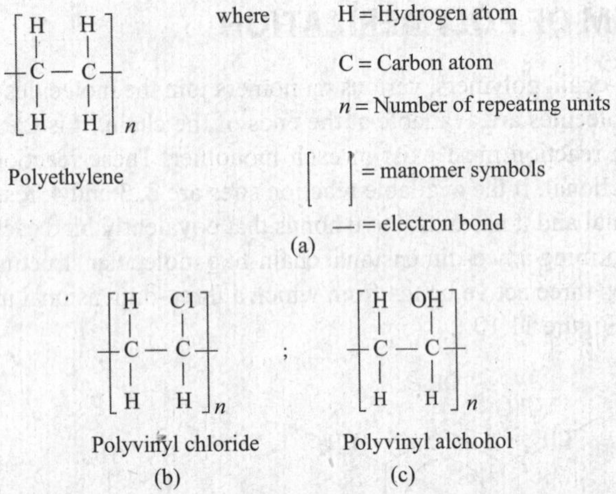

where   H = Hydrogen atom

C = Carbon atom

n = Number of repeating units

Polyethylene

$\begin{bmatrix} & | \\ | & \end{bmatrix}$ = manomer symbols

— = electron bond

(a)

Polyvinyl chloride   Polyvinyl alchohol

(b)   (c)

Figure 11.11 *(a) Polyethylene (b) Polyvinyl Chloride (c) Polyvinyl Alcohol*

11.7 HOMOPOLYMERIZATION AND COPOLYMERIZATION

In polymerization, long chains are connected together often by relatively short cross-links. The polymerization reaction involves the breaking down of double covalent bonds between the two carbon atoms (within ethylene molecules) and the subsequent redistribution of these bonds between a whole series of carbon atoms.

Various types of polymerization processes are as follows:

1. Addition polymerization
2. Copolymerization
3. Condensation polymerization

The addition of *monomers of the same kind* is known as homopolymerization and the addition of *different kinds of monomers* is known as copolymerization. In case of addition polymerization, the covalent bonds of monomers are broken and the monomers are combined together by single bonds. Addition homopolymerization of polypropylene is shown in Figure 11.12.

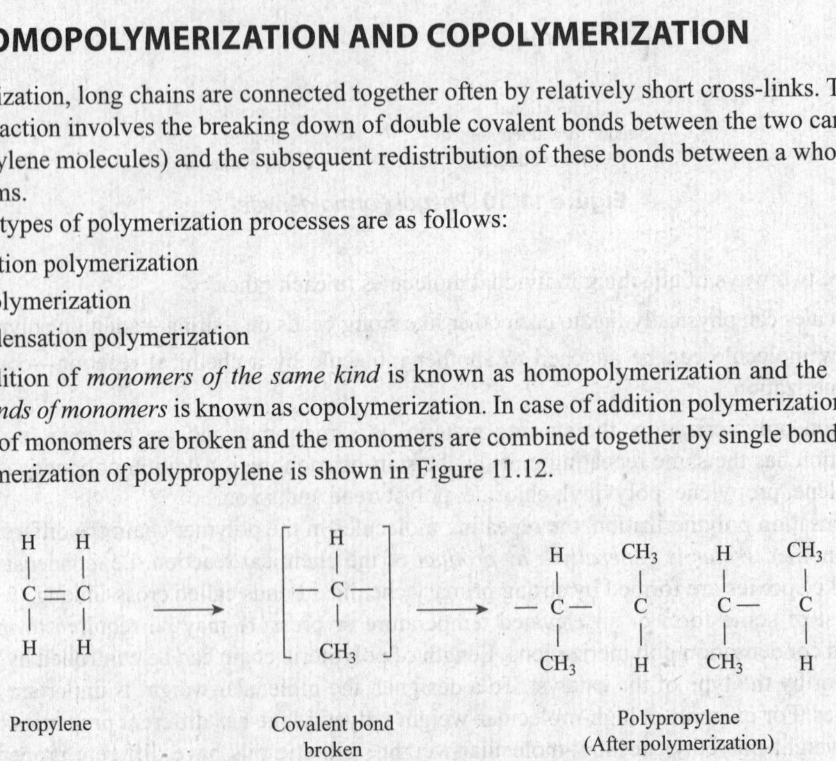

Propylene   Covalent bond
broken   Polypropylene
(After polymerization)

Figure 11.12 *Homo-polymerization of Polypropylene*

The formation of copolymers extends the possibilities of creating new types of plastics with improved physical and mechanical properties.

It is possible to form a copolymer by joining together different monomers in the same chain where A and B represent different monomer units.

Copolymers with different monomer units are as follows:

Linear polymers   A — A — A — A — A
                      B — B— B — B — B

Regular polymers   A — B —A — B — A — B

Random polymers   A — B — B — A — A — A — B — B — A — B

Block polymers   A — B — B — B — A — A — A — B — B — B — A — A — A — B

Following are few examples:

1. Chain may be composed of vinyl chloride and vinyl acetate.
2. Chain of butadiene–styrene.
3. Phenol and formaldehyde—resulting structure is phenol formaldehyde (bakelite).

Figure 11.13 shows copolymerization of butadiene and styrene.

where Ⓡ is

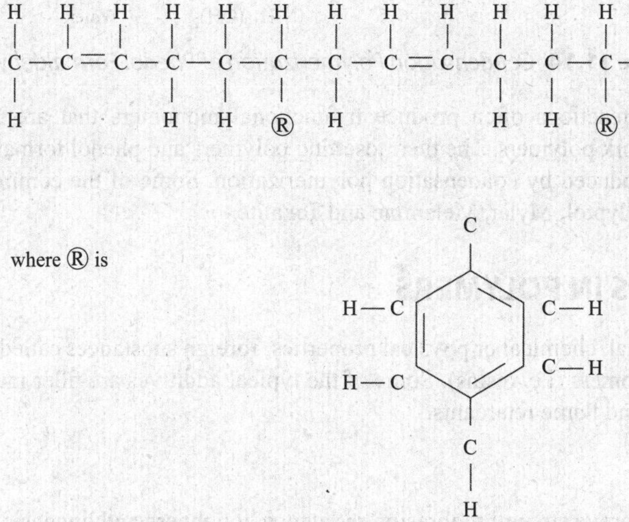

Figure 11.13 *Copolymerization of Butadiene and Styrene*

11.8 CONDENSATION POLYMERIZATION

The process in which two or more chemically different monomers are polymerized to form a cross-link polymer along with a by-product such as water and ammonia is known as condensation polymerization. For example,

$$\text{Methyl alcohol + acetic acid} \rightarrow \text{ester + water}$$

In addition to chain polymers, three-dimensional network polymers can also be formed, which are known as cross-linked polymers. For example,

Formaldehyde (HCHO) + phenol (C_6H_5OH) → cross-linked phenol formaldehyde + water (bakelite)

Figure 11.14 shows the condensation polymerization of phenol formaldehyde.

$$CH_2O \qquad C_6H_5OH \qquad C_6H_5OH$$
Formaldehyde   Phenol

⟶   Phenol formaldehyde + H₂O

$$C_{12}H_{10}(OH)_2 \qquad Water$$

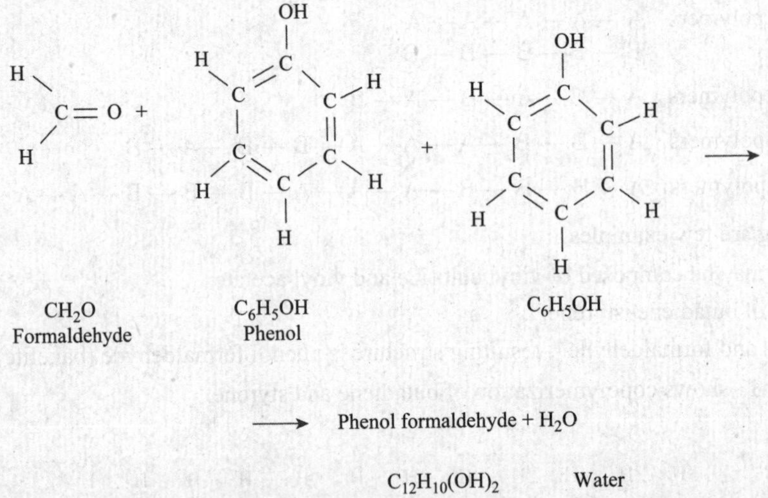

Figure 11.14 *Condensation Polymerization of Phenol Formaldehyde*

The condensation reactions often produce trifunctional monomers that are capable of forming cross-linked and network polymers. The thermosetting polymers and phenol formaldehyde, nylons and polycarbonates are produced by condensation polymerization. Some of the commercial condensation polymers are Durez, Glyptol, Mylar, Melamine and Texalite.

11.9 ADDITIVES IN POLYMERS

To modify the medicinal, chemical or physical properties, foreign substances called additives are intentionally added in monomers (i.e. resins). Some of the typical additives are filler materials, plasticizers, stabilizers, colorants and flame retardants.

11.9.1 Fillers

Additives of fillers improve strengths, abrasion resistance, toughness and dimensional and thermal stability of the plastic material. Particle fillers such as wood flour, silica flour, sand, glass, clay, talc, limestone and even some synthetic polymers are added, which are inexpensive materials and reduce the cost of the final products.

11.9.2 Plasticizers

Plasticizers improve flexibility, ductility and toughness of polymers and brittleness of plastics is reduced. In effect, plasticizers lower the glass transition temperature, for example some plasticizers are tricresyl phosphate, camphor, resins and organic solvents. Plasticizers are used in the production of thin sheets, films, tubings, rain coats and curtains. For example, PVC is hard at room temperature, but is plasticized by tricresyl phosphate.

11.9.3 Stabilizers

Some polymeric materials have poor mechanical integrity and they rapidly deteriorate under normal environmental conditions, especially UV rays and oxidation cause deteriorations. Additives that counteract these deterioration processes are called stabilizers. For example, hindered amines and benzophenones act as UV stabilizers, and organophosphites act as heat stabilizers.

11.9.4 Catalysts

Catalysts act as accelerators and hardeners. They increase the rate of reaction of polymerizations. For example, benzoyl peroxide with tricresyl phosphate in the form of paste acts as catalyst. Similarly, acetyl peroxide in liquid form act as catalyst.

11.9.5 Initiators

The addition of hydrogen peroxide helps to initiate the polymerization process.

11.9.6 Colourants

Colourants impart specific colour to the polymer in the form of dyes and pigments. Dyes are dissolved and become a part of molecular structures of polymers. Pigments are filler materials that do not dissolve. They remain in small particle size and are transparent. Generally, metallic oxides act as pigments, e.g. sulphur diodes, quinacridones and titanium dioxide.

11.9.7 Flame Retardants

For the manufacture of children's toys and textiles, flammability of polymer is of important considerations. Flame retardants enhance the flammability resistance. The retardants interface with the combustion process through the gas phase or by initiating a chemical reaction that causes a cooling of combustion region and cessation of burning. For example, antimony oxides and reactive bromates act as flame retardants.

11.10 STRENGTHENING MECHANISMS OF POLYMERS

Polymers are generally weak polymeric chains and to increase their strengths several techniques are used: (1) crystallization, (2) cross-linking and (3) chain stiffening.

Crystallization Crystallization is obtained by mechanical working or by the formation of hydrogen bond. Long chain molecules are either non-crystalline or semi-crystalline. By mechanical working, the long chains are aligned, for example, a low-density polyethylene (LDPE) with a relative density of 0.92 and crystallinity of 50% is converted into a high-density polyethylene (HDPE) with a relative density of 0.96 and crystallinity of 80% with the help of mechanical deformation as shown in Figure 11.15.

Non-crystalline   Semi-crystalline   Crystalline

Figure 11.15 *Alignment of Long Chain Molecules*

Polymers are bonded by weak Van der Waal's bonds between the polymeric chains. If these Van der Waal's bonds are replaced by hydrogen bonds, the crystallinity of polymer is increased, thereby increasing the strength. For example, cellulose and nylon are strengthened by this mechanism.

Cross-linking During cross-linking, covalent bonds are formed in segments of polymeric chains. Cross-linking is an irreversible process and very much dependent on the temperature. During vulcanization, cross-linking of isoprene polymers takes place by sulphur atoms. Cross-linking greatly improves the mechanical strength as in the case of vulcanized rubber, which is 10 times the strength of unvulcanized rubber.

Cross-linking of rubber by oxygen is harmful, and it leads to loss of flexibility and increased brittleness. This is called *ageing of polymer*.

The phenomenon of cross-linking involves primary bonds between polymer chains as shown in Figure 11.16. Greater the degree of cross-linking, greater is the rigidity of the material and the lesser it responds to remelting.

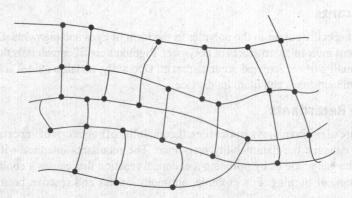

Figure 11.16 *Cross-linked Polymers*

Chain stiffening In general, in polymeric chains, carbon-to-carbon bonds act as pivot points for the chain to bind. This bonding is presented if a pendant group is present at pivot points, marking the polymer as rigid, for example, the presence of a large benzene ring as an integral part of the polystyrene polymer causes a reduction in mobility of chain and increase its rigidly as shown in Figure 11.17.

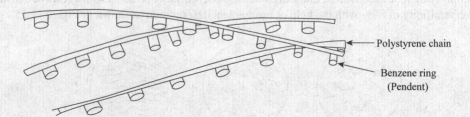

Polystyrene chain

Benzene ring
(Pendent)

Figure 11.17 *Polystyrene Chains with Benzene Rings*

Larger pendant groups on the chain specially increase the stiffness and strength. By stiffening methods, polymers acquire various structural shapes like network and frame work as shown in Figure 11.18.

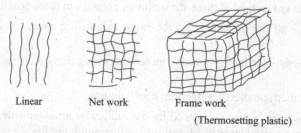

| Linear | Net work | Frame work |

(Thermosetting plastic)

Figure 11.18 *Structural Shapes of Polymers*

Ethylene is a bifunctional monomer producing a linear structure, but phenol formaldehyde produces a network and a framework.

11.10.1 Graft Copolymers

When branches of different monomers are added to a linear chain, a graft copolymer is obtained as a branched chain polymer as shown in Figure 11.19. Natural rubber and acrylonitrile are examples of graft-branched copolymer.

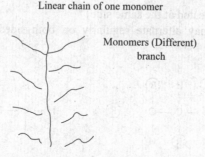

Linear chain of one monomer

Monomers (Different) branch

Figure 11.19 *Grafted-branched Chain*

11.10.2 Deformation of Polymers

Deformation of polymers is affected by their structural configuration. As the bonding force between the molecules is small, permanent deformations takes place due to slip between the adjacent molecules; however, the intermolecular bonds do not break due to this deformation by slip. Plastics deform early under pressure and high temperature, which are called thermoplastics.

If there is a continuous three-dimensional network or frame work of molecules, slip does not take place between the molecules. Moreover, primary covalent bonds exist throughout the structure. This type of polymerized plastic is known as thermosetting plastic, e.g. phenol formaldehyde and epoxy.

11.11 STEREOTACTIC SYNTHESIS

In stereotactic synthesis, the term 'stereo' stands for space and 'tactic' stands for arrangement, i.e. three-dimensional synthesis or three-dimensional configurations.

Long molecular chains are formed in three-dimensional network in three possible ways as follows:

1. Isotactic synthesis—all the molecules on the same side of the chain (molecules having high symmetry)
2. Syndiotactic synthesis—for less symmetric molecules or regularly alternating from one side to the other
3. Atactic—least symmetric molecules, random configuration

Properties of molecules are highly influenced by the molecular arrangements as explained earlier. For a polymer, the melting point, density, crystallinity and strength are higher in the case of isotactic arrangement than in other two types of arrangements.

The methyl group (CH_3) in polypropylene may all be on one side as shown in Figure 11.20, i.e isotactic arrangements.

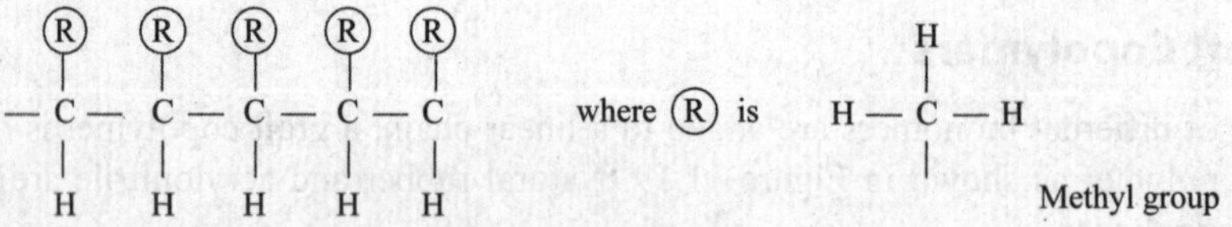

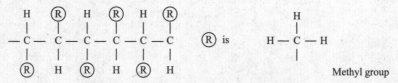

Figure 11.20 *Isotactic Arrangements*

Isotactic—(pendant® groups located at the same side)
Syndrotactic—methyl group may alternate regularly on both sides of the chain as shown in Figure 11.21.

Figure 11.21 *Syndrotactic Arrangements*

Actactic—methyl group may be randomly placed anywhere along the chain as shown in Figure 11.22.

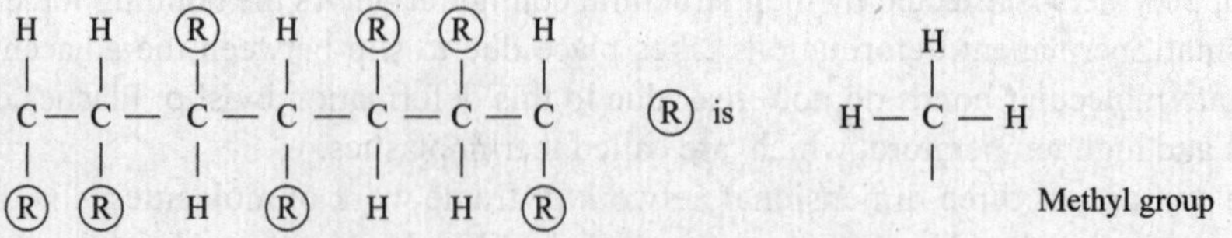

Figure 11.22 *Actactic Arrangements*

Example: Draw molecular chain of polystyrene (PS) (Figure 11.23).

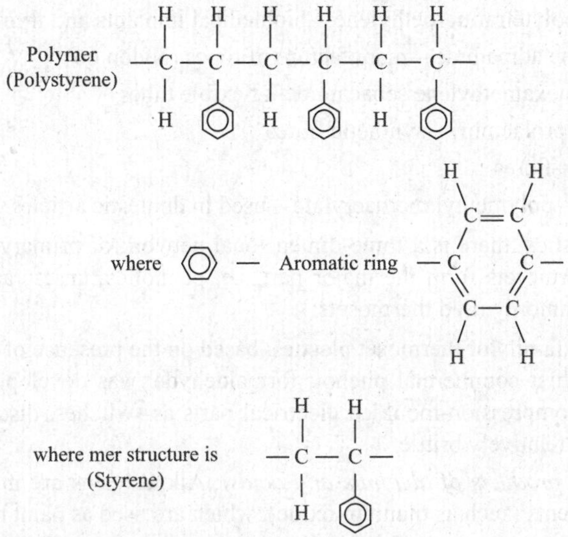

Figure 11.23 *Molecular Chain of Polystyrene*

11.12 PLASTICS

Generally, polymer is termed as plastic. ASTM defines plastic as a material that contains an essential ingredient, an organic substance of large molecular weight, which is solid in its finished state and at some stage in its manufacture or processing into finished article, can be shaped by flow. 'Basically, plastic is a mixture of resin, catalyst, accelerator, inhibitor and pigment'. Resin forms the major part of this mixture, i.e. 80–90 per cent.

Plastics can be broadly classified into two categories depending upon their elevated temperature characteristics: (1) thermoplastic and (2) thermosetting plastics. A thermoplastic material will flow at elevated temperature (above the glass transition temperature) and solidified polymer can be repeated as many times as desired and it will behave in the same manner.

Thermoplastics contain linear chains, a two-dimensional structure and are termed as '*linear polymers*'. But in thermosetting plastics, once the shape is formed by casting or plastic flow, it will no longer melt or flow on reheating. In thermosetting plastics, cross-linking takes place during polymerization and a strong network is formed. Strong covalent bonds formed prevent the material from remelting. During reheating, they burn a sublime.

There are many low-cost fabrication techniques available for thermoplastics, but for thermosetting materials, more expensive fabrication processes are required.

Thermoplastics become soft on heating and no hardening takes place. They possess excellent plasticity, but have a low melting point. A few examples of commonly used thermoplastics are as follows:

1. Polyethylene—for bags, toys and containers
2. Polypropylene—used for ropes, moulded bottles, carpeting and fibres

3. Polystyrene—used for sound proofing in buildings, refrigerators and consumer products
4. Polyvinyl chloride—Gramophone records, electrical insulators, piping, guards, ducts and tanks
5. Teflon (PTFE)—polytetrafluoroethylene—biomedical implants and frying pans
6. Polyhexamethylene adipamide—manufacture of ropes (Nylon 66)
7. Nylon 610—polyhexamethylene sebacamide—flexible tubes
8. Nylon 6—(polycaprolactum)—synthetic fibres
9. Cellulose acetate—fibres
10. Perspex–PMMA—polymethyl methacrylate—used in domestic articles

In thermosetting plastics, there is a three-dimensional network of primary bonds in all directions. These categories of thermosets form the major part, i.e. phenolics, unsaturated polyesters and urea. Following are some commonly used thermosets:

1. *Phenolics*: Oldest family of thermoset plastics, based on the presence of a ring structure alcohol and phenol. The first commercial phenol, formaldehyde, was developed as 'bakelite'. It was widely used for compression-moulded electrical parts as switches, distributor caps and so on. But phenolics are relatively brittle.

2. *Alkydes (reaction products of alcohols and acids)*: Alkyd resins are mixed with oils (such as linseed) and pigments (such as titanium oxide), which are used as paint bases.

3. *Melamine formaldehyde*: Melamine formaldehyde is a rigid thermosetting polymer with a network type of structure, resistant to UV rays. Many plastic dishes are made from this material. These are also used for electrical devices and laminates for surfaces.

4. *Urea formaldehyde*: They are often used as adhesives for large moulded building trusses and beams. They are also used for electrical devices, circuit breakers and switches. They are not resistant to UV rays. Urea is used in making plywoods.

5. *Unsaturated polyesters*: There are a number of polyesters with a significant range of properties. There are two groups in this category: (1) thermosetting resins with cross-linking structure and (2) thermoplastic polyester, highly crystalline in structure and with high melting points. Most important use of polyesters is in composites with polyester resin acting as matrix. Other uses of polyesters are in tanks and portable shelters, boats, fishing poles and autos, and also in GRP (glass fibre-reinforced plastic composites).

6. *Epoxy*: This is more expensive. In addition to commercial applications, it is extensively used in polymer matrix composites (PMCS) of aerospace application .

7. *Silicones*: These are used as composite matrix resins for special application, where operating temperature is high, as high as 340°C. These are available as rigid thermosets.

11.13 FIBRES AND FILAMENTS

The fibre polymers can be drawn into long filaments with minimum length to diameter ratio of 100:1. These drawn fibres are used in textile industry to make fabric or cloth. They have much higher stiffness and strength along the axial direction, but in the transverse direction both stiffness and strength are very less. These fibres must have several mechanical properties as they are subjected to mechanical deformation as stretching, twisting, shearing and abrasion. So, they have high tensile modulus and high tensile strength, as well as good abrasion resistance. *Aramid fibres* possess high strength comparable to the strength of metals and are used in making *high-strength composites*.

There are natural fibres like wool, cellulose, cotton, jute and silk, and synthetic fibres like nylon, terylene, rayon, orlon and Kevlar. In sanforized cotton clothes, long chains are made to align and they are made non-shrinkable. Nylon 66 (a thermoplastic) does not soften easily under temperature and they are used in automobile tyres as nylon cords.

Synthetic fibres are produced by three-different methods like: (1) melt extrusion, (2) wet spinning and (3) dry spinning.

Nylon (polyamides) and terylene fibres are melt spun. Viscous rayon fibres are produced by wet spinning cellulose acetate and polyacrylonitriles (orlon or acrilan) are the products of dry spinning.

When the polymer is fast spun into a filament, chain molecules are arranged randomly, but in the next step, chains are straightened and oriented parallel to the direction of fibre axis. Stretching or cold working of fibres gives high tenacity and melting point to them.

11.14 ELASTOMERS AND RUBBERS

Elastomers are rubbery materials capable of extending to several times of its length under the applied load. When the load is removed, they return to their original dimensions. In addition to natural elastomer (rubber), there are several man-made elastomers. Natural rubber is derived from latex, a viscous milky fluid containing a linear polymer of isoprene. The monomer of isoprene is given in Figure 11.24.

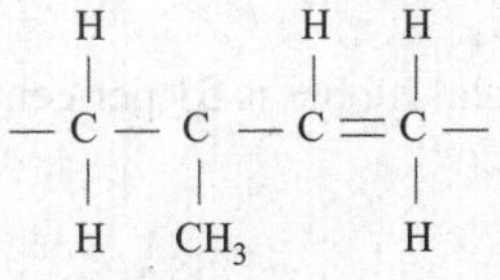

Figure 11.24 *Isoprene Monomer*

This arrangement results in a natural tendency for the chain to bend, promoting rubbery behaviour. For a polymer to be an elastomer at room temperature, its glass transition temperature T_g must be well below the room temperature and the chain molecule segments must be in a state of constant translational motion with respect to neighbouring atoms. Additives are blended in raw rubber to get desired properties. Examples of commonly used additives are accelerators (catalyst) like lime, magnesia, and litharge; antioxidants (negative catalyst), organic compounds and reinforcing agents such as carbon black and zinc oxide; and plasticizers such as stearic acid, vegetable oils and sulphur.

The tear resistance and low hysteresis make natural rubbers useful for shock-absorbing parts and for large vehicle tires.

11.14.1 Vulcanization

One requisite property for elastomer behaviour is that the molecular structure is lightly cross-linked. This cross-linking is provided by vulcanization, obtained by a non-reversible chemical reaction normally carried out at higher temperatures (110–140°C). In most vulcanizing reactions, sulphur compounds are added to the heated elastomers, and chains of sulphur atoms bond with adjacent polymer backbone chain and cross-link as shown in Figure 11.25.

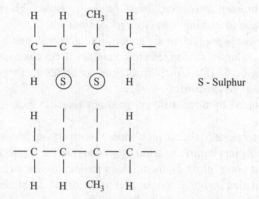

Figure 11.25 *Sulphur Cross-linking the Chain of Isoprene During Vulcanization*

More the number of cross-links, more will be the degree of vulcanization, resulting in stiffer and rigid rubber. Tensile modulus of vulcanized rubber is about 100 times the tensile modulus of unvulcanized rubber and its tensile strength (30 MPa) is about 10 times the tensile strength of unvulcanized rubber (3 MPa).

Unvulcanized rubber is soft and tacky, and has a poor resistance to abrasion. Useful rubber results when about 1–5 parts (by weight) of sulphur are added to 100 parts of rubber. These are thermosetting in nature due to cross-linking. The cross-links enable the chains to be pulled back to their original positions without slipping past one another.

Constitutional composition of a typical rubber is 51 per cent isoprene, 27 per cent butadiene, 16 per cent sulphur and 6 per cent carbon black.

11.14.2 Synthetic Rubbers

Synthetic rubbers are superior to natural rubbers. These are manufactured from raw materials like coal tar, petroleum, coke, limestone, natural gas, alcohol, ammonia, salt and sulphur. Most important synthetic elastomer is styrene butadiene rubber (SBR), used commonly in automobile tires reinforced with carbon black and NBR, which is highly resistant to degradation and swelling.

SBR is a copolymer of polystyrene and polybutadiene. Due to its low cost, it is used for hoses, belts, gaskets, shock mounts and automobile tires.

Chloroprene rubber (CR) is a carbon chain polymer containing chlorine. It has better resistance to weather, sun light and petroleum oils, over natural rubber. It is widely used for gaskets, shock mounts, conveyor belts, seals and so on.

Nitrate rubber (NBR) is a copolymer of butadiene and acrylonitrite. This is used for gasoline hoses, fuel pump diaphragms, seals and transmission gaskets. Butyl rubber (IR) is a copolymer of isobutylene and isoprene. It has low permeability to air and excellent resistance to ageing and ozone. It is used for *puncture-proof tires* and for inner tubes.

Ethylene propylene rubber (EPM) and ethylene propylene diene monomer (EPDM) possess exceptional weathering and ageing resistance, excellent electrical properties and good heat resistance, and are used for wire insulation, weather stripping, conveyor belts and other outdoor appliances. However, they are not resistant to petroleum oils.

Chlorosulphonated polyethylene (CSM): Trade name is Hypolon. It has outstanding resistance to weathering, heat and abrasion. It is used for high-voltage insulation, tank liners and pond liners in chemical plants.

Polysulphide rubber possesses weather and ageing resistance, impermeability to gases and moisture, resistant to solvents and oils. Suitable for caulking compounds, sealants, puttying agents and castable shapes. Silicones are characterized by silicon–oxygen bonds (SiO_2), which are superior in thermal stability. They have unique ability to transfer ink and other materials (nothing sticks to them) used in printing industry.

Polyurethane is a condensation product of reaction of isocyanate and alcohol. Different polymers are made by using different reacting materials. They can behave as elastomers, as rapid hard thermosets or as an injection-moldable thermoplastic. These are used for sheets and blocks, die springs, forming dies, wear pads, ski boots and sports equipment, and are also suitable for floor covering (to withstand truck traffic, scuffing and chipping).

11.15 MECHANICAL AND THERMAL BEHAVIOUR OF POLYMERS

Polymers have low strength and poor dimensional stability, are poor conductors of electricity and are unsuitable for high-temperature applications. Yet, they have excellent combination of properties: (1) low specific gravity, (2) high dielectric constant, (3) resistance to corrosion, (4) equally transparent to glass and (5) less brittle than glass, which make them suitable for extensive applications in photography, consumer goods, engineering products and as electrical insulators.

The mechanical behaviour of polymers is very much dependent on the molecular structure of polymers and on crystallinity as cross-linking effect. The elastomers exhibit non-linear stress–strain curve and a hysteresis loop is formed as shown in Figure 11.26. The hysteresis effect enables rubber to absorb vibrational energy and is used as a shock absorber. Rubber heats up on rapid stretching and coils down on rapid compression.

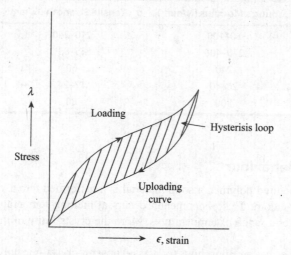

Figure 11.26 *Elastomer*

Cross-linking of polymers reduces viscous flow in polymers and tensile stress–strain curve for nylon is more or less linear as that of steel. The material elongates elastically up to yield point and then deforms plastically up to the ultimate tensile strength and extends by 50–150 per cent. But rubber extends up to 400–600 per cent and even more [Figure 11.27(a)].

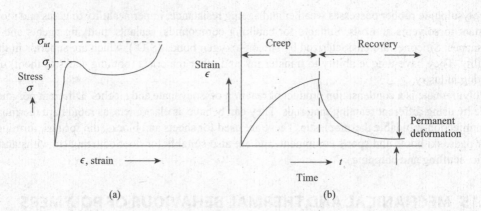

Figure 11.27 (a) Stress–strain Behaviour of Polymer (b) Viscoelastic Behaviour of Polymer

In general, polymers exhibit viscoelastic behaviour, i.e. they respond to both recoverable and time-dependent permanent deformation. Under rapidly applied loads, polymers respond to partially elastic behaviour because the structured molecules cannot be instantaneously stretched. But under a slowly applied load, they slip past each other in plastic flow. This phenomenon is both time and temperature dependent and non-recoverable [Figure 11.27(b)].

The average mechanical properties of some common polymers are given in Table 11.2.

Table 11.2 Average Mechanical Properties of Some Common Polymers

Materials	E, Young's Modulus (N/mm²)	σ_{ut}, Tensile Strength (N/mm²)	Elongation (%)
Polyethylene	50–100	210–240	50–600
Polystyrene	270–400	35–83	1–2.5
Polyvinyl chloride	240	60	2–40
PTFE	26–40	17–24	250–300
Nylon 66	300	80	40–80

11.15.1 Thermal Behaviour

During melting of a structured polymer, a solid material is transformed into a viscous liquid, in which the structure is highly random. This phenomenon occurs at melting temperature T_m. The melting of polymers takes place over a range of temperatures. More the crystallinity of the polymer, more is the melting temperature.

Then, glass transition occurs in amorphous (or glassy) or semi-crystalline polymers, due to the reduction in motion of large segments of molecular chains with decreasing temperature. Upon cooling, the glass transition corresponds to the gradual transformation from a liquid to a rubbery material, and finally to a rigid solid state. This temperature at which the polymer experiences the transition from rubbery to rigid state is known as glass transition temperature, T_g. At temperature, T_g, there are abrupt changes in E, heat capacity and coefficient of thermal expansion.

The glass transition temperature generally occurs at temperatures between 0.5 and 0.65 T_m, where T_m is the absolute melting temperature in Kelvin. For some common polymers, T_m and T_g are given in Table 11.3.

Table 11.3 *Melting and Glass Transition Temperature of Polymers*

Polymers	T_m, Melting Point (°C)	T_g, Glass Transition Temperature (°C)
Polyethylene	140	−78
Epoxy	Does not melt	50–200
Polyester	Does not melt	50–200
PMMA	–	100
Polyvinyl chloride	212	87
Polystyrene	240	100
Polycarbonate	270	180
Nylon 6	265	60

11.16 SPECIAL PURPOSE PLASTICS

Plastics with properties comparable to those of metals have been developed. These plastics can be broadly classified as: (1) conducting polymers, (2) expanding plastics, (3) plastics used in electronics, (4) thermoplast–thermoset plastics, (5) Liquid crystal polymers, (6) biomedical polymers and (7) polymer foams.

11.16.1 Conducting Polymers

Conducting filler materials such as metal wires and powders, graphite powder and transition metal compounds are mixed in non-conducting polymers such as poly acetylenes (PAC) and the conductivity of PAC is further enhanced by 10 times when iodine is doped into it. This doped PAC possesses electrical conductivity of range almost of metals.

These conducting polymers can generate electric signals by ion exchange mechanism. The conducting electro active polymers are termed as 'smart materials'.

11.16.2 Expanding Plastics

These expanding plastics have zero shrinkage during polymerization. These are resistant to corrosion and abrasion. Expanding plastics are used in coatings, adhesives, electro-optics, dentistry, medical prosthesis and electronic applications.

The polyacrylic ring opening monomers are combined with conventional monomers and oligomers to produce expanding polymers.

Expanding polymers provide superior fillings in dentistry and are used in dentures and crowns. In electronics, they produce advanced microchip sealants.

11.16.3 Plastics in Electronics

Many polyimides are used for interlayer insulations and crossovers for microwave-integrated circuits, aviation radome, anti-radar paints and heat shields.

11.16.4 Thermoplast–Thermoset Plastics

Polyphenylene sulphide (PPS) is a unique polymer that possesses the properties of both thermoplast and thermosetting plastics. They possess excellent properties like (1) high temperature resistance, (2) corrosions resistance, (3) flame resistance, (4) low moisture absorptions, (5) easy processability and (6) good electrical and mechanical properties.

11.16.5 Liquid Crystal Polymers (LCP)

These polymers are crystalline in solid as well as liquid state. They are high-strength fibres, e.g. Kevlar is a liquid crystal. They have good stability, low flammability, good electrical properties at elevated temperatures and very low coefficient of thermal expansions, and are easily moulded. These are used in telecommunications and fibre optics.

11.16.6 Biomedical Polymers

A biomaterial must be mechanically adaptable for its desired functions. Biomedical polymers should be such that the blood, enzymes and proteins should not cause adverse immune response to cancer, toxic and allergic reactions.

The materials used for artificial heart, heart valve and vascular tubing are: (1) segmented polymethane, (2) polydimethyl siloxane and (3) segmented co polydimethyl siloxane–methane.

The materials used in membrane oxygenator are as follows:

1. Perfluorobutyl ethyl cellulose
2. Polyalkyl sulphone

11.16.7 Polymer Foams

Gas-filled solid materials are generated using synthetic organic compounds. Nomex honey comb structure is an elastic and rigid gas-filled material. Foamed polymers are polyolefins, polyvinyl chloride and polymethanes.

=== KEY POINTS TO REMEMBER ===

❏ The material in which carbon is the basic component is known as organic material.

❏ A monomer is a small molecule, which on polymerization converts into a large molecule called a polymer.

❏ Molecular weight of a polymer is important in the determination of its properties.

❏ There are different types of polymers depending upon (a) arrangement of repeating subunits, (b) chemical nature of subunits and (c) presence or absence of multifunctional junctions.

❏ Degree of polymerization n is the ratio of the number of average molecular weight/molecular weight of mer.

❏ Average end-to-end distance to a freely rotating polymeric chain is $l_a = r_0 \sqrt{\lambda n}$, where λ is a constant, r_0 is the interatomic distance and n is the number of bonds.

❏ Cross-linked linear chains are connected to each other by covalent bonds. Branches are connected to linear chain to produce cross-linked polymer.

❏ Trifunctional mer units having three-dimensional covalent bonds form three-dimensional network.

❏ In the formation of long-chain polymers, various monomers join together. It is necessary that sites for polymerization reactions must exist in each monomer. These reactions may be bifunctional, trifunctional or tetrafunctional.

❏ Addition of monomers of the same type is known as homopolymerization.

❏ Addition of different kinds of monomers is called copolymerization.

❏ Condensation polymerization is a process in which two or more chemically different monomers are polymerized to form a cross-linked polymer along with a by-product.

❏ To modify mechanical, chemical or physical properties, additives are intentionally added in monomers (resin) such as fillers, plasticizers, colourants and flame retardants.

❏ Polymers are strengthened by (a) crystallization, (b) cross-linking and (c) chain stiffening.

❏ In polymers, if Van der Waal's bonds are replaced by hydrogen bonds, crystallinity of polymer is increased.

❏ Long molecular chains are formed in three-dimensional network in three possible ways: isotactic, syndiotactic and atactic syntheses.

❏ Thermoplastic material flows at elevated temperature (above glass transition temperature) and solidified polymer can be reheated as many times as desired.

❏ In thermosetting plastics, cross-linking has taken place during polymerization and a strong network is formed. During reheating either they burn or sublime.

❏ The fibre polymers can be drawn into long filaments with minimum length to diameter ratio of 100.

❏ Aramid fibres possessing high strength are used in composites.

❏ Elastomers are rubbery materials capable of extending to several times of its length under the applied load. Loading and unloading curve of an elastomer results in hysteresis loop. Elastomers are used in shock-absorbing mounts.

❏ During vulcanization, sulphur cross-links the isoprene molecules (of rubber).

❏ Synthetic rubbers are superior to natural rubbers. Commonly used synthetic rubbers are SBR, CR, NBR, IR, EPM, CSM, polysulphides and polymethanes.

❏ In general, polymers exhibit viscoelastic behaviour, i.e. they respond to both recoverable and time-dependent permanent deformation.

❏ Glass transition occurs in amorphous (or glossy) or semi-crystalline polymers due to the reduction in motion of large segments of molecular chains with decreasing temperature.

❏ Liquid crystal polymers (LCPs) are crystalline in solid as well as liquid state. High-strength aramid fibre, i.e. Kevlar is an LCP.

❏ Biomedical polymers should be such that the blood, enzymes and proteins should not cause adverse immune response to cancer, toxic and allergic reactions.

MULTIPLE CHOICE QUESTIONS

1. If degree of polymerization is 100,000, what is the molecular weight of Teflon?
   - (a) 6×10^6
   - (b) 8×10^6
   - (c) 10×10^6
   - (d) None of these

2. Polystyrene can be classified as
   - (a) Linear polymer
   - (b) Branched polymer
   - (c) Cross-linked polymer
   - (d) None of these

3. How many sites are available in phenol formaldehyde molecule?
   - (a) 4
   - (b) 3
   - (c) 2
   - (d) None of these

4. Chemical formula of a monomer is $-\overset{\displaystyle H}{\underset{\displaystyle H}{C}}-\overset{\displaystyle OH}{\underset{\displaystyle H}{C}}-\cdot$

   What is the name of the monomer?
   - (a) Ethylene
   - (b) Vinyl alcohol
   - (c) Vinyl chloride
   - (d) None of these

5. Which one of the following is copolymerized?
   - (a) Phenol formaldehyde
   - (b) Polyvinyl chloride
   - (c) Polypropylene
   - (d) All the above

6. What function is achieved by adding tricresyl phosphate?
   - (a) Catalysts
   - (b) Stabilizers
   - (c) Plasticizers
   - (d) None of these

7. Acrylonitrile is an example of
   - (a) Cross-linked polymer
   - (b) Branched polymer
   - (c) Graft copolymer
   - (d) None of these

8. Polypropylene is an example of what type of synthesis?
   - (a) Isotactic
   - (b) Syndioctactic
   - (c) Actactic
   - (d) None of these

9. Identify the thermosetting plastics in the following.
   - (a) PTFE
   - (b) Urea formaldehyde
   - (c) Nylon 6
   - (d) Epoxy

10. Which of the following fibres is used in automobile tires?
    - (a) Silk
    - (b) Nylon 66
    - (c) Kevlar
    - (d) Orlon

11. What reinforcing agents are used in rubber?
    - (a) Carbon black
    - (b) Sulphur
    - (c) Zinc oxide
    - (d) All the above

12. Which synthetic rubber is used for high-voltage insulation?
    - (a) NBR
    - (b) CR
    - (c) CSM
    - (d) EPM

13. What is the glass transition temperature of nylon 6?
    - (a) 100°C
    - (b) 87°C
    - (c) 75°C
    - (d) 60°C

14. Which one is the thermoplast–thermoset plastics?
    - (a) PPS
    - (b) PAC
    - (c) PTFE
    - (d) LCP

Answers

1. (c)   2. (a)   3. (b)   4. (b)   5. (a)   6. (c)   7. (c)   8. (a)   9. (b) & (d)
10. (b)   11. (d)   12. (c)   13. (d)   14. (a)

REVIEW QUESTIONS

1. What are monomer and polymer? Write the chemical formulae for polyethylene and polyvinyl chloride.

2. What are the different types of polymers depending upon the presence of multifunctional junction sites?

3. In a polymeric chain, what are backbone atoms and bond angle?

4. What is the molecular weight of monomers of teflon, ethylene, PMMA and styrene?

5. With the help of neat sketches explain linear, branched, cross-linked and network polymers.

6. Explain the mechanism of polymerization.

7. Differentiate among homopolymers, copolymers and condensation polymers.

8. What are fillers, plasticizers and stabilizers in polymers? Give two examples of each?

9. What is the crystallinity in polymers? How is it achieved?

10. Explain the process of cross-linking and chain stiffening in polymers.

11. Write a shot note on stereotactic synthesis.

12. What is the basic difference between thermoplastic and thermosetting plastics? Give three examples of each.

13. What are the different organic fibres used in composites to achieve higher strength?

14. Explain vulcanization in rubber.

15. Describe the following and give their applications.

    SBR, CR, NBR, EPM and CS

16. Why elastomers are used in shocker mounts? Explain.

17. Explain melting point and glass transition point for polymers.

=========== **PRACTICE PROBLEMS** ===========

1. Styrene monomer is polymerized to a DOP of 10,000. Calculate the molecular weight of polystyrene.

   (Styrene C_8H_8)

   Ans. $[1.04 \times 10^6]$

2. The average molecular weight of a polyvinyl chloride is 9600. What is its degree of polymerization ?

   Ans. [154]

3. Monomer of PMMA is given below

$$CH_3 = \underset{\underset{COOCH_3}{|}}{\overset{\overset{CH_3}{|}}{C}}$$

   What is its molecular weight if degree of polymerization is 2000?

   Ans. $[2 \times 10^5]$

12 CERAMIC MATERIALS

12.1 INTRODUCTION

Most of the ceramics are compounds of metallic and non-metallic elements. The crystal structure of ceramics is more complex because at least two elements are involved in making a ceramic compound. Their importance lies in the fact that *ceramics can be used at low as well as at high temperatures*. Ceramic materials are obtained by firing them at high temperatures. Traditional ceramics are clay products likes bricks, tiles and porcelain. China ceramics are obtained by firing clay products, which are made by shaping when they are in dough form and after drying they are fired. These ceramic materials have poor strength and are brittle in nature. The interatomic bonds in ceramics are ionic to covalent.

Now, a new generation of ceramics have been developed, which are used in electronic, computer, communication and aerospace industries.

Advanced ceramics have been developed for use as tools, rockets, missile applications and wear coating on components subjected to high stresses. Powders of ceramic materials like SiC, WC, Al_2O_3 and TiC are mixed and glued with the help of glass powder (vitrification) and pressed in mould and then sintered. These ceramics possess high Young's modulus, high strength and high fracture toughness, and can be used at high and low temperatures.

This chapter discusses ceramics of engineering design, refractories, silicates, structure of glass, various types of glasses, thermal behaviour of glass, polymorphs of carbon, clay-based ceramics, carbon products and hard ceramics, cement and concrete along with their mechanical properties and applications.

12.2 CLASSIFICATION OF CERAMICS

Ceramics are inorganic and non-metallic materials. Many combinations of metallic and non-metallic atoms are possible and several structural arrangements of each combination are produced. A wide range of ceramic materials are found in the nature and are used for various engineering applications.

Major applications of ceramics are in furnaces, ovens as insulators and crockeries. Other important applications are (1) in artificial limbs and teeth, (2) as super conducting materials, (3) in explosive forming, (4) as ferrites in microwave gyrators, (5) as memory cores of computers, (6) as garnets in microwave isolators and (7) in sonar devices.

General classification of ceramics is as follows:

1. Refractories
2. Glasses
3. Silicates
4. Limes
5. Cements
6. Plain concrete
7. Rocks and stones
8. Clay and clay products
9. Abrasives

Moreover, carbides of tungsten, titanium, zirconium, silicon, alkali halides and silicon nitride are important ceramics used in engineering applications such as (1) carbon brushes, (2) abrasives, (3) tiles, (4) cutting tool inserts, (5) spark plugs, (6) different types of glasses, (7) earthenwares, (8) ceramic insulators as electrical goods, (9) cermets and (10) diamond saws to cut wafers.

Table 12.1 gives a list of typical ceramics used in engineering design.

Table 12.1 *Typical Ceramics of Engineering Design*

Class	Examples	Uses
Single oxides	Alumina Al_2O_3	Electrical insulation
	Chromium oxide Cr_2O_3	Wear coatings
		Thermal insulation
	Zirconia ZrO_2	Pigment
	Magnesium oxide MgO	Wear parts
	Silica SiO_2	Abrasives, glass
Mixed oxides	Kaolinite ($Al_2O_3.2SiO_2.2H_2O$)	Clay products
Carbides	Vanadium carbide VC	Wear resistant
	Tantalum carbide TaC	Wear resistant
	Tungsten carbide WC	Cutting tools
	Titanium carbide TiC	Wear resistant
	Silicon carbide SiC	Abrasive
	Chromium carbide Cr_3C_2	Wear coatings
	Boron carbide B_4C	Abrasives
Sulphides	Molybdenum disulphide MoS_2	Lubricant
	Tungsten disulphide WS_2	Lubricant
Nitrides	Boron nitride BN	Insulator
	Silicon nitride Si_3N_4	Wear products
Metalloid elements	Ge (Germanium)	Electronic devices
	Si (Silicon)	Electronic devices
Intermetallics	Nickel aluminide (NiAl)	Wear coatings

12.3 REFRACTORIES

Materials that withstand high temperatures under various environments are termed as 'refractories'. Basically, ceramic materials are used in the construction of linings of furnaces, boilers, flues, regenerators, crucibles, dryers, pyro-tubes and other similar applications. Salient features of these materials are as follows: (1) capacity to withstand high temperatures without melting or decomposing, (2) remains unreactive and inert when exposed to severe environments, (3) provide thermal insulation, (4) low thermal expansion or contraction, (5) low electrical conductivity, (6) long life without cracking or spalling and (7) impermeable to liquids and gases. A general form of refractories is brick.

Performance of any refractory depends on its composition. Compositional elements of refractory are Al_2O_3, SiO_2, MgO, Cr_2O_3, Fe_2O_3, CaO and TiO_2. Five common refractories are the following:

1. Fireclay (SiO_2 70–80, Al_2O_3 25–45 + small percentages of MgO + Fe_2O_3 + Cao + TiO_2)
2. High alumina fireclay (Al_2O_3 50–90, SiO_2 10–45 + small percentage of MgO, Fe_2O_3, CaO, TiO_2)
3. Silica (SiO_2 96.3, CaO 2.2, small amounts of MgO, Al_2O_3)
4. Periclase (MgO 90, SiO_2 3, Fe_2O_3 3, small amounts of Al_2O_3, Cr_2O and CaO 2.5)
5. Periclase chrome (MgO 73, Cr_2O_3 8.2, Al_2O_3 9, SiO_2 5, CaO 2.2)

Apparent porosities of these refractories vary from 18 to 25 per cent.

Fireclay bricks are mainly used in furnace constructions to confine hot atmosphere and to thermally insulate structural members from excessive temperatures. For fireclay bricks, strength is not an important factor.

Silica refractories are acid refractories. Because of load-bearing capacity, these are commonly used in arched roofs of steel and glass-making furnaces; temperatures can be as high as 1000°C. These refractories are also resistant to slags (rich in silica–acid slags), but are readily attacked by basic slags (MgO, CaO slags).

Periclase (or MgO) is termed as 'basic refractory'. Presence of silica is injurious to its high-temperature performance. Basic refractories are resistant to attack by slags, because they contain high concentrations of MgO and CaO. They are used in steel-making open hearth furnaces.

Recently, new refractories have been developed for service at high temperatures in gas turbines, jet engines, missiles, nuclear reactors and so on. These refractories are simple crystalline bodies composed of metallic oxides, carbides, borides, nitrides and sulphides. Latest refractories are cermets and alloys like Nimonic and Incoloy. A typical neutral character is shown by such refractories as carbon, graphite, carbide, chromite, bauxite and forsterite.

Required properties of basic refractories are as follows:

1. *Refractoriness:* Ability to withstand high temperature.
2. *Ceramic bond:* is a glassy matrix formed on cooling the liquid produced from the more fusible constituents of the mixture on firing. Presence of ceramic bond greatly increases the cold strength of a refractory, but it lowers refractoriness at high temperatures.
3. *Dimensional stability:* That is, resistance of a material to any volume change when exposed to a high temperature for long duration. Both physical and chemical stabilities at high temperatures are the primary requirements of a refractory material. Therefore, refractory materials must withstand (1) pressures from weights of parts of furnaces, (2) thermal shock due to rapid cooling and heating and (3) chemical attack by heated solids, liquids and gases.

12.4 SILICATES AND SILICA

Silicates are composed of silicon and oxygen, which are abundantly available in the Earth's crest. For example, rocks, soils and clay come under the classification of silicates. A unit cell of silicate is a tetrahedron on which each atom of silicon is bounded to four atoms of oxygen as shown in Figure 12.1.

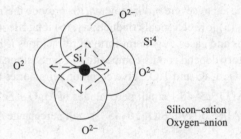

Figure 12.1 *Silicate Structure*

Oxygen atoms are located on the edges of a tetrahedron structure and silicon atoms are located at the centre. This basic unit of silicate is treated as negatively charged. There is a covalent bond between Si and O, i.e. Si–O. These are strong and directional. SiO_4 has a negative charge, i.e. –4, hence silicate unit cell is represented by Si_4^{4-}. These Si_4^{4-} units are combined in one-, two-, or three-dimensional arrangements to produce stable electronic structure.

12.4.1 Silica

Silica (SiO_2) is the simple form of silicate. This is a three-dimensional network of tetrahedron when every corner oxygen atom is shared by adjacent tetrahedral, and the material becomes electrically neutral but electronically stable. Under this arrangement, the ratio of Si to O becomes 1:2 as given by chemical formula, SiO_2. There are three polymorphic forms of silica: (1) quartz, (2) cristobalite and (3) tridymite. Structures of these three forms are complicated as atoms are not closely packed. They have low density but high melting point. Silica is used in the manufacture of different varieties of glasses.

12.5 STRUCTURE OF GLASSES

Generally, solids have three-dimensional periodic structures as shown in Figure 12.2. This is a crystalline structure. But the materials, which do not have three-dimensional structures, but random structure as shown in Figure 12.3 are said to be amorphous or glassy. Many metal alloys, oxide compounds and

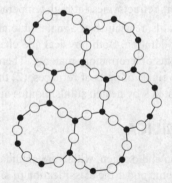

Figure12.2 *Crystalline Structure (Orderly Repeated)*

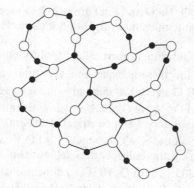

Figure 12.3 *Random Structure (Amorphous)*

non-oxide compounds form glassy structure. Fused silica or vitreous silica has high degree of atomic randomness. Similarly, oxides as B_2O_3 and GeO_2 may also form glassy structure. The common inorganic glasses that are used for products like containers and windows are silica glasses to which oxides such as CaO and Na_2O are added.

12.6 GLASSES

Solids that do not have three-dimensional periodic structures are called 'amorphous' or 'glassy'. Many materials such as metal alloys, organic polymers, oxide compounds and non-oxide compounds have glassy structure. The amorphous or glassy structure is a super cooled liquid, i.e. if a liquid is cooled fast enough to prevent crystallization, a glass may be formed. To form a metallic glass, the quench rate must be high; vitralloy, a glass based on zirconium is commercially available. To form an oxide glass, a mixture of molten oxides is cooled rapidly. Moreover, many glass-forming oxides have relatively high viscosities even at elevated temperatures; therefore, their crystallization rates are very low.

There are oxides, which are (1) main glass formers, (2) condition glass formers, (3) intermediate oxides and (4) network modifier oxides as given in Table 12.2.

Table 12.2 *Oxides Used in Glass*

Main Glass Formers	Conditional Glass Formers	Intermediate Oxides	Network Modifiers
SiO_2	Al_2O_3	TiO_2	MgO
B_2O_3	Bi_2O_3	ZnO	Li_2O
GeO_2	WO_3	PbO	BaO
P_2O_5	MoO_3	Al_2O_3	CaO
	TeO_2	Zr_2O_3	Na_2O
			Y_2O_3
			K_2O

In addition to SiO_2, B_2O_3, GeO_2 and P_2O_5, there are elements and compounds such as tellurium, selenium and BeF_2, which also form glasses. They form a three-dimensional network. Intermediate oxides like Zr_2O_3, Al_2O_3, PbO, ZnO and TiO_2 are added in high proportions for linking up with basic glass network of glass formers.

Modifiers like MgO, LiO_2, BaO, Na_2O and K_2O are added to modify the properties of glass. Flux is added to lower down the fusion temperature of glass, but these fluxes reduce resistance of glass to chemical attack.

Commercial glasses, their composition, properties and applications are listed as follows:

1. Fused silica (99 SiO_2) very low thermal expansion, very high viscosity
2. Silica (96 per cent SiO_2, 4 B_2O_3) very low thermal expansion, very high viscosity (Vycor)
3. Borosilicate (81 SiO_2, 2 Al_2O_3, 4 Na_2O, 12 B_2O_3) low thermal expansion, low ion exchange (Pyrex) (scientific piping laboratory ware, electrical insulators)
4. Soda lime (74 SiO_2, 15 Na_2O, 5 CaO, 4 MgO, 1 Al_2O_3) easy workability, high durability (containers, window panes, electric bulbs, bottles, tablewares)
5. Thermometer (73 SiO_2, 6Al_2O_3, 10 Na_2O, 10 B_2O_3) dimensional stability
6. Fiber (54 SiO_2, 14 Al_2O_3, 16 CaO, 10 B_2O_3, 4 MgO) low alkali
7. Lead glass (tableware) (67 SiO_2, 6 Na_2O, 07 PbO, 10 K_2O), high index of refraction
8. Optical flint (50 SiO_2, 19 PbO, 13 BoO, 8 K_2O, 8 ZnO) specific index and dispersion values (used in extra dense optical glasses, shields to protect against x-ray radiations)
9. Optical crown (70 SiO_2, 8 Na_2O, 10 B_2O_3, 2 BaO, 8 K_2O) specific index and dispersion values

Coloured glasses are made by adding oxides of specific metals as follows:

1. Iron oxide (FeO) yields green colour.
2. Cobalt oxide yields blue colour.
3. Pure selenium yields red.
4. Silver chloride is mixed in ordinary glass to make photochromatic glasses used in goggles.
5. Zena glass is used to make chemical containers.

Glasses can be used at elevated temperatures. Softening points of various glasses are shown in Table 12.3.

Table 12.3 *Softening Point of Glasses*

Glass	Softening Point (°C)
Fused silica	1580
Vycor (96 SiO_2)	1500
Pyroceram	1350
Soda lime	696
Borosilicate (Pyrex)	820

Tempered glass, which fractures in small pieces when broken, is made by heating glass to a point close to its melting point and then cooling rapidly. This causes the surface of the glass to undergo compressive stress, and tendency to break and failure mode is changed.

One of the most important applications of glass in the Internet industry is in fibre optic transmission of digital information. Fiber optic cables can carry many times more information than electrical conductors.

12.7 THERMAL BEHAVIOUR OF GLASSES

By and large, glassy state is a metastable state, because the amorphous state is a type of quenched state, where liquid is cooled fast enough to prevent the formation of crystalline structure. But in many glasses, the kinetics of reaction is very slow and for all practical purposes, the glassy state is a stable state. Some compositions of glasses may be slightly stable, so that at elevated temperature, glass may transform from amorphous to crystalline state. This phenomenon is known as 'devitrification'. In glass ceramics, an object in the glassy state is transformed into predominantly crystalline state by casting and compression moulding. These glass ceramics have much better mechanical properties than amorphous glasses.

Glasses at room temperature are highly viscous; viscosity $\mu = 10^{19}$ Poise, where 10 Poise = 1 Pa-s (Pascal-second) and the viscosity of water is only 0.1 Poise. Viscous flow or creep of glass at room temperature is extremely slow. As the temperature of the glass increases, viscosity decreases.

Figure 12.4 shows a graph of viscosity versus temperature for glass. There are standard points on this graph, which are as follows:

1. Strain point
2. Annealing point
3. Softening point
4. Working point associated with melting of glass

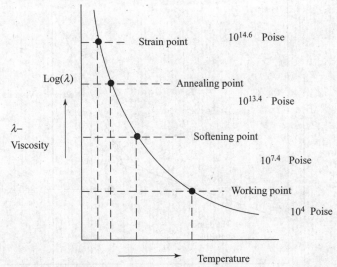

Figure 12.4 *Viscosity Versus Temperature Graph for Glass*

These points are summarized in Table 12.4.

Table 12.4 *Standard Points for Glasses*

Standard Point	Viscosity in Poise	Physical Description	Remarks
Strain point	$10^{14.6}$	Temperature at which internal stress in glass is relieved in hours	Strain point is the highest point at which glass can be put to structural use
Annealing point	$10^{13.4}$	Temperature at which internal stress in glass is relieved in minutes	
Glass transition temperature	10^{13}	Temperature at which glass transitions from super cooled liquid to glassy state	
Softening point	$10^{7.6}$	Viscosity becomes so low that glass slumps under its own weight	Most glass-forming operations occur at viscosities betwee softening point and working point
Working point	10^{4}	Viscosity of glass is low enough for forming and sealing operation	
Casting	10^{2}		Glass casting processes may occur at viscosities lower than 10^{2} Poise

12.7.1 Glass Transition Temperature, T_g

As the molten glass cools down, it contracts depending upon the coefficient of thermal expansion and viscosity increase. At same point, the viscosity of glass increases at a higher rate than the rate of structural arrangement. If a graph between volumetric strain $\Delta V/V$ and temperature is plotted, the slope of the volumetric strain versus temperature curve changes as shown in Figure 12.5, at the glass transition temperature, T_g. State of the glass changes from hard and brittle to soft and leathery, and then at higher temperature, it becomes a viscous glass. Glasses based on SiO_2 are called silicate glasses, for example, silica or fused quartz glasses, which are highly refractive. However, the addition of oxides like CaO, Na_2O and K_2O to SiO_2 reduces the working point and viscosity so that it can be used for many fabrication processes.

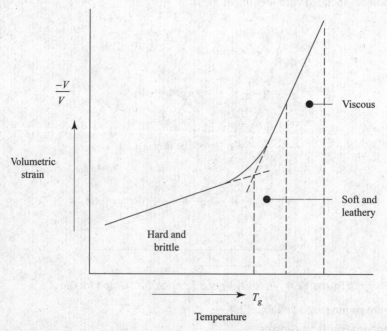

Figure 12.5 *Volumetric Strain Versus Temperature*

12.8 LIME

Lime is obtained by the process of burning lime stone. It is mainly used in building constructions. Following are different types of limes:

1. *Hydrated lime:* Calcium hydroxide, $Ca(OH)_2$. To make hydrated lime, quick lime (CaO) is mixed in water, an exothermic reaction is produced and a powder form of lime is obtained.
2. *Fat lime:* Calcium carbonate $(CaCO_3)$ is known as fat lime, a rich or pure lime. It is soluble in water and sets slowly in air.
3. *Lump lime:* These are in the form of coarse powder lumps. It is difficult to preserve lump lime. After some time lump lime is converted into a fine powder.

4. *Quick lime:* Caustic lime (CaO, calcium oxide). It has a great affinity for water and is caustic in nature.

5. *Hydraulic lime:* This is obtained from kinkar or by mixing clay with lime stone. When clay is added, it sets under water. On drying, it shrinks and cracks.

6. *Semihydraulic lime:* Contains 5–10 per cent clay. It sets in the interior of the brick walls in the absence of air.

Constituents of lime are as follows:

CaO and MgO	60–65 per cent
SiO_2, Al_2O_3, Fe_2O_3	15–20 per cent
CO_2	5 per cent
Insoluble residue	5–10 per cent

12.9 POLYMORPHS OF CARBON

Carbon exists in various polymorphic forms like (1) diamond, (2) graphite and (3) fullerenes (C_{60}) with spherical modules.

12.9.1 Diamond

With a valency of 4, carbon behaves as a metal or a non-metal. Diamond has a cubic structure while graphite has a hexagonal sheet structure (amorphous). Fullerenes are in the form of spherical molecules.

Diamond has a cubic structure, in which each carbon atom bonds with other four carbon atoms and the bonds are strong covalent bonds.

It is extremely hard (hardest known material) with a very low electrical conductivity, but unusually high thermal conductivity. It is optically transparent in the visible light and also in the infrared region. In addition, it has a high index of refraction also. It is generally used to cut and grind. Relatively large diamond single crystals are used as gem stones. Figure 12.6 shows the unit cell of diamond cubic crystal structure.

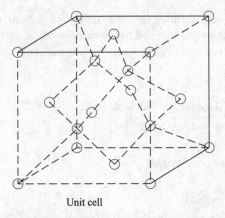

Unit cell

Figure 12.6 *Diamond Cubic Crystal Structure*

About 50 years ago synthetic diamonds were developed for industrial use in grinding wheels and glass cutters. Over the last several years, thin films of diamonds were produced by film growth techniques and film deposition by vapour phase chemical reaction. The maximum thickness of a thin film is about 1 mm. The mechanical, electrical and optical properties of a diamond film approach those of single crystal of diamond. Tools like drills, dies, bearings and knives are coated with *thin diamond film*. In addition, other components such as gears, optical recording heads and disks can also be coated with diamond film.

12.9.2 Graphite

Graphite exists in the nature and can be mined. Industrial carbons are made from coke or petroleum oils. When petroleum oil is burned in insufficient oxygen, carbon is formed in lamp black form.

Steps in the manufacture of graphite:

1. Carbon–graphite mixture with pitch is formed with a doughy consistency.
2. In this paste form, material is extruded in the form of rods, bars, sheets and so on.
3. Extruded material is sintered at 1000°C, and volatiles from the binder and impurities are driven off. At this stage, it is a mixture of graphite, ash and amorphous carbon.
4. Carbon products are now graphitized, long-duration thermal cycles at temperature range of 2500–2800°C.
5. Sintered and graphitized shapes are now impregnated with various materials.

Carbons of low-permeability grade are impregnated with phenol, furane or polyester resins and high thermal conductivity grades of carbon are impregnated with water-soluble phosphate or phosphate glass, so that pores are filled up and mechanical properties are improved. Temperature range of low-permeability grade carbons is 230–250°C and high thermal conductivity grade carbon, is 650–680°C.

Hundreds of different grades of carbon graphite are commercially available. These grades depend upon the starting material, porosity, degree of graphitization and type of surface impregnation.

The high-strength grades of carbon usually contain less graphite than lower-strength grades, which makes them abrasive in sliding systems.

12.9.3 Siliconized Grades

Silicon from silicon monoxide gas diffuses into the surface of carbons (at 1650°C); 80–90 per cent of surface is converted into silicon carbide, and the remainder of the surface still remains as graphite. Surface becomes hard, and the remaining graphite offers lubrication. These grades are used for sliding systems.

Graphite applications

Carbon products are mainly used for the following:

1. Motor brushes, electrodes, battery cores.
2. Heating elements.
3. Rocket components (nose cone shield).
4. Casting moulds.
5. Graphite as a dry film lubricant.
6. Solids made from graphite have self-lubricating properties.
7. Graphite bearings can be used at an operating temperature of 300°C.

8. Carbon graphite products when sliding against a metal surface require transfer of graphite to the metal surface, for long service life. Water vapour or contaminating gases are essential for this transfer.

9. Carbon/graphite bearings can be used in vacuums and at high temperatures.

10. Graphite materials are excellent for sliding contacts.

11. Mechanical seals (of graphite) are used as pumps, agitated tanks and so on.

12.9.4 Fullerenes

Another polymorphic form of carbon (discovered in 1985) exists in discrete molecular form, consisting of hollow spherical clusters of 60 carbon atoms, C_{60}. Each molecule is composed of groups of carbon atoms that are bonded together to form both hexagon and pentagon geometrical configurations. Material having C_{60} spherical molecules is known as Buckminster fullerene (named after its inventor R. Buckminster Fuller). In solid state, C_{60} units form a crystalline structure and pack together in an FCC structure. Technological developments have produced nanotubes of fullerene possessing very high strength (Figure 12.7).

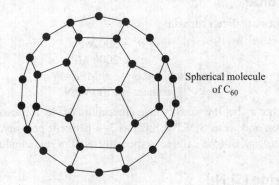

Spherical molecule of C_{60}

Figure 12.7 *Fullerenes*

12.10 CARBON PRODUCTS AND HARD CERAMICS

We have already discussed about polymorphs of carbon, i.e. diamond, graphite and fullerenes. Now, we will discuss about other carbon products, which find various industrial applications as cutting tools, abrasives, grinding wheels, rocket nozzles, pump impellers, internal combustion engines, discs and tools.

12.10.1 Cemented Carbides

Tungsten carbide and titanium carbide are used as composites bonded with a metal binder such as Ni, Co, Cr and Mo. These metal matrices with hard ceramics (WC, TiC) are known as 'cermets'.

Forty-five per cent TiC in a steel matrix is called a *cermet* and 90 per cent WC held together with 10 per cent Co binder is called a *cemented carbide*. These cermets are produced by compacting and sintering. Powders of carbides are made in size of 50 μm or less by a special chemical process.

Hardness of some cermets is

> 94 per cent WC + 6 per cent Co (matrix) – 91 RA (hardness)
> 92 per cent WC + 2 TaC + 6 Co – 92 RA

12.10.2 Aluminium Oxide (Al$_2$O$_3$)

Properties of Al$_2$O$_3$ are as follows:

$$\sigma_{uc}, \text{Ultimate strength in compression} = 2750 \text{ MPa}$$
$$\sigma_{ut}, \text{Ultimate strength in tension} = 210 \text{ MPa}$$
$$\text{Hardness} = 1600 \text{ VPN}$$
$$\text{Fracture toughness} = 1.75 \text{ MPa } \sqrt{m}, \text{KIC}$$

Environmental resistance is very good and aluminas are resistant to most oxidizing and reducing media up to their softening points.

Alumina is used for making rocket nozzles, pump impellers, pump liners, check valves and nozzles subjected to erosions. All these shapes are produced by moulding and sintering.

12.10.3 Silicon Carbide

Following are the properties of silicon carbide:

$$\sigma_{ut} = 300 \text{ MPa}$$
$$\sigma_{uc} = 2000 \text{ MPa}$$
$$\text{Fracture toughness} = 3.0 \text{ MPa } \sqrt{m}$$
$$\text{Hardness} = 2500 \text{ VPN}$$

Silicon carbide has higher σ_{ut} but low density than aluminium oxide. It is used in abrasive machining, as it is resistant to abrasion and wear. Sintered SiC has 3–4 per cent porosity, but chemically vapour-deposited SiC has zero porosity. Silicon carbide is specially used in semiconductor industry.

12.10.4 Silicon Nitride (Si$_3$N$_4$)

It is a reaction-bonded material, which has about 20 per cent porosity, therefore, it is a low-density and low-strength material. If the material is obtained by pressure sintering, 100 per cent theoretical density can be achieved.

Cutting tools, wear parts and structural shapes are usually made from full dense grades of SiC, but in furnace parts, reaction-bonded grade is often used.

Special features of silicon carbide are as follows:

1. No loss of strength up to 1000°C operation in air
2. Very good thermal shock resistance
3. Low density
4. Low thermal expansion
5. Better toughness than SiC and Al$_2$O$_3$
6. Stiffer than steel
7. Physical properties are, $\sigma_{ut} = 580 \text{ MPa}$, $\sigma_{uc} = 3500 \text{ MPa}$, VPN = 2300

Silicon nitride is widely used as a cutting tool material. Ceramic inserts of this material are better cutting tools than cemented carbides. It is used for gas turbine parts and resists thermal cycling.

12.10.5 Partially Stabilized Zirconia (PSZ)

Zirconia (ZrO_2) has been blended and sintered with other oxides such as MgO, CaO and Y_2O_3 (Yttria) by controlled crystal structure transformation.

Its toughness and steel-like properties have made PSZ a prime material for the replacement of metals in internal combustion engines.

Some applications of ceramics and cermets are as follows:

1. Cemented carbide knives
2. Boron carbide abrasive blasting nozzles
3. Chromia wire guide
4. Alumina web guide
5. Cemented carbide, die and tool inserts
6. Alumina wear tiles
7. Alumina shaft sleeve
8. Chromium oxide slurry pump liner

12.11 CLAY-BASED CERAMICS

Clay, a natural amorphous inorganic material, is obtained from the remains of rocks. Clays are hydrated aluminosilicates extracted from feldspar minerals present in the rocks. Clay minerals are classified as kaolinite ($Al_2O_3.2SiO_2.2H_2O$) and (b) montmorillonite ($Al_2O_3.4SiO_2.nH_2O$). Sanitary wares and firebricks are made from kaolinite, i.e. white-coloured clay, whereas steatite used in high-frequency electrical applications is made from montmorillonite.

Water content in the clay decides its plasticity. Drying, shrinking and vitrification properties of clay-based ceramics are based upon additions of non-plastic materials such as crushed and powdered quartz, talc, feldspar and so on.

Table 12.5 shows temperature range and applications of clay-based ceramics.

Table 12.5 *Temperature Range and Applications of Clay-based Ceramics*

Ceramic	Temperature ranges in °C	Applications
Stoneware	1125 °C	Roof tiles, glazed pipes
Earthenware	800–1000 °C	Drainage pipes, water filters, bricks, wall tiles
Porcelain	1125–1300 °C	Scientific and electrical items
China clay	1000–1200 °C	Tableware

12.12 CEMENT

It is the most important civil engineering construction material. Depending upon the requirement, various types of cements are available: (a) Portland cement, (b) Pozzolana cement, (c) white cement, (d) coloured cement, (e) quick-setting cement, (f) blast furnace cement, (g) high alumina cement, (h) low-heat cement, (i) rapid-hardening cement and so on.

Table 12.6 *List of Various Ingredients at Raw Stage in Portland Cement*

Chemical Ingredient	Formula	Proportion
Lime	CaO	60–65
Silica	SiO_2	17–25
Alumina	Al_2O_3	3–7
Iron oxide	Fe_2O_3	0.5–6%
Gypsum	$CaSO_4$	3–4
Magnesium oxide	MgO	0.5–4%
Sulphur trioxide	SO_3	1–2%
Potash and soda alkali	$Na_2O.K_2O$	0.5–1%

The maximum consumption of Portland cement occurs in the construction of buildings, bridges and dams. It is produced by grinding and intimately mixing clay and lime-bearing minerals in specific proportions. This mixture is heated at about 1400°C in a rotary kiln. This process is called 'calcination', which produces physical and chemical changes in the raw materials. In the rotary kiln, clinker is produced, which is ground to extremely fine powder in which a small amount of gypsum ($CaSO_4$–$2H_2O$) is added so as to retard the setting time. The product is called Portland cement. The strength and setting time of Portland cement largely depends upon its composition (Table 12.6).

Several different constituents are found in the final finely ground Portland cement. The main constituents are tricalcium silicate ($3CaO$–SiO_2) and dicalcium silicate ($2CaO$–SiO_2). The setting and hardening time of this cement results from the complicated hydration reactions that occur between various cement constituents and water that is added. The reaction of dicalcium silicate is as follows:

$$2CaO \cdot SiO_2 + xH_2O = 2CaO \cdot SiO_2 \cdot xH_2O$$

where x is a variable depending upon the quantity of water added. The hydrated product is in the form of gels forming cementitious bond.

Hydration reaction begins as soon as water is added to the cement. Stiffening and hardening of cement take place in different stages: (1) cement–water paste stiffens within a few hours and (2) hardening of mass follows as a result of further hydration, a slow process—may continue for several months. In this process, water actually participates in chemical bonding reaction.

Portland cement is also called hydraulic cement, because its hardness develops by chemical reaction with water.

Table 12.7 *Final Ingredients of Portland Cement*

Compound	Chemical Formula	Proportion (%)
Dicalcium silicate	$2 (CaO) SiO_2$	20–45
Tricalcium silicate	$3 (CaO) SiO_2$	25–45
Tricalcium aluminate	$3 (CaO) Al_2O_3$	8–12
Tetracalcium alumina ferrite	$4 (CaO) Al_2O_3.Fe_2O_3$	9–14

Table 12.7 gives the final ingredients of Portland cement. Cement is primarily used in mortar and concrete to bind into a cohesive mass, an aggregate of inert particles.

12.13 CONCRETE

Concrete is the most widely used construction material in the world, i.e. buildings, roads, bridges, dams, airports, ducts and so on. It is not a ceramic but a master piece of ceramic engineering. Concrete is a composite of sand, aggregate and cement. Cement bonds the aggregate by forming a ceramic-like structure around each grain of sand and rock fragment aggregates.

Mortars were discovered by Greeks and Egyptians thousands of years ago. By heat, chalk ($CaCO_2$) is converted into CaO (lime). When lime is mixed with water, it hardens. Lime reacts with water to form CaO, which in turn reacts with silica (SiO_2) to make a compound that hardens and bonds stones, bricks and other structural materials. But this masonry cement is very strong.

In nineteenth century, Portland cement was invented, which allowed formation of concrete; bricks and stones were no longer necessary and structures could be made from concrete.

Portland cement is the bonding agent for sand and aggregate, which makes up concrete. Cement bonds by chemical reaction with water that is added to dry mix to start the reaction. Chemical reaction starts within minutes and continues for more than 2 months. The strength of a particular mix is advanced after 30 days; but the concrete has to be kept wet for this length of time for the best strength.

There are an infinite number of compositions of concrete. Following are some typical properties using Portland cement (ASTMC150):

> Density is 2.44 g/cc
> 28-day compressive strength is 20–35 MPa
> Elastic modulus is 30–35 GPa
> Approximate tensile strength is 4 MPa
> Approximate fracture toughness is 0.5 MPa $\sqrt{m}$

Concrete is not intended to be used in tension. When it is used in bridges, floors, slabs and so on, steel reinforcement is used to essentially carry the tension loads. Regardless of brittleness of concrete, it is the most widely used construction material for infrastructure and building.

KEY POINTS TO REMEMBER

❏ Ceramics are compounds of metallic and non-metallic elements. Their crystal structure is complex. Generally, these are oxides of metals and non-metals.

❏ Ceramics of engineering design are oxides of Al, Cr, Zn, Mg and Si, carbides of V, Ta, W, Ti, Si, Cr and B, and sulphides of W and Mo; nitrides of B and Si and metalloid elements of Ge and Si are used in electronic industry.

❏ Materials that can withstand high temperatures under various severe environments are refractories. They are used in furnaces, boilers, flues, crucibles and so on.

❏ Fireclay, high alumina fire clay, silica, periclase and periclase chrome are refractories.

❏ A unit cell of silicate is a tetrahedron in which each silicon atom is bounded to four atoms of oxygen at corners of the tetrahedron.

❏ Amorphous material—structure of atoms is random.

❑ Oxides used in glass manufacture are: (a) main glass formers, (b) conditional glass formers, (c) intermediate oxides and (d) network modifiers.

❑ Borosilicate (Pyrex) glass is used for scientific piping, laboratory ware and electrical insulators.

❑ Soda lime glass is used in containers, window panes, electric bulbs, table wares and so on.

❑ Lead glass has high index of refraction.

❑ Various oxides of Fe, Co, Fe and Ag are used to introduce colour in glasses.

❑ Softening point of fused silica glass is 1580°C.

❑ Working point viscosity of glass is 10^4 Poise.

❑ Casting point viscosity of glass is 10^2 Poise.

❑ Lime is obtained by burning limestone, used in building construction.

❑ Polymorphs of carbon are: (a) diamond, (b) graphite and (c) fullerenes, C_{60}.

❑ Clay-based ceramics are used in stoneware, earthenware, porcelain, china clay, roof tiles, glazed tiles and table ware.

❑ Cemented carbides are WC in cobalt matrix or WC and TaC in cobalt matrix.

❑ Partially stabilized zirconia is blended with other oxides as MgO, CaO, Y_2O_3 and then sintered by controlled crystal structure transformation.

❑ Main ingredients of Portland cement are dicalcium silicate and tricalcium silicate. Cement is set by hydration reaction, which continues for several months to achieve maximum strength of cement.

❑ Concrete is a composite of sand, aggregate and Portland cement. When water is added, cement bonds aggregate by forming a ceramic-like structure around each grain of sand and rock fragments.

MULTIPLE CHOICE QUESTIONS

1. Which one of the following is not an application of boron nitride and silicon nitride?
   - (a) Insulators
   - (b) Wear products
   - (c) Lubricant
   - (d) None of these

2. Which is a correct statement?
   - (A) Graphite bearings can be used in vacuums and at high temperatures.
   - (B) Silicon monoxide gas diffuses into surface of carbons to produce silicon carbide.
   - (a) A only
   - (b) B only
   - (c) A and B
   - (d) Neither A nor B

3. Match the list of ceramics and uses

A Silicon carbide	I Pigment
B Zirconia	II Lubricant
C Tungsten disulphide	III Cutting tools
D Tungsten carbide	IV Abrasive

	A	B	C	D
(a)	IV	I	II	III
(b)	IV	II	I	III
(c)	II	IV	I	III
(d)	IV	I	III	II

4. Which one of the following is an acid refractory?
   - (a) MgO
   - (b) Silica
   - (c) CaO
   - (d) None of these

5. Which one is the network modifier in glass?

    (a) MoO_3 (c) Li_2O

    (b) Al_2O_3 (d) WO_3

6. What is the percentage silica in fused silica glass?

    (a) 90   (c) 96

    (b) 94   (d) 99

7. Which of the following yields blue colour in glass?

    (a) Iron oxide

    (b) Cobalt oxide

    (c) Silver chloride

    (d) Pure selenium

8. What is the viscosity of glass at which it can be cast in moulds?

    (a) 10^4 Poise   (c) $10^{3.4}$ Poise

    (b) 10^3 Poise   (d) 10^2 Poise

9. What is quick lime?

    (a) CaO   (c) $CaCO_3$

    (b) $Ca(OH)_2$ (d) None of these

10. Coating of which material is provided on tools such as drills, dies and knives

    (a) Diamond film

    (b) Tungsten carbide

    (c) Molybdenum disulphide

    (d) None of these

11. Arrange the following ceramics in decreasing order of their maximum operating temperature range.

    (a) Porcelain, earthenware, stoneware

    (b) Porcelain, stoneware, earthenware

    (c) Earthenware, stoneware, porcelain

    (d) Stoneware, earthenware, porcelain

12. What is hardness of Al_2O_3?

    (a) 1200 VPN   (c) 2500 VPN

    (b) 1600 VPN   (d) None of these

13. Which is the main ingredient in raw materials for making cement?

    (a) $CaSO_4$ (c) CaO

    (b) MgO   (d) Fe_2O_3

Answers

1.(c)   2. (c)   3. (a)   4. (b)   5. (c)   6. (d)   7. (b)   8. (d)

9.(a)   10. (a)   11. (b)   12. (b)   13. (c)

REVIEW QUESTIONS

1. Make a list of carbides used as ceramics and write their applications.

2. Mention six ceramics, which are used as wear-resistant materials.

3. What is a refractory? What is the difference between acidic and basic refractories? What are the applications of refractories?

4. What is the basic difference between silicate and silica?

5. Differentiate between crystalline and amorphous structures. Show with one example each.

6. Differentiate between

    (a) Soda lime glass and fused silica glass

    (b) Vycor and Pyrex glasses

7. Explain the thermal behaviour of glass. Explain various standard points.

8. What is lime? What are the differences between quick lime and fat lime?

9. Make a sketch of a unit cell of diamond? What is the difference between natural diamond and synthetic diamond?

10. What is a diamond film? How is it produced? What are its applications?

11. Differentiate between graphite and fullerene structures. Show sketches.

12. What are clay-based ceramics? How are they made? What are their limitations?

13. Explain how cemented carbides are made?

14. What are the applications of SiC and SiN?

15. Write a short note on PSZ.

16. What are the applications of cermets?

17. What do you mean by Portland cement? What is hydration reaction? Explain.

18. What is concrete? How is it made? What are its applications?

13

COMPOSITE MATERIALS

13.1 INTRODUCTION

With the advancement of technology, especially in the field of aerospace engineering, there is increasing need of lightweight materials with unusual combination of properties of high strength, high elastic modulus and at the same time suitability at high temperature operation. This combination of properties is not obtainable from conventional materials like alloys, high-speed steels, stainless steels, superalloys and so on. A composite material is developed with different phases, and the properties of the composite are better than the properties of the individual phases (constituents) making the composite. Common example of a composite is glass-reinforced plastics (GRP), in which polymer resin is reinforced with glass fibres. The polymer resin matrix has low strength but high ductility, while glass fibres have high strength and very low ductility; but GRP possesses high strength derived from glass fibres and good ductility derived from polymer matrix.

In composites, the matrix can be of metal, polymer or ceramic. Similarly, the reinforcement can be of any material, i.e. metal, thermoplasts or ceramic depending upon the requirement. Moreover, the form of the reinforcement can be fibres (continuous, discontinuous or chopped), particles (large size or very fine particles of size 0.1 μm) or a structure (as a honeycomb structure in between two sheets).

This chapter discusses various types of matrices and fibres like carbon, glass, boron and so on. It also discusses the effect of fibre and matrix phases of the strength of the composite. Besides fabrication techniques of most commonly used polymer composites will also be dealt with. At the same time to get the maximum strength, hybrid composites are developed in which there two types of fibres (as carbon and boron fibres) and polymer matrices.

Advanced composites like metal matrix composites (MMCs) and ceramic matrix composites (CMCs) are also included in this chapter.

13.2 TYPES OF COMPOSITES

Composite is a multiphase material, developed with a specific purpose of improvement in properties, i.e. the properties of resultant composite made from different phases are better than the properties of individual phases. Following are few examples of composites:

1. *Pearlite:* It is a composite of ferrite and cementite. The strength of pearlite is more than the strength of ferrite and its ductility is more than the ductility of cementite phase.

2. *Wood:* It is a natural fibre composite consists of strong and flexible fibres of cellulose surrounded by matrix of lignin, which provides binding.

However in man-made composites, phases are chemically dissimilar (e.g. polymer matrix and glass fibre in which two phases are chemically dissimilar), separated by distinct interfaces.

Most of the composites of general commercial purpose consist of only two phases: (1) matrix that surrounds the other phase and (2) dispersed phase (dispersed in matrix).

There are three types of dispersed phases:

1. Fibres of different materials are reinforcements.

2. Particles as reinforcements.

3. Structural members.

Figure 13.1 shows a simplified scheme of classification of composites. All these types of composites will be discussed in this chapter.

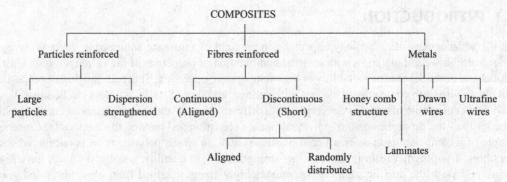

Figure 13.1 *Classification of Composites*

13.3 LARGE PARTICLE COMPOSITES

In the case of large particle composites, the matrix and particle interface is not treated on atomic or molecular scale, but are treated on macroscopic scale. The particulate phase is harder and stiffer than the matrix. The particles provide the strength to the composite and restrict the movement of matrix phase in the vicinity of each particle. Basic function of matrix is to transfer the applied stress to the reinforcing particles, and these particles share a portion of the load depending upon the volume fraction of particles in the composite. The bonding between particles and matrix is very important because the efficiency of reinforcement and improvement in mechanical properties depend upon the strength of bond between matrix and particles. Concrete is an example of large particle composite. In some polymers, fillers are added as large size particles with the purpose of (1) filler materials, (2) plasticizers, (3) stabilizers, (4) colourants and (5) flame retardants.

Filler materials: These are used in polymers to improve tensile and or compressive strengths, to provide abrasion resistance, toughness, dimensional stability and thermal stability, for example, wood flour, silica flour, sand particles, glass powder, clay, talc, limestone and even some synthetic polymers. Carbon black consists of very small and spherical particles of carbon, when added to vulcanized rubber, this extremely inexpensive material enhances tensile strength, toughness and tear and abrasion resistance of rubber. Automobile tires contain 15–30 vol% of carbon black. A strong bond exists between rubber matrix and carbon particles.

Plasticizers: The flexibility, ductility and toughness of polymers can be improved by the addition of plasticizers. The addition of plasticizers reduces hardness and stiffness of the composite. Moreover, they reduce the glass transition temperature. They are commonly used in polymers that are intrinsically brittle at room temperature such as polyvinyl chloride (PVC). Plasticizers are used in the manufacture of sheets or films, tubes, raincoats and curtains.

Some polymers under normal environmental conditions are subjected to rapid deterioration as a result of exposure to light, UV rays and also to oxidation. Addition of stabilizers counteracts these deteriorations processes.

Colourants: These impart a specific colour to a polymer and may be added as dyes or pigments. Dyes dissolve and become part of the molecular structures, but pigments are filler materials that do not dissolve but remains as a separate phase. Pigments are transparent or opaque.

Flame retardant: In the manufacture of textiles and children's toys, flammability of a polymer is of serious concern. Flame retardants enhance the flammability resistance of combustible polymers. These retardants may function by interfering with the combustion process, when the gas phase and combustion region may be cooled.

Particles can have large varieties of geometries. For effective reinforcement, the particles should be as small as possible and uniformly distributed throughout the matrix phase (Figure 13.2).

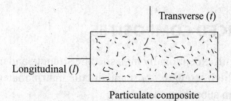

Particulate composite

Figure 13.2 *Particulate Composite*

Rule of mixtures gives the elastic modulus of the composites.

$$E_1 = E_p V_p + E_m V_m, \quad \text{in longitudinal direction}$$

$$E_t = \frac{E_p E_m}{E_p V_m + E_m V_p}, \quad \text{in transverse directions}$$

where E_p, E_m are the elastic modulus of particulate and matrix and V_p, V_m are the volume fractions of particulates and matrix, respectively.

Large particle composites are made in all the three forms, i.e. metals, polymers and ceramics. Cermets are examples of ceramic–metal composites. These are the cemented carbides, consisting of extremely hard particles of refractory carbides like tungsten carbide (WC) and titanium carbide (TiC) embedded in a metal matrix of cobalt or nickel. Cermets are used as cutting tools for cutting hardened steels. Carbides are hard and brittle, and provide cutting action. These are embedded in ductile metal matrix.

Both elastomers and plastics are frequently reinforced with various particulate materials as carbon black in rubber to produce vulcanized rubber as explained before.

Concrete is the most common example of very large-sized particles of gravel, mixed in a slurry of cement and sand. In RCC, steel serves as a suitable reinforcement material because its coefficient of thermal expansion is nearly the same as of concrete. Cement provides a cover on steel reinforcement and hence the corrosion of steel is prevented.

13.4 DISPERSION-STRENGTHENED COMPOSITES

Dispersion-strengthened composites differ from particulate composites in the size of dispersed particles and their volume fraction. In these composites, uniformly dispersed fine hard particles of size less than 0.1 μm are used as reinforcement. These particles are stronger than the pure metal matrix. These can be metallic, intermetallic or non-metallic. Generally, very few particles of carbides, oxides and borides are used as dispersion particles. Shape of these particles can be round, disc or needle like. Needle-shaped particles provide maximum strengthening and volume fraction of these dispersed particles can be 0.05–0.15.

Strengthening mechanism involves interactions between the particles and dislocations within the matrix and this strengthening is retained at an elevated temperature that too for long extended period of time because the dispersed particles used in these composites are unreactive with the matrix phase.

The high-temperature strength of nickel alloys may be enhanced significantly by the addition of about 3 vol% of thoria (ThO_2) as finely dispersed particles. Similar is the case with aluminium–aluminium oxide system. A very thin and adherent alumina coating is formed on extremely small aluminium flakes, which are dispersed within an aluminium metal matrix. This is known as sintered aluminium powder (SAP).

13.5 FIBRE-REINFORCED COMPOSITES

Fibre-reinforced composites with exceptionally high specific strength and modulii have been developed, which utilize the low-density, high-strength fibres and ductile matrix materials. Materials for fibres and matrix will be dealt in details in subsequent articles.

Let us discuss the mechanical aspects of the fibre-reinforced composite.

13.5.1 Effect of Fibre Length

The mechanical strength of a fibre-reinforced composite depends not only on the properties of fibre and matrix, but also on the degree to which an applied load is transmitted to the fibres by the matrix phase. The magnitude of interfacial band between the fibre and the matrix plays the most important role. Under an applied stress, the fibre–matrix bond ceases at the fibre ends, meaning thereby that there is no load transmission from matrix at each fibre end. Some critical length is necessary for affecting strengthening and stiffening of composite material as shown below.

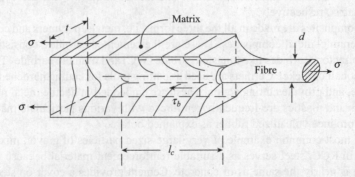

Critical fibre length,
$$l_c = \frac{\sigma_{ut}^f d}{2\tau_b}$$

where σ_{ut}^f = ultimate tensile strength of fibre

d = fibre diameter

τ_b = fibre–matrix bond strength

If the length of the fibre inside the matrix is less than l_c, then it will pull out under the action of stress σ applied on the fibre. For a number of fibres of glass and carbon in a polymer matrix, critical length is of the order of 1 mm, or $l_c = 20d$–$150d$, where d is the diameter of the fibre.

If the fibre length $l \gg l_c$ or (normally $l > 15l_c$), the fibre is termed as continuous fibre.

Discontinuous or short fibres have lengths smaller than, $l = 15l_c$. However, if the discontinuous fibres are of length less than l_c (critical length), then there is no transfer of stress from matrix to fibre, and no effect of reinforcement by the fibres.

To obtain a significant improvement in strength of the composite, the fibres must be continuous. There are three types of fibre arrangements in a matrix:

1. Continuous and aligned
2. Discontinuous and aligned
3. Discontinuous and random as shown in Figure 13.3(a)–(c).

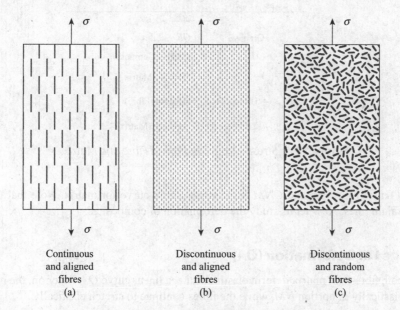

Continuous and aligned fibres
(a)

Discontinuous and aligned fibres
(b)

Discontinuous and random fibres
(c)

Figure 13.3 *Fibre Arrangement in a Matrix*

13.5.2 Stress–strain Diagram (Composite)

A fibre-reinforced composite consisting of fibres and matrix will exhibit the stress–strain curve under uniaxial tension as shown by curve *OAB* in Figure 13.4. In the same diagram, *OF* is the stress–strain curve

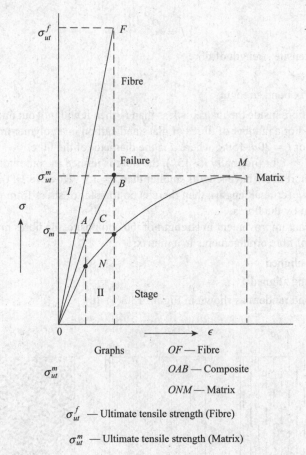

Figure 13.4 *Stress–strain Diagram of Fibre and Matrix*

under uniaxial tension for fibre and *ONM* is the stress–strain curve for matrix. Note that *OF*, *OA*, *AB* and *ON* are straight lines. Now let us study the deformation of composites.

13.5.3 Stage I of Deformation (*OA*)

In this stage, both fibres and matrix deform elastically, i.e. a linear curve *OA*. Later on, the matrix yields and deforms plastically in portion *NM*, while the fibres continue to stretch elastically.

$$\sigma_{ut}^{f} \gg \sigma_{ut}^{m}$$

13.5.4 Stage II (A to B)

Stage II is generally linear but with a reduced slope in comparison to the slope of stage I curve. While passing from stage I to II, the proportion of the applied load that is shared by the fibre increases.

The onset of failure of composite begins as the fibres start to fracture, but the composite failure is not catastrophic, because of the following reasons:

1. All the fibres do not fracture at the same time.
2. Although the fibres have failed, matrix is intact.
3. Fractured fibres (which have become shorter than original fibres) are still embedded within the intact matrix.
4. Fractured fibres are capable of sustaining the diminished load as the matrix continues to deform plastically.

13.5.5 Law of Mixture

If the applied force on composite $= F_C$

$$F_C = F_f + F_m$$

$$= \text{load shared by fibres} + \text{load shared by matrix}$$

$$F_f = \sigma_f A_f \text{ (where } A_f \text{ is area of fibres)}$$

$$F_m = \sigma_m A_m \text{ (area of matrix section, } A_m)$$

$$F_C = \sigma_C \times A_C \text{ (} A_C - \text{area of composite)}$$

$$A_C = A_m + A_f$$

Finally, we have

$$\sigma_C A_C = \sigma_f A_f + \sigma_m A_m$$

Multiplying througout by length l, for continuous fibres

$$\sigma_C A_C \times l = \sigma_f A_f l + \sigma_m A_m l$$

$$\sigma_C = \sigma_f \times \frac{A_f l}{A_C l} + \sigma_m \frac{A_m l}{A_C l}$$

$$\sigma_C = \sigma_f \times V_f + \sigma_m \times V_m$$

$$V_f = \text{Volume fraction of fibres}$$

$$V_m = \text{Volume fraction of matrix}$$

composite strength, $\qquad \sigma_C = \sigma_m V_m + \sigma_f V_f \qquad$ (13.1)

is known as law of mixtures in strength of composite. For longitudinal loading, the law of mixtures can be applied for Young's modulus also.

$$E_C = E_m V_m + E_f V_f$$

To prove this
composite stress, $\qquad \sigma_C = \epsilon E_C$

matrix stress, $\qquad \sigma_m = \epsilon E_m$

fibre stress, $\qquad \sigma_f = \epsilon E_f$

since in a composite, strain for fibre, matrix and composite is the sum, therefore

$$\epsilon E_C = \epsilon E_m V_m + \epsilon E_f V_f$$

or $\qquad E_C = E_m V_m + E_f V_f \qquad$ (13.2)

13.5.6 Transverse Modulus

A continuous and oriented fibre composite can be loaded in the transverse direction as shown in Figure 13.5.

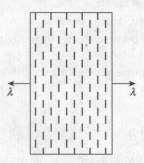

Figure 13.5 *Transverse Loading (Fibre-reinforced Composite)*

In this case, stress in composite, matrix and fibre will be the same, i.e.

$$\sigma_C = \sigma_m = \sigma_f = \sigma(\text{say})$$

Strain in composite $\qquad \epsilon_c = \epsilon_m + \epsilon_f$, strain in matrix and fibre

But $\qquad \epsilon_c = \dfrac{\sigma_C}{E_C}, \epsilon_f = \dfrac{\sigma_f}{E}, \epsilon_m = \dfrac{\sigma_m}{E}$

putting these values

$$\frac{\sigma_C}{E_C} = \frac{\sigma_m}{E_m} \times V_m + \frac{\sigma_f}{E_f} \times V_f$$

But $\qquad \sigma_C = \sigma_m = \sigma_f,$

so $\qquad \dfrac{1}{E_C} = \dfrac{V_m}{E_m} + \dfrac{V_f}{E_f} = \dfrac{V_m E_f + V_f E_m}{E_m E_f}$

or $\qquad E_C = \dfrac{E_m E_f}{V_m E_f + V_f E_m}$

Moreover, the ratio of load carried by fibre and matrix is

$$\frac{F_f}{F_m} = \frac{E_f V_f}{E_m V_m}$$

Example 13.1 A continuous and aligned glass fibre-reinforced composite consists of 45 per cent volume of glass fibres. If E for glass fibres = 70 GPa and E for polyester resin is 3.5 GPa, determine

1. Modulus of elasticity in longitudinal direction, E_C
2. Modulus of elasticity in transverse direction, E_t
3. If the cross-sectional area of the composite is 300 mm² and a stress of 60 MPa is applied in the longitudinal direction, compute the magnitude of load carried by each fibre and matrix.

Solution:

Volume fraction of fibre, $V_f = 0.45$

Volume fraction of matrix, $V_m = 1 - 0.45 = 0.55$

$$E_f = 70 \text{ GPa}, E_m = 3.5 \text{ GPa}$$

1. $\quad E_c = E_f V_f + E_m V_m$

$$= 70 \times 0.45 + 3.5 \times 0.55$$

$$= 31.5 + 1.925 = \underline{33.425 \text{ GPa}} \text{ , in longitudnal direction}$$

2. $\quad E_t = \dfrac{E_m E_f}{E_f V_m + E_m V_f} = \dfrac{70 \times 3.5}{70 \times 0.55 + 3.5 \times 0.45}$

$$= \dfrac{245}{38.5 + 1.575} = \dfrac{245}{40.075} = 6.11 \text{ GPa, in transverse direction}$$

3. $\quad$ Load as composite, $F_C = \sigma_C A_C$

$$= 60 \times 300 = 18,000 \text{ N}$$

$$\text{Ratio } \dfrac{F_f}{F_m} = \dfrac{E_f V_f}{E_m V_m} = \dfrac{20 \times 0.45}{3.5 \times 0.55}$$

$$= \dfrac{31.5}{1.925} = 16.36$$

$$F_f = 16.36 \, F_m$$

$$\text{or} \quad F_f + F_m = F_C = 18,000$$

$$16.36 \, F_m + F_m = 18,000$$

Load shared by matrix = 1036.87N

Load shared by fibres = $18,000 - 1036.87$

$$= \underline{16,963.17 \text{ N}}$$

Longitudinal and transverse strength for volume fraction of fibre, $V_f = 0.5$ for most commonly used fibre-reinforced composites is given in Table 13.1.

Table 13.1 *Strength of Fibre-reinforced Composite*

Material	Longitudinal Strength (MPa)	Transverse Strength (MPa)
Glass–polyester	700	20
Carbon (high modulus) epoxy	1000	35
Kevlar–epoxy	1200	20

13.5.7 Discontinuous and Aligned Fibre Composites

The discontinuous and aligned fibre composites are in more demand in commercial application than continuous fibre composites, because the composite of discontinuous fibres nearly reach 90 per cent of strength of continuous fibre composites. Similarly, the Young's modulus of discontinuous fibre composite is nearly 50 per cent of the Young's modulus of continuous fibre composites.

Chopped glass fibres and discontinuous fibres of carbon and aramid are being used in commercial composites.

Taking the reinforcement efficiency of a composite with all fibres parallel and aligned to direction of stress as 1 and perpendicular to the direction of stress as 0, the fibre efficiency of other cases of reinforcement are given in Table 13.2.

Table 13.2 *Reinforcement Efficiency*

Fibre Orientation	Stress Direction	Reinforcement Efficiency
All fibres are parallel	Stress parallel to fibres	1.0
	Stress perpendicular to fibres	0.0
Fibres uniformly but randomly distributed within a specific plane	Stress in any direction in the plane of fibres	0.375
Fibres uniformly and randomly distributed in three dimensions of the structure/composite	Any direction	0.125

13.6 FIBRE PHASE

A small-diameter fibre possesses much more strength than the large-diameter wires. In bigger-size wires there is more probability of critical surface flaws, than in fine-diameter fibres. This is especially true in the case of wires and fibres of brittle materials like glass. As the size continuously decreases, the strength of the fibre gradually increases. For the following strength goes on increasing.

$$\text{Wires} \rightarrow \text{fibres} \rightarrow \text{whiskers}$$
$$\text{(minimum strength)} \rightarrow \text{moderate strength} \rightarrow \text{maximum strength}$$

Whiskers are very fine crystals (grown in the laboratory) having a large length to diameter ratio. They are exceptionally strong and virtually free from flaws. The materials such as graphite, silicon carbide, silicon nitrides and aluminium oxide are used for growing their whiskers.

Fibres are either polycrystalline or amorphous having small diameters (5–10 μm). These are made of ceramics or polymers, for example:

1. Polymer aramid
2. Glass, carbon, brass, aluminium oxide and tungsten

13.6.1 Wires

Fine wires of steel, molybdenum and tungsten are used in (1) radial steel reinforcement in automobile tires, (2) filament-wound rocket casings and (3) wire-wound high-pressure hoses.

13.7 MATRIX PHASE

General metal (in metal–metal matrix composites) and polymer (in polymer composites) are used as matrix phase, because ductility of matrix phase is utilized in improving the mechanical properties of the composite. In ceramic matrix composite, the reinforcing component is added to improve fracture toughness. In fibre-reinforced composite, the functions of matrix phase are summarized as follows:

1. Matrix binds the fibres together.
2. Matrix acts as a mechanism by which an external load/stress is transmitted and distributed to the fibres (through shear tractions along the length of fibres).

3. Only a small fraction of applied load is sustained by the matrix, and majority of the load is carried by fibres.

4. Matrix material is ductile in nature so as to improve fracture toughness of the composite.

5. Matrix protects the individual fibres from surface damage.

6. At the same time, matrix separates the fibres and prevents the propagation of brittle cracks.

7. The adhesive bonding forces between fibres and matrix should be high to minimize the fibre pullout.

8. Ultimate strength of the composite depends on the magnitude of bonding strength between fibre and matrix.

13.8 POLYMER MATRIX COMPOSITES

A composite is a material composed of two or more materials, with the properties of the resultant material superior to the properties of individual materials making the composite. For example, glass fibre plastic composites take the advantage of high strength of glass fibre and high ductility of plastic matrix. As per the terms even an alloy is a composite, but the term 'composite' is used for polymeric composite in which matrix is of a polymeric material.

Polymers used in composite manufacture are epoxy, unsaturated polyesters, a few thermoplastics and some thermosetting polymers as silicones, phenolics and polyimides. In a polymeric composite, there is a continuous resin matrix in which there is controlled distribution of reinforcements such as glass, graphite, aramid, thermoplastic fibres, metals and ceramics. The reinforcement can be continuous woven fabric, chopped fibres, particles or flakes. In general composites, reinforcement is of the order of 20–50 per cent by weight, but in advanced composites, reinforcement can be as high as 70 per cent by weight. Graphite or carbon fibres are most common reinforcements.

The purpose of reinforcement is to enhance mechanical properties, but chopped fibres, flakes and particles are not as effective as continuous fibres, because the continuous fibres distribute the applied load throughout the entire field of composite and enhance strength.

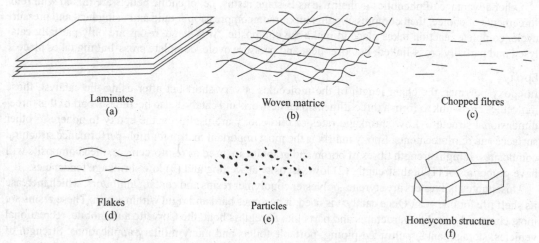

Laminates
(a)

Woven matrice
(b)

Chopped fibres
(c)

Flakes
(d)

Particles
(e)

Honeycomb structure
(f)

Figure 13.6 *Forms of Reinforcements in Polymer Matrix*

High-performance grades of polymer composites, i.e. with stronger matrix and continuous reinforcements have high specific strength and high specific modulus.

Cellulose fibres reinforce the plants and enhance their mechanical properties and hence wood is a natural composite. The first commercial composite was developed by using paper lamination as reinforcements in phenolics. Then, there were further developments in glass–epoxy composites used in items as boats, piping and vessels, because of their strength and resistance to environment.

Different forms of reinforcements are (1) laminations, (2) particles, (3) woven fibres, (4) chopped fibres, (5) flakes and (6) honeycomb structural elements (Figure 13.6).

13.8.1 Matrix Materials

There are two main types of polymer composite matrix materials: (1) thermoplastic and (2) thermosets. In the beginning, glass reinforcement in the form of chopped fibres were reinforced in thermoplastic by injection moulding process, but these composites of short length, discontinuous forms do not posses high strength. Later on, techniques were developed for reinforcement in continuous forms in thermoplastic by passing through continuous fibres as of glass through the molten bath of thermoplastic polymer. But the viscosity of thermoplastic polymer is high and a number of problems are associated in this process. After passing through the molten bath, the continuous bunch of fibres was wound on a mandrel in a specific sequence. Then, the other process was developed in which polymer is dissolved in a solvent. The fibres are drawn through the bath of polymer–solvent solution and thus solvent gets volatized and coating on fibres remains only of polymer. This proved to be a better technique and is being used as thermoplastics like polyamide-imide, polysulfones, polyetherimide and so on. Solution-coated materials have better flexibility. The most common reinforcements in thermoplasts are glass fibres, carbon fibres and aramid fibres.

Thermosetting resins generally have lower viscosity than thermoplastics and become cross-linked by using a catalyst. Earlier, composites were made by using phenolic thermosetting matrix. Then, epoxies, unsaturated polyesters, silicones and polyimides resins are being used.

Phenolics are hard and rigid and possess good electrical properties, and all normal reinforcements can be used with phenolics. Depending upon specific requirements, paper, cloth, glass and aramid fibres are used as reinforcements. Applications include brake and clutch pads moulded from phenolics and reinforcements of asbestos, powdered metals and friction modifiers as MoS and graphite.

Other advantage of phenolics is their use as B-stage resins, i.e. phenolic pellets are mixed with reinforcements of choice, then compressing this mixture in compression mould and using heat and pressure cycle, complete reaction takes place to make the composite. At B stage, resins are only partially catalysed and partially cross-linked, but after heat and pressure cycle, complete cross-linking takes place.

Epoxy

In epoxy polymer, the chain length of the molecules is very short but after using the catalyst, those molecules cross-link to form a three-dimensional network and catalyst also becomes a part of this three-dimensional structure. Low shrinkage rates of thin epoxy are useful for the epoxy to adhere to other surfaces and reinforcements. Epoxy matrix is the most important matrix for high-performance structural composites. If high-strength fibres of boron and graphite are used as reinforcement, then composite will have properties of (1) high strength, (2) low viscosity at wetting and (3) low shrinkage tendencies.

Unsaturated polyesters are styrene–polyester copolymer resins and contain inhibitors, which increase its shelf life for one year. Once catalyst is used, it becomes hard and rigid within 1 min. These resins are most commonly used for structures and parts like fibreglass boat, the Corvette automobile, recreational vehicles, storage tanks, pultruded piping, portable toilets and many military applications. Strength of unsaturated polyesters is slightly less than that of epoxies.

Glass is the most commonly used reinforcements in polyester. Big boats are often made by hand lay-up, small boats are made by chopped glass fibres and the hull is formed by simply spraying the mould to the desired hull thickness.

Pipe and structural shapes are pultruded and fibre reinforcement and resins are extruded from a die.

Silicones

Silicones are used as matrix for special applications, which can withstand a service temperature of 300°C. Printing blankets are made from silicones because they will transfer ink completely to the other surface. Nothing sticks to silicone elastomers. Silicones are also available as rigid thermosets.

Polyimides are also used for special applications, usually in high-temperature composites. Polyimides prepregs are available that can be fabricated from partially polymerized matrix resins. Prepregs can be placed in moulds and cured to final form with the application of heat, and the composites can sustain service temperatures up to 250°C. These resins are very costly and are used only in aerospace applications.

General guidelines for the use of polymers as resins are as follows:

1. Thermosetting matrix materials include polyimides, urea, melamine formaldehydes and furans, which are commercially available in desirable properties.
2. Melamines are widely used in fillers for unbreakable dinner wares.
3. Ureas are used for laminating resins.
4. Furans are used in chemical process industry for tanks to hold aggressive chemicals.
5. Composites for elevated service temperatures usually use polyimide and silicone.
6. Most of the thermoplastics are available in glass-reinforced form; content of glass is 10–40 percent.
7. For continuous fibre reinforced, thermoplastic composites include polyether imide, polyphenylene sulphide and thermoplasts polyimides.
8. For short, chopped fibres, commonly used thermoplasts are polyamides, poly carbonate, acetals, polystyrene, polyethers and fluorocarbons.

13.8.2 Reinforcements

The first composites were laminated of paper saturated with phenolic resin, and compression moulded into sheets for electrical applications. Net cotton fabrics were used as canvas–phenolic composites using woven cotton fabrics. Hard, inorganic reinforcements such as glass and metal cause excessive tool wear in secondary operations. A brief description of reinforcement is as follows:

1. Metals are used in the form of drawn wires, ultrafine wires, laminates and honeycomb structure. Beehive pattern honeycombs are often made from aluminium foils. For structural members of the aircraft, laminates with honeycomb structure in the core with metal or fabric reinforced polymers as the facing of the laminate are used. Metal/plastic/ metal laminates have been developed for panels of automobiles.
2. *Asbestos:* It is a naturally occurring mineral with a fibrous structure and can be wet with low viscosity resins. Asbestos used for resin is *chrystolite asbestos*, a hydrated magnesium silicate $(3MgO.2SiO_2.2H_2O)$. Asbestos fibres wet in water can be woven into fabrics. These fibres are non-flammable and are relatively inert from chemical attack. But asbestos fibres are injurious to health.
3. *Ceramics:* Ceramics such as silicon carbide, silicon nitride and aluminium oxide can be made into small-diameter fibres, whiskers or particles and can be used to reinforce polymer matrix.

4. *Polymers:* These are liquid crystal polymers with extremely high strength. These liquid crystal polymers and some olefins have been used as reinforcement in thermosets and thermoplastics. Kevlar fibre, an aramid fibre, has a strength of the order of 3000 MPa. These Kevlar fibres are available in continuous fibres, woven fabrics and as chopped fibres. Another polymer called Nomex, a high-temperature nylon, is not as strong as Kevlar, but it is easier to process and less expensive. During synthesis, the rigid molecules (of Kevlar) are aligned in the direction of fibre axis. They have high longitudinal strength and high modulus. Matrix material is epoxy or polyester. Major applications are in (1) bullet proof vests, (2) sports goods, (3) ropes and tires, (4) missile cases and (5) pressure vessels.

5. *Boron:* Continuous filaments of boron are made by chemical deposition of boron from boron-rich gas. Boron fibres are of high strength and are used in composites for aerospace and military applications.

6. *Carbon graphite:* Carbon fibres (CFs) (used as reinforcement in polymers) are obtained by heating precursor fibres of organic materials to very high temperatures of the order of 1000–3000°C, in the absence of air and under tension. These are the fibres of rayon, pitch or polyacrylonitrile (PAN). Graphite crystals have a hexagonal structure with the basal plane aligned parallel to the fibre axis.

Carbon fibres (CFs) are grown in diameters of smaller than 5 μm. They are made into strands for weaving or winding and they are available as chopped strands for use in injection moulding resin. But these carbon fibres are very costly.

7. *Glass:* The most common reinforcement is glass fibres. Fibre glass is the trade name of first important structural composites. Glass fibres are made by flowing molten metal through tiny holes in dies. There are two types of glasses: E (electrical applications) and S (high strength) glasses. S glass is a magnesia/silica/alumina material with high tensile strength, and the diameter of fibres range from 5 to 25 μm. E glass fibres (55 per cent SiO_2, 16 CaO, 15 Al_2O_3, 10 B_2O_3, 4 MgO) are easily drawn into fibres. Glass reinforcements are available in continuous filaments, strands, rovings, weaves, chopped strands and non-woven mat forms.

Mat cloths are made from randomly intertwined discontinuous fibres of moderate lengths. When bundles of strands are formed into a large continuous strand, the product is called roving and heavy composites are often made from cloths that are woven from roving.

To get good mechanical strength between glass fibres and resin matrix, bond between the two is most important. Glasses are often treated by silane compounds that tend to enhance this adhesion between glass fibres and resin matrix. The coupling of silane (A_3Si B) provides high performance of composites.

8. Fine wires of steel, molybdenum and tungsten are utilized as a radial steel reinforcement in automobile tires, in filament-wound rocket casings and wire-wound high pressure hoses.

13.8.3 Fabrication Techniques

Detailed discussions of fabrication techniques are beyond the scope of this book, however, these techniques will be briefly described as follows:

1. Contact moulding or hand lay-up involves coating a mould with a layer of resin; thin glass reinforcements are laid up in mould. The process is repeated till the desired thickness of composite is developed and reinforcement is thoroughly saturated with resin.

2. *Filament winding:* Glass reinforcement continuous strand is wound around mandrel. Strand is saturated with resin in online bath. Winding pattern can be controlled depending upon the desired mechanical strength. This process is used for making pipes and tanks to carry chemicals.

3. *Compression moulding:* A catalyst is used in resin, and the catalysed polyester or epoxy resin is kneaded into glass reinforcement by rollers. Special fillers are added to keep the resin from being tacky (thick) and inhibitors are added to increase the hot life of catalysed resin. Finished sheet is called sheet moulding compound (SMC). This sheet can be cut into different sizes to match the mould to make the finished part. The mould is finally heated to cross-link the polymer resin. Similarly, the bulk moulding compound (BMC) is made by adding thickness to the resin in place of thinners as in the case of SMC. Both SMC and BMC are used for large moulding such as automobile fenders.

13.8.4 Continuous Pultrusion

In this process, resin-impregnated glass strands are pulled through a heated die. Before the die, there is a heated bath and the resin cross-links in the heated die. Different shapes as channel, I and pipe sections are generated.

Chopped fibre spraying: The resin and catalyst are mixed in a hand-held gun and sprayed at a mould surface. A chopper is incorporated in the gun. It chops continuous strands of glass into small length to act as reinforcement in the composite. This type of composite is not as strong as hand lay-ups, however, the process is used for making boats, shower stalls and bath tubs.

Resin transfer moulding: In this case, we get two finished surfaces instead of one. A close fitting mould is required. Glass reinforcement is cut and shaped to desired thickness in the open mould. Then the mould is closed and evacuated, and the catalysed resin is pumped into the bottom of the mould. After the mould is filled, part is allowed to cure. This is used in RTP boats (reinforced thermosetting plastics).

13.8.5 Vacuum Bag Forming

SMC is cured in the vacuum bag rig using temperature-resistant silicon rubbers for forming bladder or vacuum bag to make a preform and cure the preform in another mould.

Table 13.3 shows a comparison of properties of glass fibres, carbon fibres and Kevlar fibres in a composite with volume fraction, $V_f = 0.6$.

Table 13.3 *Comparison of Properties of Fibres*

Property	Glass Fibres (E Glass)	Carbon Fibres (High Strength)	Aramid Fibres (Kevlar-49)
Specific gravity	2.1	1.6	1.4
Tensile modulus (Longitudinal) (GPa)	45	145	76
Tensile modulus (transverse) (GPa)	12	10	5.5
Tensile strength Longitudinal (MPa)	1020	1240	1360
Ultimate tensile strain (%)	2.3	0.9	1.8

Table 13.4 gives the mechanical properties of various reinforcements used in composites.

Table 13.4 *Fibre Reinforcement Materials*

Material	SG	σ_{ut} (GPa)	E (GPa)
Whiskers			
Graphite	2.2	20	700
Silicon nitride	3.2	5–7	350–400
Aluminium oxide	4.0	10–18	700–1500
Silicon carbide	3.2	20	480
Fibres			
Aluminium oxide	3.95	1.38	380
Aramid (Kevlar-49)	1.44	3.6–4.0	131
Carbon	1.8–2.1	1.5–4.8	220–700
E glass	2.58	3.45	70
Boron	2.57	3.6	400
Silicon carbide	3.0	3.9	400
Metallic wires			
High-strength steel	7.9	2.39	210
Molybdenum	10.2	2.2	324
Tungsten	19.3	2.89	407

13.9 CERAMIC MATRIX COMPOSITES

Ceramics are generally resistant to oxidation and deterioration at elevated temperature. Various components in aircraft gas turbine engines and IC engines of automobiles are subjected to high temperatures during operation. Therefore, ceramic–ceramic matrix composites (CMCs) can be used for aircraft and automobile parts.

Fracture toughness of ceramic materials is low because of their brittle behaviour, but by the development of new generation of ceramic matrix composites, the fracture toughness is highly improved. Reinforcements of ceramics in the form of fibres, particulates or whiskers are embedded in the matrix of another ceramics. Improvement in fracture toughness is due to the interaction between the advancing cracks (initiating in matrix) and dispersed phase of ceramic particles.

Fracture toughness of most ceramic materials varies from 1 to 5 MPa $\sqrt{m}$, but in ceramic matrix composites it is improved to 6–20 MPa$\sqrt{m}$. This is K_{IC} value, i.e stress intensity factors in mode I.

Several techniques are employed to retard the crack propagation as follows.

13.9.1 Transformation Toughening

Small particles of partially stabilized zirconia (ZrO_2) are dispersed within the matrix such as matrix of Al_2O_3. Partial stabilization allows retention of the metastable tetragonal phase at ambient conditions. The stress field in front of a propagating crack causes these metastable, retained tetragonal particles to undergo transformation to the stable monoclinic phase. During this process, there is a slight increase in particle volume, with the net result that compressive stresses are developed as the crack surface near the crack tip, tending to pinch the crack and arresting its growth.

In another technique, whiskers of SiC and Si_3N_4 are used. These whiskers inhibit crack propagation by (1) deflecting the crack tip, (2) forming bridges across crack faces, (3) absorbing energy during pull out as whiskers debond from the matrix and (4) redistributing the stresses in the region adjacent to crack tips.

These CMCs exhibit improved high-temperature creep behaviour, resistance to thermal shock. SiC whiskers–reinforced aluminas are being used as cutting tool inserts for machining hardmetal alloys.

13.10 CARBON–CARBON COMPOSITES

In this, the carbon fibres are reinforcing the carbon matrix to obtain high tensile strength and high elastic modulus retained at high temperatures of the order of 2000°C.

Carbon–Carbon composites are employed in rocket motors, as a frictional material in aircraft and high-performance automobiles, as ablative shield for re-entry vehicles. To make this composite, two- or three-dimensional patterns of carbon fibres are made. This pattern is impregnated often with a phenolic resin, and the work piece is formed into final shape. Resin is allowed to cure. Now, the matrix (phenolic resin) is pyrolyzed by heating in an inert atmosphere and resin is converted into carbon by heating. All the molecular components like oxygen, hydrogen and nitrogen are driven off leaving behind large carbon chain molecules. Subsequent heat treatment at higher temperature causes this carbon matrix to densify and strengthen the composite.

13.11 METAL MATRIX COMPOSITES

Metal matrix composite stands for metal fibres in a metal matrix (a ductile matrix). Strength of MMC is much better than the strength of the base metal. The metallic reinforcement improves specific stiffness (E/ρ) and specific strength (σ/ρ), where ρ is the specific gravity, along with abrasion resistance, creep resistance, thermal conductivity and dimensional stability. These MMCs are very expensive, therefore used only in restricted applications. But these composites have many advantages over polymer matrix composites (PMCs) such as (1) higher operating temperature, (2) non-flammabilities and (3) more resistance to degradation by organic fluids.

The super alloys and alloys of Al, Mg, Ti and Cu are employed as metal matrix. The reinforcement can be in the form of particulates, continuous or discontinuous fibres or whiskers with volume fraction of reinforcement as 0.1–0.6. Continuous fibres can be of carbon, silicon carbide, boron, alumina and other refractory metals, while the discontinuous fibres are primarily of SiC whiskers, chopped fibres of Al_2O_3, chopped fibres of carbon, and in particulate form, fine particles of SiC and Al_2O_3. Cermets can be classified as MMCs.

An example of MMC is as follows:

Fibre	Boron
Matrix	Aluminium
Fibre fraction	0.48
E (GPa)	207
σ_{ut} (MPa)	1515

Processing of MMCs is done in two steps:

1. Introduction of fibres into matrix, e.g. thorough mixing of silicon carbide particles in hot aluminium alloy by churning at high speed.
2. Shaping operation—by standard metal forming operation as forging, extrusion, rolling and so on.

13.11.1 Applications of MMC

Major applications of MMCs are as follows:

1. Advanced aluminium alloy metal matrix with boron fibres—used in space shuttle orbiter.
2. Continuous graphite fibres in aluminium alloy—used in Hubble Telescope.
3. High-temperature creep and rupture properties of some superalloys are enhanced by reinforcement of tungsten fibres.

13.12 HYBRID COMPOSITES

In hybrid composites, there are more than two different phases as two different kinds of fibres in a single matrix for better overall combinations of properties than the composites with single fibre plus matrix. A combination of glass and carbon fibres in epoxy matrix results in a better hybrid composites. Carbon fibres are much stronger than glass fibres; at the same time, glass fibres are cheaper and carbon fibres are very costly. Under the applications of load, first of all glass fibres will fracture, then carbon fibres will fail, resulting in a stress–strain diagram with a double slope as shown in Figure 13.7. Slope OA is initial elastic modulus and slope BC is final elastic modulus of the composite. Fall A to B in the curve is due to the failure of the first fibre system (carbon) at strain ϵ_A. The second fibre system continues to take the load until another fibre fracture at ϵ_C strain at stress σ_C. In glass–carbon–epoxy system, I curve OA is of carbon plus glass fibres, and II curve BC is of glass fibres.

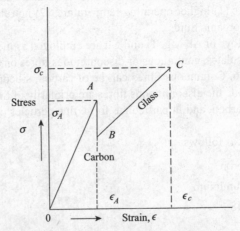

Figure 13.7 *Stress–strain Curve of a Hybrid Composite*

In a hybrid composite, failure is not generally catastrophic. In carbon–glass–epoxy hybrid, carbon fibres are the first to fail, and the load is transferred to glass fibres. Upon failure of the glass fibres, the matrix phase sustains the applied load. When matrix also fails, eventually the composite fails.

Applications of hybrid composites are as follows:

1. Antenna discs made of CFRP (carbon fibre reinforced plastic) + aluminium honeycomb
2. CFRP and GRP for leaf springs
3. Helicopter rotors of CFRP and GRP
4. Lightweight land, water and air transport structural components
5. Lightweight orthopaedic components

13.13 STRUCTURAL COMPOSITES

A structural composite is generally composed of both homogeneous and composite materials. The properties of this structural composite depend not only on the properties of its constituent materials, but also on the geometrical design and orientation of various structural elements.

Laminar composites and sandwich panels are the two most common structural composites. Laminar composites are made up of many laminae, i.e. layers of laminae as shown in Figure 13.8. A lamina is a ply or a layer (very thin). A single lamina can be used because it is very thin. A number of lamina are glued together to form a laminate of desired thickness. Following are the examples of laminates:

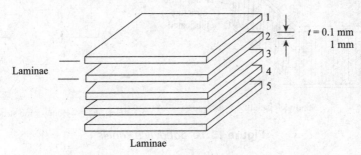

Figure 13.8 *Structural Composite*

1. Plywood.
2. Sheet moulding compounds (SMC) discussed earlier.
3. In a ply board, odd numbers of plies are glued together to build a board of 6–12 mm thickness or even up to 18 mm thickness. Successive plies have different grain orientations to develop biaxial strength of ply board, as shown in Figure 13.9.

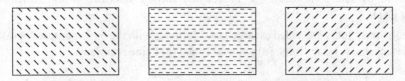

Figure 13.9 *Plies with Different Grain Orientations*

Normally, five to seven plies are glued together so that shrinkage stresses are symmetrical about mid ply and tendency of warping is minimized.

13.13.1 Sandwich Panels

In a sandwich panel, a layer of less dense material or core is provided with two strong outer sheets or faces. The core has lower stiffness and lower strength and the faces bear most of the in-plane loading. Typical facing materials are aluminium alloys, fibre-reinforced plastics, steel sheets or ply wood. There are two basic structural purposes of the core:

1. It separates the faces and resists deformation in the direction perpendicular to face plane.
2. It provides a certain degree of shear rigidity along planes.

Sandwich panels as shown in Figure 13.10 are found in various applications like roofs, floors, walls of buildings, air crafts, wings, fuselage and tail plane skins.

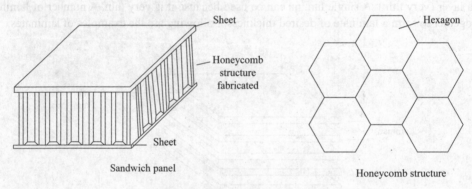

Figure 13.10 *Sandwich Panels*

=== **KEY POINTS TO REMEMBER** ===

❏ Composite is a multiphase material, developed with a specific purpose of improvement in properties, i.e. the properties of resultant composite made from different phases are better than the properties of individual phases.

❏ Wood is a natural composite with cellulose fibres in lignin matrix.

❏ In large-sized particle composites, the matrix and particle interface is not treated on atomic or molecular level.

❏ In some polymers, fillers are added as large-sized particles with the basic purposes of (a) filler materials, (b) plasticizers, (c) stabilizers, (d) colourants and (e) flame retardants.

❏ Cermets, vulcanized rubber and concrete are examples of large particle composites.

❏ In dispersion-strengthened composite, particle size is about 0.1 μm or less, with volume fractions of 0.05–0.15. The high-temperature strength of nickel alloys is enhanced significantly by the addition of 3 vol% of thoria.

❏ Critical fibre length so that it is not pulled out of matrix

$$l_c = \frac{\sigma_{ut}^f d}{2\tau_b},$$

where σ_{ut}^f is ultimate tensile strength of the fibre, d is the fibre diameter and τ_b is the fibre matrix bond strength.

❏ If fibre length $l > 15l_c$, it is a continuous fibre.

❏ Continuous fibre

$$E_1 = E_m V_m + E_f V_f, \text{ elastic modulus in longitudinal direction}$$

$$E_t = \frac{E_m E_f}{E_f V_m + E_m V_f}, \text{ elastic modulus in transverse direction}$$

❏ Whiskers are very fine single crystals having large length to diameter ratio.

❏ Basic functions of matrix are (a) binding the fibres together, (b) external load is transmitted by matrix to the fibres by shear tractions, (c) separates the fibres and (d) prevents propagation of brittle cracks.

❏ Polymers used in composite manufacture are epoxy, unsaturated polymers, a few thermoplastics and thermosetting plastics as silicones, phenolics and polyimides.

❏ Reinforcements are (a) metal (wires, very fine wires, honeycomb structure), (b) asbestos fibres, (c) ceramic fibres and whiskers, (d) polymer–like Kevlar fibre, (e) carbon–graphite fibres, (f) glass fibres and (g) cloth mats of glass fibres.

❏ *Ceramic matrix composites:* Reinforcement of ceramics in the form of fibres and whiskers are embedded in the matrix of another ceramic. There is improvement in fracture toughness. Transformation toughening retards the crack propagation in CMC.

❏ *Carbon–Carbon composites:* Carbon fibres are impregnated with phenolic resin, which is burnt in inert atmosphere leaving carbon matrix.

❏ Metal matrix composites (MMC). Superalloys are employed as metal matrix in which reinforcement in the form of fibres, whiskers and particulates of SiC, Al_2O_3 and other refractory metals are provided. MMC of boron fibre in aluminium matrix has a strength of 1515 MPa.

❏ *Hybrid composites:* More than two different phases are present as two types of fibres in a single matrix.

❏ Laminar composites and sandwich panels are examples of structural composites.

MULTIPLE CHOICE QUESTIONS

1. In a dispersion-strengthened composite, the size of the particles is
   - (a) 1 μm
   - (b) 0.1 μm or less
   - (c) 1 nm
   - (d) None of these

2. In wood, what is the matrix material.
   - (a) Cellulose
   - (b) Glucose
   - (c) Lignin
   - (d) None of these

3. Which one is a correct statement
   - A. Fillers added in large particle composites are wood flour, silica flour, glass powder and so on.
   - B. Addition of plasticizers in large particle composites improves the elastic modulus of the composite.
   - (a) Both A and B
   - (b) A only
   - (c) B only
   - (d) Neither A nor B

4. Vulcanized rubber is an example of
   - (a) Large particle composite
   - (b) Dispersion-strengthened composite
   - (c) Discontinuous fibre composite
   - (d) None of these

5. In dispersion-strengthened composite, which shape of particle reinforcement provides maximum strength?
   - (a) Round
   - (b) Needle
   - (c) Disc
   - (d) Cube

6. The ultimate strength of a fibre is 1600 MPa, fibre diameter is 10 μm and shear strength between fibre and matrix is 100 MPa. What is the critical length of fibre?
   - (a) 100 μm
   - (b) 80 μm
   - (c) 40 μm
   - (d) None of these

7. Young's modulus of a fibre is 72 GPa and of a matrix is 3.6 GPa. If $V_f = 0.6$, what is Young's modulus of the composite in longitudinal direction?
   - (a) 30.96 GPa
   - (b) 37.8 GPa
   - (c) 45.04 GPa
   - (d) None of these

8. What is the approximate ratio of E_c/E_t of a Kelvar–epoxy composite with 0.5 V_f?
   - (a) 60
   - (b) 40
   - (c) 30
   - (d) 20

9. Which one is not a correct statement for a matrix phase?
   - (a) Matrix prevents the individual fibres from surface damage
   - (b) Matrix binds the fibres together
   - (c) Matrix prevents the propagation of brittle cracks
   - (d) None of above

10. Which of the following has maximum strength?
    - (a) Carbon fibre
    - (b) Aramid fibre
    - (c) Glass fibre
    - (d) Asbestos fibre

11. In ceramic matrix composite, which process retards the crack propagation?
    - (a) Precipitation hardening
    - (b) Strain hardening
    - (c) Transformation toughening
    - (d) None of these

Answers

1. (b)   2. (c)   3. (b)   4. (a)   5. (b)   6. (b)   7. (c)   8. (a)
9. (d)   10. (b)   11. (c)

REVIEW QUESTIONS

1. What is a composite? Why composites are developed?

2. Differentiate among continuous, discontinuous and choppers of glass? What are their applications?

3. What are the basic functions of fillers, plasticizers and stabilizers in the manufacturer of large-particle composites?

4. Explain the following:
   Cermets, vulcanized rubber, concrete and RCC

5. What are dispersion-strengthened composites? What is a strengthening mechanism and what is its advantage?

6. What are thoria, SAP and zirconia?

7. Explain with the help of a sketch the critical length of a short fibre in a fibre matrix composite.

8. Compare the stress–strain behaviour of continuous fibre composite with stress–strain behaviour of fibre and matrix.

9. What is rule of mixture in strength and elastic modulus for a fibre matrix composite?

10. What are different types of wire reinforcements and what are their applications?

11. What are functions of matrix phase in a composite?

12. What are different forms of reinforcements in composites?

13. Differentiate among phenolics, epoxy and unsaturated polyester resins as matrix material.

14. Explain the following.
    Filament winding, compression moulding and continuous pultrusion techniques for fibre-reinforced composites.

15. Write a short note on ceramic matrix composites.

16. What are metal matrix composites? Where are they used?

17. What is a hybrid composite? Explain with the help of an example.

18. What are laminar composites and sandwich panels? What are their applications?

PRACTICE PROBLEMS

1. Elastic modulii of glass and epoxy are 70 GPa and 3.5 GPa, respectively. A glass–fibre–epoxy composite is made up of (a) 15 per cent fibre by volume and (b) 40 per cent fibre by volume. Obtain the fraction of load carried by glass fibres in these two composites.

   Ans. [(a) 0.779 (b) 0.93]

2. A Kevlar-49–epoxy unidirectional composite is made with 65 per cent fibre volume fraction. Properties of Kelvar and epoxy are as follows:

Material	σ_{ut} (GPa)	E (GPa)
Kelvar 49	1.4	70
Epoxy	0.0025	3.5

(a) Calculate the following:
   (i) Longitudinal strengths
   (ii) Longitudinal modulus
   (iii) Transverse modulus

(b) Determine the fibre volume fraction if $\sigma_c = 358$ MPa, i.e. composite strength.

Ans. [910.88 MPa; 46.72 GPa; 0.915 GPa; (b) 0.254]

14

WEAR OF MATERIALS

14.1 INTRODUCTION

This chapter explains the basics of friction and wear. The term 'tribology' stands for the 'study of friction, wear and lubrication'. From the beginning of civilization, people are confronted with the good and bad effects of friction between two contacting surfaces having relative sliding motion. Invention of a wheel brought relief by converting sliding friction into rolling friction, and rolling friction on any object is much less than the sliding friction.

Best example of friction and wear is an automobile, in which friction between tyre and road is necessary for the starting and stopping motion of the automobile, while friction in moving parts of the engine is responsible for loss of power and wear of the engine parts ultimately leading to its failure.

Earth quake is due to the stick–slip movement of rock plates supporting the land mass. When the rock plates slip past each other, earth quake results. In human beings, hip and knee joints suffer from wear due to friction. Result of wear of lubricating cartilage in knee joints is the 'arthritis disease'.

In a survey, it is estimated that 5 per cent of gross domestic product (GDP) is wasted into wear. However, lubrication can help reduce wear due to friction, adhesion, abrasion and erosion. Friction and wear cannot be completely eliminated, but these can be reduced to a minimum level.

This chapter discusses different types of wear, contact stresses, friction and measurement of frictional effects and techniques employed for protection against wear.

14.2 HISTORY OF FRICTION AND WEAR

Ancient people used to rub stones to produce sparks and create fire in dry grass. They used to kill their prey with the stone weapons. They knew that it was easier to drag their kill than to carry the kill on the shoulder as the dragging force on the kill is much less than the weight of the kill. It was assumed to be the third rule of Thumb. Egyptians have used lubrication to slide their stones for building monuments. In 1789, Coulomb investigated friction variables and observed that frictional force is independent of the area of contact.

A general definition of friction is that 'friction consists of forces on object resisting motion when motion is attempted'. Wear is the cause of friction and the development of tools very much depends upon wear. The first tools developed were of wood, but wood does not last long. Then stones were attached to wood to make hatchets, hammers, knives and arrows. Wear rate of stone was much less than wear rate of wood, but stone is a brittle material and breaks easily. Then, the tools made of wrought iron were developed, having more life, more strength and hardness. Now, there are tools made of various types of steels, with multipoints for gradual and continuous cutting of metals and are provided with lubrication to reduce the effect of heat produced during cutting operations. Now, we have many ingenious devices in our arsenal to combat friction, wear and erosion.

14.3 CONTACT MECHANICS

Wear between two surfaces occurs when there is relative motion between the two surfaces in contact. Amount of wear highly depends on the physical properties of two surfaces, roughness of two surfaces, geometry of the surface—whether two flat surfaces are in contact, one flat and one curved surface in contact or two curved surfaces are in contact—and the magnitude and type of stresses developed at the contact points between the two. Contact mechanics is a form of engineering mechanics, dealing with stresses and deformation at microscopic areas that form the real area of contact.

Moreover, various other aspects of contact surfaces are of equal importance such as (1) atomic aspects of contacting surfaces, (2) organic materials required to separate and lubricate the two surfaces, (3) mechanical aspects of tribe system as fluid mechanics, effect of rise in temperature, effect of contact stresses developed, (4) response of various materials to wear processes and (5) reduction in cost of friction and wear.

However, in this section we will study the effect of forces on the stresses developed between two surfaces, where (1) two surfaces are flat, (2) one flat surface and other curved surface, and (3) two curved surfaces are in contact.

14.3.1 Two Surfaces are Flat

Two flat surfaces are most common in sight, while dragging a box on a floor, one plate sliding over another plate, a flat belt rubbing on flat surface of a pulley and so on. Figure 14.1 shows two flat surfaces of blocks A and B at the interface.

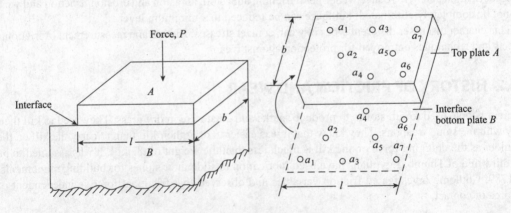

Figure 14.1 *Two Flat Surfaces*

Apparent area in contact $= l \times b$. But due to surface irregularities (unevenness in the surfaces) the contact takes place at very small areas $a_1, a_2, \ldots a_7$.

Apparent contact stress under force, P

$$\sigma_a = \frac{P}{l \times b}$$

Real contact stress under force, P

$$\sigma_r = \frac{P}{\text{summation of areas } a_1, a_2, a_3, \ldots a_7}$$

Real contact stresses are much more than apparent contact stresses and surfaces get severe deformation at these contact points. Real surfaces contain errors of form due to manufacturing processes. Ridges of surfaces contact each other and produce junctions of various sizes depending upon the load.

Now, if one block A is pushed over the surface of block B, then coefficient of friction between the two surfaces (depending upon surface texture of both surfaces) is the deciding factor so as to know the force required to push one block over another. Figure 14.2 shows how the ridges of two surfaces contact each other. Wear does not always involve contact between two conforming surfaces.

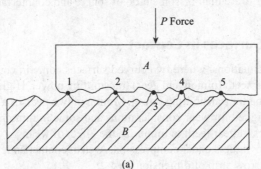

(a)

Figure 14.2 *(a) Contact of Ridges of Two Surfaces*

One of the most useful aspects of contact mechanics is the determination of point and line contact stresses using Hertzian stress equation.

14.3.2 One Flat and Other Curved Surface

Heinrich Hertz developed models for the calculation of elastic stresses for systems such as a ball on a flat surface, crossed cylinders, two cylinders making line contact and so on.

The stress at a point contact is a function of the geometry and elastic properties (E, v) for contacting materials. Hertz equations for the contact of a sphere on a flat surface Fig 14.2(b) under elastic conditions, i.e. deformation is recoverable, are

Radius of contact area,

$$a = 0.721 \sqrt[3]{PD\left(\frac{1 - v_1^2}{E_1} + \frac{1 - v_2^2}{E_2}\right)}$$

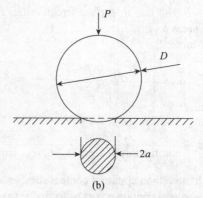

Figure 14.2 *(b) One Flat and Other Curved Surface in Contact*

Maximum stress,

$$\sigma_{max} = \frac{1.5P}{\pi a^2}$$

where a is the radius of contact area, D is the diameter of sphere, E_1, E_2 are the elastic modulus of sphere and counterface, v_1, v_2 are the Poisson's ratio of sphere and counterface and P is the force on the sphere.

14.3.3 Two Curved Surfaces in Contact

There are many practical situations, where two curved surfaces come in contact and then going out of contact, for example, a gear teeth (pinion and gear) transmitting power. High contact stresses are developed with two teeth meshing for transmitting power. Motion of two gears is a combination of rolling and sliding. Gear teeth are designed for wear considerations and some minimum hardness (350–400 BHN) is necessary on the surfaces of gear teeth to minimize the effect of wear.

Figure 14.3 shows two cylinders under compression. Area of contact under load P (uniformly distributed along length l) is a narrow strip of dimension $2w \times l$.

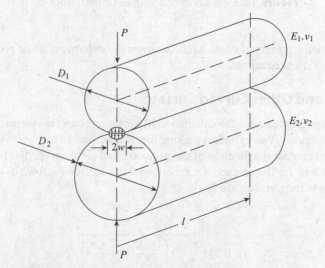

Figure 14.3 *Cylinders Under Diametral Compression*

As per Hertzian equations,

Semiwidth,
$$w = \sqrt{\frac{2P}{\pi l} \left\{ \frac{(1 - v_1^2)}{E_1} + \frac{(1 - v_2^2)}{E_2} \right\} \times \frac{D_1 D_2}{(D_1 + D_2)}}$$

where P is the applied diametral load, uniformly distributed along the of cylinders, w is the semiwidth of contact area, D_1, D_2 are the diameters of cylinders, E_1, E_2 are the modulii of elasticity of two materials and v_1, v_2 are the Poisson's ratio of two materials.

Maximum compressive stress

$$\sigma_{average} = \frac{P}{2wl}$$

$$\sigma_{max} = 2\sigma_{av} = \frac{P}{wl}$$

There is variation of stress along the width $2w$, and maximum stress occurs at the centre.

14.4 FRICTION

About the causes of friction between two contacting surfaces, there are several schools of thoughts as follows:

1. Some feel that when atoms of two contacting surfaces come in the range of attraction, friction is created.
2. Many feel that it is due to the films of two surfaces sticking to each other, as in humid atmosphere one's hands stick on the table.
3. Yet, many realize that it is the action of a third body as sand particles, which cause friction.
4. Many are of the view that it is the nature of the materials, which is responsible for friction as copper and polytetrafluoro ethylene (PTFE) readily adhere to any other surface.
5. Many think that errors in the form of surfaces produced on account of errors in machine tools is the source of frictional force.

However, shear force can be considered as the shear resistance offered by the real area of contact.

Shear force, $\qquad\qquad F = \tau A_r$,

where τ is the shear stress or shear resistance and A_r is the real area of constant.

If H is the hardness of the material in terms of force/area,

then

$$A_r = \frac{N}{H} = \frac{\text{normal force between two surfaces}}{\text{penetration hardness}}$$

From these two equations,

$$F = \tau \frac{N}{H}$$

or
$$\frac{F}{N} = \frac{\text{shear force}}{\text{normal force}} = \frac{\text{shear resistance}}{\text{penetration hardness}}$$

$$= \mu, \text{ coefficient of friction, in case of sliding friction.}$$

In the case of rolling friction, stiffness (i.e. Young's modulus) of contacting surfaces is of important consideration.

Let us consider two surfaces supporting a normal force W, its reactions N and the external tangential force P tends to slide one block over the other. Friction force opposes the sliding motion as shown in Figure 14.4.

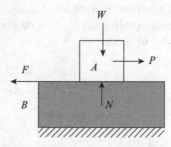

Figure 14.4 *Sliding Motion of Two Surfaces*

In actual machines, there is loss of energy due to friction and this energy is dissipated in the form of heat energy, for example, friction between brake shoe and drum generates heat and the temperature of both drum and brake is increased. However, in the case of wheeled vehicles, friction is necessary for starting, moving and stopping the vehicle.

Figure 14.5 shows the enlarged view of the contacting surfaces. At each point, there is a reaction R_1, R_2 ... etc. At each contact point, there are two components of reaction, i.e. R_i has components N_i and F_i as shown in the Figure 14.5.

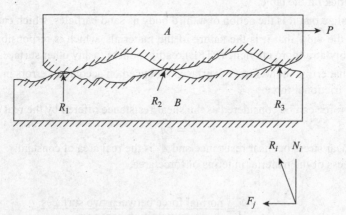

Figure 14.5 *Enlarged View of the Contacting Surfaces*

Then, normal reaction,

$$N = \sum_{i=1}^{n} N_i$$

Frictional force, $F = \sum_{i=1}^{n} F_i$

At the contact points, yielding, crushing or tearing of asperities (raised edges) takes place and the force of friction depends on the following:

1. Generation of local high temperature
2. Adhesion at contact points
3. Relative hardness of mating surfaces
4. Presence of thin films of oxides
5. Presence of oil dirt or dust particles

Now, as the applied force is gradually increased, the frictional force also increases gradually but up to a limit F, beyond which there is no increase in frictional resistance and the body starts slipping, as the motion starts there is slight reduction in the frictional resistance. Figure 14.6 shows a relationship between the applied force P and the force of friction F. Once the motion starts, maximum force of friction F (at A) is reduced to F_k, kinetic force of friction.

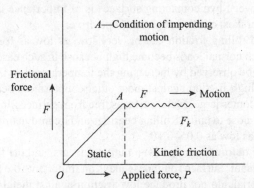

Figure 14.6 *Relationship Between Applied Force and the Force of Friction*

Coefficient of static friction,

$$\mu = \frac{F}{N}$$

Coefficient of kinetic friction,

$$\mu_k = \frac{F_k}{N}$$

Friction between two dry surfaces or unlubricated surfaces is called 'Coulomb's friction'. Coulomb's law states that the force of friction is independent of the magnitude of apparent area of contact between the two surfaces.

14.5 MEASUREMENTS

In mechanics laboratory, there are many apparatuses to determine the coefficient of static friction by using inclined plane, horizontal plane and belt on pulley as shown in Figure 14.7.
In the case of belt and pulley,

$$\mu = \frac{\ln(T/W)}{\theta}$$

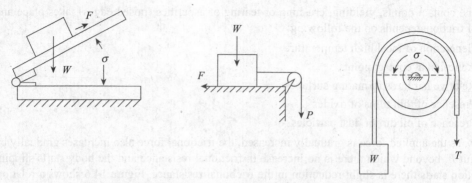

Figure 14.7 *Measurement of Coefficient of Static Friction*

But these tests are performed between two dry or unlubricated surfaces. However, the knowledge of coefficient of friction between two contacting surfaces is of importance in many engineering applications as journal bearing, brakes, clutches, belt and rope drive.

But the lubricated and rolling friction can be very low, as low as 0.15. Most metals and plastics exhibit lower friction when normal loads become high because in such cases surface deformation dominates. Similar effects can be observed by increasing the temperature and the velocity.

Rubbers tend to have high friction against most other counterfaces because rubbers are compliant. The friction shear area becomes large. Metal surfaces free from surface films and contaminates can have a friction coefficient very close to unity. Rolling bearings and hydrodynamically lubricated bearings can have friction coefficients as low as 0.05–0.10.

At high speeds, plastic deformation and even melting occurs, and the friction is reduced because of liquid melt acting as lubricant. Surface roughness plays an important role in decreasing the friction.

Brake and clutch materials do not produce low friction against metal counterfaces, because brake materials are often made by adding friction modifiers to a polymer base until a particular friction/pressure/velocity profile is achieved.

Measurement of friction in lubricated system is often made on actual machinery by measuring power expanded by prime movers.

In hydrodynamic lubrication, rubbing surfaces are completely separated by a film of lubricant, and the wear will be nil. In boundary lubrication, some solid contact remains, and wear will occur if boundary lubrication exists. For example, an electric motor running at 300 rpm may result in boundary lubrication and if speed is increased to 1000 rpm, lubrication becomes hydrodynamic.

The friction of oil and grease films can be measured in laboratory in rolling element bearings. Finally, it can be said that friction is a factor in lubricated systems, because different lubricants lead to different frictions in the system.

Figure 14.8 shows the Stribeck curve between characteristic of lubricant (ZV/P) and coefficient of friction, μ, useful in lubricated journal/shaft system.

Friction coefficient is important because of the following:

1. Value of controlled friction is of utmost importance: we take single coefficient of friction between tyres and road for efficient running of vehicle, but low value of coefficient of friction is desired between engine parts of an automobile, as sizeable amount of heat energy supplied by the fuel is lost in overcoming friction.

2. PTFE displays a low friction in sliding contact; it has poor wear qualities, so it is reinforced with glass when used as a bearing.

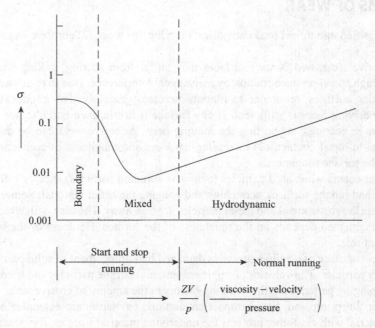

Figure 14.8 *Stribeck Curve*

3. Rubber has high friction against most other surfaces, so used as abrasion-resistant material.
4. However, friction data alone cannot be used to select materials for wear resistance.
5. Design of rotating machinery should always be checked for friction.
6. Testing of components under simulated service conditions can produce most valid data.

14.6 DEFINITION OF WEAR

ASTM defines wear as 'damage to a solid surface, generally involving progressive loss of material due to relative motion between the surface and a contacting substance or substances'. ASTM also defines erosion as a progressive loss of original material from a solid surface due to mechanical interaction between that surface and a fluid; a multicomponent fluid or an impinging liquid or solid particles. G 40 standard on wear and erosion terminology provides these definitions.

A common example of wear is wearing out the gear teeth in mesh for power transmission. As the pinion and gear come in contact, high contact stresses are developed and a small area (or pit) is plastically deformed. During the sliding motion (pinion slips past the gear), small particles of material that are crushed are displaced, causing pitting on the surface of weaker of the two. As there is continuous power transmission, there is progressive wear of the material of teeth. To minimize wear, surfaces of gear teeth are hardened by surface-hardening techniques. Moreover, the gears remain continuously lubricated by the oil in the sump of the gear box.

A few examples of erosion are soil erosion during floods, erosion of cast components by sand blasting and changes in sea-shore line erosion of abrasive particles from grinding.

14.7 FORMS OF WEAR

Wear can be classified into three broad categories: (1) adhesive wear, (2) abrasive wear and (3) erosive wear.

Due to adhesive wear, two contact surfaces may suffer from scoring, galling and scuffing. The asperities (tiny high spots) produce friction by mechanical interference. Due to relative motion between the two contacting surfaces, resistance to motion increases gradually. The interlocked particles are deformed if the driving force is sufficient. If any surface is brittle, then particles are torn off. Adhesive wear occurs in bearings, supporting the moving parts. Adhesive wear can be minimized by (1) preventing metal-to-metal contact, (2) increasing hardness and toughness of contacting surfaces and (3) decreasing the surface roughness.

Abrasive wear occurs when hard particles (acting as abrading particles) slide or roll under pressure across a surface and rub the surfaces, scratching and gouging the softer material. Sometimes these hard particles penetrate the softer metal and metal particles are torn away. The ease with which the deformed metal may be fragmented depends on the toughness of the surface. Hardness of the surface plays an equally important role.

In erosive wear, surface of a solid material is damaged by impingement of solid particles through an air jet containing particles. The velocity of impingement, mass of the particles and hardness and sharpness of hard impinging particles are the deciding factors in the amount of erosive wear.

Sand blasting, slurry erosion, liquid impact erosion and cavitation are examples of erosive wear. Coating of a material with elastomer protects the underlying material from erosive wear.

14.8 SLIDING CONTACT WEAR

There are various forms of the wear like adhesive, galling, scuffing, scoring, oxidative and fretting wear caused by sliding contact.

14.8.1 Adhesive

When two surfaces are in contact subjected to external normal load, bonding of asperities (or high spots) on mating surfaces occurs. If bonding is significant, particles from one surface can adhere to the other surface and during sliding, this adhered part is removed from one surface causing wear. ASTM defines this wear as 'wear due to localized bonding between the contacting solids leading to material transfer or removal from either contacting surfaces'. All materials are susceptible to this type of wear.

Figure 14.9 shows how in adhesive wear, fragment of high spot of B surface adheres to surface A and gets transferred during sliding.

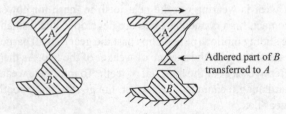

Figure 14.9 *Adhesive Wear*

Archard has provided equation for volume of adhesive wear as follows.

Volume of wear,
$$V_w = k\frac{dN}{H}$$

where V_w is the volume of wear (mm³), k is the constant, d is the sliding displacement (mm), H is the hardness of softer material (kg/mm²) and N is the normal force in Newtons (N).

This type of wear is system dependent and the coefficient of variation is very high.

14.8.2 Galling

When the adhesive wear becomes severe, it leads to galling, i.e. the formation of macroscopic excrescences. The material flows up from the surface and then flowing up of particle leads to seizure, where the sliding members rub against each other with little clearance. Soft single-phase metals are particularly prone to galling. Figure 14.10 shows galling in two surfaces A and B, and the materials flowing up the surface at A and B, respectively. Plug valves are prone to galling.

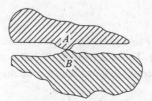

(Formation of flowing up particles)

Figure 14.10 *Galling*

14.8.3 Scuffing

Scratches and surface deformations occur along the direction of motion on two surfaces. These are moderate forms of adhesive wear. If piston in a cylinder is working properly, only mild wear occurs, but inside, the diameter of the cylinder is slightly increased due to wear. If the surfaces are roughened, scoring occurs, leading to unacceptable high rates of wear. This type of wear can be observed in unlubricated and overloaded gear teeth. By proper lubrication and optimum clearance, this type of wear can be avoided.

14.8.4 Oxidative Wear

Adhesive wear takes place at real areas of contact, due to repeated rubbing action, and wear particles are formed, which get oxidized due to reaction with environment. In ferrous materials, surfaces appear to be rusted. This type of wear is quite common in household applications like nails, locks, screw, hinges of doors and hot plates. Hardened steels often display this type of wear and can be avoided by proper oiling of hinges, objects having sliding motion.

14.8.5 Fretting

Oscillatory relative motion (repeated motion) between two contacting surfaces causes fretting wear or fretting corrosion. Fretting corrosion-affected surface looks like a pitted rusted surface.

Due to oscillatory motion of small amplitude, repeated rubbing of surfaces can cause adherence as on high spots adhered junctions are broken. The broken particles roll back and forth between the two surfaces during oscillatory motion, at the same time reacting with environment. This type of damage is known as *fretting corrosion*. Ferrous materials exhibit fretting corrosion, while plastics exhibit fretting wear. Fretting wear can be avoided by preventing the fretting motion. High hardness also reduces the fretting wear.

14.9 ABRASIVE WEAR

Abrasive wear is the unintentional wear caused by hard and sharp particles or by asperities moving on a softer surface. There are two types of abrasive wear: (1) two-body abrasion and (2) three-body abrasion, in which loose abrasive particles between two conforming surfaces produce wear. Two-body abrasion is more damaging. Sand papers (abrasive particles glued on paper) and grinding wheels (abrasive particles in vitrified glass powder) are examples of two-body abrasion.

Abrasive wear is further classified into (1) low-stress abrasion, (2) high-stress abrasion, (3) gouging and (4) polishing abrasion.

14.9.1 Low-stress Abrasion

Low-stress abrasion is characterized by fine scratches on the surface, as in the case of coal sliding down a chute producing low-stress abrasion. The mechanism of metal removal chip formation from a fixed grain sliding on a surface or the grain could just produce a scratch, i.e. no chip is fractured off but grain plows a furrow.

14.9.2 High-stress Abrasion

In high-stress abrasion, abrasive substance is imposed on the surface with sufficient stress to cause the abrasive to fracture or crush, i.e. abrasive grains fracture during the process as in the case of surface grinding. Moving parts of bull dozers, drag line and shovel bucket teeth suffer from this kind of abrasion. Edges of abrasive (sand particles in the case of earth-moving machines) usually scratch the material and form chips. Crushing of abrasives is shown in high-stress abrasion in Figure 14.11.

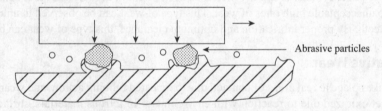

Abrasive particles

Figure 14.11 *High-stress Abrasion*

14.9.3 Gouging Abrasion

In gouging abrasion, gouge groove or deep scratches are formed by plastic deformation of a single impact.

If a rock is crushed against a solid surface, this type of damage is produced. This type of abrasion takes place in teeth of bucket of shovel, stone crushers and in mining equipments. But there is special use of this type of abrasion in processing ores, building roads and infrastructural development.

14.9.4 Polishing Abrasion

In polishing abrasion, polished surfaces are produced by fine abrasives, and no scratches or furrows are produced. Steel surfaces are polished by fine abrasives of aluminium oxide or diamond particles with mean a diameter of 1 μm. These fine particles rather remove the scratches and polish the surface. Abrasive particles are carried in a fluid, which corrode the surface and remove the oxides, producing a polished surface.

14.10 TYPES OF EROSION

There are five types of erosion: (1) solid erosion, (2) slurry erosion, (3) liquid impact erosion, (4) liquid erosion and (5) cavitation.

14.10.1 Solid Erosion

In solid erosion, surface of a solid material is damaged by the impingement of solid particles carried in a gas (generally air). Air jet containing oxide particles are directed on the surface. The degree of damage is a function of mass of abrasive particle (m), velocity of impingement (V), angle of impingement (φ) and particle sharpness factor (P).

$$\text{Erosion (particle)} = A\,m\,V^2\,\varphi P,$$

where A is a constant.

In brittle materials, erosion is maximum with normal impact and material is removed by spalling action. In ductile materials, $\varphi; \simeq 20\text{--}30°$, and the material is removed by cutting action when abrasive particles impact on the surface. It rotates and cuts the material as shown in Figure 14.12. Abrasive particles behave as tiny cutters.

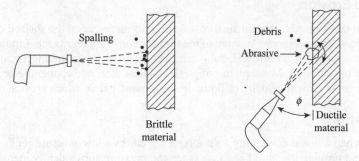

Figure 14.12 *Solid Erosion*

A few examples of solid erosion are as follows:

1. In particle conveying systems as soot blowers and cyclone separators
2. Fans used in dirty areas
3. Jet engine blades
4. Sand blasting

14.10.2 Slurry Erosion

Slurry erosion commonly occurs in pipe conveying slurries, as in coal pipe lines, which are several hundred kilometres long. Removal of the material is caused by slurry motion across a solid surface. Slurry system involves more or less parallel flow and scratching of solid surface by particles in motion (in slurry). Slurry erosion depends upon (1) the mass of the particles that contact the solid surface, (2) the velocity and (3) the shape factor of the particles. It occurs in pumps handling drilling and mine waters damaging pump impellers. Figure 14.13 shows the damage of elbow of a pipe due to slurry erosion.

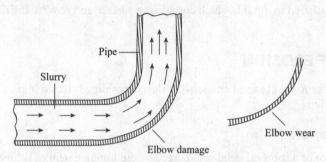

Figure 14.13 *Slurry Erosion*

14.10.3 Liquid Impact Erosion

In liquid impact erosion, the liquid droplets impinge on a solid surface with a very high velocity. Rain erosion of aircraft surface is the classic example, as the aircraft travels at a speed of 300–400 m/s and the relative velocity of rain drop with respect to aircraft is very high, windshields, nose and leading edges of the spar get damaged. In stream turbines, if condensate is present in the steam, liquid impact erosion occurs on blades. This type of erosion is restricted in special turbo systems.

14.10.4 Liquid Erosion

This type of erosion takes place in a solid surface when liquid impinges on the surface or moves along the surface. This occurs in pipe, having passive oxide film for corrosion resistance. Liquid impingement removes the protective oxide. It is reformed, but is removed again by liquid impingement. This repeated action can perforate pipe elbows. Metal piping of steel, stainless steel and copper are prone to this type of erosion. There is some critical velocity of liquid impingement, below which erosion does not occur.

14.10.5 Cavitation

Cavitation occurs when a liquid containing a dissolved gas enters a low-pressure region. Gas bubbles, which precipitate and grow in the liquid collapse when the pressure subsequently increases. The high-pressure, local shock wave that is produced may exert a pressure of thousands of atmosphere on the surrounding material. Cavitation is frequently encountered in propellers, dams' spillways and hydraulic pumps.

The wide industrial use of ultrasonic debubblers and cleaners has made this form of erosion a very formidable factor to be dealt with. Organic coatings like elastomer on a material permit the organic polymer to absorb the shock of cavitation and protect the underlying material from erosion.

14.11 SURFACE FATIGUE

Two surfaces come in contact and are then separated under repeated cyclic loads or stress that suffer from pitting, wear, spalling and indentations on account of high contact stresses of compressive nature. The damage due to repeated loads is termed as 'surface fatigue'.

Pitting is the most common form of surface fatigue and is evident in meshing gears, which transmit power. Pits initiate as subsurface cracks and these cracks propagate to allow ejection of fragment during sliding motion of two gear teeth. If the fragments contaminate the rolling surface, fragments are rolled into the surface under compressive stress and, further, pits are formed. The debris from the pits move to the oil sump and the lubricating oil gets contaminated. Pitting also takes place in bearings. Pitting occurs on almost all heavily used rail road tracks.

Impact wears occur on surfaces, which are subjected to repeated impact as in the case of sledge hammer. The end of the sledge hammer can be examined for this type of impact wear. One can see that chips are removed from the end of the sledge hammer. Sometimes, subsurface cracks occur leading to fragmentation. Many a times, it is the plastic flow. This type of impact wear occurs in cold chisels, impact drivers and hammers. To minimize impact wear, special hardness profiles are used for high-quality hammers.

Spalling is defined as the fracture of a portion of the surface of a material by repeated stresses under Hertzian compressive stresses (Figure. 14.14).

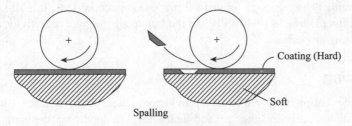

Figure 14.14 *Spalling*

Figure 14.14 shows a fragmented portion of hard coating from a surface under Hertzian contact stress. If hard and brittle coating is applied to a soft substrate, spalling can take place under Hertzian loading. Graded coatings are used in PVD cutting tools for stress accommodation as to reduce the risk of spalling. Surface of the material should be only 20 per cent softer than coating.

Brinelling means indentation of a surface by static overload of balls and rollers. It destroys the bearing in the same way as pitting and spalling. To minimize brinelling, shock loads must be avoided.

14.12 PROTECTION AGAINST WEAR

Protection of engineering components from various types of wear like adhesive, abrasive and erosive using various processes depends upon the following factors:

1. Actual service conditions as temperature, pressure and surroundings
2. Type of loads on components
3. Type of stresses developed under applied load as compressor stress or Hertzian stresses
4. Limitation of particular materials and processes
5. Selection of the material of component to withstand wear

Mainly, wear damage is a surface phenomenon and protection of the surface or improving the properties of the surface is of utmost importance. Various techniques used for protection against wear are (1) electroplating, (2) anodizing, (3) diffusion, (4) metal spraying and (5) hard facing.

14.12.1 Electroplating

In electroplating, a harder material is electroplated on the surface of a metal part such as chromium, nickel and rhodium. For the reduction of wear of lead bearings, indium coating is used.

There are two types of chromium coating: (1) hard chromium and (2) porous chromium. Hard chromium plating is generally used for decorative purposes, while porous chromium plate can hold lubricants. Hardness of chromium plating lies between 950 and 1050 VPN and the thickness variation can be 25 μm–2.5 mm. Due to high hardness and low coefficient of friction, this is very useful in applications such as follows:

1. Cylinders and piston rings of IC engines.
2. Chromium-plated steel parts are forced fitted and seizing and galling are prevented.
3. Corrosion resistance of chromium is very high, so chromium-plated parts are used in corrosive atmosphere.

Hardness of nickel plating is much lower than that of chromium plating, which lies between 140 and 425 VPN. Nickel plating is hard enough for general-purpose applications and it is also economical.

Hardness of rhodium plate is 540–640 VPN, but rhodium plate has high reflectivity, high heat resistance and non-tarnishing properties.

14.12.2 Anodizing

In anodizing, an oxide coating is formed on metals to improve their wear resistance. Anodizing process is employed on aluminium, zinc, magnesium and their alloys. In anodizing, the work is in the anode, and oxide layers are gradually built up on the base metal. These oxide layers are porous enough to allow the passage of oxygen ions.

In anodizing of aluminium, sulphuric acid is used as an electrolyte in the process called alumilite. The aluminium oxide layers formed by this process are transparent, thicker and porous than those produced by other electrolytes (other than sulphuric acid).

Aircraft materials like hydraulic pistons, guide tracks, cams, gears, screws, friction locks and swivel joints are all made by hard-coated aluminium alloys.

The production of hard wear-resistant coating by anodizing has greatly extended the applications of Mg alloys. Anodic zinc coatings are used for cartridge cases, propeller blades of aircraft, wire screw cloth and refrigerator shelves.

14.12.3 Diffusion

There are several diffusion-controlled processes, which improve wear resistance of the surface layers of the metals. These are (1) carburizing, (2) cyaniding, (3) carbonitriding, (4) nitriding, (5) chromizing and (6) siliconizing.

By using carburizing process, carbon content of the surface layers is increased. Carburizing is generally done on steels with 0.2 per cent carbon. In pack carburizing, the part to be carburized is packed in a steel container so that it is completely surrounded by granules of charcoal. Charcoal is treated with barium carbonate and carbon monoxide is formed, which reacts with low-carbon steel surface to form atomic carbon that diffuses with steel. In gas carburizing, carbonaceous gas like natural gas and propane gas are most frequently used (at 930°C).

In cyaniding, there is diffusion of carbon and nitrogen into the steel surface through a molten cyanide bath such as sodium cyanide, at about 760–850°C. Normally, low-carbon steels are cyanided, with a depth variation of 0.25–0.75 mm. Nitriding provides lower distortion and carburizing provides better case depths.

Carbonitriding is a surface-hardening process that involves the diffusion of both nitrogen and carbon into the steel surface, in a carburizing gas atmosphere (methane or propane mixed with ammonia), and process performed at 870°C. Case depths up to 0.25 mm on plain carbon steels are obtained.

Nitriding is a very useful surface-hardening technique, in which monoatomic nitrogen is diffused into the surface of the steel being treated. Hardening is accomplished by a nitrogen atmosphere that prevents scaling and discolouration.

Source of nitrogen is ammonia (at 500–570°C).

$$\text{Reaction,} \quad 2NH_3 \rightarrow 2N + 3H_2$$

Nitrogen diffuses into the steel and hydrogen is exhausted. Nitrided layers are, however, brittle and prone to spalling. Nitrided layer is white in colour, and the fatigue life of nitrided layer is badly affected.

Chromizing consists of introduction of chromium into the surface layers of the base metal. The surface layer of steel is converted into stainless steel. Chromium is transferred through a gas phase, at 900–1100°C.

Chromized high-carbon steel has hardness of 800–1000 VPN and low coefficient of friction. Chromizing is used on tools, hydraulic rams, pistons, pump shafts and drop forging dies.

Siliconizing consists of impregnation of silicon into iron base material. Work is heated in contact with silicon carbide and chlorine gas (acting as catalyst) at 900–1100°C. Core produced contains about 14 per cent silicon. Hardness of siliconized cores ranges from 80 to 85 Rockwell B, yet they are difficult to machine. Siliconizing is used on pump shafts, chain links of conveyors, cylinder liners, valve guides, valves and fittings of chemical and oil industries.

14.12.4 Metal Spraying

Metal spraying has been used for many years to build up dimensions of undersized or worn-out surfaces. Now, metal spraying has found increased utility in wear-resistant applications.

Metallizing is done by automatic feeding of a metal wire at a controlled speed through a metallizing tool or gun. Air, oxygen and combustible gas are supplied to the gun and a high-temperature, high-velocity flame is generated around the wire tip. The wire tip is continuously melted, and the flame containing molten metal of wire strikes the surface of the base metal. These particles flatten out to form irregularly shaped discs. At the same time, molten metal particles fill the surface pores and irregularities providing mechanical interlocking. Cooling of discs is very rapid, and a thin oxide film is formed on the exposed surfaces of the deposited particles. Metals that form dense, tenacious oxides are chromium steel and aluminium bronze. Silicon–aluminium alloys show relatively high strength in sprayed form. Brass and copper produce coatings of low strength.

In one method, oxyacetylene powder gun is utilized for spraying metal powder on preheated surfaces and coated surface is postheated to get hard, corrosion-resistant alloy coating. Most of these alloys are nickel-base or cobalt-base materials containing chromium, boron and silicon.

Plasma flame permits deposition of highest melting metals, as plasma produces a luminous, stream of ionized gas produced by a gas through an electric arc, at temperatures up to 16,000°C, which are easily obtainable, but plasma arc spraying is characterized by high temperatures, high noise level, toxic waste products and radiation.

In general, a sprayed metal coating is harder and porous, but brittle. Salient features of sprayed coatings are as follows:

1. High-chromium (13.5 per cent chromium) stainless steel is used in application such as armature shafts, cylinder liners, piston, valve stems and hydraulic rams.

2. Molybdenum coatings combine a hard wearing surface with a good adhesion. They have good wear resistance and abrasion resistance. These coatings are used on aluminium pulleys, iron brake drums and presses.

3. Aluminium bronze is highly wear resistant and corrosion resistant, and is used in parts as pump impellers, bronze castings, split motor bearings and air brake valves.

4. Monel and nickel coatings are wear resistant and corrosion resistant, and are used in parts as pump plungers, shafts and hydraulic pumps.

5. Several tungsten carbide compositions applied by flame plating are wear resistant, heat resistant and shock resistant, and are recommended for general wear applications such as seals, valve plates, bearings and shafts.

Metallizing is best suited for applications where abrasive wear resistance is required and boundary lubrication exits.

14.12.5 Hard Facing

The production of a hard wear-resistant layer on metals by welding is known as hard facing and this process will be discussed in detail.

14.13 HARD FACING

Welding of hard wear-resistant layer on the surface of the metals is known as hard facing. Hard facing alloys are in the form of welding rods, and using oxyacetylene gas or electric arc, welding can be done on the surfaces of the base metals. Main advantages of hard facing are as follows: (1) it can be applied on localized area wherever required, (2) wear-resistant compounds are readily available and (3) there is effective use of expensive alloys.

If oxyacetylene gas is used, then electrodes are bare, but in electric arc, electrodes are coated with flux, which provides stability of arc, protection of molten weld from oxidation, fluxing of impurities, thermal and electrical insulation and controlled matter transfer. However, due to sharp thermal gradients, cracks tend to develop in such coatings.

Hard facing can be done on most ferrous metals, but it is not advisable to use on non-ferrous metals. Carbon steel with 0.35 per cent C are relatively easy to hard face, as welding becomes more difficult on steels with increasing carbon percentage. High-carbon and alloy steels must be preheated before the application of hard facing and postheated after hard facing.

Hard facing is most extensively used where systematic lubrication against abrasion is not possible as in oil well drilling tools, earth-moving equipments, mining tools, engine valves and chemical-processing equipment. Hard faced surfaces are generally wear resistant, heat resistant and corrosion resistant. By hard facing, life of a part can be extended, and operating efficiency also is increased.

There are more than 100 different compositions of hard facing materials. The properties of some special hard facing materials are given below.

1. Tungsten carbide hard facings have highest hardness and best wear resistance. This is used on rock drill bits.

2. High-chromium irons (17–32 per cent Cr) are available in many compositions.

3. Addition of tungsten, molybdenum and vanadium are sometimes made to increase the hot hardness and abrasion resistance.

4. Combination of martensite and carbide matrix provides a hard composite structure with good abrasion resistance.

5. Where wear and abrasion resistance along with heat and oxidation resistance are required, cobalt-base alloys (45–63 per cent Co, 24–29 per cent Cr, 5–13 per cent W and 1–3.0 per cent C) are used. These have been used in hard facing materials for ladle lining and pouring spouts to resist hot gases and liquids.

6. The nickel-base alloys (70–80 per cent Ni, 11–17 per cent Cr and 2.5–3.5 per cent B and small amounts of Co and Si) are highly wear resistant and oxidation resistant and are used for hard facing of hot heading dies, piercing mandrels and shear blades exposed to hot solid metals.

7. Austenitic manganese steels are very tough and work-harden rapidly under impact. These are used in moderate service conditions as crushing and grinding of coal, lime stone and aggregates.

14.14 BEARINGS

Bearing is the most important turbocomponent used to support and locate the rotating or sliding element with respect to other parts of a machine or a structure. There are two types of bearings: (1) plain bearing and (2) rolling element bearing. In plain bearing, there are sliding surfaces of some geometric shape and rubbing occurs within a defined area of contact. In rolling element bearing, load is shared by balls or rollers and Hertzian contact occurs between the turboelements (e.g. balls, inner race, outer race)

Plain bearings are two-body sliding systems, while rolling bearings are three-body rolling systems. In plain bearing, there are three types of lubrications.

1. *Hydrodynamic lubrication:* Wear due to friction occurs during start up or shut down.

2. *Hydrostatic bearing:* Sliding member can be supported by pumping a pressurized fluid into the bearing moving member interface to create a hydrostatic bearing or air bearing (air acts as a separating medium).

3. Self-lubricated plastic bearing or oil-impregnated porous metal bearing. Oil trapped in pores wicks into the bearing clearance in operation and hydrodynamic bearing is possible.

The design of plain and roller bearings depends upon coefficient of friction between the surfaces, viscosity of the lubricant and the speed of rotation of the shaft.

Greased precision rolling element bearing is the first choice for manufacturing equipment that must run continuously. If designed properly, these bearings are to last as long as desired.

Following equation is used to determine the rated life of ball and roller bearings.

$$L_{10} = \frac{74332}{N} \left(\frac{C}{P}\right)^k$$

where L_{10} is the rated life in revolutions, C is the basic dynamic load in Newtons, P is the equivalent radial load in Newtons and k is a constant, which is equal to 3 for ball bearing and 10/3 for roller bearing and N is rpm.

The basic load rating (C) is the radial load that a ball bearing can withstand for one million revolutions of the inner ring.

Discussion on various types of ball and roller bearings is beyond the scope of this book.

14.15 LUBRICATION

To reduce the effect of wear due to friction, abrasion, adhesion and erosion, it is essential to separate the two contacting surfaces by a layer of lubrication in the interface and to avoid metal to metal contact. A lubricant is defined as a substance, which separates the rubbing surfaces and is ready to shear while adhering to the surfaces. Therefore, the viscosity of lubricant is a very important factor. Different types of lubricants are: (1) oils, (2) greases and (3) solid film lubricants.

14.15.1 Oils

Mineral oil is a crude oil that is refined to remove certain molecular reactions. So refined crude oil is a base oil in which chemicals are added to change pour point (low temperature fluidity) and modifiers are added to change viscosity. Viscosity is a key parameter in film formation. Additives include (1) chemicals to form bonds to the rubbing surfaces, (2) oxidation and corrosion inhibitors, (3) foaming reducers and (4) detergents.

Some synthetic oils also have exactly similar molecules as the base oils. They are manufactured by chemical processes. Commonly used synthetic oil is polyalphaolefins (PAOs). Synthetic oils are expensive, but they have better heat resistance, longer life, less evaporation and produce lower friction.

It is appropriate to use oil for a specific system, which can be splash lubricated or pump lubricated. Oils remove heat from tribosystems. Lubricants can attack plastics, but self-lubricating plastics generally do not need any lubrication.

14.15.2 Greases

In grease, it is the oil that does lubrication. Grease lubrication is of the lowest cost to lubricate a rolling element bearing. There are three main categories of greases based on the operating temperature and the type of thickener (Table 14.1).

Table 14.1 *Types of Greases*

Operating Temperature (°C)	Type of Thickener
120	Lithium, sodium
175	Polyurea, lithium complex, aluminium complex
180	Bentonite clay, polytetrofluoro ethylene (PTFE), perfluoropolyether

Bearing speed affects lubrication. Value of dn is commonly used to rate speed limit of the bearings, and the dn values are different for oils and greases (Table 14.2).

$$dn = \text{diameter of bore of bearing in mm} \times \text{speed (rpm)}$$

In the case of seals, grease is the most convenient and easiest lubricant to use.

Table 14.2 *Values of dn for Some Oils and Greases*

	dn Value	
Example	Grease	Oils
Double row ball bearing	160,000	220,000

14.15.3 Solid Film Lubricants

In many systems, oils and greases cannot be used, instead they need solid film lubricants, e.g. sanitary system, vacuum, in liquids, in wire drawing, extrusion and rolling processes. There are two types of solid film lubricants: organic and inorganic. Application processes are physical vapour deposition, spraying, burnishing and impingement. Table 14.3 shows the limiting value of operating pressure for some solid film lubricants.

Following solid film lubricants are used in the industry:

1. Antimony trioxide
2. Boric acid
3. Bismuth
4. Calcium fluoride
5. Indium
6. Lead oxide
7. Molybdenum disulphide
8. Silver
9. Tungsten disulphide
10. Zinc oxide

Table 14.3 *Operating Pressure of Solid Film Lubricants*

Lubricants	Pressure (N/mm²)
Molybdenum disulphide	700
Graphite	280
PTE fluorocarbon	400

KEY POINTS TO REMEMBER

- ❑ Tribology is the science of friction, wear and lubrication.
- ❑ Earth quake is a result of stick and slip movement of rock plates supporting the land mass.
- ❑ Frictional force is independent of the area of contact of two the contacting surfaces.
- ❑ Real contact stress,

$$\sigma_r = \frac{\text{force}}{\text{summation of actual areas of contact}}$$

- ❑ A sphere in contact with a flat surface under normal force P

Radius of contact area,

$$a = 0.721 \sqrt[3]{PD \frac{1 - v_1^2}{E_1} + \frac{1 - v_2^2}{E_2}}$$

$$\sigma_{max} = \frac{1.5P}{\pi a^2}$$

where D is the diameter of sphere, E_1, E_2 are the Young's modulii of sphere and flat surface and v_1, v_2 are the Poisson's ratio of sphere and flat surface, respectively

Real area of contact,

$$A_r = \frac{N}{H} = \frac{\text{normal force between two surfaces}}{\text{penetration hardness}}$$

❑ At the contact points, yielding, crushing or tearing of asperities (high spots) takes place.

❑ Friction between two dry surfaces or unlubricated surfaces is called Coulomb's friction.

❑ In hydrodynamic lubrication, rubbing surfaces are completely separated by a film of lubricant.

❑ In boundary lubrication, some solid contact remains, and wear occurs.

❑ Rubber has high friction against most other surfaces, so it is used as abrasion-resistant material.

❑ *Definition of wear by ASTM:* 'Damage to a solid surface, generally involving progressive loss of material due to relative motion between the surfaces and a contacting substance or substances'.

❑ ASTM defines erosion as 'progressive loss of original material from a solid due to mechanical interaction between that surface and a fluid, a multicomponent fluid or an impinging liquid or solid particles'.

❑ *There are three forms of wear:* Adhesive, abrasive and erosive.

❑ Sliding contact wear, volume of wear,

$$V_w = k \frac{dN}{H}$$

where k is a constant, d is the sliding displacement, N is the normal force and H is the hardness of softer material.

❑ Fretting corrosion-affected surface looks like pitted and rusted surface.

❑ Abrasive wear is caused by hard and sharp particles or by asperities moving in a softer surface.

❑ Polished surfaces are produced by fine abrasives, and no scratches or furrows are produced.

❑ Solid erosion (particles) = $AmV^2\varphi P$, where A is a constant, m is the mass, V is the velocity of impingement, φ is the angle of impingement and P is the particle sharpness factor.

❑ Pitting, impact, spalling and brinelling are produced by surface fatigue.

❑ Wear damage is a surface phenomenon; surfaces are protected against wear by electroplating, anodizing, diffusion processes and metallizing the surface by coating of wear-resistant hard materials.

❑ The production of a hard wear-resistant layer on metals by welding (using electrodes of hard materials) is known as hard facing.

❑ Hard facing is generally done on ferrous metals by arc welding or by oxyacetylene welding.

❑ Tungsten carbide hard facing has highest hardness and best wear resistance.

❑ Plain bearings are two-body sliding systems and rolling element bearings are three-element rolling systems.

❑ To reduce friction through lubrication, viscosity of the lubricant and the speed of rotation of the shaft are the deciding factors.

❑ Refined crude oil is a base oil in which certain chemicals are added to improve its properties so that it can be used as a lubricant.

❑ Grease lubrication is of lowest cost, to lubricate a rolling element bearing.

❑ Solid film lubricants are used where oils and greases cannot be used, e.g. in sanitary systems, wire drawing operations, extrusion and rolling.

MULTIPLE CHOICE QUESTIONS

1. Earth quake is a result of

   (a) Stick–slip movement of rock plates

   (b) Dislocation of heavy land mass

   (c) Severe vibrations in the Earth crest

   (d) None of these

2. A sphere exerts force P on a flat surface. If a is the radius of indent between the sphere and the flat surface, maximum stress is equal to

   (a) $\dfrac{1.0P}{\pi a^2}$

   (b) $\dfrac{1.5P}{\pi a^2}$

   (c) $\dfrac{2P}{\pi a^2}$

   (d) None of these

3. Coefficient of sliding friction is

   (a) $\dfrac{\text{Shear resistance}}{\text{Area of contact}}$

   (b) $\dfrac{\text{Shear resistance}}{\text{Penetration hardness}}$

   (c) Penetration hardness × real area of contact

   (d) None of these

4. A load W is lifted through belt passing over a pulley by applying a pulling force P on the other side of the belt. The coefficient of friction is equal to

   (a) $\dfrac{\text{In } (W/P)}{\pi}$

   (b) $\dfrac{\text{In } (P/W)}{\pi}$

   (c) $\dfrac{2\text{In } (P/W)}{\pi}$

   (d) None of these

5. Which one of the following is not an erosion process?

   (a) Sand blasting

   (b) Sea-shore line change

   (c) Grinding wheel operation

   (d) Damage due to mechanical interference

6. In galling, what happens?

   (A) Material flows up from the surface causing seizure.

   (B) Sliding members rub against each other with little clearance.

   (a) Both A and B

   (b) Neither A nor B

   (c) Only A

   (d) Only B

7. In which type of abrasions deep scratches are formed due to single impact as rock getting crushed against a solid surface?

   (a) Low-stress abrasion

   (b) Gouging abrasion

   (c) Polishing

   (d) None of these

8. What type of erosion occurs in pumps handling drilling and mine waters?

   (a) Solid erosion

   (b) Liquid erosion

   (c) Slurry erosion

   (d) None of these

9. Hertzian contact stresses can cause

   (a) Spalling

   (b) Galling

   (c) Scuffing

   (d) None of these

10. Hardness of chromium plating lies between

    (a) 400–500 VPN

    (b) 600–800 VPN

    (c) 900–1050 VPN

    (d) None of these

11. In which process, surface layer of steel is converted into stainless steel?

    (a) Chromizing

    (b) Nitriding

    (c) Anodizing

    (d) None of these

12. Production of a hard wear-resistant layer on metals by welding is known as
    - (a) Hardening
    - (b) Hard facing
    - (c) Metallizing
    - (d) None of these

13. What is the life of a bearing in million of cycles if C/P ratio is 2, where C is the basic dynamic load and P is the equivalent radial load?

    - (a) 2 million cycles
    - (b) 4 million cycles
    - (c) 8 million cycles
    - (d) None of these

14. Which one of the following is not a solid film lubricant?
    - (a) Graphite
    - (b) Bentonite
    - (c) Calcium fluoride
    - (d) Lead oxide

Answers

1. (a) 2. (b) 3. (b) 4. (b) 5. (d) 6. (a) 7. (b) 8. (c)
9. (a) 10. (c) 11. (a) 12. (b) 13. (c) 14. (b)

REVIEW QUESTIONS

1. What do you understand by wear between two contacting surfaces? On what factors this wear depends?

2. What do you understand by apparent contact area, real contact area and real contact stress? Explain with the help of a sketch.

3. What do you mean by Hertzian contact stresses? Why stresses depend on elastic constants?

4. Prove that coefficient of sliding friction is the ratio of shear resistance/penetration hardness.

5. How the friction is measured? Give two methods.

6. Explain the differences among hydrodynamic lubrication, boundary lubrication and hydrostatic lubrication.

7. Prove that Coulomb's friction is independent of area of contact.

8. Explain the following in sliding contact wear volume of wear. Galling, seizure and fretting corrosion

9. Differentiate between low-stress and high-stress abrasions.

10. What is a slurry erosion? Give three examples.

11. What type of surface damage occurs in surface fatigue? Explain spalling and brinelling with the help of sketches.

12. What is electroplating? How does it protect the surface from wear?

13. What are the effects of chromizing the surface of steel?

14. Differentiate among nitriding, carbonitriding and cyaniding processes.

15. Give a few examples of sprayed metal coating.

16. What are self-lubricated plastic bearings?

17. What is rated life of a rolling element bearing?

18. Why viscosity is a key parameter of oil lubrication?

19. What are synthetic oil lubricants?

20. Where solid film lubricants are used? Give few examples? Name five solid film lubricants.

CORROSION AND OXIDATION

15.1 INTRODUCTION

The unintentional deterioration of a material by an electrochemical process is known as corrosion. More-over, corrosion process is the reverse process of producing/extracting metal from ores, because pure metals tend to revert to their original state of oxides, sulphides and so on. Except noble metals, gold and platinum, all other metals exist in nature in the form of oxides, sulphides, carbonates and silicates. Lot of energy is consumed in extracting pure metal from its ores as iron is extracted from haematite (Fe_2O_3). So pure metals are of high-energy state, which is unstable, therefore when they come in contact with environment, gases and liquids, they tend to revert to their original form or in electrochemical terms, they want to be oxidized. Rusting of iron occurs when iron is exposed to humid atmosphere or water.

Corrosion takes place in the presence of an electrolyte, an aqueous solution of acid, salt or alkali. This type of corrosion is known as 'wet corrosion'. If corrosion takes place without the presence of an electrolyte, as in oxidation of metal in furnace, it is known as 'dry corrosion'.

Corrosion is a localized surface phenomenon,which cause a reduction in mechanical strength of the metal. Sometimes, severe pitting occurs on the metal, creating holes and cracks in the metal. Replace-ment of such parts causes loss of productivity. Moreover, corrosion deposits in the inner surface of the pipes cause reduction in efficiency of heat transfer, overheating and rupture of pipe.

Generally, the effects of corrosion are more pronounced on metals. In the case of ceramics, there is degradation of properties at high temperatures. Polymers may be dissolved in liquid solvents and may swell causing reduction in strength.

This chapter discusses the mechanism of corrosion, various types of corrosion and protection against corrosion.

15.2 ELECTROCHEMICAL REACTION

Corrosion of metals is an electrochemical reaction. Let us consider corrosion of steel in a solution of hydrochloride acid (HCl). Ions of hydrogen and chlorine, i.e. H^+ and Cl^- are dissolved in liquid, and the *solution of dissolved ions is known as electrolyte.* For a metal to dissolve in a liquid, it must transform from a solid atom to an ion as follows.

$$Fe \rightarrow Fe^{2+} + 2\bar{e} \quad \text{(at anode)}$$

Iron ions (cations) are positively charged and electrons are negatively charged. Liberation of electrons causes the metal to become charged (or polarized) (Figure 15.1).

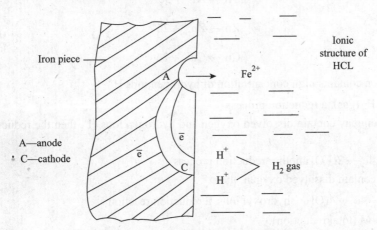

Figure 15.1 *Electrochemical Reaction*

If a sample of iron is placed in a solution of hydrochloric acid, a corrosion reaction occurs. Iron goes into solution and chlorine ion does not really go into the chemical reaction. A simplified equation will be

$$Fe + 2H^+ \rightarrow Fe^{2+} + H_2 \quad \text{(at cathode)}$$

This equation shows that elemental iron reacts with the hydrogen ions in the acid and produce dissolved iron (as ions) plus hydrogen gas.

Partial cathodic reaction

$$2H^+ + 2\bar{e} \rightarrow H_2$$

So, when iron is converted into its elemental form Fe^{2+}, it is said to be oxidized. Hydrogen ion in the acid accepts an electron to become elemental hydrogen or in a most stable state as diatomic (H_2) molecule. In this reaction, hydrogen is said to be reduced. Chemical reaction between ions and electrons is known as 'electro chemistry'.

Corrosion process requires simultaneous occurrence of both oxidation and reduction. Corrosion process will stop if any of these two processes is stopped. If either half of the process is accelerated, corrosion rate also increases.

For a metallic corrosion, an environment or a system is required, which accepts the electrons liberated during metal oxidation.

Generally, when a metal corrodes, the surface of the metal contains many microscopic anode and cathode sites. Defects, impurities, inclusion and grain boundaries act as anodic or cathodic sites.

15.3 ELECTROCHEMICAL PROCESS

Corrosion is an electrochemical process, in which a metal is corroded and metal ions are removed at anode from the anode (an oxidation reaction) as follows

$$M \rightarrow M^{n+} + n\bar{e} \quad \text{(oxidation reaction)}$$

A metal is oxidized to metal ions M^{n+} and electrons $n\bar{e}$, where n is the number of valency electrons. This process of oxidation occurs at anode. Following are few examples of this process:

$$Fe \rightarrow F^{2+} + 2\bar{e}$$

$$Al \rightarrow Al^{3+} + 3\bar{e}$$

$$Zn \rightarrow Zn^{2+} + 2\bar{e}$$

$$Cu \rightarrow Cu^{2+} + 2\bar{e}$$

1. Acid solution contains high concentration of hydrogen ions H^+

   $2H^+ + 2\bar{e} = H_2$ (gas), a reduction process

2. Acid solution may contain dissolved oxygen and hydrogen ions H^+, then the reduction reaction will be

   $O_2 + 4H^+ + 4\bar{e} \rightarrow 2H_2O$, another reduction process

3. Water may contain dissolved oxygen, then

   $2H_2O + O_2 + 4\bar{e} \rightarrow 4(OH)^-$, hydroxyl ions, a reduction reaction

4. $M^{n+} + n\bar{e} \rightarrow M$ (total reduction)

Site at which reduction takes place is called a 'cathode'. Overall electrochemical reaction must consist of an oxidation and a reduction process. Individual oxidation reaction or reduction reaction is known as 'half reaction'.

15.3.1 Standard Hydrogen Reference Electrode

Figure 15.2 shows a zinc electrode placed in a solution with a standard concentration of zinc ions, Zn^{2+}. Platinum electrode on the other side is used as a reference. A voltmeter connected between the two electrodes measures the voltage difference between them.

Now,
$$E_{cell} = E_{reduction} - E_{oxidation}$$

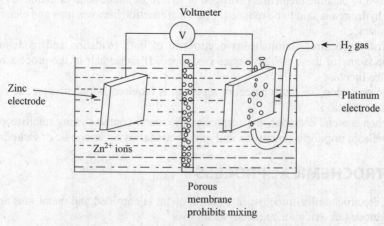

Figure 15.2 *Standard Hydrogen Reference Electrode*

The potential of hydrogen reduction process that occurs at the hydrogen reference electrode provides a reference for all other redox (reduction + oxidation) processes.

Hydrogen reduction process has 0 volt as reference volt.

or
$$E_{H2} = 0.000 \text{ V}$$

The redox potential of zinc oxidation process, E_{Zn}

$$Zn \rightarrow Zn^{2+} + 2\bar{e}$$

$$E_{Zn} = -0.763 \text{ V,}$$

relative to hydrogen reduction reaction.

This technique has been used to find out the redox potentials of many metals and metal ions. Some typical redox potentials are presented in Table 15.1.

Table 15.1 *Standard Electrode Potentials (or emf) of Metals and Chemical Species*

	Equilibrium Equation	Potential (Redox) at 25°C (V)
(Noble end)	$Au^{3+} + 3\bar{e} = Au$	+1.50
	$O_2 + 4H^+ + 4\bar{e} = 2H_2O$	+1.23
	$Pt^{2+} + 2\bar{e} = Pt$	+1.20
	$Ag^+ + \bar{e} = Ag$	+0.80
	$Fe^{3+} + \bar{e} = Fe^{2+}$	+0.77
	$O^2 + 2H_2O + 4\bar{e} = 4(OH)^-$	+0.40
	$Cu^{2+} + 2\bar{e} = Cu$	+0.34
	$Pb^{2+} + 2\bar{e} = Pb$	−0.13
	$Mo^{3+} + 3\bar{e} = Mo$	−0.20
	$Ni^{2+} + 2\bar{e} = Ni$	−0.25
	$Fe^{2+} + 2\bar{e} = Fe$	−0.44
	$Zn^{2+} + 2\bar{e} = Zn$	−0.76
	$Mn^{2+} + 2\bar{e} = Mn$	−1.18
	$Al^{3+} + 3\bar{e} = Al$	−1.66
	$Be^{2+} + 2\bar{e} = Be$	−1.85
	$Na^+ + \bar{e} = Na$	−2.71
	$Ca^{2+} + 2\bar{e} = Ca$	−2.87
	$K^+ + \bar{e} \rightarrow K$	−2.924
	$Li^+ + \bar{e} = Li$	−3.05 (Active end)

Gold at the top of the list is the most noble metal and will not dissolve easily. Lithium at the bottom of the list is the most active metal, which will go into solution readily.

Example 15.1 Calculate the potential between copper and iron galvanic cell when the temperature is 25°C.

Solution:

$$E_{Cu} = +0.34 \quad \text{(anode)}$$

$$E_{Fe} = -0.44 \quad \text{(cathode)}$$

Potential between Cu and Fe electrodes $= -0.44 - (+0.34)$

$$= -0.78 \text{ V}$$

Exercise 15.1

1. Determine the potential between Cu and Au electrodes.

Ans. [−1.16 V]

2. Calculate the potential between Al and Fe electrodes.

Ans. [−2.43 V]

The measured cell voltages represent only differences in the electrical potential when compared with a reference cell. The reference cell is a standard hydrogen electrode. It consists of an inert platinum electrode, in solution of H^+ ions, saturated with hydrogen gas bubbled through the solution at a pressure of 1 atm and temperature of 25°C. Platinum does not take part in electrochemical process. It acts only as a surface on which hydrogen atoms are oxidized or hydrogen ions are reduced. The electromotive force (emf) series shown earlier is generated by coupling standard halves of various metals to the standard hydrogen electrode. Metals are thus ranked as per the measured voltages. Voltages shown in Table 15.1 are the half reactions or reduction reactions.

15.4 ELECTROLYTES

Electrochemical corrosion takes place in the presence of an electrolyte, which is simply a fluid conducting electricity, by migration of ions. Water generally contains mineral ions, hydrogen ions and hydroxyl ions $(OH)^-$. In the case of atmospheric corrosion, *humidity in the air* does the job of an electrolyte.

Rusting in desert-type atmosphere is low, because of low humidity and dry air being a poor electrolyte.

Sometimes, *metal oxide coating acts as an electrolyte*, because most of the metals, which are used at high temperatures in furnaces oxidize and deteriorate with time (Figure 15.3). This type of corrosion

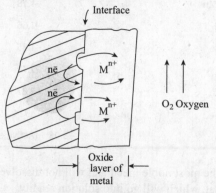

Figure 15.3 *Electrochemical Corrosion*

is also electrochemical. The oxide layer conducts metal ions (M^{n+}) from the metal surface. Metal ions (anions) combine with oxygen (cations) produced at oxide layer, i.e. oxygen interface to produce metal oxide. In furnaces, the *oxide layer becomes thicker and metal parts get thinner*.

15.5 GALVANIC CELL

A galvanic cell is formed between two dissimilar electrodes and electrolyte. One electrode becomes the anode and the other becomes the cathode. As we have already learnt that *lithium is the most active* element, it is most anodic and *gold is most cathodic*. Considering Zn and Ni system, zinc is anodic and nickel is cathodic. Table 15.2 shows the relative position of metals in the emf series.

The emf series shown in Table 15.1 is generated under highly idealized conditions and its utility is limited. But the table indicates the relative reactivities of the metals.

Table 15.2 *Relative Position of Metals in emf Series*

Anodic (active end)	Li, K, Ca, Na, Mg, Be, U, Al, Ti, Zr, Mn, Zn, Cr, Ga, Fe, Cd, In, Tl, Cu, Ni, Mo,
	Sn, Pb, H, Bi, Cu, Hg, Ag, Pd, Pt, Au cathode (inactive end)

A more realistic and practical ranking is provided by galvanic series. A number of metals and alloys are tested in sea water for their relative reactivities. The alloys near the top are cathodic, whereas those at the bottom of the series are anodic. In this table no voltages are provided. A comparison of the standard emf and galvanic series ranking has a high degree of correspondence between the relative positions of pure base metals. Table 15.3 shows galvanic series.

15.6 TYPES OF CORROSION

Process of corrosion can be broadly classified as follows:

1. Oxidation
2. Degradation
3. Radiation damage
4. Rusting

High-temperature corrosion is termed as 'oxidation'. The serviceability of plastic products is often impaired by pronounced swelling and cracking of plastic in the presence of organic solvents. This is known as 'degradation'. In nuclear reaction, the components are subjected to *radiation damage*. Neutron radiation produced by nuclear reaction can cause enormous damage and can penetrate up to 100 mm or so into typical structural materials. Iron gets rusted in humid atmosphere conditions.

Corrosion is further classified as (1) wet or liquid corrosion and (2) dry or gaseous corrosion. Galvanic cell (corrosion in the presence of an electrolyte) is an example of wet corrosion, while dry corrosion occurs in gaseous environments (without the presence of an electrolyte) as corrosion of metal in furnaces.

Table 15.3 *Galvanic Series*

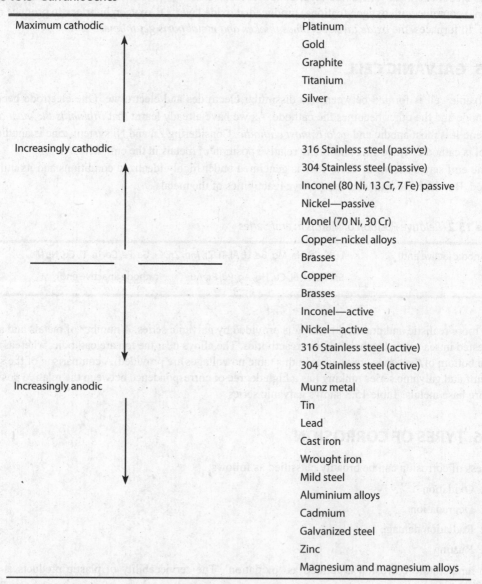

Maximum cathodic	Platinum
	Gold
	Graphite
	Titanium
	Silver
Increasingly cathodic	316 Stainless steel (passive)
	304 Stainless steel (passive)
	Inconel (80 Ni, 13 Cr, 7 Fe) passive
	Nickel—passive
	Monel (70 Ni, 30 Cr)
	Copper–nickel alloys
	Brasses
	Copper
	Brasses
	Inconel—active
	Nickel—active
	316 Stainless steel (active)
	304 Stainless steel (active)
Increasingly anodic	Munz metal
	Tin
	Lead
	Cast iron
	Wrought iron
	Mild steel
	Aluminium alloys
	Cadmium
	Galvanized steel
	Zinc
	Magnesium and magnesium alloys

Then, there are porous and non-porous types of corrosion. When the corrosion products (powder form) are very dense and do not permit corrosion to proceed further, it is known as *non-porous corrosion*. Corrosion proceeds by diffusion process in non-porous medium, i.e. between copper and oxygen. But, if the electrolyte penetrates through the powder as the *powder contains pores*, then it is known as 'porous corrosion'.

15.7 LAWS OF CORROSION

During the electrochemical process, the corrosion products form a film on the metal surface, which can be either porous (non-protecting) or non-porous (protecting). There are two types of films: (1) adherent film, in which corrosion products compress upon the surface and (2) expanding film, i.e. in porous corrosion, the film expands to cover up the surface. Based on the nature of films produced on metals, there are three laws of corrosion:

1. Linear law
2. Parabolic law
3. Logarithmic law

If x is the thickness of the film and t is the time for corrosion process, then

Linear law, $\qquad x = A_L t,$
where A_L is the constant for linear corrosion,

Parabolic law, $\qquad x = A_P \sqrt{t},$
where A_P is the parabolic rate constant,

Logarithmic law, $\qquad x = A_O \log\left(1 + \dfrac{t}{t_1}\right),$

where A_O is the logarithmic rate constant and t_1 is any arbitrary time.

Following are few examples of laws of corossion:

1. Corrosion in plain carbon steels, magnesium, barium and niobium follows linear law.
2. Corrosion in copper, stainless steel, and silicon follows parabolic law.
3. Corrosion in nickel, aluminium, zinc and chromium follows logarithmic law.

Example 15.2 Oxidation loss on the copper surface is 0.05 mm in 15 h. How much will be the loss in 225 h?

Solution:
Copper: oxidation in copper follows parabolic law.

$$x = A_P \sqrt{t}$$
or
$$x^2 = A_P^2 \times t$$
$$x_1 = 0.05 \text{ mm}, t_1 = 15 \text{ h}$$
$$x_2 = ? \qquad t_2 = 225 \text{ h}$$

Pulling the values

$$(0.05)^2 = A_P^2 \times 15$$
$$(x^2)^2 = A_P^2 \times 225$$
$$\frac{x_2^2}{(0.05)^2} = \frac{225}{15} = 15$$
$$x_2 = 0.194 \text{ mm}$$

Exercise 15.2   In a corrosion process, nickel loses 0.08 mm in 500 h due to oxidation. Estimate this loss after 4000 h.

Ans. [0.17 mm]

15.8 CORROSION RATE

The rate of material removal by a chemical action during corrosion is called 'corrosion rate' or corrosion penetration rate, i.e. the loss of thickness of material per unit time.

Corrosion penetration rate,
$$CPR = \frac{K.w}{\rho.A.t}$$

where w is the weight loss after exposure time, t, ρ is the density, A is the area of specimen exposed and K is a constant.

CPR can be expressed in terms of either mils per year (mpy) or millimetres per year (mm/year). For most applications a corrosion penetration rate less than 20 mpy (0.5 mm/year) is acceptable. Using electrode kinetic principle, it is possible to make rate estimates for some corrosion systems.

15.9 DRY CORROSION

Corrosion of a metal by a gas (without an electrolyte) is known as 'dry corrosion'. It is produced by a simple chemical reaction as

$$4Fe + 3O_2 \rightarrow 2Fe_2O_3 \quad \text{(iron oxide)}$$

Some combination of metals and gases are more active at room temperature, while other combinations are active at elevated temperatures. A clear surface of an aluminium plate quickly reacts with air and forms aluminium oxide, but iron in dry air requires high temperature to produce a significant reaction. The corrosion product is generally a film on surface, which can be porous or non-porous.

The actual type of the film, i.e. adherent or porous depends on the ratio of

$$\frac{M_c}{\rho_c} > \frac{M_m}{\rho_m} \quad \text{for adherent film}$$

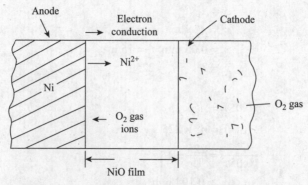

Figure 15.4 *Dry Corrosion in Nickel and Oxygen System*

$$\frac{M_c}{\rho_c} < \frac{M_m}{\rho_m} \quad \text{for porous film}$$

where c stands for corrosion product, m stands for metal, M stands for molecular weight and ρ stands for density.

Figure 15.4 shows the mechanism of corrosion by diffusion of a non-porous medium formed between nickel and oxygen. The metal–film interface acts as anode and gas–film interface acts as cathode. The film acts as external circuit in conducting the electrons from anode to cathode and as internal circuit in conducting ions.

Example 15.3 Find out the likelihood that oxidation product of Mg, i.e. MgO (magnesium oxide) will form a protecting film on magnesium. Densities of magnesium and magnesium oxide are 1738 and 3650 kg/m³, respectively. Atomic weight of magnesium is 24.31 g.

Solution:

Densities:

$$\rho_{Mg} = 1738 \text{ kg/m}^3 = 1.738 \text{ g/cm}^3$$

$$\rho_{MgO} = 3650 \text{ kg/m}^3 = 3.650 \text{ g/cm}^3$$

$$M_{Mg} = \text{molecular weight of magnesium} = 24.31 \text{ g}$$

$$M_{MgO} = 24.31 + 16 = 40.31 \text{ g}$$

$$\frac{M_c}{\rho_c} = \frac{M_{Mgo}}{\rho_{Mgo}} = \frac{40.31}{3.650} = 11.0438$$

$$\frac{M_m}{\rho_m} = \frac{M_{Mg}}{\rho_{Mg}} = \frac{24.31}{1.738} = 13.988$$

$$\frac{M_c}{\rho_c} < \frac{M_m}{\rho_m},$$

porous film is formed.

Exercise 15.3 Find out whether oxidation product of Ni, i.e. Mo forms a protective film over nickel or not.

Densities:

$$\rho_{Ni} = 8.9 \text{ g/cm}^2$$

$$\rho_{Nio} = 7.08 \text{ g/cm}^3$$

Atomic weight of Ni = 58.69

$$\text{Ans. } \left[\frac{M_c}{\rho_c} > \frac{M_m}{\rho_m}, \text{ a protective film is formed} \right]$$

15.9.1 Scale Types

The rate of oxidation of the metal and the tendency of the oxide film to protect the film from further oxidation are related to the relative volume of oxide and metal. Ratio of these volumes is known as PB ratio (Pilling–Bedworth ratio), which is determined by the expression

$$\text{PB radio} = \frac{M_o \rho_m}{M_m \rho_o}$$

where M_o is the molecular weight of oxide, M_m is the molecular weight of metal, ρ_o is the density of oxide and ρ_m is the density of metal.

PB ratio <1 results in porous film, which is unprotective, and insufficient to fully cover the metal surface. PB ratio >1, as the film forms compressive stresses are developed in the film. For PB ratio 2–3, oxide films may crack and can flake off (Table 15.4).

Table 15.4 *PB Ratio for Some Metals*

Protective		Non-protective	
Al	1.28	K	0.45
Ni	1.52	Li	0.57
Cu	1.68	Na	0.57
Fe	1.76	Cd	1.21
Co	1.99	Ag	1.59
Cr	1.99	Ti	1.95
Si	2.27	Sb	2.35
		Mo	3.40
		W	3.40

Factors influencing the oxidation resistance imparted by film are as follows:

1. High degree of adherence between the film and the metal.
2. Comparable coefficient of thermal expansion for metal and oxide.
3. High melting point and high temperature plasticity for oxide.

15.9.2 Kinetics

Oxide scale reaction product generally remains on the surface and the rate of reaction may be calculated by measuring weight gain per unit area as a function of time.

For the non-porous oxide film that adheres to the surface, parabolic relationship exists between weight gain per unit area w and time t, because the rate of layer growth is controlled by basic diffusion.

$$w = \sqrt{C_1 t} + C_2 \tag{15.1}$$

where C_1 and C_2 are time-dependent constants at a particular temperature. Oxidation of Fe, Cu and Co follows this parabolic rate relationship.

If the oxidation film is porous or flakes off, a PB ratio is <1 or >2, the oxidation reaction rate is linear.

$$w = C_3 t,$$

where C_3 is a constant. Oxide film being porous does not act as a barrier. Oxygen is always available for reaction. Sodium, tantalum and potassium oxidize as per this linear rate.

In very thin oxide layers (<100 nm), which are formed at relatively low temperature, weight gain rate is logarithmic, and the relationship is

$$W = C_4 \log (C_5 t + C_6)$$

where C_4, C_5 and C_6 are constants.

Figure 15.5 shows oxidation behaviour of aluminium, iron and copper at ambient temperature.

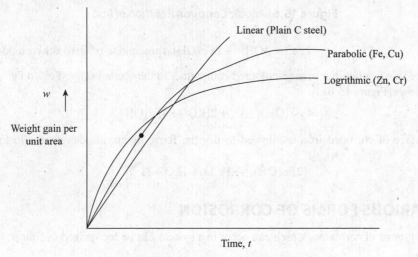

Figure 15.5 *Oxidation Film Growth*

15.10 RUSTING OF STEEL

If an article of steel is left in the open, rain water (in which oxygen is dissolved from air) causes rusting of steel (Figure 15.6).

Anodic corrosion reaction of iron (or oxidation)

$$Fe \rightarrow Fe^{2+} + 2\bar{e} \text{ (anodic partial process)}$$

Cathodic or reduction reaction

$$O_2 + 2H_2O + 4\bar{e} \rightarrow 4OH^-$$

Oxygen dissolved in water is converted into OH^- hydroxyl ion.

Overall corrosion reaction is

$$2Fe + 2H_2O + O_2 \rightarrow 2Fe^{2+} + 4OH^-$$

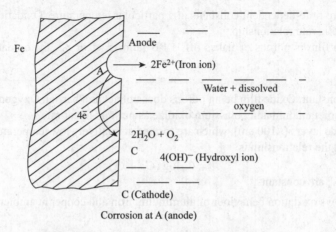

Figure 15.6 *Anodic Corrosion Reaction of Iron*

$$2Fe^{2+} + 4OH^- \rightarrow 2Fe(OH)_2 \text{ (precipitate of ferrous hydroxide)}$$

Ferrous hydroxide is a familiar orange-coloured compound. In the second stage, Fe^{2+} to Fe^{3+}, as per the equation follows (Figure 15.6)

$$4\,Fe(OH)_2 + O_2 + 2H_2O \rightarrow 4Fe(OH)_3$$

If the surface of corroded iron is allowed to dry the ferric hydroxide dehydrates to form Fe_2O_3 (redrust).

$$2Fe(OH)_2 \rightarrow Fe_2O_3 + H_2O + H_2 \uparrow$$

15.11 VARIOUS FORMS OF CORROSION

Various basic forms of corrosion, which can occur in a system can be recognized as follows:

1. Uniform
2. Pitting
3. Crevice
4. Galvanic
5. Stress corrosion
6. Hydrogen Embrittlement
7. Intergranular attack
8. Dealloying

15.11.1 Uniform Corrosion

Uniform attack on all surfaces exposed to corrosion atmosphere is called uniform corrosion. Most of the plastics and ceramics are poor conductors of electricity and are corroded by direct attack. For example, nylon in strong oxidizing acids becomes soft and gooey. Molybdenum is another example of direct attack. At elevated temperature in air (>760°C), no film is formed, and the metal slowly sublimes (disappears). Chlorine gas causes direct attack on many metals.

Moreover, uniform corrosion involves electrochemical reactions as follows:

1. Rusting in atmosphere can be uniform.
2. Cell action between the metal grains and the grain boundaries is uniform.
3. A metal pickling operation (used for car bodies) usually results in uniform attack.

Uniform corrosion can be prevented by (1) removing the electrolyte and (b) selecting a material that is not affected by a specific corrodent after consulting detailed corrosion data.

15.11.2 Pitting

Pitting is a local corrosion damage characterized by cavities. It is a particularly insidious form of corrosion, because even if one pit perforates the side of a tank, serviceability is lost until the tank is repaired. Chemical nature of the environment causes pitting which are as follows:

1. Halogen-containing solutions
2. Brackish water
3. Salt water
4. Chloride bleaches
5. Reducing inorganic acids are solutions that tend to produce pitting.

Stainless steels are particularly prone to pitting. Pitting of brass conductive tubes sometimes occurs due to dezincification. This consists in the solution of the brass followed by precipitation of copper by zinc in the brass. The net result is selective removal of zinc. A localized attack frequently occurs near the inlet ends of the condenser tubes, due to impingement of air bubbles, which carry away the corrosion products. Pumps and ship propellers are liable to an attack known as *cavitation*, an impact caused by the collapse of vapour bubbles.

Prevention

Major preventive measures are as follows:

1. Austenitic steels pit in salt water, so most designers tend to use copper alloys, bronzes, monels and other materials having lower pitting tendencies.
2. Some use carbon steels in salt water, in which corrosion rate is much higher than with stainless steels, but attack is more uniform and no pitting takes place.

15.11.3 Crevice

A local attack in a crevice between metal and metal surfaces or between metal and non-metal surfaces is known as 'crevice'. One side of the crevice must be exposed to corrodent or the corrodent must be in the crevice. This type of corrosion generally occurs in poorly gasketed pipe flanges, under bolt heads and attachments immersed in liquids.

It is generally believed that the chemistry of corrodent changes in the stagnant area of crevice (Figure 15.7). If the solution chemistry differs between the crevice and the bulk solution around the crevice, the area within the crevice becomes anodic. A decrease in pH has been measured in crevices in metals immersed in sea water.

Because of localized damage, crevice corrosion is very destructive. Good gasketing must be done to avoid crevice corrosion.

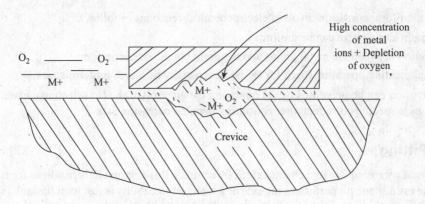

Figure 15.7 *Crevice Corrosion*

15.11.4 Galvanic Corrosion

If two dissimilar metals are connected electrically in an electrolyte, an electrochemical cell is formed. If the two metals are significantly dissimilar, then one metal will become anodic and corrode. Galvanic series of metals is established in sea water. Farther apart, two metals in the list (galvanic series of metals). The greater is the potential for corrosion, when they are coupled in an electrolyte. Magnesium to steel is a bad combination, while monel to stainless steel is a good combination (with negligible corrosion).

The other factor that controls galvanic corrosion is the relative size of the anode and the cathode. If the anode is smaller in comparison to the cathode, the attack on anode will be more, but if the size of the anode is bigger, then the situation is reversed. A steel bolt in an aluminium plate wherein aluminium becomes the anode, anode plate is large in comparison to steel bolt (cathode), and hence attack will be less.

If two metals are immersed in electrolyte and they are not mixed, galvanic corrosion is avoided. Galvanic series is given in Table 15.3.

15.11.5 Stress Corrosion Cracking

Stress corrosion cracking takes place under the combined action of applied tensile stress and corrosive environment. Some materials, which are inert in a particular corrosive medium become susceptible when a tensile stress is applied. Small cracks are developed, which propagate in a direction perpendicular to tensile stress, resulting in eventual failure of the material. Most alloys are susceptible to stress corrosion under specific environments. For example, *stainless steels corrode in solution of chloride ions and brasses corrode when exposed to ammonia.*

It is not necessary that the stress has to be externally applied. Even a residual stress can cause this type of corrosion. It is a form of environmentally assisted cracking (EAC). Hydrogen embrittlement, caustic embrittlement and liquid metal corrosion are all forms of EAC. This corrosion is time dependent, sometimes take months to occur.

Common remedies to eliminate stress corrosion cracking are (1) stress relieving heat treatment, (2) use of pure metals, which are immune to corrosion and (3) to consult available corrosion data and to avoid the environment–material combination that tends to cause stress corrosion cracking.

15.11.6 Hydrogen Embrittlement

Hydrogen in its atmospheric form diffuses interstitially through the crystal lattice and concentration as low as several parts per million can lead to cracking. Hydrogen-induced cracks are more often transgranular. Hydrogen embrittlement is similar to stress corrosion, in that a normally ductile material experiences brittle fracture when exposed to both tensile stress and corrosion atmosphere.

In order for hydrogen embrittlement to occur, some source of hydrogen must be present in addition to the possibility for the formation of atomic hydrogen.

These conditions exist in (1) pickling of steels in sulphuric acid, (2) electroplating and (3) presence of hydrogen-bearing atmosphere at elevated temperature as during welding and heat treatments.

Sulphuric and arsenic compounds accelerate hydrogen embrittlement, because these retard the formation of molecular hydrogen. Hydrogen sulphide found in petroleum fluids is most aggressive and is termed as 'poison'.

Martensitic steels are especially vulnerable to this type of failure but austenitic steels, alloys of copper, aluminium and nickel are relatively resistant to hydrogen embrittlement.

15.11.7 Intergranular Attack

This is a type of corrosion that occurs preferentially at the grain boundaries of the metals, due to alloy segregation at the grain boundaries. The grain boundaries are somewhat higher-energy areas than the grains. In uniform corrosion, the *grain boundaries may be anodic to grains*. If something is done to an alloy to make the grain boundaries dissimilar to grains, then intergranular attack will occur.

For example, sensitization of stainless steels. If austentic stainless steels are heated in temperature range of 400–850°C, chromium carbides tend to form in the grain boundaries. Chromium diffuses from matrix to form thick carbides, and the material adjacent to the grain boundaries become low-alloy steel. Many corrosive environments will readily attack the chromium-depleted grain boundary regions.

Most common *cause of sensitization in stainless steels is welding*. The metal adjacent to weld deposits cycles through the sensitizing temperature of 1650°C, and corrosive atmosphere causes intergranular attack. Low-carbon grade steels resist sensitization, because there is no enough carbon present to form chromium carbides. In stabilization approach, scavenger elements are added that tie up carbon atoms and prevent chromium depletion. Intergranular attack also occurs in many high-strength aluminium alloys and in some copper alloys.

15.11.8 Dealloying

One microconstituent of a metal alloy is preferentially removed from the alloy—leaving altered residual microconstitutent, for example, dezincification of brass—removal of zinc from brass leaving copper and graphitization of grey cast iron—the dissolution of iron from grey cast iron leaving only the graphite. Most of the large-diameter underground water and fire pipes are of grey cast iron, with a life span of 30–100 years. Graphitization occurs in corrosive soils, cinder fills and soils contaminated with industrial wastes. To avoid graphitization of grey CI pipes for water and fire mains, pipes are wrapped with polyethylene film before installation. Dezincification can be eliminated by not using yellow brasses in hot water systems. Copper base alloys with at least 85 per cent copper will be immune to dezincification.

15.12 FACTORS AFFECTING CORROSION

Although there are a number of factors affecting corrosion, the most important ones are as follows:

1. Redox potential
2. Metallurgical considerations
3. Passivity
4. Chemical nature
5. Operating conditions
6. Polarization

15.12.1 Redox Potential

Redox potential measured is a function of the metal and there is a definite relationship between the nature of material and its possible corrosion.

$$E_{cell} = E_{redox} = E_{reduction} - E_{oxidation}$$

15.12.2 Metallurgical Effects

Electrochemical corrosion requires one anode and one cathode. In pure metals, usually grain boundaries are anodic. In alloys and other materials, impurities such as chemical segregations, presence of multiphases, inclusions, degree of cold work and non-uniform stresses in components affect corrosion, as these impurities create anodic areas. Following are few examples:

1. In a bolted assembly, plates are in compression, area under bolt is in compression, bolt are in tension, metals react differently to corrodent and cell corrosion can occur.
2. Shot peening is a cause of corrosion.
3. Difference in grain size in metals performs a cell action.
4. Wrought iron contains a very small percentage of slag (silicate), which does not corrode, so wrought iron does not corrode or rust in water.
5. In austenitic stainless steels, there is presence of ferrite phase in addition to austenite phase, and the corrosion tendency is increased.

15.12.3 Passivity

Some metals form a passive film and this film imparts corrosion resistance by acting as a barrier in between the metal surface and the corrodent. If an environment is not attacking a particular metal, even though it is capable of attacking, it is known as passivity of the surface of the metal. Some metals have a tendency to form passive surface, for example, chromium, nickel, cobalt, iron and molybdenum.

For example, dilute solution of nitric acid causes rapid attack on steel while concentrated nitric acid causes a surface film to form, which imparts passivity. Passivity is the formation of a protective film.

Any operational conditions such as surface abrasion and impingement on a high-velocity solution contact will tend to break the film by a mechanical action, which can lead to corrosion.

15.12.4 Chemical Nature

Different materials react differently with different environments. Different types of environments are acids (oxidizing and reducing), bases, salts (acidic, alkaline or neutral), gases and solvents. Some materials like oxidizing, some like reducing and many like alkaline environments. Some gases are oxidizing, while some are reducing. pH concentration of an environment serves as a measure of the strength of acids or base (Table 15.5). pH stands for positive hydrogen ion.

Table 15.5 *pH Concentration of Different Environments*

pH value	Environment
<7	Acid
7	Neutral
7–12	Alkaline

Presence of halogen ions (e.g. chlorine and iodine) in a solution can lead to corrosion in solutions that would not normally cause corrosion.

15.12.5 Operating Conditions

Some essential operating conditions that must be considered while selecting a material are velocity, temperature, concentration, impurities and aeration. Some important observations are as follows:

1. Increasing the temperature of most chemical reactions increases the rate of corrosion.
2. Increasing fluid velocity increases the rate of corrosion due to erosive effect.
3. Increasing the concentration of corrosive species (H^+ ions in acids) in some situation produces more rapid rate of corrosion.
4. If the impurity is abrasive particles, it may accelerate corrosion by the removal of passive film.
5. If the impurity is a trace chemical such as water in an organic solvent, pitting may occur.
6. Metals that do not depend on passive surface films for corrosion resistance usually show increased corrosion rates in aerated solutions.

15.12.6 Polarization

If corrosion reactions are studied under controlled conditions and corrosion current and corrosion potential are noted, then change in potential with increasing or decreasing corrosion current flow is called polarization. Different types of polarization are: (1) activation polarization, (2) concentration polarization and (3) IR potential drop.

Activation Polarization

In a corrosion cell, this type of polarization can be seen at cathode where hydrogen is being reduced.

$$2H^+ + 2e^- \rightarrow H_2\uparrow$$

Hydrogen goes off as gas bubbles. Sometimes this reaction can be sluggish and thus polarization is said to occur.

The gas bubbles at cathode keep other hydrogen ions from reaching the surface and corrosion rate is decreased.

Concentration Polarization

This occurs when reacting species are not enough at an active electrode, i.e. enough hydrogen ions are not available at cathode, and hence corrosion potential will decrease.

IR Drop

IR drop simply means the drop of IR or potential drop in the electrochemical cell due to resistance in electrolyte. The flow of corrodent to the metal surface is impeded by the surface film and corrosion decreases.

15.13 CORROSION FATIGUE

The components subjected to repeated stress cycles are known to have suffered fatigue damage. Fatigue damage is characterized by pitting, impact wear, spalling and dent formation due to Hertzian contact stresses. If the environments of fatigue loading are corrosive, then fatigue damage is accelerated. Crack nucleation will take place at much less number of cycles, than without corrosive atmosphere. Crack propagation will be faster at much less number of fatigue cycles, and the specimen will fail. Moreover, the endurance limit of the material will be drastically reduced. Therefore, it is almost necessary that the components subjected to cyclic stresses must be provided with protective coating as in the case of turbine blades operating in steam or gas are provided with protective tungsten carbide facing. Wet portion of the steam must be removed from steam turbine to prevent corrosion.

15.14 CORROSION OF CERAMIC MATERIALS

Ceramic materials at room temperature are highly immune to corrosion in all types of environments. In metals, corrosion takes place due to electrochemical process, but in ceramics, corrosion (degradation) is due to simple chemical reaction. Ceramics are frequently employed due to their resistance to corrosion.

Refractory ceramics in addition to provide thermal insulation have to withstand high temperatures and high temperature attacks by molten metals, salts and slags.

Ceramic refractories operate in furnaces and other high-temperature devices between 1000°C and 3000°C and the refractories based on alumina (Al_2O_3) or magnesia (MgO) may undergo damaging reactions with environments of high temperatures. In steel-making furnaces, slags rich in silica (SiO_2) attack the surface of MgO refractories by forming a compound that is liquid at high operating temperature. Non-oxide refractories such as tantalum carbide (TaC) and titanium nitride (TiN) retain their strength at very high temperatures, but suffer from the disadvantage of reacting with oxygen at about 1000°C. For this reason, non-oxide refractories are generally used within a protective atmosphere.

15.15 DEGRADATION OF POLYMERS

Polymeric materials are susceptible to both chemical reaction and disintegration of long-chain molecules. The fumes produced by thermal degradation of polymers are sometimes dangerous. In particular, polyvinyl chloride, polyvinylidene-chloride and neoprene can give off small amount of poisonous gas, $CoCl_2$.

Taking two agents jointly, oxygen and ultraviolet rays cause deterioration of polymers at room temperature. Ultraviolet rays can break bonds in a manner similar to thermal energy. In the absence of oxygen, there is slow degradation of polymer, but the presence of oxygen accelerates the degradation.

The rate of oxidative deterioration of polymers can be significantly reduced by incorporating antioxidants (amines of phenols) in the polymers.

Some polymers such as synthetic or natural rubber contain regularly spaced double-bonded carbons, which are especially susceptible to attack by ozone (O_3). There are anti-ozonants such as primary diamines, which decrease the rate of attack by ozone.

However, some polymers decompose into compounds that enrich the soil environment, which is called 'biodegradation'. A useful example of polymer degradation is the fiery ablation of a *sacrificial polymer coating* on the nose cone of a space craft during re-entry into the Earth's atmosphere.

Suitable treatment of the surface of the polymers can improve their properties. For example, a typical effect of treatment of polyethylene with fluorine gas is to improve resistance to chemical attack.

When polymers are exposed to liquids, the main forms of degradation are swelling and dissolution. With swelling, the liquid or solute diffuses into the polymer and is absorbed within the polymer, and the small solute molecules fit into and occupy positions among the polymer molecules. The material becomes rubbery and weak.

15.16 GUIDELINES FOR PROTECTION AGAINST CORROSION AND OXIDATION

15.16.1 Metals and Alloys

Many alloys offer good resistance to corrosion and oxidation in different environments and are briefly listed as follows:

1. Brasses and bronzes offer good resistance against environments of water and salty air.
2. Titanium and zirconium resist chlorine environment.
3. 18–8 stainless steel is excellent against all types of environments.
4. Addition of Cr, Ni and Al in steel as alloying elements provides excellent resistance at elevated temperatures.
5. Addition of niobium in steel offers very good corrosion resistance.
6. Chromium steel used in oil refinery, chromel in thermocouples, stainless steel (chromium 12–17 per cent) used in turbine blades, valves of IC Engines and inconel used in turbine blades are good oxidation-resistant alloys.
7. 18–8 stainless steel (used in utensils and heat exchangers), Nichrome (Cr 20 per cent, Ni 80 per cent) used for strain gauges and Alumel (Al 2 per cent, Mn 2 per cent, Si 1 per cent, rest Ni) as heat-resisting wires are oxidation-resistant alloys.

Guidelines for Protection

Following are the guidelines for protection against corrosion and oxidation:

1. There is sizable loss to the industrial economy of the country due to corrosion and oxidation of domestic, commercial and industrial parts. Corrosion can be prevented by the use of the following:
   (a) Noble metals
   (b) Oxidation- and corrosion-resistant materials
   (c) Preventive coatings
   (d) Inhibitors

Moreover, deaeration of water, cathodic protection techniques and proper design of components so as to avoid formation of galvanic cells.

2. Simplest coating for corrosion control is conversion coating obtained by simple immersion treatments. Most often, it is only an atmospheric corrosion and there is no effect in chemical environment.

3. Affecting corrosion control with polymer coatings requires that the coating should be more than 1 mm thickness, free from pin holes, impermeable and inert to desired environments. This is also true to ceramic and glass coatings.

4. Metal coatings that are anodic to substrate, as zinc galvanizing, are very effective for control under atmospheric corrosion because they are not sensitive to pin holes.

5. Chromizing is effective in improving corrosion resistance of steels.

6. Diffusion-controlled cyaniding helps in preventing atmospheric rusting of steels. But nitriding of stainless steels lowers their chemical resistance.

7. When stainless steels are sensitized by welding or similar operation, they can be returned to un-sensitized condition by solution annealing and water quench.

8. Some cast alloys are annealed or normalized before using them in corrosion environments.

9. A good surface greatly aids in cleanability, which in turn prevents under-deposit attack and crevice corrosion.

15.16.2 Environmental Control

For stainless steels:

1. Dissolved gases lower pH values. Small chloride concentrations, e.g. a few parts per million, cause stress corrosion cracking of stainless steels.

2. Tanks holding organic solvents have been destroyed by corrosion, as trace impurities of water in chlorinated solvents can form galvanic cell.

3. Cleaning of pipes and vessels holding corrodents is essential.

4. Crevices under deposit and concentration cell for corrosion are promoted by deposits and build up in containers holding corrodents.

15.16.3 Inhibitors

Inhibitors are complex compounds, for example, sulphites, chromates, alcohol, polar nitrogen compounds, salts of arsenic and antimony are physically added to corrodents in a small concentration, as they remove oxygen and lower corrosion.

Other inhibitors called absorptive inhibitors attack the rate-controlling steps in electrochemical corrosion cell, and slow down the anodic and cathodic reactions. Put some species into the corrodent that will interfere with hydrogen ion reduction at a cathode.

Other inhibitors work by making passivation easier. They help to establish passive film that many metals depend on for corrosion protection.

15.16.4 Design

An appropriate design is essential for preventing corrosion and oxidation. Following points should be taken care of during the process of design:

1. Crevices usually occur by design errors.
2. If the design is faulty leading to cleaning and drainage problems at the time of cleaning, solids in pipes and tanks usually occur.
3. *Welding carbon steel to stainless steel:* Fusion welding involves melting of base metal. It is possible for the steel weld to locally dilute the stainless steel.
4. A good flush-fitting gasket must be used. If a gasket sticks out from a mechanical joint, the gasket itself can form a crevice.
5. If a tank cannot completely empty during cleaning process, the residue corrodent can concentrate and produce abnormal corrosion effects.
6. Corrosion monitoring is a part of corrosion control.
7. Galvanic couples can be prevented by using insulating materials.
8. Incomplete welds should be avoided as this can cause crevice corrosion, concentration of electrolytes.
9. Avoid recesses in the supports of pipes and vessels, where a solution can be collected.
10. Design a flow path that does not involve any impingement.
11. Principles of galvanic corrosion can be used to provide cathodic protection. There are special magnesium drain plugs in automobile engine crank cases that provide cathodic protection.
12. Zinc anode plates are available for steel boat hulls. Zinc collars are available that can be put on boat propeller shafts to take the bulk of corrosion and prevent galvanic attack.
13. In anodic protection, the potential of the object to be protected is controlled so that the metal stays passive in the vessels and chemical process equipments.

KEY POINTS TO REMEMBER

❏ Unintentional deterioration of a material by an electrochemical process is known as corrosion.
❏ In an electrolytic cell, metal is oxidized at anode.
❏ Ions are reduced at the cathode.
❏ Oxidation and reduction processes occur simultaneously and at the same rate.
❏ An electrolyte must be present and electrical path must be completed for corrosion.
❏ There is a potential between anode and cathode.
❏ $E_{cell} = E_{reduction} - E_{oxidation}$ (a redox process)
❏ Corrosion that takes place without the presence of an electrolyte is dry corrosion, e.g. oxidation of metal in a furnace.

❏ When a metal corrodes, the surface of the metal contains many microscopic anode and cathode sites. Defects, impurities, inclusions and grain boundaries act as such anodic and cathodic sites.

❏ The potential of hydrogen reduction process that occurs at the hydrogen reference electrode provides a reference for all other redox processes. Platinum acts as an inert electrode.

❏ In corrosion process, electrolyte is simply a fluid, conducting electricity by migration of ions.

❏ Water generally contains mineral ions, hydrogen ions and hydroxyl ions.

❏ In atmospheric corrosion, humidity in the air does the job of ion of an electrolyte.

❏ *Galvanic series:* A number of metals and alloys are tested in sea water for their relative reactivities.

❏ Alloys near the top of the series are cathodic and near the bottom of the series are anodic.

❏ *Classification of corrosion:* (a) oxidation, (b) degradation, (c) radiation damage and (d) rusting.

❏ *Laws of corrosion:* (a) linear law, e.g. corrosion in plain carbon steels, (b) parabolic law, e.g. corrosion in copper and stainless steels and (c) logarithmic law, e.g. corrosion in nickel, aluminium, zinc and chromium.

❏ Corrosion penetration rate
$$\frac{kw}{\rho At}$$

where k is a constant, w is the weight loss in exposure time t, ρ is the density and A is the area of specimen exposed. CPR less than 0.5 mm/year is acceptable.

❏ Dry corrosion

Adherent film $\qquad \dfrac{M_c}{\rho_c} > \dfrac{M_m}{\rho_m}$, porous film $\dfrac{M_c}{\rho} < \dfrac{M_m}{\rho_m}$

where M_c and M_m are molecular weights of corrosion product and metal and ρ_c, ρ_m are densities of corrosion product and metal, respectively.

Pilling bedworth rate, $\qquad\qquad \text{PBR} = \dfrac{M_c \rho_m}{M_m \rho_c}$

❏ Rain water (in which oxygen is dissolved from air) causes rusting of steel articles left in the open.

❏ Various forms of corrosion are uniform, pitting, crevice, galvanic, stress corrosion cracking, intergranular attack and dealloying.

❏ Crevice between metal and metal surfaces or between metal and non-metal surfaces is corroded if one side of the crevice is exposed to a corrodent.

❏ Under combined attack of applied tensile stress and corrosion environment, stress corrosion cracking occurs.

❏ *Sensitization of stainless steels:* If austentic stainless steels are heated in temperature range of 400–850°C, chromium carbides tend to form along the grain boundaries, chromium diffuses from the matrix to the boundaries and material adjacent to the grain boundaries become low-alloy steels.

❏ Dezincification of brass and graphitization of grey CI are dealloying processes. Factors affecting corrosion are redox potential, metallurgical considerations, passivity, chemical nature, operating conditions and polarization.

❏ Some metals form a passive film, which acts as a barrier between the metal surface and the corrodent.

❑ If pH value is less than 7, the environment is acidic and if pH value is between 7 and 12, the environment is alkaline.

❑ Fatigue under corrosive environment is corrosion fatigue.

❑ Ceramics have excellent resistance to corrosion.

❑ When polymers are exposed to liquids, the main forms of degradation are swelling and dissolution.

MULTIPLE CHOICE QUESTIONS

1. Which is a correct statement?

   (a) Corrosion is a localized surface phenomenon

   (b) Pitting due to corrosion causes holes and cracks in metals

   (c) Corrosion causes reduction in mechanical strength

   (d) All the above

2. Which is a correct statement?

   (a) Solution of dissolved ions is known as electrolyte

   (b) Electrolyte is a fluid conducting electricity

   (c) Both (a) and (b)

   (d) Neither (a) or (b)

3. In the following elements which is most anodic?

   Zr, Mg, Ga, Cu, Mn

   (a) Mn   (c) Cu

   (b) Mg   (d) Zr

4. Arrange the following metals in galvanic series with increasingly anodic

   Zinc, cadmium, tin

   (a) Tin, zinc, cadmium

   (b) Tin, cadmium, zinc

   (c) Cadmium, tin, zinc

   (d) None of these

5. Corrosion of copper follows which law of corrosion?

   (a) Linear law   (c) Parabolic law

   (b) Logarithmic law   (d) None of these

6. If M_m, M_o are molecular weights of metal and oxide, ρ_m, ρ_o are densities of metal and oxide, then PB ratio is

   (a) $\dfrac{M_m \rho_m}{M_o \rho_o}$

   (c) $\dfrac{M_o \rho_m}{M_m \rho_o}$

   (b) $\dfrac{M_m}{M_o} \times \dfrac{\rho_o}{\rho_m}$

   (d) None of these

7. Which one is a correct statement?

   (a) A metal pickling (used for car bodies) is a uniform attack

   (b) Halogen is contained in salt water

   (c) Both (a) and (b)

   (d) Neither (a) nor (b)

8. What is necessary to avoid crevice corrosion?

   (a) A good gasketing between two surfaces

   (b) Avoid collapse of air bubbles

   (c) Both (a) and (b)

   (d) Neither (a) nor (b)

9. Which one is not a correct statement?

   (a) Stainless steels corrode in solution of chloride ions

(b) Brasses corrode when exposed to ammonia

(c) Stress corrosion cracking is environmentally assisted cracking

(d) None of the above

10. Sensitization of stainless steel causes

(a) Formation of chromium carbides in grain boundaries

(b) Diffusion of chromium into grain boundaries

(c) Material adjacent to grain boundaries becomes low-alloy steel

(d) All the above

11. Which one is not a cause of corrosion?

(a) Shot peening

(b) Difference in grain sizes

(c) Slag inclusion in wrought irons

(d) Presence of ferrite phase in austenic steels

12. For the environment to be neutral what is its pH value?

(a) 04   (c) 10

(b) 07   (d) None of these

13. Which one of the following is subjected to corrosion fatigue?

(a) Bolted assembly

(b) Gas turbine blade

(c) Steel plate in sea water

(d) None of these

14. Which one is an incorrect statement?

(a) Polymeric materials are susceptible to disintegration of long-chain molecules

(b) TiN, titanium nitride, loses its strength at high temperature

(c) Treatment of polyethylene with fluorine gas improves its resistance to chemical attack

(d) None of these

Answers

1. (d)	2. (c)	3. (b)	4. (b)	5. (c)	6. (c)	7. (a)	8. (a)
9. (d)	10. (d)	11. (c)	12. (b)	13. (b)	14. (b)		

REVIEW QUESTIONS

1. Explain the corrosion of iron in ionic solution of HCl.

2. What is electrochemical process of corrosion? What is standard hydrogen reference electrode?

3. Explain the following:

Redox potential, electrolyte and inert platinum electrode.

4. What is galvanic cell? What is the significance of galvanic series?

5. Draw a comparison among degradation, radiation damage and rusting.

6. Explain various laws of corrosion? Give examples of two metals following the law in each case.

7. What is dry corrosion? What are porous and non-porous films?

8. Discuss PB rate of Al, Cr and Li.

9. Describe the process of rusting of steel.

10. Differentiate between pitting and crevice corrosion.

11. Differentiate between intergranular attack and dealloying corrosion.

12. What is a passive film? How is it formed and how does it act as a protective film?

13. What is polarization? Explain various types of polarization.

14. Differentiate between corrosion of ceramics and degradation of polymers.

THERMAL PROPERTIES

16.1 INTRODUCTION

From the beginning of civilization, people know that materials expand during heating and contract during cooling. These concepts have been used to melt the solids and then to solidify them. Blacksmiths have been using the concept of heat and temperature by heating the steel tires and then to slip over the wooden wheel for reinforcement, and to provide shrinkage fit between wooden wheel and steel tire. Study of the response of the materials is of much importance to design and production engineers. Manufacturing processes like casting, forging and welding can be performed efficiently only after thorough knowledge of thermal properties of the solids. Refractories in furnaces are provided for thermal insulation and to minimize heat transfer from the furnace to the surroundings. Power generation in plants very much depends upon the heat capacity of coal, various temperatures of steam, super-heated steam and so on.

Two materials are joined together after taking into account their coefficients of thermal expansion. Otherwise, thermal stresses will be developed. Various thermal properties such as melting point, boiling point, softening point, specific heats and thermal conductivity will be studied in this chapter. Special cylinders are designed to store liquid gases like oxygen, nitrogen and helium and then use for industrial processes.

In this chapter, we will also study about materials for high-temperature and low-temperature applications.

16.2 TEMPERATURE SCALE

The accurate measurement of temperature is of utmost importance in an industry, especially in heat treatment processes; therefore, scale of temperature has to be understood thoroughly.

The absolute fundamental temperature scale is based on the second law of thermodynamics applied to a 'perfect gas' for which

$$\text{Pressure} \times \text{volume} = \text{constant} \times \text{temperature (K)}$$

The unit degree on the scale is defined arbitrarily as one hundredth of the temperature interval between the freezing point of water (273°C) and the boiling point (373°C) of pure water. Although no perfect gas is available, hydrogen or nitrogen can be used in an instrument known as 'constant volume gas thermometer' and slight corrections can be made for lack of perfection.

The zero point is chosen as the lowest conceivable temperature corresponding to −273° on the centigrade scale, which has its zero at the freezing point of water.

Gas thermometer is a complicated instrument to use, and it can be regarded as a primary instrument, which has been used to measure freezing points of a number of metals and substances that can be employed to calibrate secondary pyrometers of greater flexibility.

The International Temperature Scale is similar to the thermodynamic scale, but uses the platinum-resistance thermometer and the disappearing filament-type pyrometer. The unit interval is called 'degree Celsius'.

Following principles are used for temperature measurement in various types of thermometers (Table 16.1).

Table 16.1 *Principles of Temperature Measurement in Various Thermometers*

Thermometer	Thermometric Property	Temperature Measurement Equation
Constant volume gas thermometer	Pressure (P)	$T(P) = 273 \times \dfrac{P}{P_t}$
Constant pressure gas thermometer	Volume (V)	$T(V) = 273 \times \dfrac{V}{V_t}$
Mercury in glass thermometer	Length (L)	$T(L) = 273 \times \dfrac{L}{L_t}$
Thermocouple	Thermal emf (e)	$T(e) = 273 \times \dfrac{e}{e_t}$

P_t, V_t, L_t and e_t are the respective thermometric property for unit degree of temperature change.

16.3 MELTING POINT

At the melting point, the solid phase of a material starts transforming into liquid phase and solid plus liquid phases coexist. The melting point temperature of a material depends upon the type of chemical bond existing in the material and the thermal energy required in breaking the chemical bond. Therefore, materials having strong bond will have high melting point. The strength of the bonds increases in the order of molecular bond, metallic bond, 'ionic' bond and covalent bond; therefore, melting points of these bonds will be in the increasing order for molecular, metallic, ionic and covalent bonds. Crystalline solids after melting solidify as they cool down to room temperature. But for non-crystalline polymeric materials, after melting irreversible chemical changes take place. Melting point temperature T_{mp} and linear coefficient of thermal expansions α are related together by

$$\alpha T_{mp} = \text{constant, i.e. } \lambda$$

Values of λ for different materials are listed in Table 16.2.

Table 16.2 *Values of λ for Different Materials*

λ	Types of Materials
0.02	Ionic compounds and metals
0.03	Some salts
0.07	Covalent bonded oxides and glasses

Table 16.3 provides the list of melting point temperatures for some materials.

Table 16.3 *Melting Point Temperatures*

Materials	T_{mp} (K)
Aluminium	930
Aluminium alloy 5% Cu	780
Copper	1355
Brass	1280
Silver	1335
Gray cast iron	1425
Mild steel	1785
High-carbon steel	1760
18–8 stainless steel	1765
Polystyrene	510
Teflon	600
Nylon	500
Fused silica	2000
Alumina	2320

16.4 HEAT CAPACITY

Heat capacity is the ability of a material to absorb heat from external surroundings, and it indicates the amount of heat energy required to produce a unit rise in temperature.

Heat capacity,

$$C = \frac{dQ}{dT} = \frac{\text{energy required}}{\text{change in temperature}}$$

Units of C are J/mol.K or cal/mol.K.

Heat capacity per unit mass of material,

$$c = \frac{C}{m}$$

where m is the mass of the material. 'Specific heat' is the energy required to raise temperature by 1 unit for unit mass of the material or this is the heat capacity per unit mass. Units of c, specific heat, are J/kg.K or cal/g.K, where 'g' stands for gram and K for Kelvin.

There are two types of specific heat: (1) C_p, specific heat of a material while maintaining its pressure constant and (2) C_v, specific heat of a material while maintaining its volume constant. Sometimes specific heat of a material is defined as the ratio of its heat capacity to the heat capacity of water in the same units. In this manner, specific heat becomes dimensionless. The magnitude of C_p is always greater than C_v, but the difference $C_p - C_V$ is very small for most of the solid materials.

'Mole' is defined as the quantity of a material contained in a fixed number of molecules given by Avogadro's number, $N_A = 6.023 \times 10^{26}$, mass is taken in kilograms.

The weight of a 'mole' of a substance is the sum of the 'atomic weights' of atoms in a molecule of the material. The specific heat capacity per mole is called 'molar heat', which is given by C in cal/mol.K or J/kg.K.

In most of the solids, thermal energy is mainly absorbed by the increase in vibrational energy of the atoms. The atoms in a substance are constantly vibrating with high frequencies but with small amplitude. Since atoms are bonded together, vibrations of adjacent atoms are coupled, and due to these coupled vibrations lattice waves are produced. These are considered as elastic waves travelling with velocity of sound, having short wave lengths but high frequencies. A series of elastic waves with different frequencies are generated. Only certain energy values are allowed in the crystal, and a single quantum of vibrational energy is called a 'phonon'. Sometimes 'vibrational waves' themselves are termed as 'phonons'. These vibrational waves participate in the transport of energy during 'thermal conduction'. Specific heats, C_P of some materials are given in Table 16.4.

Example 16.1 How much heat must be supplied to a piece of iron of mass 100 g, if its temperature is raised to 600°C from room temperature of 25°C?

Solution:

Specific heat of iron,

$$C_P = 448 \text{ J/kg.K} = 448 \text{ J/kg.C (Table 16.4)}$$

$$\text{Mass} = 100 \text{ g} = 0.1 \text{ kg}$$

$$\Delta T = 600 - 25 = 575°C$$

Heat supplied,

$$Q = C_p m \Delta T$$

$$= \frac{448 \text{ J}}{\text{kg.C}} \times 0.1 \text{ kg} \times 575°C$$

$$= 25{,}760 \text{ J}$$

or

$$C_P = \frac{448}{4148} = 0.108 \text{ cal/g.K (Table 16.4)}$$

$$= 0.108 \text{ cal/g.K}$$

$$\Delta T = 575°C$$

$$\text{Mass} = 100 \text{ g.}$$

Heat supplied,

$$Q = 0.108 \times \frac{\text{cal}}{\text{g.C}} \times 100 \text{ g} \times 575°C$$

$$= 6210 \text{ cal}$$

$$1 \text{ cal} = 4.18 \text{ J}$$

$$Q = 25{,}960 \text{ J (approximately same as before)}$$

Table 16.4 *Specific Heat, C_p*

Materials	C_p (J/kg.K)
Metals	
Aluminium	900
Copper	386
Boron	1020
Au	129
Iron	448
Nickel	443
Molybdenum	270
Silver	235
Sb	200
Tungsten	138
Magnesium	1008
Lead	158
Silicon	697
Titanium	518
Zinc	386
Brass (70 Cu, 30 Zn)	375
Invar (36 Ni, 64 Fe)	500
Ceramics	
Alumina (Al_2O_3)	780
Magnesia (MgO)	940
Spinel ($MgAl_2O_4$)	790
Fused silica (SiO_2)	740
Soda lime glass	840
Borosilicate glass (Pyrex)	850
Polymers	
High-density polyethylene	1850
Low-density polyethylene	2280
6/6 Nylon	1670
Polystyrene	1170
Polypropylene	1425
Water	4148
Nitrogen	1033

16.5 TEMPERATURE DEPENDENCE OF HEAT CAPACITY

As the temperature of material increases, amplitude of vibration of atoms increases and thermal scattering of free electrons during electronic conduction takes place by the vibrations and these elastic waves participate in the process of transport of energy during thermal conduction. The vibrational contribution of energy increases with increase in temperature and for many crystalline materials, heat capacity C_V rises rapidly with temperature starting from 0 at 0 K, till the curve between C_V and temperature T becomes asymptotic, at $C_V = 3R$, where R is a gas constant (Figure 16.1).

At low temperatures, relation between C_V and T is

$$C_V = AT^3$$

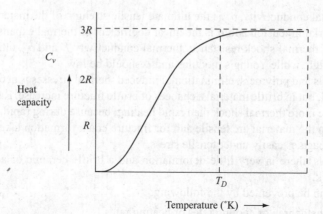

Figure 16.1 *Variations of C_V with Temperature*

where A is a constant independent of temperature T. C_V abruptly increases up to T_D (Debye's temperature) and there it becomes constant when $T > T_D$, and the constant value of $C_V \approx 3R$. For many materials values of T_D are below the room temperature.

With increasing temperature, total energy in the material increases, but the quantity of energy required to produce unit degree change in temperature is constant. For many materials, approximate value of C_V is 25 J/mol.K or 6 cal/mol.K. Table 16.4 gives experimental values of C_P, specific heat for commonly used materials.

The 'Debye theory' for specific heat is based on quantum principles and accounts for variations of C_V with temperature, for simple solids. A characteristic temperature, T_D also known as 'Debye temperature' can be determined for each material. At temperature T_D, C_V is considerably less than the constant value of 25 J/mol.K. At room temperatures greater than T_D, C_V approaches $3R$ (as per Dulong–Petit principle). At low temperatures

$$C_P \approx C_V \approx 3R \left(\frac{4}{50}\, \pi^4\right)\left(\frac{T}{T_D}\right)^3$$

$$\approx 46.5 \left(\frac{T}{T_D}\right)^3,$$

taking gas constant,
$$R = 1.987\,\frac{\text{Cal}}{\text{mol}}$$

This equation shows that C_P varies with temperature as per cubic relationship. In most engineering calculations, specific heat is used conveniently rather than heat capacity. Moreover, specific heat or heat capacity does not depend on structure of the material, changes in dislocation density, grain size or vacancies.

16.6 THERMAL SHOCK

Whenever a material is rapidly cooled or heated, it may fracture due to thermal stresses produced by thermal shock. If a thermometer is dipped suddenly into a hot liquid, glass of thermometer will break because of high tensile stresses developed in the glass, as α for glass is much less than α for mercury.

Thermal shock resistance (TSR) is given by

$$\text{TSR} = \frac{K\sigma_{ut}}{E_t \times \alpha}$$

where K is the thermal conductivity, σ_{ut} is the ultimate tensile strength of the material, E_t is the Young's modulus of the material in tension and α is the linear coefficient of thermal expansion.

For high value of thermal shock resistance, thermal conductivity K and σ_{ut}, ultimate strength of the material should be high, while Young's modulus and α should be low.

In ductile materials and polymers, elimination of induced thermal stresses is accomplished by plastic deformation in metal, but in brittle materials, chances of brittle fracture increase. Rapid cooling of a brittle material can cause more thermal shock than rapid heating, because during rapid cooling, the resisting stresses developed in the material are tensile and for fracture crack formation takes place under tensile stress and crack propagates easily under tensile stress.

In brittle materials, there is very little deformation and a brittle ceramic or a brittle metal cannot sustain thermal shock.

Thermal shock can be prevented by the following:

1. Reduction in the degree of cooling rates or heating rates.
2. Minimizing temperature gradients across the body.
3. Use borosilicate glass in place of soda lime glass, because α for Pyrex (borosilicate) glass is $3.3 \times 10^{-6}/°C$ and α for soda lime glass is $9 \times 10^{-6}/°C$.
4. Removing thermal stresses in ceramic materials by a special heat treatment (annealing).

Example 16.2   Determine the thermal shock resistance R of a steel body with

$$\alpha = 12 \times 10^{-6}/°C, \quad K = 80 \text{ W/mK}$$
$$\sigma_{ut} = 650 \text{ N/mm}^2, \quad E_t = 200,000 \text{ N/mm}^2$$

Solution:

$$K = 80 \text{ W/mK} = 80 \text{ W/m°C}$$

Thermal shock resistance,

$$R = \frac{K\,\sigma_{ut}}{E_t \times \sigma}$$

$$= \frac{80 \text{ W}}{\text{mC}} \times \frac{650 \times 10^6 \text{ N/m}^2}{200,000 \times 10^6 \text{ N/m}^2} \times \frac{\text{C}}{12 \times 10^{-6}}$$

$$= 21.667 \times 10^3 \text{ W/m}$$

16.7 THERMAL CONDUCTIVITY

The ability of a material to transfer heat is called thermal conductivity, and the 'thermal conduction' is the phenomenon by which heat is transferred from higher temperature to low temperature regions of a substance.

Thermal conductivity generally denoted by symbol K is a measure of rate of heat transferred through a material. Thermal conduction is similar to the time-dependent process of diffusion.

Heat flux,

$$q = \frac{Q}{A} = -\frac{\text{total heat/second}}{\text{area of plane}}$$

Negative sign indicates that heat flow is in the direction of thermal gradient.

$$\frac{Q}{A} = -K \times \frac{\Delta T}{\Delta x}$$

where

$$\Delta T = T_1 - T_2$$
$$\Delta x = x_1 - x_2$$

Therefore, thermal gradient is $\Delta T/\Delta x$, and K is the thermal conductivity. Thermal conduction in metals takes place through *free electron cloud*. Atoms vibrate and it is appropriate to consider each mode of vibration of atoms as a transient type of imperfection called phonons. As the temperature of a solid increases, it results in increased atomic vibrations represented by increasing number of phonons through the crystal.

So heat is transported in solids by both vibration of atoms (phonons) and free electrons. Total conductivity is the sum of the two contributions.

$$K = K_v + K_e$$

= thermal conductivity due to atomic vibrations
+ thermal conductivity due to electrons.

Thermal energy associated with phonons is in the direction of motion of phonons. K_v contribution is from the net movement of phonons from high- to low-temperature regions of a body across which the temperature gradient exists.

Free electrons produce electronic thermal conduction. Electrons in hot region gain kinetic energy and migrate to colder regions. This kinetic energy is directly transferred to atoms as a result of collisions with phonons. Mean free path of phonons is of the order of 10^{-9} to 10^{-8} m, and the mean free path of conduction electrons in metals is considerably larger, and thermal conductivity in metals proceeds similar to electrical conduction.

It can be shown that ratio of thermal to electrical conductivity in metals is proportional to the absolute temperature.

16.7.1 Weidemann–Franz Law

As per this law, 'The ratio of thermal and electrical conductivities is the same for all metals at the same temperature and this ratio is directly proportional to the absolute temperature of the metal'.

Mathematically,

$$\frac{K}{\sigma_e} \, aT = CT$$

where K is the thermal conductivity, σ_e is the electrical conductivity, T is the absolute temperature and C is a constant.

$$C = \frac{K}{\sigma_e T}$$

$C = 2.44 \times 10^{-8}$ WΩ/K^2 (for all metals) is known as Lorenz number. Thermal conductivity K is expressed in watt/metre. Kelvin (W/m.K). Experimentally determined values of constant C are given in Table 16.5. These experimental values of C are very close to 2.44×10^{-8}.

Alloying elements with impurities result in a reduction of the thermal conductivity. Impurity atoms especially in a solid solution act as scattering centres, lowering down the efficiency of electron motion.

Table 16.5 *Weidmann–Franz Law (Values of C)*

	Al	Cu	Au	Fe	Ni	Ag	W	Invar 64 Fe 36 Ni
$C \rightarrow (\Omega\text{-W/K}^2) \times 10^{-8}$	2.20	2.25	2.50	2.70	2.08	2.13	3.20	2.75

Thermal insulating materials are used to resist transfer of heat by thermal conduction. These materials are mixtures of cellular, granular and fibrous ceramics with pores (or air pockets) so as to reduce thermal conductivity. Heat flow through pores takes place by convection, radiation or molecular radiation or by a combination of these processes.

Moreover, ceramics are thermal insulators as they lack large number of electrons, as are available in metals in the form of electron clouds, and phonons are generally responsible for thermal conduction, but they are not as effective as free electrons.

Thermal conductivity of some metals and ceramics is given in Table 16.6.

Table 16.6 *Thermal Conductivity*

Metals	K (W/mK)	Ceramics	K (W/mK)
Aluminium	248	Al_2O_3	15–40
Copper	400	Carbon (diamond)	200
Gold	315	Carbon (graphite)	335
Iron	80	Fire clay	0.26
Nickel	90	Magnesia	38
Silver	428	Spinel ($MgAl_2O_4$)	15 (mean value from 0 to 1000°C)
Tungsten	180	Fused silica (SiO_2)	1.4
316 Stainless steel	16	Soda lime glass	1.7
Brass (70 Cu, 30 Zn)	120	Pyrex glass (Borosilicate)	1.4
Invar (64 Fe, 36 Ni)	10		

Scattering of lattice vibrations becomes more pronounced with increasing temperature; therefore, for most ceramics, generally with increasing temperature, the thermal conductivity decreases.

Porosity in ceramics plays an important part in thermal conductivity. Increasing the volume fraction of pores results in decrease in thermal conductivity. Moreover, heat transfer through pores is ordinarily low and inefficient and gaseous convection within the pores is also ineffective.

Ceramic materials subjected to temperature variations must have low coefficient of thermal expansion and should be isotropic. Ceramic materials are generally brittle in nature and if there is non-uniform dimensional change, these may fracture due to thermal shock.

16.7.2 Polymers

Many polymers have large coefficients of thermal expansion ranging from 50×10^{-6} to $400 \times 10^{-6}/°C$. Thermosetting plastics have very low coefficient of thermal expansion (as 120×10^{-6} for phenoformaldehyde) and thermoplastics have large values of coefficient of thermal expansion (polyethylene $110–200 \times 10^{-6}/°C$).

In polymers, heat energy is transported by vibration and rotation of chain molecules. Vibration of molecular chains occurs more effectively in crystalline materials. Therefore, thermal conductivity depends on the crystallinity of polymers.

Polymers are also used as insulators. Polymers produced by foamed polymerization are good thermal insulators because of the presence of small pores in the formed polymers. Styrofoam (foamed polystyrene) is commonly used for making drinking cups and insulating chest.

Example 16.3 Determine the thickness of a glass window 120×120 cm^2 that separates a room at temperature of 25°C from outside temperature of 44°C and allows not more than 7×10^6 cal of heat to enter the room each day. Assume thermal conductivity of glass as 0.0024 cal/cm.s.K.

Solution:

Flux,

$$q = \frac{Q}{A} = \frac{\text{total heat transferred per second}}{\text{area of window}}$$

$$1 \text{ day} = 24 \times 3600 = 8.64 \times 10^4 \text{s}$$

$$A = 120 \times 120 = 14{,}400 \text{ cm}^2 = 1.44 \times 10^4 \text{ cm}^2$$

$$Q = \frac{7 \times 10^6 \text{ cal/day}}{8.64 \times 10^4 \text{s/day}} = 81.02 \text{ cal/s}$$

$$\frac{Q}{A} = \frac{81.02 \text{ cal}}{\text{S} \times 1.44 \times 10^4 \text{ cm}^2}$$

$$= 56.26 \times 10^{-4} \text{ cal/cm}^2.\text{s}$$

$$\Delta T = \text{temperature difference} = 44 - 25 = 19°\text{C} = 19\text{K}$$

$$56.26 \times 10^{-4} \frac{\text{cal}}{\text{cm}^2 \times \text{s}} = 0.0024 \times \frac{\text{cal}}{\text{cm.s.K}} \times \frac{19\text{K}}{\Delta x}$$

$$\Delta x = 8.10 \text{ cm}$$

Thickness of glass window required is 81 mm.

16.8 THERMAL EXPANSION

Materials when subjected to increase in temperature expand and when subjected to decrease in temperature they contract. Figure 16.2 shows a bar of length L, at temperature T, which is subjected to increase in temperature T to T_f (final temperature) and length of the bar increases to L_f.

Change in length,

$$\Delta L = L_f - L$$

$$= \alpha L(T_f - T)$$

$$= \alpha L \Delta T$$

where ΔT is the net increase in temperature and α is the linear coefficient of thermal expansion.

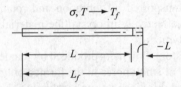

Figure 16.2 *A Bar Subjected to Temperature Variation*

Or

$$\frac{\Delta L}{L} = \alpha \Delta T$$

apparent strain in bar due to thermal expansion. Similarly, if a volume V of a material is subjected to increase in temperature (ΔT),

$$\frac{\Delta V}{V} = \gamma \Delta T$$

where γ is the volume coefficient of thermal expansion.

There are isotropic materials, in which linear thermal coefficients in three directions (defining the volume) are the same.

The volume coefficient of thermal expansion, $\gamma = 3\alpha$. But, there are some anisotropic materials, in which the volume coefficient of thermal expansion γ depends on the crystallographic directions, along which linear coefficients of thermal expansions are measured.

Due to thermal expansion, the interatomic distance between atoms also changes (or increases). The interatomic spacing at $0°K$ is r_0, which increases to r_1 at temperature T_1, and r_2 at temperature T_2 due to asymmetric curvature of potential energy curve as shown in Figure 16.3.

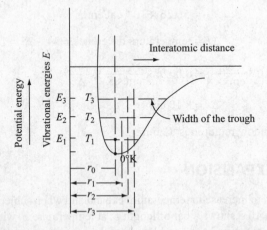

Figure 16.3 *Potential Energy Versus Interatomic Distance*

At $0°K$, interatomic distance is r_0. When the temperature rises to T_1, the interatomic spacing increases to r_1. Similarly, at increased temperature T_2, the interatomic spacing increases to r_2. So when the temperature increases, the interatomic spacing also increases.

$$0°K \rightarrow T_1 \rightarrow T_2 \rightarrow T_3$$
$$r_0 \rightarrow r_1 \rightarrow r_2 \rightarrow r_3$$

If the potential energy curve is symmetric, then r_0 does not change and the thermal expansion will not occur.

With rising temperature, vibrational energy change to $E_1 \to E_2 \to E_3$ as shown in Figure 16.3. The average vibrational amplitude corresponds to width of the trough at each temperature and average interatomic distance corresponds to the centre of the trough (Figure 16.3).

For any material, greater the atomic bonding energy, deeper and narrower will be the potential energy trough; as a result, increase in interatomic distance will be less for a given temperature, and consequently smaller value of coefficient α.

Table 16.7 provides values of linear coefficient of thermal expansion for various metals, alloys, ceramics and polymers at room temperature.

Table 16.7 *Linear Coefficient of Thermal Expansion*

Material	$\alpha \times 10^{-6}/°C$	Material	$\alpha \times 10^{-6}/°C$
Metals		**Ceramics**	
Aluminium	23	Aluminium oxide	74
Copper	17	Concrete	10–13.6
Silicon	2.5	Diamond (natural)	0.11–1.23
Gold	14.2	Soda lime glass	9.0
Platinum	9.1	Borosilicate glass (Pyrex)	3.3
Iron	11.8	Graphite (extruded)	2–2.7
Nickel	13.3	Graphite (moulded)	2.2–6.0
Tin	23.8	Fused silica	0.4
Silver	19.7	Zirconia	9.6
Tantalum	6.5		
Tungsten	4.5	**Polymers**	
Molybdenum	4.9	Elastomers (rubbers)	220–270
Zinc	22.5	Epoxy	80–116
		Nylon 6.6	144
Alloys		Phenolic	122
Invar (64 Fe, 36 Ni)	1.6	PBT (polybutylene tetraphthalate)	108–170
Super Invar (63 Fe, 32 Ni, 5 Co)	0.72	PC (polycarbonate)	122
Plain carbon steels	12.0	HPPE (polyethylene high density)	106–198
Stainless steel 316	15.9	PMMA (polymethyl methacrylate)	90–160
Grey cast Iron	11.4	PVC (polyvinyl chloride)	90–180
Ductile iron	11.0	PTFE (polytetra fluoroethylene)	126–216
Beryllium copper	16.7	PP (polypropylene)	146–180
Cartridge brass	20.0		
Bearing bronze	18.0		
Lead tin solder (60 Sn, 40 Pb)	24.0		
Monel 400	13.9		

16.8.1 Metals

For most of the metals in common use, linear coefficients of thermal expansion vary from 4.5×10^{-6} – $24 \times 10^{-6}/°C$. Many a times, dimensional stability of measuring instruments and gages is of utmost importance, for which alloys with very low linear coefficients of thermal expansion are developed such as Invar (64 Fe, 36 Ni) with $\alpha = 1.6 \times 10^{-6}/°C$ and superinvar (63 Fe, 32 Ni, 5 Co) with $\alpha = 0.72 \times 10^{-6}/°C$, which is used in slip gauges, measuring tapes and inspection gauges used in tool rooms. Linear coefficient of thermal expansion plays an important role in the thermal stresses developed between two materials joined together and subjected to temperature change. Linear coefficients of thermal expansion of steel ($\alpha = 12 \times 10^{-6}/°C$) and concrete ($\alpha = 10 - 13.6 \times 10^{-6}/°C$) are really the same and thermal stresses due to temperature variation in reinforced cement concrete (RCC) are the minimum.

16.8.2 Ceramics

In ceramics, there are strong interatomic bonding forces resulting in low coefficient of thermal expansion varying from 0.4×10^{-6} to $15 \times 10^{-6}/°C$. Non-crystalline ceramics are isotropic, but crystalline ceramics are anisotropic, i.e. while heating, ceramics expand in one direction and contract in the other direction. The low linear coefficient of thermal expansion, i.e. $0.4 \times 10^{-6}/°C$ of fused silica (SiO_2) is due to low atomic packing factor, producing very small microscopic dimensional changes.

Ceramics in general use should have low α and should be isotropic in thermal behaviour; otherwise, a ceramic being brittle fractures while heating due to non-uniform dimensional changes—a phenomenon known as thermal shock.

16.8.3 Polymers

Some polymers experience large values of α, i.e. 80×10^{-6} to $270 \times 10^{-6}/°C$. Higher values of α are found in thermoplastics as PVC, as these are linear and branched polymers with weak secondary bonds. As the cross-linking increases, coefficient of thermal expansion decreases. Lowest values of α are found in thermoset plastics as polyester, epoxy and phenol-formaldehyde, in which the bonding is entirely covalent.

Example 16.4 Aluminium and mild steel bars of equal lengths at 25°C differ in length by 1.0 mm at 350 K. If the coefficient of linear expansion of aluminium and mild steel are $23.7 \times 10^{-6}/°C$ and $15.2 \times 10^{-6}/°C$, respectively, what is the length of each rod at 0°C?

Solution:

Temperature
$$25°C = 25 + 273 = 298 \text{ K}$$

Say length at 25°C is L for both aluminium and mild steel bars, then

$$L \times 23.7 \times 10^{-6} (350 - 298) - L \times 15.2 \times 10^{-6} (350 - 298) = 1 \text{ mm}$$

$$L [4.42 \times 10^{-4}] = 1 \text{ mm}$$

$$L = \frac{1 \times 10^4}{4.42} = 2262.4 \text{ mm at 25°C}$$

Length at 0°C

$$L = L_A [1 + 23.7 \times 10^{-6} \times 25] = 2262.4 \text{ mm}$$

$$2262.4 = L_A [1 + 5.925 \times 10^{-4}]$$

$$L_A = 2261.06 \text{ mm, length of aluminium bar at 0°C.}$$

Similarly,

$$L = L_m [1 + 25 \times 15.2 \times 10^{-6}] = 2262.4 \text{ mm}$$

$$2262.4 = L_m [1 + 3.8 \times 10^{-4}]$$

$$L_m = 2261.54 \text{ mm, length of mild steel bar at } 0°C$$

16.9 THERMAL STRESSES

Stresses due to temperature variations are induced in materials if (1) free thermal expansion or contraction is restrained, (2) thermal gradient exists in a material and (3) two dissimilar metals are joined together.

Thermal stresses are developed in (1) welding of structures, (2) joints of two rails when expand due to temperature increase, (3) shrink fitted cylinders, (4) bimetallic strips used for temperature control, (5) refractory bricks used in furnaces and ovens, (6) outer skin of rockets and missiles subjected to fractured heat, (7) components of IC engines as piston, cylinder and cylinder liner and (7) concrete structures and dams. Let us take following cases.

16.9.1 Restrained Thermal Expansion or Contraction

Consider a bar of length L and area of cross section A held between two rigid walls. E is the Young's modulus of the material of the bar (Figure 16.4). Bar is subjected to increase in temperature by $\Delta T°C$. Free expansion of the bar (if allowed) = $\alpha \Delta T L$

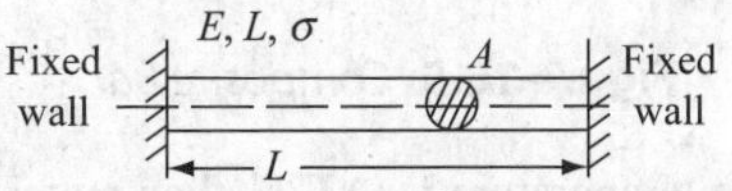

Figure 16.4 *A Bar Between Two Rigid Walls*

If free expansion is restrained, compressive force will be developed in the bar resulting in compressive stress, e.g. σ_{CT} and the bar may buckle if σ_{CT} is large enough.

$$\frac{\sigma_{CT}}{E} = \text{strain bar}$$

$$= \frac{\alpha \Delta T \cdot L}{L}, \text{ strain restrained}$$

or

$$\sigma_{CT} = E \cdot \alpha \cdot \Delta T \text{ (compression)}$$

where α is the linear coefficient of thermal expansion. If rod is cooled and temperature is decreased by ΔT, then tensile stresses will be developed in the bar.

$\sigma_{CT} = E\alpha\Delta T$ (tensile), the bar may break or will be subjected to plastic deformation depending upon the magnitude of the thermal stress σ_{CT} developed.

16.9.2 Stresses due to Temperature Gradients

When a body is heated or cooled, the temperature change is not uniform throughout the section and the depth of the body, rather there is temperature variation. The temperature distribution within the body depends upon the size and shape of the body, thermal conductivity of the material and rate of temperature change. As a result of temperature gradients, thermal stresses are developed in the body. Generally, these thermal stresses develop during rapid cooling or rapid heating.

If a body is rapidly heated, then the temperature at the outer surface of the body will be more than the temperature at the interior. As a result, there is more thermal expansion at the outer surface than at the interior of the body. This variation in thermal expansion from outer to interior, resulting in differential change in dimensions act to restrain the free expansion or free contraction in the adjacent volume elements of the body. Restraining the free expansions causes compressive surface stresses and tensile interior stresses during rapid heating of the body. Similarly, during rapid cooling, tensile surface stresses and compressive interior stresses are developed. For example, while pouring a hot liquid in a cold glass tumbler, the glass tumbler may crack due to differential expansion and development of compressive and tensile stresses.

16.9.3 Thermal Stresses in Components of Two Dissimilar Metals

When a composite bar is made of two dissimilar metals 1 and 2, with different Young's modulii $E_1 \neq E_2$ and different linear coefficients of thermal expansion $\alpha_1 \neq \alpha_2$, then thermal stresses are developed in two different materials during heating or cooling. Let us take a composite bar of length L, as shown in Figure 16.5.

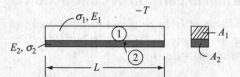

Figure 16.5 *Composite Bar*

If $\alpha_1 > \alpha_2$ and there is increase in temperature by $\Delta T°C$, then material 1 will try to expand more than material 2, but in a composite bar both materials expand by the same amount, as a result compressive thermal stress is developed in material 1 and tensile thermal stress in material 2.

For equilibrium,

$$\sigma_{1T} \cdot A_1 = \sigma_{2T} \cdot A_2, \tag{16.1}$$

where σ_{1T} is the thermal stress in material 1 (compressive) and σ_{2T} is the thermal stress in material 2 (tensile).

Moreover,

$$\frac{\sigma_{1T}}{E_1} + \frac{\sigma_{2T}}{E_2} = (\alpha_1 - \alpha_2)\Delta T \tag{16.2}$$

where E_1 and E_2 are Young's modulii of materials 1 and 2, respectively, and ΔT is the change in temperature.

From Eqs (16.1) and (16.2), thermal stresses σ_{1T} and σ_{2T} are determined. If the composite bar is cooled by temperature ΔT, then tensile thermal stress in bar 1 and compressive thermal stress in bar 2 are developed. For example, bimetallic strip, due to differential expansion, acts as a temperature controller in a refrigerator.

If $\alpha_1 = \alpha_2$, no thermal stresses are developed during heating or cooling of the composite bar. In RCC, effort is made to have equal linear coefficients of thermal expansion for concrete mix and reinforcing steel bars, so that thermal stresses are minimized during heating or cooling of RCC slabs or columns.

Example 16.5 A mild steel bar, 1.2 m long and 5 cm in diameter, is held between two rigid supports. Value of α for mild steel is $12 \times 10^{-6}/°C$ and Young's modulus is 200 GPa. By how much temperature the bar must be heated above room temperature so that the maximum compressive stress developed in the bar is 80 N/mm².

Solution:

$$\alpha = 12 \times 10^{-6}/°C$$

$$E = 200 \text{ kN/mm}^2$$

Strain in bar, if stress is 80 N/mm²,

$$\epsilon = \frac{80}{200 \times 1000}$$

$$= 4 \times 10^{-4}$$

$$= \alpha \Delta T$$

$$= 12 \times 10^{-6} \times \Delta T$$

Increase in temperature,

$$\Delta T = \frac{4 \times 10^{-4}}{12 \times 10^{-6}}$$

$$= 333.3°C$$

Example 16.6 A thin copper strip of rectangular section 6×1 mm² is perfectly joined to a steel strip of same section. The composite strip is subjected to a temperature drop of 40°C. Determine thermal stresses developed in copper and steel strips. Given $E_C = 105$ kN/mm², $E_S = 210$ kN/mm²

$$\alpha_C = 17 \times 10^{-6}/°C,$$

$$\alpha_s = 12 \times 10^{-6}/°C$$

Solution:

There is a drop in temperature and $\alpha_{Cu} > \alpha_{steel}$, tensile thermal stress in copper and compressive thermal stress in steel will be developed. For example, if stresses are σ_{CT} and σ_{ST}, then

$$\sigma_{CT} \times A_C = \sigma_{ST} \times A_S$$

But

$$A_C = A_S = 6 \times 1 \text{ mm}^2$$

So

$$\sigma_{CT} = \sigma_{ST} \tag{16.3}$$

$$\frac{\sigma_{CT}}{E_C} + \frac{\sigma_{ST}}{E_S} = (\alpha_C - \alpha_S) \times \Delta T$$

$$\frac{\sigma_{CT}}{105 \times 1000} + \frac{\sigma_{ST}}{210 \times 1000} = (17 - 12) \times 10^{-6} \times 40$$

$$\sigma_{CT} + 0.5\sigma_{ST} = 5 \times 10^{-6} \times 40 \times 105 \times 1000$$

or

$$1.5 \ \sigma_{CT} = 21$$

$$\sigma_{CT} = +14 \text{ N/mm}^2 \text{ (tensile)}$$

$$\sigma_{ST} = -14 \text{ N/mm}^2 \text{ (compressive)}$$

Example 16.7 To what temperature must a cylindrical rod of tungsten of 12 mm diameter and a plate of 1025 steel having a circular hole of 11.987 mm diameter have to be heated for the rod to just fit into the hole? Assume that initial temperature is 24°C.

$$\sigma_{steel} = 12 \times 10^{-6}/°C; \; \sigma_w = 4.5 \times 10^{-6}/°C$$

Solution:

For example, both rod and plate are heated by ΔT temperature (increase). After heating, final dimensions of hole in steel plate and diameter of the rod will be equal, therefore

$$11.987 \times 12 \times 10^{-6} \times \Delta T + 11.987 = 12 \times 4.5 \times 10^{-6} \, \Delta T + 12.000$$

$$\Delta T \times 10^{-6} \, [143.844 - 54] = 0.013$$

$$\Delta T = \frac{0.013 \times 10^{6}}{89.844} = 144.7°C$$

Final temperature,

$$T_f = 144.7 + 24 = 168.7°C$$

16.10 MATERIALS FOR HIGH-TEMPERATURE APPLICATIONS

With the advancement of technology, the need for materials resisting high temperature is increasing day by day as in applications such as gas turbines, jet engines, rockets, missiles and supersonic aircrafts. Moreover, there must be materials to resist very high temperature in furnaces and ovens. In turbines, the order of temperatures encountered is about 1000°C and in automobiles it is more than 1000°C, while several thousand degrees Celsius in fast-breeding reactions. The detrimental effects of high temperature are: (1) loss of strength, (2) reduced stiffness, (3) loss of cohesive strength, (4) polymorphic transformation and (5) decrease in hardness. Therefore, for high-temperature applications, the material should be able to maintain its strength and hardness at elevated temperatures or the property of red hardness.

In sophisticated aircraft applications, superalloys are used. There are three types of superalloys: (1) iron–nickel base, (2) nickel base and (3) cobalt base. These alloys are creep-resistant alloys.

In iron–nickel superalloys, the composition is 15 per cent Cr, 20–40 per cent Ni, remainder is iron, and the two alloys, discalloy and incoloy are nickel–base alloys.

Nickel-base alloys are best creep-resistant alloys, for example, nimonic, inconel and waspalloy are the commonly used ones. A particular Nimonic alloy contains 0.2 per cent C, 10 per cent Cr, 20 per cent Co, 5 per cent Mo, 5 per cent Al, 1.3 per cent Ti, and the remainder is Ni. The creep-resistant property of cobalt alloy lies in between Cu–Ni superalloy and Ni-base superalloys. A typical composition of cobalt-base alloy is 25 per cent Cr, 10 per cent Ni, 8 per cent W, 2 per cent Fe, 0.5 per cent C and rest is Co. Vitallium is a cobalt-base superalloy.

High melting point is a primary requirement of a refractory metal. Therefore, melting point is the criterion used to differentiate between refractory metals and ordinary metals. A temperature of 2000°C is most frequently used to determine whether it is a refractory metal or an ordinary metal.

There are four refractory metals that have a BCC crystal structure and display a ductile-to-brittle transition temperature. These metals are listed in Table 16.8.

Table 16.8 *Refractory Metals Having a BCC Crystal Structure*

Metal	T_{mp} (Melting Point Temperature) (°C)
Nb (Niobium)	2468
Mo (Molybdenum)	2623
Ta (Tantalum)	2996
W (Tungsten)	3410

Refractory metals have a strong tendency to oxidize even at moderately high temperatures. These metals are alloyed to enhance their mechanical properties at room temperature and at high temperatures.

16.11 MATERIALS FOR LOW-TEMPERATURE APPLICATIONS

There is sizable requirement of materials used in refrigerators, cold storage, fertilizers, chemical processing and medicinal industries. Liquid oxygen and liquid nitrogen are used for preserving skin, semen and vital parts of the body. Liquid nitrogen cylinders are in demand for food preservations. Dry ice is made by liquefying carbon dioxide gas at −190°C. For various gases used in industry/research activities, the liquefying temperatures are as follows (Table 16.9).

Table 16.9 *The Liquefying Temperatures of Gases*

Gas	Liquefying Temperature (°C)
Ammonia	−190
Oxygen	−183
Nitrogen	−196
Carbon dioxide	−190
Hydrogen	−253

Storage of these gases in cylinders, which can sustain high bursting pressures is of serious concern. LPG gas cylinders burst in the presence of hot environment.

A temperature lower than −157.5°C is known as a cryogenic temperature. Following are the effects of low temperature on various mechanical properties:

1. Yield strength and ultimate strength of ductile materials are increased.
2. Reduction in ductility or toughness of the material.
3. Young's modulus of the material is slightly increased.
4. Improvement in fatigue resistance of the material.

The increase in strength and decrease in ductility are gradual in metals with FCC structure, but in metals of BCC structure, these phenomena are rapid. At low temperatures, stiffness of elastomers (rubber) increases, but reduction in toughness makes instability of automobile tyres.

Some materials used for low-temperature application are as follows:

1. Plain low-carbon, high-strength, low-alloy steels as A516, with σ_{ut} = 485 MPa and σ_{ut} = 280 MPa and ductility is 21 per cent, used for low-temperature pressure vessels.

2. Austenite stainless steel S30400, with 0.08 C, 19 Cr, 9 Ni, 2 Mn, rest Fe, under annealed condition with σ_{ut} = 515 MPa, σ_{yp} = 205 MPa, elongation is 40 per cent, used for chemical and food-processing equipment and cryogenic vessels.

3. Aluminium–lithium alloy 2090, with 2.7 Cu, 0.25 Mg, 2.25 Li, 0.12 Zr, rest Al with σ_{ut} = 435 MPa, ductility is 5 per cent, used for aircraft structure and cryogenic tankage structures.

4. Nickel-based steels have been developed for use in cryogenic industries. The nickel composition and service temperatures are given in Table 16.10.

Table 16.10 *Composition of Nickel Based Steels and Service Temperatures*

Nickel percentage in steel	3.5	5.0	9.0
Service temperature (°C)	−100	−120	−190

KEY POINTS TO REMEMBER

❑ Absolute fundamental temperature scale is based on the second law of thermodynamics applied to 'perfect gas'.

Pressure × volume = constant × temperature (K)
Zero point (−273°C absolute)—freezing point of water
(373°C absolute)—boiling point of water

❑ Melting point temperature T_{mp} and linear coefficient of thermal expansion are related.

$$\alpha, T_{mp} = \text{constant}, \lambda$$

$$\text{Heat capacity, } C = \frac{dQ}{dT} = \frac{\text{energy required}}{\text{change in temperature}}$$

$$\text{Specific heat } c = \frac{C}{m} = \text{heat capacity per unit mass}$$

❑ Heat capacity at constant volume, $C_V = 3R$, where R is a gas constant.

❑ $C_V = AT^3$, where A is a constant and T is the absolute temperature.

❑ Thermal shock resistance,

$$\text{TSR} = \frac{K\sigma_{ut}}{E \times \alpha},$$

where K is the thermal conductivity, σ_{ut} is the ultimate tensile strength, E is the Young's modulus and α is the linear coefficient of thermal expansion.

❑ $K = K_v + K_e$ = thermal conductivity due to atomic vibrations + thermal conductivity due to electrons

❑ Weidemann–Franz Law,

$$\frac{K}{\sigma_e} = CT,$$

where K is the thermal conductivity, σ_e is the electrical conductivity, T is the absolute temperature and C is a constant.

❑ Ceramic materials generally brittle in nature have low coefficients of thermal expansion.

❑ Polymers have large linear coefficients of thermal expansion $50-400 \times 10^{-6}/°C$

❑ $\frac{\Delta V}{V} = \gamma \Delta T$, where γ is the volume coefficient of thermal expansion.

❑ For isotropic materials, $\gamma = 3\alpha$ (linear coefficient of thermal expansion).

❑ In potential energy versus interatomic distance curve, the average vibrational amplitude corresponds to the width of the trough and interatomic distance corresponds to the centre of the trough, at a particular temperature.

❑ For invar (64 Fe, 36 Ni) $\alpha = 1.6 \times 10^{-6}/°C$ used in measuring instruments.

❑ In polymers, as the cross-linking increases, the coefficient of thermal expansion decreases.

❑ Thermal stress in restrained thermal expansion or contraction, $\sigma_{CT} = \alpha \Delta T$, compression when expansion is restrained.

❑ In two dissimilar metals joined together with E_1, E_2, α_1 and α_2, respectively $\sigma_{1T} A_1 = \sigma_{2T} A_2$, where A_1 and A_2 are the area of cross section respectively,

$$\frac{\sigma_1 T}{E_1} + \frac{\sigma_2 T}{E_2} = (\alpha_1 - \alpha_2)\Delta T$$

where σ_{1T} and σ_{2T} are thermal stresses in two metals, one in compression and the other in tension.

❑ Superalloys are used in high-temperature applications of jet engines and gas turbines.

❑ Liquid nitrogen is used for preserving skin, semen and vital parts of the body.

❑ Dry ice is carbon dioxide at $-190°C$.

MULTIPLE CHOICE QUESTIONS

1. Arrange the following bonds in the increasing order of strength: covalent bond, ionic bond and molecular bond
   - (a) Molecular bond, covalent bond, ionic bond
   - (b) Molecular bond, ionic bond, covalent bond
   - (c) Ionic bond, molecular bond, covalent bond
   - (d) Covalent bond, ionic bond, molecular bond

2. What is the melting point of grey CI?
   - (a) 1335°K
   - (b) 1425°K
   - (c) 1280°K
   - (d) None of these

3. If $C_p = 450$ J/kg.K of iron, how much heat is needed to heat 1 kg of iron by 10°C?
   - (a) 4.5 J
   - (b) 450 J
   - (c) 4500 J
   - (d) None of these

4. What is the maximum value of C_v, heat capacity in terms of R (gas constant)?
   - (a) 2R
   - (b) 2.73R
   - (c) 3R
   - (d) None of these

5. What is the expression for thermal shock resistance?
   - (a) $\dfrac{K\sigma_{ut}}{E_t}$
   - (b) $\dfrac{K\sigma_{ut}}{E_t \alpha}$
   - (c) $\dfrac{KE_t}{\sigma_{ut} \alpha}$
   - (d) None of these

where K is the thermal conductivity, E_t is the Young's modulus in tension, σ_{ut} is the ultimate tensile strength and α is the linear coefficient of thermal expansion.

6. Thermal energy is associated with

   (a) Direction of motion of phonons

   (b) Net movement of phonons from high- to low-temperature regions

   (c) Both (a) and (b)

   (d) Only (a)

7. Arrange the following materials with decreasing order of thermal conductionTungsten, magnesia and gold

   (a) Magnesia, tungsten, gold

   (b) Gold, tungsten, magnesia

   (c) Tungsten, magnesia, gold

   (d) Tungsten, gold, magnesia

8. A solid is subjected to increase in temperature by 100°C, if volumetric strain is 30×10^{-6}, what is the coefficient of linear thermal expansion α?

   (a) $1 \times 10^{-6}/°C$ (c) $100 \times 10^{-4}/°C$

   (b) $10 \times 10^{-6}/°C$ (d) None of these

9. What is the linear coefficient of thermal expansion for superinvar?

   (a) $0.45 \times 10^{-6}/°C$ (c) $0.72 \times 10^{-6}/°C$

   (b) $0.60 \times 10^{-6}/°C$ (d) None of these

10. A copper strip of 6×2 mm² is perfectly joined with aluminium strip of 6×1 mm². If due to temperature change stress in copper strip is +50 N/mm², what is the stress in the aluminium strip?

   (a) +100 N/mm²   (c) −50 N/mm²

   (b) +50 N/mm²   (d) −100 N/mm²

Answers

1. (b)   2. (b)   3. (c)   4. (c)   5. (b)   6. (c)   7. (b)   8. (b)   9. (c)   10. (d)

REVIEW QUESTIONS

1. What is absolute fundamental temperature scale? What are freezing point and boiling point of pure water in absolute scale?

2. What do you mean by melting point of a solid? What is the relationship between melting point temperature and linear coefficient of thermal expansion?

3. Differentiate between heat capacity and specific heat.

4. Explain the graph among heat capacity, C_V and absolute temperature. What is Debye's temperature?

5. Explain how thermal shock is developed during rapid cooling or rapid heating? Why rapid cooling is more dangerous than rapid heating? Discuss the expression for TSR.

6. What do you understand by thermal conductivity? Explain the relation between thermal conductivity and electrical conductivity.

7. What is the difference between isotropic expansion and anisotropic expansion? Name (a) a metal with minimum expansion, (b) ceramic with minimum expansion and (c) polymer with maximum expansion coefficient.

8. Explain the different causes of thermal stresses developed in a material subjected to temperature variation.

9. Derive expression for thermal stresses in a composite bar of two materials subjected to temperature change.

10. What are superalloys? Where are they used? Name three superalloys.

11. What are cryogenic temperatures? What are the effects of cryogenic temperatures on the mechanical behaviour of a material?

PRACTICE PROBLEMS

1. A 150 g piece of nickel is heated, so that its temperature is increased by 250°C. If specific heat of nickel is 0.106 cal/g.K, how much heat must be supplied to nickel piece?

Ans. [3975 cal]

2. A slab of cork $100 \times 100 \times 1.2$ mm^3 thick is used as thermal insulator. Calculate the heat flow through the slab per day if the temperature difference between the opposite faces is 125°C. Thermal conductivity of cork is 0.0001 cal/cm.s.

Ans. [900 kcal/day]

3. Determine the thermal shock resistance of an aluminium component with $\alpha = 23 \times 10^{-6}/°C$, $K = 248$ W/mK, $\sigma_{ut} = 230 \times 10^6$ N/m^2, $E_t = 66 \times 10^9$ N/m^2.

Ans. [37.58×10^3 W/m]

4. Two bars, one of invar (Fe 36, Ni 64) and other of copper are heated by 150°C each so that their lengths are increased to 1000 mm. What are the initial lengths of invar and copper bars, respectively at room temperature of 25°C? What will be the difference in their lengths at a temperature of 200°C?

Given $\alpha_{invar} = 1.54 \times 10^{-6}/°C$, $\alpha_{Cu} = 16.6 \times 10^{-6}/°C$

Ans. [$L_{invar} = 999.769$ mm, $L_{Cu} = 997.516$ mm, $\Delta L = 0.3765$ mm]

5. A brass rod is held between two rigid ends. The rod is stress-free at 25°C, and its temperature is increased by 65°C. What is the magnitude and nature of the stress developed in the brass bar? Given $E = 100$ kN/mm^2, $\alpha = 20 \times 10^{-6}/°C$

Ans. [130 N/mm^2, compressive]

6. A nickel bar of diameter 10 mm and length 100 mm is held between two rigid supports. The bar is stress-free at 25°C. What is the change in diameter of bar if its temperature is raised to 150°C.

Given α for nickel $= 13.2 \times 10^{-6}/°C$, Poisson's ratio of nickel $= 0.31$

Ans. [0.00307 mm]

7. A composite bar of steel and aluminium is made by joining perfectly a steel flat of 10×1 mm^2, 100 mm long with aluminium flat 20×1 mm^2, 100 mm long. At 20°C, there is no stress in any strip. Now the temperature is raised to 100°C. What are the stresses developed in aluminium and steel strips?

Given $E_{steel} = 3$, $E_{aluminium} = 210$ kN/mm^2

$\alpha_s = 12 \times 10^{-6}/°C$, $\alpha_{Al} = 23.6 \times 10^{-6}/°C$

Ans. [$\sigma_{aT} = -38.98$ N/mm^2, $\sigma_{ST} = +77.95$ N/mm^2]

8. A copper wire is stretched with a stress of 80 MPa at 25°C. If the length is held constant, to what temperature must the wire be heated to reduce the stress to 40 MPa?

$$\alpha_{copper} = 17 \times 10^{-6}/°C$$

Ans. [46.4°C]

9. Rail road tracks made of 1025 steel are to be laid at average temperature of 15°C. If a joint space of 5 mm is allowed between standard 11.9 m long rails, what is the maximum possible temperature that can be tolerated without the introduction of thermal stress?

$$\alpha = 12 \times 10^{-6}/°C$$

Ans. [50°C]

17

Electrical Conductivity and Insulating Properties

17.1 INTRODUCTION

The property of 'electric conduction' is most important because by virtue of this property a material can transmit electric current under the applied electric field. There is a large variation of electric conduction from superconductors to semiconductors and conductors. The study of electric current is related with electron configuration, number of free electrons, electron bond energy and electron states. A valence bond is separated from an empty conduction band by a band gap. The energy of band gap is important to decide whether it is an insulator or a semiconductor. In the case of semiconductor or conductor, the electrons are excited and the excitation energy is greater than the band gap energy. Total conductivity of a material is the sum of the electronic and ionic conductivities.

The electrons or charged ions are accelerated by an applied electric field, but there is frictional force on these charged particles due to the scattering of free electrons by thermal energy, impurity atoms and crystal imperfections or dislocations depending upon deformation.

Resistivity of a conductor changes with temperature and its temperature coefficient of resistivity is equally important and resistor can be used as an instrument to measure temperature.

Commercial alloys with high and low conductivity find different industrial applications. Insulation of antennas and electrical apparatus is as important as the conduction of a material. Different materials available for insulation are also discussed in this chapter.

17.2 OHM'S LAW

The most important electrical property of a solid material is the ease with which the material can transmit electric current, which is known as 'electric conduction or conductivity'. Ohm's law provides a relationship between the current transmitted and the voltage applied between the two points on a material separated by a distance L.

Applied voltage,

$$V = I \times R$$

$$= \text{current} \times \text{resistance}$$

or electrical current, $\quad\quad I = V/R$

Figure 17.1 shows the application of voltage V and current measured I.

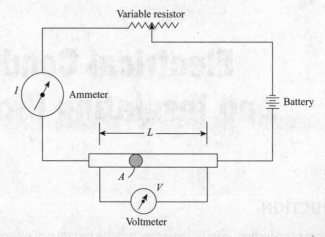

Figure 17.1 *Voltage Applied on Solid*

Units of voltage, current and resistance are volt (V), ampere (A) and ohm (Ω).

Resistance, $\quad\quad\quad\quad\quad\quad\quad\quad R \propto L,$

where L is the separation distance.

$$\propto \frac{1}{A},$$

where A is the area of cross section of the solid bar.

or

$$R = \rho \frac{L}{A},$$

where ρ is known as resistivity of solid bar.

Resistivity,

$$\rho = \frac{RA}{L} = \frac{\text{ohm.m}^2}{\text{m}} = \text{ohm.m}$$

Unit of resistivity is ohm.m (Ωm).

Current density,

$$J = \frac{I}{A} = \text{intensity of current per unit area of cross section}$$

Electric field intensity,

$$\varsigma = \frac{V}{L}, \text{ i.e. volts per unit length.}$$

Electrical resistivities for some materials are given in Table 17.1.

Table 17.1 *Electrical Resistivity, $\rho\,(\Omega m)$*

Material	ρ at Room Temperature (Ωm)	Material	ρ at Room Temperature (Ωm)
Metals		Constantan 55% Cu, 45% Ni	49×10^{-6}
Silver	10^{9}	Nichrome 80% Ni, 20% Sr	108×10^{-6}
Gold	10^{-9}	**Insulators**	
Copper	10^{9}	Alumina	10^{11}
Aluminium	10^{8}	Ramand	10^{12}
Nickel	10^{7}	Glass	10^{5}
Antimony	10^{-5}	PVC	10^{15}
Bismuth	10^{4}	Bakelite	10^{9}
Alloys		**Semiconductors**	
Copper annealed	1.67×10^{-6}	Germanium (pure)	10^{-1}
Aluminium annealed	2.65×10^{-6}	Doped germanium	10^{-3}
Iron annealed	9.71×10^{-6}	Pure silicon	10^{-2} to 10^{-3}

17.2.1 Electrical Conductivity

Electrical conductivity is the reciprocal of resistivity, i.e. more resistivity amounts to less conductivity. Electrical conductivity,

$$\sigma = \frac{1}{\rho} = \frac{1}{\text{resistivity}}, \text{ which is measured in } (\Omega m)^{-1}.$$

Conductivity is one of the electrical properties of the material, which varies most widely from 10^{7} to $10^{-20}\ (\Omega m)^{-1}$. For example, conductivities of some of the materials are as follows:

$$10^{7}\ (\Omega m)^{-1} \text{ for metals}$$
$$10^{-20}\ (\Omega m)^{-1} \text{ for good electrical insulators}$$
$$10^{-6} \text{ to } 10^{4}\ (\Omega m)^{-1} \text{ for semiconductors}$$

Example 17.1 A copper wire of commercial purity is to conduct 12 A of current with a maximum voltage drop of 0.5 V/m. What is the minimum diameter of the wire?

Conductivity of commercially pure copper is $5.84 \times 10^{7}\ \Omega m^{-1}$

Solution:

$$\text{Voltage drop} = 0.5\ \text{V/m} = IR$$
$$I = \text{current} = 12\ \text{A}$$

Resistance,

$$R = \frac{0.5}{12} = 0.041667\ \Omega/\text{m}$$
$$= \frac{\rho L}{A} = \frac{L}{\sigma A}$$

So, area of cross section,

$$A = \frac{0.041667 \times 1\ \text{m}}{\sigma}$$

As length, $L = 1$ m

$$\sigma = 5.84 \times 10^7 \ \Omega m^{-1}$$

Area of cross section,

$$A = \frac{0.041667}{5.84 \times 10^7} = 7.1347 \times 10^{-7} \ m^2$$

$$= \frac{\pi}{4} d^2$$

Wire diameter,

$$d^2 = 7.1347 \times \frac{4}{\pi} \times 10^{-7}$$

$$= 0.9084 \times 10^{-6}$$

$$d = 0.95 \times 10^{-3}$$

For this application, copper wire of commercial purity must have a diameter of 0.95 mm or more.

17.3 COMMONLY USED CONDUCTING MATERIALS

Following are the commonly used conducting materials:

1. *Copper:* This is one of the best conductors of electricity. Its conductivity is highly sensitive to impurities. It is used in wires, cables, windings of generators and transformers, overhead conductors and bus bars. Hard- and cold-drawn copper is used in line conductors having high tensile strength.
2. *Aluminium:* It is next to copper in the usage of electrical conductors. It is essentially used in overhead transmission lines, domestic wiring, flexibility tires, bus bars and rotor bars of squirrel cage induction motors. However, due to the insulating properties of aluminium oxide formed on the surface of aluminium, it is difficult to solder aluminium wires.
3. *Steels:* low-, medium- and high-carbon steels are also used as conducting materials.
4. Low-resistivity copper alloys like brass and bronze are used in industrial applications. Bronze has lower conductivity than copper, but more resistant to corrosion.

17.4 HIGH-RESISTIVITY MATERIALS

A few examples of high-resistivity materials are as follows:

1. *Tungsten:* The principal uses of tungsten are as filaments in incandescent lamps and wires in electrical furnaces. It is used in the manufacture of spark plugs, electrical contact points and as a target in X-ray tubes.
2. *Carbon:* Carbon products are used in current-carrying elements. It has a very high value of resistivity and has a negative temperature coefficient of resistance. Electrical resistance of carbon contact decreases as the pressure increases. Carbon is used in brushes for electric machines and apparatus. Carbon finds applications in carbon resistors, both film type and solid type. Carbon pile resistors are made up of a number of carbon plates under pressure.
3. *Mercury:* It is used in arc rectifiers, gas-filled tubes, a liquid contact material, electric switches and so on.
4. *Constantan:* This is extensively used in thermocouples, in making electric resistance elements for items like rheostat and starters for electric motors.
5. *Nichrome:* This is used in making heating elements of electric irons, ovens, room heaters and electric furnaces.

6. *Platinum:* It is used for contact points in electrical apparatus and in instruments used for measuring high temperatures.

7. *Manganin:* It is an alloy of 86 per cent copper, 12 per cent manganese and 2 per cent nickel. Its coefficient of resistance is large at higher temperatures, and is used in wire-wound precision shunts and resistances, resistance boxes and coils.

17.5 ELECTRON CONFIGURATION

For each individual atom, there exist discrete energy levels that may be occupied by electrons. These electrons are arranged in shells and subshells. Shells are designated by K, L, M and N and subshells are designated as s, p, d and f. For each subshell there exist one, three, five and seven states, i.e. for s, p, d and f, respectively. Figure 17.2 shows Sommerfeld atomic model showing various suborbits in N-shell.

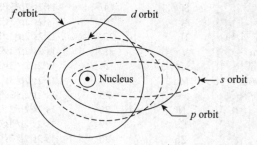

Figure 17.2 *Sommerfeld Atomic Model Suborbits in N-shell*

The electrons in most atoms fill just the states having the lowest energy; two electrons of opposite spin per state, i.e. 2 electrons for s state, 6 electrons for p state, 10 electrons for d state and 14 electrons for f state as per Pauli exclusion prinic
ple.

Pauli exclusion principle states that 'no two' electrons in an atom can have the same quantum state. In other words, not more than one electron can occupy each quantum state.

Table 17.2 gives the available electron states in electron shells and subshells. Electronic configurations for some elements are given in Table 17.3.

Table 17.2 *Available Electron States*

Principal Quantum Number (n)	Shell Designation	Subshells	Number of States	Number of Electrons Per Subshell	Per Shell
1	K (1)	s	1	2	2
2	L (2)	s	1	2	8
		p	3	6	
3	M (3)	s	1	2	18
		p	3	6	
		d	5	10	
4	N (4)	s	1	2	32
		p	3	6	
		d	5	10	
		f	7	14	

Table 17.3 *Electronic Configurations*

Element	Symbol	Atomic Number	Configuration
Hydrogen	H	1	$1s^1$
Helium	He	2	$1s^2$
Carbon	C	6	$1s^2 2s^2 2p^2$
Nitrogen	N	7	$1s^2 2s^2 2p^3$
Oxygen	O	8	$1s^2 2s^2 2p^4$
Neon	Ne	10	$1s^2 2s^2 2p^6$
Sodium	Na	11	$1s^2 2s^2 2p^6 3s^1$
Magnesium	Mg	12	$1s^2 2s^2 2p^6 3s^2$
Aluminium	Al	13	$1s^2 2s^2 2p^6 3s^2 3p^1$
Silicon	Si	14	$1s^2 2s^2 2p^6 3s^2 3p^2$
Argon	Ar	18	$1s^2 2s^2 2p^6 3s^2 3p^6$
Titanium	Ti	22	$1s^2 2s^2 2p^6 3s^2 3p^6 3d^2 4s^2$
Vanadium	V	23	$1s^2 2s^2 2p^6 3s^2 3p^6 3d^3 4s^2$
Chromium	Cr	24	$1s^2 2s^2 2p^6 3s^2 3p^6 3d^5 4s^1$
Manganese	Mn	25	$1s^2 2s^2 2p^6 3s^2 3p^6 3d^5 4s^2$
Iron	Fe	26	$1s^2 2s^2 2p^6 3s^2 3p^6 3d^6 4s^2$
Nickel	Ni	28	$1s^2 2s^2 2p^6 3s^2 3p^6 3d^8 4s^2$
Copper	Cu	29	$1s^2 2s^2 2p^6 3s^2 3p^6 3d^{10} 4s^1$
Zinc	Zn	30	$1s^2 2s^2 2p^6 3s^2 3p^6 3d^{10} 4s^2$
Germanium	Ge	32	$1s^2 2s^2 2p^6 3s^2 3p^6 3d^{10} 4s^2 4p^2$

For example,

1. Nitrogen 7 electrons,
   two electrons in *s*-orbit of 1 shell
   two electrons in *s*-orbit of 2 shell
   three electrons in *p*-orbit of 2 shell

Note that superscripts denote the number of electrons.

2. Argon 18 electrons,
   two electrons in *s*-orbit of 1 shell
   two electrons in *s*-orbit of 2 shell
   six electrons in *p*-orbit of 2 shell
   two electrons in *s*-orbit of 3 shell
   six electrons in *p*-orbit of 3 shell

3. Copper 29 electrons,
   two electrons in *s*-orbit of 1 shell
   two electrons in *s*-orbit of 2 shell
   six electrons in *p*-orbit of 2 shell
   two electrons in *s*-orbit of 3 shell
   six electrons in *p*-orbit of 3 shell
   ten electrons in *d*-orbit of 3 shell
   one electron in *s*-orbit of 4 shell

17.6 ELECTRON ENERGY BAND

As long as the atoms are separated at large distances, each atom behaves independently as if isolated from the adjacent atoms, but if the atoms come closer to each other, electrons of one atom are disturbed by the presence of electrons and nuclei of the adjacent atoms. Influence of close proximity is such that each distinct atomic state may split into a series of closely spaced electron states in the solid, forming an electron energy band. Extent of splitting of atomic state depends upon interatomic separation and begins with the outermost electron shell as these are the first to be disturbed when atoms coalesce.

Within each band, the energy states are discrete, though the difference between the adjacent states is very small. At the equilibrium spacing, band formation may not occur for electron subshell very close to the nucleus.

Moreover, gaps may exist between the adjacent bands, and normally the energies lying within these band gaps are not available for electron occupancy (Figure 17.3).

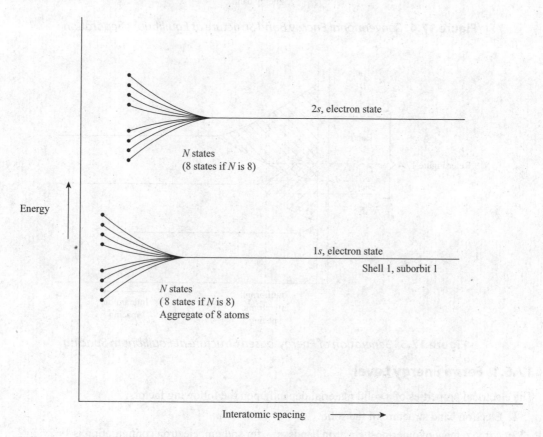

Figure 17.3 *Graph Between Electron Energy and Interatomic Spacing*

Figure 17.4 shows electron energy versus interatomic separation for an aggregate of N atoms; if $N = 8$, electron band consists of 8 states.

Figure 17.4 shows conventional energy band structure at equilibrium separation and Figure 17.5 shows the generation of energy band structure at equilibrium spacing for N aggregate of atoms. In other words, N states at s-band, $3N$ states at p-band and $5N$ states at d-band.

With regard to occupancy of electrons, each energy state may accommodate two electrons (oppositely directed spins). Moreover, there may be empty bands and bands that are only partially filled.

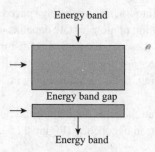

Figure 17.4 *Conventional Energy Band Structure at Equilibrium Separation*

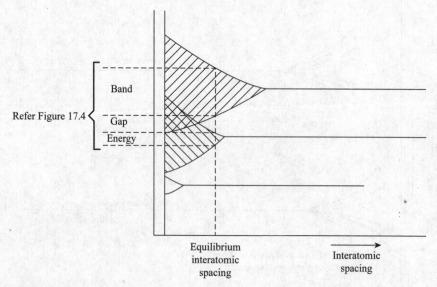

Figure 17.5 *Generation of Energy-based Structure at Equilibrium Spacing*

17.6.1 Fermi Energy Level

The electrical properties of a solid material depend upon the following factors:

1. Electron band structure of the solid.
2. Arrangement of outermost electron bands, e.g. for sodium, electron configuration is $1s^2 2s^2 2p^6 3s^1$, and there is only one electron in the outermost electron band $3s$.
3. The manner in which outermost electron bands are filled with electrons.

The energy corresponding to highest filled state at 0 K is called Fermi energy, E_f.

17.7 DIFFERENT TYPES OF BAND STRUCTURES

There are four types of band structures that are possible at 0 K, which are given as follows:

1. One outermost band is partially filled with electrons, which are found in metals. For example, an isolated atom of copper has one $4s$ electron in outermost band, but in aggregate of N atoms of

copper, i.e. a solid copper, 4s band is capable of accommodating 2N electrons. So, only half the available electron portions are filled within 4s band [Figure 17.6(a)].

2. There is an overlap of an empty band and a filled band (found in metals). Each isolated atom of magnesium has two electrons in 3s orbit. But when solid is formed, the 3s and 4p bands overlap. The Fermi energy is taken as that energy, below which N states (for N atoms) are filled, two electrons per state [Figure 17.6(b)].

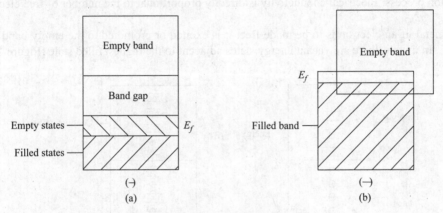

Figure 17.6 *Band Structure*

3. A valency band completely filled with electrons is separated from an empty conduction band, by an energy band gap. Band gap is large for insulators [Figure 17.7(a)]. Gap > 2 electron volt (eV).

4. A filled valency band is separated from an empty conduction band by an energy band gap. Band gap is smaller for semiconductors [Figure 17.7(b)]. Gap < 2 eV.

The Fermi energy, E_f for these two band structures lies near the centre of the band gap, within the band gap.

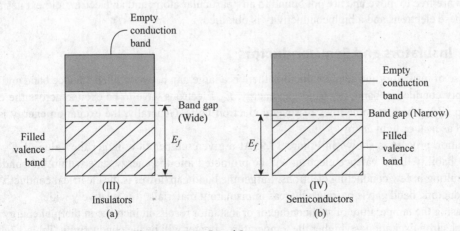

Figure 17.7 *Band Structure*

17.8 BAND AND ATOMIC BONDING MODEL FOR CONDUCTION

Only those electrons (in valence band) with energy levels greater than Fermi energy, E_f can be acted upon by an electric field and can be accelerated. These electrons participate in conduction process and are called free electrons. Another electronic entity is a hole, found in insulators and semiconductors. *Holes have energy levels smaller than Fermi energy, E_f* and holes and free electrons participate in conduction process. Electrical conductivity is directly proportional to the number of free electrons and holes.

In a metal, if an electron is to be made free, it is excited or promoted to the empty band available above E_f. In metals, there are vacant energy states adjacent to the highest filled state [Figure 17.8(a)].

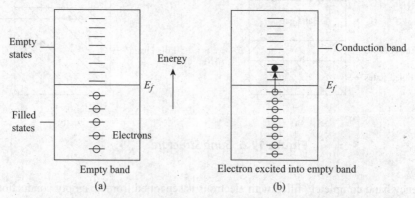

Figure 17.8 *(a) Empty band (b) Electron excited into empty band*

The energy is produced by an electrical field and a large number of electrons are excited into the conduction band, as shown in Figure 17.8(b). A very little energy is needed to promote electrons into the low-lying empty states. Energy provided by an electric field is sufficient to promote large number of electrons into the conductivity states. In metals, valence electrons form electron gas. These valence electrons are free to move and are not bound to any particular atom, and an electric field excites a fraction of these electrons and a high conductivity is obtained.

17.8.1 Insulators and Semiconductors

In the case of insulators and semiconductors, there is a large gap between filled valence band and available empty conduction band, i.e. band gap energy, E_g. Electrons have to be excited across the energy band gap (E_g), which is sometimes of several electron volts. Generally, the excitation energy is non-electrical as heat or light energy.

Excitation process is shown in Figure 17.9. At a given temperature, larger the value of E_g, lower is the probability that a valence electron will be promoted into the energy state within the conduction band, resulting in few conducting electrons. Larger the band gap, lower is the electrical conductivity. In semiconductors, band gap is narrow, whereas in insulating materials, it is relatively wide.

Increasing the temperature of semiconductor or insulator results in increase in thermal energy available for electron excitation; so higher the temperature, greater will be the conductivity. Table 17.4 gives the number of free electrons for some metals.

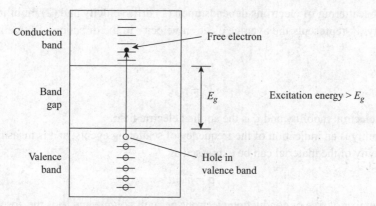

Figure 17.9 *Excitation Process*

Table 17.4 *Free Electrons*

Metal	Free Electron per m³	Metal	Free Electron per m³
Silver	6.10×10^{28}	Copper	6.30×10^{28}
Gold	5.65×10^{28}	Zinc	3.0×10^{28}
Aluminium	1.67×10^{29}	Silicon	2.0×10^{29}

17.9 ELECTRON MOBILITY

Under the influence of an applied electric field ζ, electrons of a solid get accelerated in a direction opposite to the direction of the electric field, because electrons are negatively charged. There is no interaction between the accelerated electrons and the atoms in a perfect lattice. Since all the electrons get accelerated as long as the electric field is applied, current should continuously increase with time, but the current reaches a constant value, the moment electric field is applied. This shows that the electrons are subjected to some type of frictional forces, which cause deceleration of electrons. These frictional forces are a result of scattering of electrons due to impurities in solids, i.e. imperfections in crystal lattice and thermal vibrations of atoms. Imperfections such as vacancies, impurity atoms and dislocations are present in the crystal structure and depend on the temperature and plastic deformation of solid.

Each scattering event causes an electron to lose kinetic energy and change in the direction of motion of electrons shown in Figure 17.10. However, there is some net electron motion in the direction opposite to the direction of applied field ζ, and this flow of charge is the electric current.

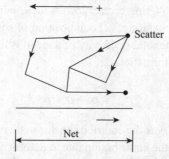

Figure 17.10 *Motion of Electrons*

The extent of scattering of electrons depends upon (1) drift velocity and (2) mobility of electrons. The drift velocity, V_d represents the average electron velocity in the direction of force imposed by the applied velocity.

Drift velocity,

$$V_d = \mu_e \zeta$$

where, μ_e is the electron mobility and ζ is the applied electric field.

Electron mobility is an indication of the frequency of scattering events, and is measured in m^2/V-S.

The conductivity of the material can be expressed as

$$\sigma = n|e|\mu_e$$

where n is the number of free or conducting electrons per unit volume and $|e|$ is the absolute magnitude of electric charge on an electron.

$$= 1.6 \times 10^{-19} \text{ C}$$

μ_e = electron mobility.

So, electrical conductivity is proportional to both number of free electrons and electron mobility. Table 17.5 gives electrical conductivity σ of most common metals at room temperature.

Table 17.5 *Electrical Conductivity*

Metal	σ $(\Omega m)^{-1}$	Metal	σ $(\Omega m)^{-1}$
Aluminium	3.8×10^7	Gold	4.3×10^7
Iron	1.0×10^7	Brass (70/30)	1.6×10^7
Silver	6.8×10^7	Plain carbon steel	0.6×10^7
Copper	6.0×10^7	Stainless steel	0.2×10^7

17.10 ELECTRICAL RESISTIVITY OF METALS

Most of the metals are very good conductors of electricity, because of the presence of large number of free electrons, which have been excited into empty conduction band, from the Fermi energy level. As the crystalline defects and impurities in solids serve as scattering centres for conducting electrons in metals, increase in the number of scattering centres lowers the conductivity. The concentration of these imperfections depends upon (1) temperature, (2) composition of solid and (3) degree of cold working or plastic deformation. Therefore, the total resistivity of a metal is the sum of resistivity due to thermal vibrations, impurities and plastic deformations.

Total resistivity,

$$\rho_{\text{total}} = \rho_T + \rho_i + \rho_d$$

known as Matthiessen's rule, where ρ_T is the contribution due to thermal resistivity, ρ_i is the contribution due to impurity resistivity and ρ_d is the contribution due to deformation resistivity.

17.10.1 Influence of Temperature

General relationship between resistivity and temperature is

$$\rho_T = \rho_0 + aT$$
$$\rho_0 = \text{constant}$$
$$a = \text{constant for each particular metal}$$

The thermal resistivity, ρ_T depends on the increase in thermal vibrations with temperature and lattice irregularities as vacancies.

17.10.2 Influence of Impurities

Impurity resistivity depends on the impurity concentration c_i (in terms of atom fractions)

$$\rho_i = Ac_i(1 - c_i)$$

where A is a composition-independent constant and a function of impurity and host metals.

For example, nickel atoms in copper act as scattering centres, and increasing the concentration of nickel in copper results in an enhancement of resistivity.

For a two-phase alloy, α and β phases, rule of mixture can be applied for resistivity.

$$\rho_L = \rho_\alpha V_\alpha + \rho_\beta V_\beta,$$

where V_α and V_β are volume fractions of α and β phases and ρ_α and ρ_β are resistivities of α and β phases, respectively.

17.10.3 Influence of Plastic Deformation

Plastic deformation increases the electrical resistivity because of increased number of electron-scattering dislocations due to deformation. Although the resistivity is high in cold-worked metals, it can be reduced by annealing. Table 17.6 gives resistivity and temperature coefficient of resistivity for some materials.

Table 17.6 *Resistivity and Temperature Coefficient of Resistivity*

Material	ρ (Ωm)	a (1/K)
Gold	22×10^{-9}	0.0035
Silver	15×10^{-9}	0.0040
Copper	17×10^{-9}	0.0044
Aluminium	28×10^{-9}	0.0042
Nichrome	1.1×10^{-9}	0.0001

Example 17.2 What is the electrical resistivity of pure copper at 150°C. The temperature resistivity coefficient of copper is 0.00385 C^{-1}.

Solution:

From Table 17.5, electrical conductivity of copper at room temperature (20°C) is

$$\sigma = 6 \times 10^7 \ (\Omega m)^{-1}$$
$$\rho = \frac{1}{s} = 1.66 \times 10^{-8} \ \Omega m$$

$$\rho_t = 1.66 \times 10^{-8} \, \Omega m \, (1 + a\Delta T)$$

$$\Delta T = 150 - 20 = 130°C$$

$$a = 0.00385 \, C^{-1}$$

$$\rho_t = 1.66 \times 10^{-8} \, \Omega m \, (1 + 0.00385 + 130)$$

$$= 2.49 \times 10^{-8} \, (\Omega m)$$

17.11 ELECTRONIC AND IONIC CONDUCTION

Forces due to externally applied electric field act on electrically charged particles and as these particles move, electric current is produced. Positively charged particles are accelerated in the field direction and negatively charged particles are accelerated in the opposite direction. Current arising from the flow of electrons is known as 'electronic conduction'. In ionic materials, net motion of charged ions produce an electric current known as 'ionic conduction'. Both anions and cations in ionic material possess an electric charge and consequently they are capable of migration or diffusion when an electric field is applied. Total conductivity of an ionic material σ_{total} is equal to the sum of both electronic and ionic contributions.

$$\sigma_{total} = \sigma_{electronic} + \sigma_{ionic}$$

A mobility μ_i is associated with each ionic species

$$\mu_i = \frac{n_i e D_i}{kT}$$

where n_i is the valence of a particular ion, D_i is the diffusion coefficient of a particular ion, e is the absolute magnitude of electrical charge on ion, k is the Boltzmann's constant and T is the absolute temperature.

Inspite of the contribution from electronic conductivity, most ionic materials remain insulative. Table 17.7 shows electrical conductivities for some non-metals at room temperature.

Table 17.7 *Electrical Conductivity on Non-metals*

Material	Electrical Conductivity $(\Omega m)^{-1}$
Graphite	3×10^4 to 2×10^5
Ceramics	
Porcelain	10^{-10} to 10^{-12}
Borosilicate glass	$\sim 10^{-13}$
Aluminium oxide	$< 10^{-13}$
Fused silica	$< 10^{-8}$
Polymers	
Phenol formaldehyde	10^{-9} to 10^{-10}
Nylon 6.6	10^{-12} to 10^{-13}
Polystyrene	$< 10^{-14}$
Polyethylene	10^{-15} to 10^{-17}
PTFE	$< 10^{-17}$

17.12 COMMERCIAL ALLOYS

The best material for electrical conduction is silver, but it is very expensive and hence its use is restricted. Electrical and other properties (e.g. ductility and strength) of copper make it the most widely used conductor. Oxygen-free high-conductivity (OFHC) copper, having extremely low oxygen and other impurities is produced for many electrical applications. Electrical conductivity of aluminium is only half the conductivity of copper, yet it is frequently employed in aircraft industry, where weight is the basic consideration. Aluminium is more corrosion resistant than copper. Sometimes, the strength of a conductor is more important than its conductivity and the strength may be enhanced by a second phase that does not have much adverse effect on conductivity. Copper–beryllium alloys are precipitation hardened.

For some applications as furnace, high-resistivity materials are desirable. Energy loss of electrons due to scattering is dissipated as heat energy. Nichrome, a nickel–chrome alloy is commonly used in heating elements.

17.13 INSULATION

An object intended to support or separate electrical conductors without passing current through it is called an 'insulator'. Electrical insulation in a material or object contains no free electrons to permit the flow of electric current. When a voltage is applied across an insulator, no charge or electric current flows.

Many materials like silicon dioxide and Teflon are very good insulators. Many other materials like rubber-like polymers and plastics are good to insulate electrical wiring and cables. These materials serve as safe practical insulators for low to moderate voltages (hundreds to thousands of volts).

As per electron band theory, a charge will flow whenever there are states available into which the electrons can be excited. But in insulators no such states are available.

Most insulators are characterized by having a large band gap between valence band (containing highest energy electrons in full) and the next band above it. There is always voltage (called the breakdown voltage), which will give enough energy to electrons to be excited into this band. Once this breakdown voltage is exceeded, the material ceases to act as an insulator and charge will begin to pass through it. However, this electric break-down causes physical and chemical changes in the insulator and the insulating properties of the material are permanently degraded.

Materials that lack electron conduction must also lack other mobile charges as well. For example, a liquid or gas containing ions. These ions can be made to flow as an electric current and the material becomes a conductor. Electrolytes and plasma contain ions and act as conductors, whether or not electron flow is involved.

17.14 HIGH-VOLTAGE INSULATORS

Insulators for high-voltage transmission are made from glass, porcelain or composite polymer materials. Porcelain insulators are made from clay, quartz or alumina and feldspar, and are covered with smooth glaze to shed dirt and dust. Insulators made from porcelain rich in alumina are used where high mechanical strength is desired. Glass insulators were used to suspend electric power lines, but these are now rarely used.

Recently, insulators made from polymer composite materials have been developed, which consist of a central rod made of fibre-reinforced plastic and outer weathershed made of silicone rubber (SR) or ethylene-propylene-diene monomer (EPDM). Composite insulators are less costly and lighter in weight, having excellent hydrophobic capacity. These are ideal in polluted areas. However, their long-term service life is less than that of glass and porcelain.

17.15 INSULATION OF ANTENNAS

Antenna of a broadcasting radio station requires an insulating mounting. So insulators of steatite are used. They have to withstand not only the voltage of the mast radiator to ground, which can reach up to 400 kV, but also the weight of the mast construction and dynamic forces. Arcing horns and lightning arrestors are necessary as lightning strikes in the mast are common.

At guyed mast radiators, insulators in the guy (if they are not grounded or a coil at the anchor base) are used to prevent undesired electrical resonances. The insulators also have to be equipped with an overvoltage protection equipment.

17.16 INSULATION OF ELECTRICAL APPARATUS

Air is the most important insulation material. A wide variety of solid, liquid and gaseous insulators are used in electrical apparatus. Following are some examples:

1. In small transformers, generators and electric motors, insulation on the wire coils consist of up to four thin layers of polymer varnish film.
2. Film-insulated magnet wire permits a manufacturer to obtain the maximum number of turns within the available space.
3. Windings that are thicker conductors are often wrapped with supplemental fibreglass insulating tape.
4. Windings may also be impregnated with insulating varnishes to prevent electrical corona and reduce magnetically induced wire vibrations.
5. Large power transformer windings are mostly insulated with paper, wood, varnish and mineral oil.
6. Bus bars and circuit breakers in switch gear may be insulated with glass-reinforced plastic insulation.
7. In old apparatus, boards made of compressed asbestos may be found, but handling or repairs of asbestos material release dangerous fibres into the air.
8. Live-front switch boards were made of slate in marble in old apparatus.
9. Electrical wires may be insulated with polyethylene, cross-linked polyethylene, PVC, rubber-like polymers, oil-impregnated paper, Teflon, silicone or ETFE (modified ethylenetetrafluoroethylene).
10. Large power cables may use compressed inorganic powder depending upon application.
11. Flexible PVCs are used to insulate the circuit and prevent human contact with a live wire.

17.17 CLASS I AND CLASS II INSULATION

Requirement of a class I insulator is that the metal body of apparatus is solidly connected through a 'grounding wire', which is earthed at the main service panel, but only basic insulation of the conductors is needed. This equipment is easily identified by a round pin for the grounding connections.

Class II insulation stands for double insulation, used in appliances as electric shaver, hair dryers and portable power tools. Double insulation requires that the device have basic and supplementary insulation, each of which is sufficient to prevent electric shock. All internal electrically energized components are fully enclosed within the insulated packaging, which prevents any contact with live parts. They can be recognized because their leads have two pins or three-pin plugs, the third pin (earth) is made of plastic rather than metal. Double insulated appliances are marked by double square, one inside the other as ▣.

Various insulating materials used in electrical apparatus are shown in Table 17.8.

Table 17.8 *Various Insulating Materials*

Class of Insulator	Temperature Range of Use	Applications	Insulators
Class Y	Up to 90°C	Seldom used in machines	Paper, cotton silk and wool
Class A	Up to 105°C	Widely used in electrical machines	Enamelled wire, varnished paper and laminated board
Class E	Up to 120°C	Not widely used due to difficultmanufacturing process	Enamelled wire insulations on a base of polyvinyl formal cotton and paper laminates
Class B	Up to 130°C	Widely used in electrical machines	Organic materials or mica
Class F	Up to 155°C	Not widely used due to difficultmanufacturing process	Epoxy and polyurethane
Class H	Up to 180°C	Used in traction motors and dry transformers	Built-up mica, fibre glass and asbestos
Class C	More than 180°C	Used in heavy electrical machines	Ceramics, quartz, asbestos, glass and mica

17.18 PROPERTIES OF INSULATING MATERIALS

The properties of insulating materials are given as follows:

1. Paper is an important insulating material. These are commercially available as cable paper, capacitor paper and press board.

2. *Jute, cotton, hemp and silk:* These are textiles used for insulation. Cloth materials are impregnated with oils and varnishes. Jute is cheaper than cotton. Silk materials are extra thin and comparatively stronger but costlier.

3. Wool has high tensile strength and elasticity, making it especially desirable for industrial use because of its lightness, ability to absorb moisture and to provide insulation.

4. *Rayon, Nylon and Capron:* These are synthetic polyamide fibres. Rayon is a modified wood cellulose transformed into long fibres. These are used only after impregnation.

5. *Asbestos:* This is a fibrous form of several minerals and hydrous silicates of magnesium. Asbestos fibres can be moulded or woven into various fabrics. Since it is non-flammable and a good heat insulator, it was formerly widely used to make fireproof products such as safety clothing

for fire fighters and insulation products such as hot-water piping. It can withstand a temperature of 400°C. There are two classes of asbestos: (1) amphiboles and (2) serpentines. Chrystolite belongs to serpentine class, which constitutes about 95 per cent of world supply of asbestos. It possesses high dielectric loss, low dielectric strength and is never used in high-voltage applications (above 33 kV).

6. Plastics are organic polymeric materials, which can be formed into desired shapes, through extrusions, moulding or spinning. These are characterized by high strength to density ratios, excellent thermal and electrical insulation properties, and good resistance to acids, alkalis and solvents. Linear and branched polymers are thermoplastic (soften when heated), whereas cross-linked polymers are thermosets (harden when heated).

7. Ceramics are made from earthly materials. Traditionally, clay and other minerals from earth solidify on heating. Ceramics are fired clay products including earthen ware, stone ware and porcelain. Earthen ware is low fired (900–1150°C), while stone ware and porcelains are high fired (1200–1300°C and 1200–1300°C, respectively). Traditional ceramic materials are mostly oxides, with silica, alumina, calcium oxide, iron oxide, magnesium oxide, boric oxide, soda and potash. Ceramic insulators are porcelain insulators like transformer bushing, pins, suspension insulators of transmission and distribution lines, disconnecting switches, porcelain parts used for switches, plugs, sockets, fuse holders and telephone insulators.

   Ceramics are also used in line insulators. Proper designing is required to overcome problems like effect of surface resistivity by rainfall and dirt.

8. *Rubber:* This is a natural or synthetic substance characterized by elasticity, water repellence and electrical resistance. Natural rubber is obtained from latex of rubber tree and synthetic rubbers are produced from unsaturated hydrocarbons.

   ❑ Crude rubber is insoluble in water, alkalis and weak acids, but is soluble in benzene, petroleum and chlorinated hydrocarbons and carbon disulphide. It is oxidized readily by chemical oxidizing agents and slowly to atmospheric oxygen. Simplest unit of rubber is isoprene.

   ❑ Most rubber products are vulcanized under high temperature and pressure.

   ❑ Neoprene, buna rubber and butyl rubber are examples of synthetic rubbers.

   ❑ Thiokol rubber is resistant to the action of oils and organic solvents used for lacquers, and is useful for electrical insulation because it does not deteriorate when exposed to electrical discharge and light.

9. *Wax:* It is a naturally occurring esters of fatty acids and monohydric alcohols. Wax is used with insulating oils to improve viscosity and pour point to form non-drawing cable compound, and also used with cable paper insulators.

10. *Varnish:* There are two types of varnishes: (a) spirit varnish, which is a resin dissolved in a volatile solvent that contains no drying oil and (b) asphalt varnish, which is a solution of asphalt that gives opaque, black coatings. These are used for improving the insulating properties by forming an insulating layer on the surface.

11. *Mica:* It is a group of rock-forming minerals, which form crystals in the monoclinic systems. Mica leaves are separated into very thin, elastic leaves. Micas are complex aluminium silicates. Most important micas are muscovite, phlogopite, lepidolite and biotite.

    Muscovite and phlogopite are used as insulating materials in the manufacture of electrical apparatus, particularly vacuum tubes.

12. *Asphalt:* Asphalt is a black cement-like material varying in consistency at room temperature from solid to semisolid. A small amount of asphalt is 'cracked' at temperature above 500°C to make some insulation material.

Asphalt and bitumen are used in underground cables for the protection of lead and steel armour against corrosion.

KEY POINTS TO REMEMBER

❑ The property with which a material can transmit an electric current, under an applied external voltage is known as electric conduction.

❑ Resistance,

$$R = \frac{V}{I} = \frac{\text{voltage}}{\text{current}}$$

Intensity of electric field,

$$\zeta = \frac{V}{L} = \frac{\text{voltage}}{\text{length of conductor}}$$

❑ Resistivity,

$$\rho = \frac{RA}{L} = \frac{\text{resistance} \times \text{area of cross section}}{\text{length}}$$

❑ Unit of resistivity is Ωm.

❑ Conductivity, $\sigma = 1/\rho$, unit of conductivity is $(\Omega m)^{-1}$.

❑ Copper is the best conductor of electricity, used in wires, cables, generator, transformer windings and overhead conductors.

❑ Aluminium is next to copper in electrical conductivity, which is used in overhead transmission lines, domestic wiring, flexibility tires and bus bars.

❑ Tungsten is a high-resistivity material used in filaments of incandescent lamps, spark plugs, electrical contact points and target in X-ray tubes.

❑ Mercury is also a high-resistivity material, used in arc rectifiers, gas-filled tubes and a liquid contact material.

❑ *Pauli exclusion principle:* 'No two electrons in an atom can have the same quantum state'.

❑ When the atoms come closer, electrons of one atom are influenced by electrons and nuclei of another atom; each distinct atomic state splits into a series of closely spaced electron states. Electrons in outermost shell are the first to be disturbed.

❑ Energy band structure is generated at an equilibrium spacing, producing a gap between two energy bands.

❑ The energy at the highest filled state at 0 K is called Fermi energy, E_f.

❑ A valence band completely filled with electrons is separated from an empty conduction band by an energy band gap. Gap energy, $E_g > 2$ eV in case of insulators and $E_g < 2$ eV in case of semiconductors.

Energy is provided by an electric field, and a large number of free electrons are excited into the conduction band.

In the case of insulators and semiconductors, there is a band gap between valence band and conduction band.

Increasing the temperature of semiconductor or insulator results in increase in thermal energy available for electron excitation.

❑ Free electrons are scattered by impurity atoms, imperfections and deformation of the material.

❑ Electron mobility is an indication of frequency of scattering events, μ_e and the unit is m²/V-s.

Total resistivity,

$$\rho_{total} = \rho_t = \rho_i = \rho_d \text{ contribution due to thermal resistivity}$$

$$+ \text{ impurity resistivity and deformation resistivity}$$

❑ Oxygen-free high-conductivity (OFHC) copper is produced for high-conductivity applications.

❑ In furnaces, high-resistivity materials as Nichrome are desirable.

❑ Most insulators are characterized by a large band gap between valence bend (containing highest energy electrons in full) and the next band. A breakdown voltage gives enough energy to electrons to be excited into the next band. After the application of breakdown voltage, materials of insulators are permanently degraded.

❑ Electrolytes and plasma contain ions and act as conductors.

❑ Insulators made from polymer composites are less costly and lighter in weight, having excellent hydrophobic capability, and are ideal in polluted areas.

❑ Glass insulators are used to suspend electric power lines.

❑ Insulated wire coils are used in transformers, generators and electric motors.

❑ Bus bars and circuit breakers in switch gear are insulated by glass-reinforced plastic.

❑ Flexible PVC is used to insulate the circuit and prevent human contact with live wires.

❑ Class II insulation stands for double insulation represented by ▣, used in appliances as electric shaver, hair dryers and portable power tools.

MULTIPLE CHOICE QUESTIONS

1. The conductivity of a solid material is 10^{-16} $(\Omega m)^{-1}$. Classify the material as
   - (a) Good conductor
   - (b) Good insulator
   - (c) A semiconductor
   - (d) None of these

2. What is the order of resistivity of PVC in Ωm?
   - (a) 10^{16}
   - (b) 10^{15}
   - (c) 10^{13}
   - (d) None of these

3. Resistivity of copper at room temperature is 10^{-9} Ωm. What is the resistivity of annealed copper?
   - (a) 1.67×10^{-5} Ωm.
   - (b) 1.67×10^{-6} Ωm
   - (c) 1.67×10^{-7} Ωm
   - (d) None of these

4. Match the list of conducting materials and application:

Materials	Applications
I Carbon	A Spark plugs
II Constantan	B Rectifiers
III Mercury	C Rheostats
IV Tungsten	D Pile resistors

	I	II	III	IV
(a)	C	D	A	B
(b)	D	C	B	A
(c)	B	D	C	A
(d)	None of the above			

5. Arrange copper, zinc and aluminium with decreasing order of number of free electrons per unit volume.
   - (a) Aluminium, zinc, copper
   - (b) Zinc, copper, aluminium
   - (c) Aluminium, copper, zinc
   - (d) Copper, zinc, aluminium

6. Arrange the metals in increasing order of their electrical conductivity, i.e. iron, stainless steel and brass.
   - (a) Brass, iron, stainless steel
   - (b) Stainless steel, iron, brass
   - (c) Iron, stainless steel, brass
   - (d) Brass, stainless steel, iron

7. Arrange the following materials in increasing order of electrical conductivity.

   Fused silica, nylon 6.6, PTFE
   - (a) PTFE, nylon 6.6, fused silica
   - (b) PTFE, fused silica, nylon 6.6
   - (c) Nylon 6.6, fused silica, PTFE
   - (d) Fused silica, PTFE, nylon 6.6

8. What is the temperature coefficient of resistivity of Nichrome?
   - (a) 4.4×10^{-3}
   - (b) 3.5×10^{-3}
   - (c) 1×10^{-4}
   - (d) None of these

9. What is the class of insulation used up to 155°C range of temperature?
   - (a) Class E
   - (b) Class F
   - (c) Class H
   - (d) None of these

10. Match the list of materials I with the list of applications II

I	II
I Graphite	A Heating surface elements
II Butyl rubber	B Carbon brushes
III Asbestos	C Insulator
IV Nichrome	D Thermal and electrical insulator

	I	II	III	IV
(a)	B	C	A	D
(b)	B	C	D	A

(c)	C	D	A	B
(d)	A	B	C	D

11. Type of insulation used for electric shaver and hair dryer is

  (a) Class II Insulation

  (b) Porcelain insulation

  (c) Nylon insulation

  (d) None of these

Answers

1. (b)   2. (b)   3. (b)   4. (b)   5. (c)   6. (b)   7. (a)   8. (c)
9. (b)   10. (b)   11. (a)

REVIEW QUESTIONS

1. Explain Sommerfeld atomic model of sub-orbits in *N*-shell, i.e. 4th shell.

2. Mention the electronic configuration for carbon, aluminium, argon, iron and copper.

3. What do you understand by the following in electronic configuration?
   $2s^2$; $3d^5$; $3p^6$

4. Explain the formation of energy band structure.

5. What is the difference between electronic and ionic conduction?

6. Make a list of high-resistivity materials and mention their resistivity in Ωm.

7. What are constantan, Nichrome and manganin? What are their applications?

8. What is the difference between insulators and semiconductors?

9. Explain the following:
   (a) Scattering of electrons   (c) Electronic conduction
   (b) Electron mobility   (d) Ionic conduction

10. Discuss the influence of temperature, impurities and plastic deformation on the resistivity of a metal.

11. Mention class A, B and C insulators, their temperature range and materials.

12. What is class II insulator? Where it is essential?

PRACTICE PROBLEMS

1. A wire of 1.6 mm diameter has to carry a current of 18 A. The maximum power dissipation in the wire is 3.6 W/m. What is the minimum allowable conductivity of the wire for this application?

   Ans. $[4.476 \times 10^7 \ (\Omega m)^{-1}]$

2. The number of conduction electrons in silver is 6×10^{28} per m^3. Determine the mobility of conduction electrons and the drift velocity in silver under an electric field of 1 V/m. Take standard values of electron charge and its mass.

   Ans. $[6.76 \times 10^{-3} \ m^2/Vs: 6.76 \times 10^{-3} \ m/s]$

3. For pure copper, resistivity at two temperatures is given as follows:

   $\rho_{50°c} = 1.95 \times 10^{-8} \ \Omega m$

   $\rho_{-50°c} = 1.30 \times 10^{-8} \ \Omega m$

   What are the values of ρ_{20} and a for copper?

   Ans. $[1.756 \times 10^{-8} \ \Omega m: 3.70 \times 10^{-3}]$

SEMICONDUCTORS

18.1 INTRODUCTION

Semiconductor devices, the electronic components made of semiconductor materials, are essential in modern-day electrical equipments, from computer to cellular phone to digital audio players. A semiconductor is a solid, whose electrical properties can be controlled over a wide range. Silicon is the most commercially exploited semiconductor.

The intrinsic electrical properties of a semiconductor can be permanently modified by introducing controlled quantities of impurity atoms. This process is called 'doping'.

In many semiconductors, when electrons fall from the conductor band to the valence band, they often emit light, i.e. photoemission e.g. a light-emitting diode (LED).

This chapter studies the behaviour of intrinsic and extrinsic semiconductors, the effect of temperature on the conduction of intrinsic semiconductors; *p*- and *n*-type extrinsic semiconductors and Hall effect experiment to determine the *electron mobility*. Various semiconductor devices like *p–n* junctions, forward and reverse biasing voltage, infrared detectors and photo conductors are used in thermoelectricity, transistor and MOSFET and microelectronic circuitry used in computers, calculators, watches and cell phones. In the end, there is a discussion on semiconductor applications in light-emission microwave frequency-integrated circuits, solar cells, photovoltaic cell and laser diodes.

18.2 SEMICONDUCTION

The electrical conductivity of a semiconductor is much less than that of a pure metal. However, semiconducting materials are extremely sensitive to impurities; even a minute concentration of impurity atoms changes the electrical properties of these materials. There are two types of semiconductors: (1) intrinsic, where the electrical behaviour is based on the electronic configuration of the pure material and (2) extrinsic, where the electrical properties are changed by impurity atoms.

18.2.1 Intrinsic Semiconductors

These semiconductors are characterized by the electron band structure as shown in Figure 18.1, i.e. a valence bond separated from an empty conduction band by a narrow forbidden band gap of energy E_g, generally less than 2 eV.

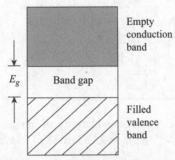

Figure 18.1 *Electron Board Structure of Semiconductor*

There are two elemental semiconductors: (1) silicon and (2) germanium having band gap energies of 1.1 and 0.67 eV, respectively. Both Si and Ge are covalently bonded. (In both Si and Ge, the valence bands correspond to sp^3 hybrid energy levels for the isolated atom. These hybridized valence bands are completely filled at 0 K.)

In intrinsic semiconductor, for every electron excited to conduction band, there is a missing electron in one of the covalent bonds, a vacant electron site or a hole in valence band as shown in Figure 18.2.

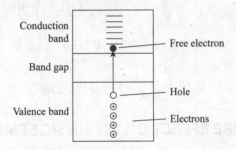

Figure 18.2 *Electron Excited to Conduction Band, Creating a Hole in Valence Band*

A hole is considered to have a charge of same magnitude as of an electron, but positive $+ 1.6 \times 10^{-19}$ C. In the presence of electric field, electrons and holes move in opposite directions. Both holes and electrons are scattered by lattice imperfections. So there are two types of charge carriers in an intrinsic semiconductor.

Electrical conduction
$$\sigma = n_e |e| \mu_e + n_h |e| \mu_h,$$

where n_e is the number of free electrons, n_h is the number of holes, e is the absolute magnitude of electrical charge on an electron or on a hole, i.e. 1.0×10^{-19} C, μ_e is the electron mobility and μ_h is the hole mobility.

Table 18.1 provides band gap energies, electron and hole mobilities and electrical conductivities for some semiconducting materials.

Table 18.1 *Band Gap Energies, Electron and Hole Mobilities and Electrical Conductivities of Some Semiconducting Materials*

Material	Band Gap (eV)	Electrical Conductivity $(\Omega m)^{-1}$	Electron Mobility, μ_e	Hole Mobility, μ_n
Si	1.11	4×10^{-4}	0.14	0.05
Ge	0.67	2.2	0.32	0.18
GaP	2.25	—	0.05	0.002
GaAs	1.42	10^{-6}	0.85	0.45
InSb	0.17	2×10^4	7.7	0.07
CdS	2.40	—	0.03	—
ZnTe	2.26	—	0.03	0.01

Example 18.1 Calculate the electrical conductivity of intrinsic silicon at 300 K. For silicon, $n_e = n_h = 1.5 \times 10^{16}$ per m³, $e = 1.60 \times 10^{-19}$ C, $\mu_e = 0.135$ m²/(Vs) and $\mu_h = 0.048$ m²/(Vs).

Solution:

Electrical conductivity,

$$\sigma = n \, |e| \, (\mu_e + \mu_h)$$

$$n_e = n_h = n = 1.5 \times 10^{16}$$

$$|e| = 1.60 \times 10^{-19} \text{ C}$$

$$\mu_e + \mu_h = 0.135 + 0.048 = 0.183 \text{ m}^2/(\text{Vs})$$

$$\sigma = \frac{1.5 \times 10^{16} \times 1.60 \times 10^{-19}(0.183)}{\text{m}^3} \times \frac{\text{m}^2}{\text{Vs}}$$

$$= 0.439 \times 10^{-3} \, \Omega\text{m}^{-1}$$

Resistivity,

$$\rho = \frac{1}{\sigma} = 2.276 \times 10^3 \, \Omega\text{m}$$

18.3 TEMPERATURE EFFECT ON INTRINSIC SEMICONDUCTOR

As the temperature increases, the Fermi distribution changes, and there is some probability that conduction band is occupied (an equal probability that a level in the valence band is unoccupied) or that a hole is present. Number of electrons in conduction band or holes in valence band is

$$n = n_e = n_h = n_0 \exp^{(-E/2kT)}$$

where n_0 is a constant.

Higher temperatures permit more electrons to cross the forbidden zone, so the conductivity

$$\sigma = n_0(\mu_e + \mu_h)\exp^{(-E/2kT)}$$

The behaviour of semiconductors is opposite to the behaviour of metals. As the temperature increases, the conductivity of a semiconductor increases because more charge carriers are present, whereas the conductivity of a metal decreases due to lower mobility of charge carriers.

Figure 18.3 shows the variation of electrical conductivity of germanium semiconductor versus temperature as compared to conductivity of a metal.

18.4 EXTRINSIC SEMICONDUCTORS

By intentionally adding a few impurity atoms to a material, an extrinsic semiconductor is produced, and the conductivity of an extrinsic semiconductor depends upon the number of impurity atoms or dopant and in a certain range; the conductivity is independent of temperature. But the conductivity of an intrinsic semiconductor changes with temperature as shown in Figure 18.3. Therefore, the conductivity of an extrinsic semiconductor is controllable and stable.

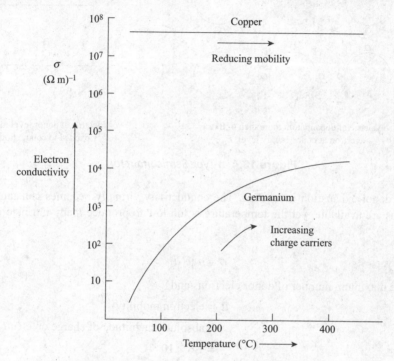

Figure 18.3 *Conductivity Versus Temperature*

18.4.1 *n*-Type Semiconductors

If an impurity like antimony having five valence electrons is added to silicon or germanium, four of the electrons of antimony atom participate in the covalent bonding process, and the remaining one electron enters an energy level in a donor state, just below the conduction band as shown in Figure 18.4. The extra electron is not tightly bound to the atom, and only a small amount of energy $E_d < E_g$ is required to enter the conduction band. No corresponding holes are created when donor electrons enter the conduction band.

Some intrinsic semiconductors still remain with a few electrons jumping the E_g gap.
Number of charge carriers

$$n_{total} = n_e \text{ (dopant)} + n_e \text{ (intrinsic)} + n_h \text{ (intrinsic)}$$

At low temperatures, few intrinsic electrons and holes are produced. As the temperature increases, more of donor electrons jump the E_g gap, eventually, all the donor electrons enter the conduction bond.

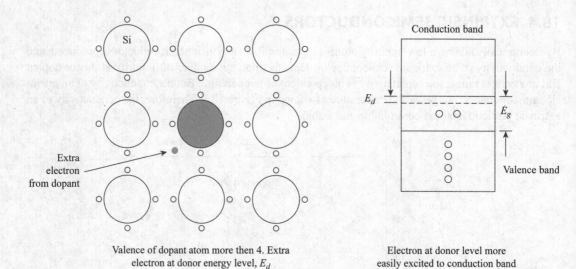

Figure 18.4 *n-Type Semiconductors*

At this point, donor exhaustion is reached. The conductivity virtually becomes constant as no more donor electrons are available, yet the temperature is too low to produce many intrinsic electrons and holes. So,

conductivity, $$\sigma = n_d |e| \mu_e$$

where n_d is the maximum number of donor electrons and

$$\mu_e = \text{electron mobility}$$
$$= \text{absolute magnitude of charge on electron or hole}$$
$$= 1.6 \times 10^{-19} \, C$$

The number of donor electrons, n_d is determined by the number of impurity atoms that are added. A material of this type is said to be an *n*-type extrinsic semiconductor. For *n*-type, the Fermi level is shifted upward in the band gap, within the vicinity of the donor state.

Example 18.2 Phosphorus is added to a high-purity silicon to give a concentration of $10^{24}/m^3$ of charge carriers at room temperature. Calculate the room temperature conductivity of this material, assuming that electron and hole mobilities are same for intrinsic material.

Solution:

Phosphorus acts as a donor in silicon. The $10^{24}/m^3$ charge carriers will be virtually all electrons. The material is extrinsically *n*-type.

$$\sigma = n |e| \mu_e$$

$$= \frac{10^{24}}{m^3} \times 1.6 \times 10^{-19} \times (0.14 \, m^2/Vs)$$

$$= 22,400 \, (\Omega m)^{-1}$$

18.4.2 *p*-Type Extrinsic Semiconductors

Gallium has a valence of 3, and if this is added to a semiconductor there are enough electrons to complete the covalent bonding process. An electron hole is produced in the valence band, which can be filled by an electron from other location as shown in Figure 18.5. The holes act as acceptors of electrons. These

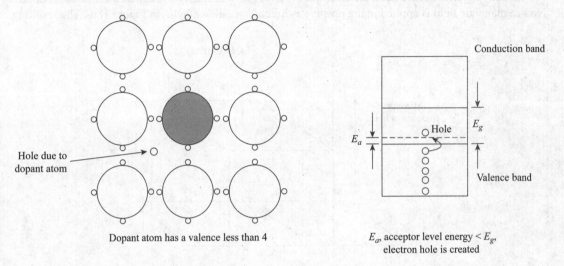

Dopant atom has a valence less than 4

E_a, acceptor level energy $< E_g$, electron hole is created

Figure 18.5 *p-Type Semiconductors*

hole sites have a somewhat higher than normal energy and create an acceptor level of possible electron energies just above the valence band, E_a. The electrons must gain energy equal to E_a in order to create a hole in the valence band. The hole moves and carries the charge. This is a *p*-type semiconductor.

If some intrinsic semiconduction occurs, total number of charge carriers is

$$n_t = n_a \text{ (acceptors)} + n_e \text{ (intrinsic)} + n_h \text{ (intrinsic)}$$

At low temperatures, the acceptor levels predominate. Eventually, the temperature is high enough to cause saturation of acceptors and the conductivity is

$$\sigma = n_a |e| \mu_h,$$

where n_a is the maximum number of acceptors or holes, e is the absolute magnitude of charge on hole and μ_h is the mobility of the hole.

Extrinsic semiconductors (both *n*- and *p*-type) are produced from materials that are of extremely high purity, and total impurity content may be as low as 10^{-7} at %. (atom per cent) Controlled concentrations of specific donors or acceptors are added, using various techniques. This process is known as doping.

In extrinsic semiconductors, a large number of charge carriers (electrons or holes) are created at room temperature by the available thermal energy, and as a result, relatively high electrical conductivities at room temperatures are obtained. Semiconductor materials are designed for use in electronic devices to be operated at ambient conditions.

18.5 HALL EFFECT

By using simple electrical conductivity measurements, the type, concentration and mobility of charge carriers in a semiconductor cannot be determined. For the measurement of these quantities, a 'Hall effect' experiment is performed. Hall effect is the creation of a voltage, the Hall voltage V_H, when a magnetic field is applied in a direction perpendicular to the motion of charged particles, which exerts a force on the particle perpendicular to both the magnetic field and the direction of particle motion.

Consider a parallelopiped specimen, base $b.a$, with origin at O of Cartesian co-ordinates. In response to externally applied electric field, the electrons or holes move in z-direction and a current I_z is produced. Now, a magnetic field is applied in the positive x-direction as shown by B_x in Figure 18.6. The resulting

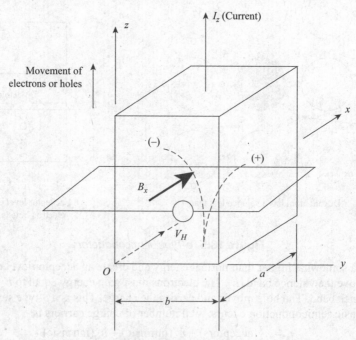

Figure 18.6 *Hall Effect*

force brought to bear on the charge carriers (moving in z-direction) will cause them to be deflected in y-directions, i.e. holes (positively charged carriers) towards the right face of the specimen and electrons (negatively charged carriers) towards the left vertical face as shown in Figure 18.6. A voltage V_H will be established in y-direction. The magnitude of V_H will depend upon I_z, B_x and the thickness of specimen a

$$V_H = \frac{R_H I_z B_x}{a} \tag{18.1}$$

where R_H is the Hall coefficient.

For metals, conduction is by electrons, and R_H is negative.

$$R_H = \frac{I}{n|e|} \tag{18.2}$$

where n is the concentration that can be determined as R_H is measured by Eq. (18.1).

$|e|$ is the absolute magnitude of charge on electron or hole. Moreover, electron mobility, μ_e is equal to

$$\mu_e = \frac{\sigma}{n|e|}$$

or

$$\mu_e = |R_H|\sigma \qquad (18.3)$$

$|R_H|$ is the absolute value of Hall coefficient from Eq. (18.3), and electron mobility μ_e can be measured.

Example 18.3   The electrical conductivity and electron mobility for aluminium are 3.7×10^7 Ωm^{-1} and 0.0012 m²/Vs. Calculate the Hall voltage for an aluminium specimen of 20-mm thickness for a current of 30 A and a magnetic field of 0.5 tesla (imposed in a direction perpendicular to current)

Solution:

Hall voltage may be determined by

$$V_H = \frac{R_H I_z B_x}{a}$$

Let us first determine Hall coefficient,

$$R_H = -\frac{\mu_e}{\sigma}$$

$$R_H = \frac{-0.0012 \text{ m}^2/\text{Vs}}{3.7 \times 10^7}$$

$$V_H = \frac{R_H I_z B_x}{a} = \frac{-3.243 \times 30 \times 0.5 \times 10^{-11}}{20 \times 10^{-3}}$$

$$= -2.43 \times 10^{-8} \text{ V}$$

18.6 VARIATION OF CONDUCTIVITY WITH TEMPERATURE AND CARRIER CONCENTRATION

In the case of intrinsic semiconductors, electrical conductivity increases with rising temperature, because due to more thermal energy on account of increase in temperature, both electrons and holes increase. Both values of n_e and n_h increase in conductivity expression. The magnitude of electron mobility and hole mobility (μ_e and μ_h) decrease slightly with temperature as a result of more *effective scattering of electrons and holes by thermal vibrations*. However, reduction in μ_e and μ_h is very much smaller than increase in n_e and n_h, with the net result that conductivity is increased.

Mathematically,

$$\ln \sigma = C - \frac{E_g}{2kT} \qquad (18.4)$$

where σ is the intrinsic conductivity, E_g is the gap energy, k is the Boltzmann's constant, T is the absolute temperature and C is a temperature-independent constant.

Since the increase in n_e and n_h is so large with increase in temperature, and there is only slight decrease in μ_e and μ_h, the dependence of carrier concentration on temperature for intrinsic behaviour is the same, i.e.

$$\ln n_e = \ln n_h = C' - \frac{E_g}{2kT} \qquad (18.5)$$

where C' is a constant, independent of temperature, but different from C.

18.6.1 Extrinsic Conductivity

At temperatures below 800 K (523°C), the boron-doped materials are extrinsically *p*-type. Virtually, all the carrier holes result from extrinsic excitations—electron transitions from valence band into the boron-acceptor band, which leaves behind valence band holes. The available thermal energies at these temperatures are sufficient to promote significant number of these excitations to acceptor level. So the extrinsic conductivity far exceeds that of intrinsic material. For example, at 127°C (400 K), σ for extrinsic silicon is 10^{-2}.

Conductivity, σ, for extrinsic silicon and 0.0013 at% boron-doped silicon is 600 $(\Omega m)^{-1}$. This comparison indicates the sensitivity of conductivity to even extremely small concentration of the same impurity atom.

Another method of representing the temperature dependence of the electrical behaviour of semiconductors is from a graph between (1) natural log of electron and hole concentration and (2) reciprocal of absolute temperature.

$$\ln n_e = \ln n_h = C' - \frac{E_g}{2kT} \tag{18.6}$$

Slope of the line segment is $-E_g/2k$.

$$E_g = -2k\left[\frac{\Delta \ln n_h}{\Delta\left(\frac{1}{T}\right)}\right] = -2k\left[\frac{\Delta \ln n_e}{\Delta\left(\frac{1}{T}\right)}\right]$$

As shown in Figure 18.7, $\ln n_h$ first increases linearly with decreasing $(1/T)$ (on increasing temperature). A large number of extrinsic excitations are possible, even at relatively low temperatures, in as much

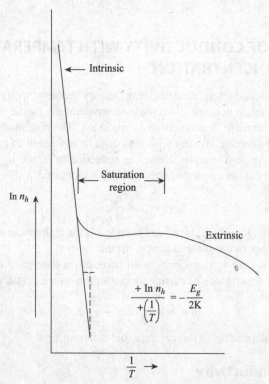

Figure 18.7 *Extrinsic Conductivity*

as acceptor level lies just above the top of the valence band. With increase in temperature or decrease in $1/T$, the hole concentration (n_h) eventually becomes independent of temperature. At this point (in the case of silicon doped with boron), virtually all the boron atoms have accepted electrons from the valence band or said to be saturated—shown by saturation region (donor impurities become exhausted instead of saturated). The number of holes in this region is approximately equal to the number of dopant impurity (boron) atoms.

Example 18.4 At room temperature of 25°C, the electrical conductivity of intrinsic silicon is 4×10^{-4}. Estimate its conductivity at 250°C.

Solution:

Constant,

$$C = \ln(\sigma) + \frac{E_g}{2kT}$$

where

$$\sigma = 4 \times 10^{-4}$$
$$E_g = 1.11 \text{ eV}$$
$$k = 8.62 \times 10^{-5}/\text{K}$$
$$T = 25 + 273 = 298 \text{ K}$$
$$C = \ln(4 \times 10^{-4}) + \frac{1.11 \text{eV}}{2 \times 8.62 \times \dfrac{10^{-5} \text{ eV}}{\text{K}} \times 298 \text{ K}}$$
$$= -7.8240 + 16.1771$$
$$= 8.353$$

At 150°C (523 K)

$$\ln\sigma = C - \frac{E_g}{2kT}$$
$$= 8.353 - \frac{1.11 \text{ eV}}{2 \times 8.62 \times \dfrac{10^{-5} \text{ eV}}{\text{K}} \times 523}$$
$$= 8.353 - 12.3107$$
$$\ln\sigma = -3.958$$

Electrical conductivity,

$$\sigma = 0.0191 \ (\Omega \text{m})^{-1}.$$

18.7 SEMICONDUCTOR DEVICES

Semiconductor devices as diodes and transistors have replaced the vacuum tubes used earlier. These are also known as solid state devices. Special features of semiconductor devices are small size, low power consumption, no warm-up time and extremely small circuits. Numerous electronic devices can be incorporated into a small silicon chip. In other words, the circuits are miniaturized. Some semiconductor devices are 'diodes', which act as rectifier and allow the current to flow only in one directions, and convert ac to dc signal. p–n semiconductor (combined) junction is a semiconducting rectifier. Figure 18.8 shows a p–n junction.

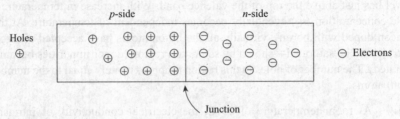

Figure 18.8 *p–n Junction*

A single piece of silicon is doped so that one side becomes *p*-side and other becomes *n*-side. Note that a piece of silicon or any semiconducting material is taken from a single crystal of the material, because the grain boundaries are deleterious to the operation of a semiconducting device.

18.7.1 Forward Bias

Before the application of any potential across the *p–n* junction, holes on *p*-side and electrons on *n*-side are the dominant carriers of charge.

Now, a battery is connected with positive terminal to the *p*-side and negative terminal to the *n*-side. This type of connection is known as *forward bias*. Under the influence of applied potential, holes on *p*-side and electrons on *n*-side are attracted towards the junction. Flow of hole and electron is shown in Figure 18.9. Holes and electrons encounter each other at the junction, recombine and cancel each other producing energy

$$\text{Hole} + \text{electron} \rightarrow \text{energy}$$

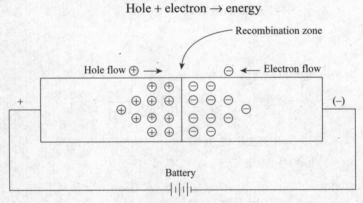

Figure 18.9 *Forward Bias*

For the forward bias, a large number of charge carriers flow across the junctions and an appreciable current is produced. The characteristics of current–voltage are shown in *I* quadrant of Figure 18.10.

18.7.2 Reverse Bias

As shown in Figure 18.11, both holes and electrons are rapidly drawn away from the junction and the junction relatively becomes free of charge carriers. Therefore, the junction is now highly insulating. The *IV* quadrant of Figure 18.11 shows the current–voltage characteristics of reverse bias on *p–n* junction. Current I_R is extremely small in comparison to I_F.

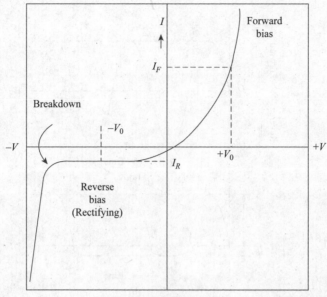

IR—Reverse bias current
IF—Forward bias current imposed maximum voltage $\pm V_0$

Figure 18.10 *Current Voltage Characteristics*

Figure 18.12(a) shows sinusoidal variation of applied voltage $\pm V_0$. Maximum current for reverse bias is very small I_R, as shown in comparison to I_F, in forward bias. Sometimes, high reverse bias voltages are applied and a large number of electrons and holes are generated. This will increase the current abruptly, a phenomenon known as *breakdown*.

Figure 18.12(b) shows voltage versus time for a *p–n* rectifying junction, while the current I_R versus time showing rectification of voltage.

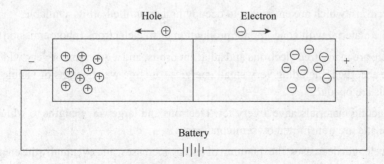

Figure 18.11 *Reverse Bias*

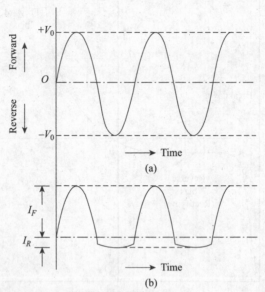

Figure 18.12 *Sinusoidal Variation of Applied Voltage*

18.8 INFRARED DETECTORS AND PHOTOCONDUCTORS

These are semiconductor devices. The energy required to break a chemical bond and to create a free electron hole pair is supplied by electromagnetic radiation of a certain wavelength. Minimum energy required to produce an electron–hole pair at 0°C absolute is E_g, gap energy between valence and conduction bands.

The electromagnetic radiation falling on a material is absorbed by the following:

1. Fee electrons in conduction band.

2. Bound electrons, which are energized to occupy higher unfilled orbits available.

3. Ionizing the material with concomitant production of free electrons (photoemission).

In metals, there are many free electrons and adjacent orbits, and a quantum of very wide spectrum of radiation will be absorbed, including very small energies (of large wavelengths of visible light), so the metallic materials are opaque.

1. Semiconducting materials have a very few electrons and large wavelengths to which the metals are opaque and are transmitted by semiconductors.

2. As the wavelength decreases, the quantum of energy increases, and eventually the energy becomes large enough to exert the electron from valence to conduction band, producing electron–hole pair and raising electrical conductivity.

3. As the wavelength becomes shorter and shorter, many electrons are produced that a semiconductor becomes opaque to these wavelengths. Shorter and shorter wavelengths beyond this stage produce photoemission.

4. Electrons from any of the orbits within the valence band can be excited to any unfilled orbits within the conduction band or to newly vacated orbits within the valence band. However, both valence and conduction bands have finite widths, and a spectrum of energies is absorbed. Whether a given semiconductor is sensitive to visible light or infrared radiation depends upon E_g, gap between valence and conductor bands.

The materials sensitive to visible light are known as 'photoconductors' and the materials sensitive to infrared radiations are known as 'infrared detectors'.

18.9 THERMOELECTRICS

Thermoelectric effects in semiconductors are 100 times greater than the effects in metals. For this reason, a semiconductor like Bi_2Te_3 (bismuth telluride) can be used to convert heat directly to electricity in a thermoelectric generator.

The principal thermoelectric effects are 'Seebeck effect, Peltier effect and Thomson effect. Thomson effect states that heat is absorbed from or liberated to the surroundings by a conductor in which both temperature gradient and current exist.

If a temperature gradient exists in a semiconductor, the otherwise uniform distribution of electrons and excess holes tend to move from the hot end of a conductor towards the cold end. An equilibrium is reached when the charge established on the cold end becomes great enough to repel the additional carriers that tend to migrate there. The open circuit current is zero, though a potential remains. The hot ends of the metals and n-type semiconductors become positively charged, while their cold ends become negatively charged. In p-type semiconductors, reverse is true.

In addition to the tendency for charge carriers to move away from hot portion of a conductor, the charge carriers possess different energies in different materials. Therefore, movement of carriers across a junction of dissimilar materials results in either liberation or absorption of energy. Conversely, if the junction is heated or cooled, there will be a movement of charge carriers across the junction.

Consider the p–n junction, a p–n device and the energy level diagrams of p- and n-type semiconductors (Figures 18.13 and 18.14).

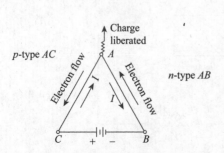

Figure 18.13 *p–n Device*

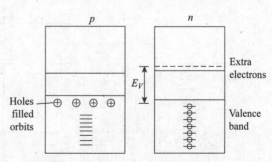

Figure 18.14 *Energy Level Diagrams*

If the applied voltage causes electrons to flow from *n*-material across the junctions to *p*-material, heating of the junction will occur. This is because the high-energy electrons from donor levels will move down the energy barrier and liberate energy as they occupy the acceptor levels in the valence band of *p*-material. In this case, the device can be used as a heat pump.

If the applied voltage is reversed so that the electrons move from acceptor levels near the valence band to donor levels near the conductor band, energy has to be supplied to the electrons. This energy is obtained in the form of heat from the surroundings, causing the junctions to become cold. This device is called a 'refrigerator'.

Semiconductors have two advantages over metals when used in thermoelectrics:

1. The voltages produced in semiconductors are 10 times greater than that for a given temperature difference in the metals.

2. Most of the semiconductors are relatively poor conductors of heat, so it is easier to maintain a large temperature difference between hot and cold junctions under given conditions.

18.10 TRANSISTORS

Transistors are most important semiconducting devices in microelectronic circuitry and can perform two basic functions:

1. They can amplify an electrical signal like a triode.

2. In computers, they can serve as switching devices for processing and storage of data.

There are two types of transistors: (1) junction transistor and (2) MOSFET (metal oxide semiconductor field effect transistor) transistor.

18.10.1 Junction Transistor

In this transistor, there are two *p–n* junctions arranged back to back as shown in Figure 18.15. A very thin *n*-type base region is sandwiched between *p*-type emitter on one side and *p*-type collector on the other side. Base–emitter junction is forward biased, while base–collector junction is reverse biased.

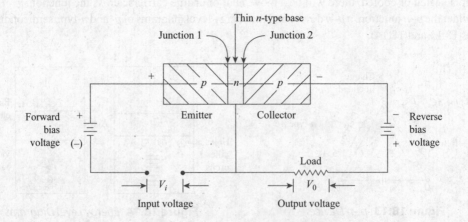

Figure 18.15 *Junction Transistor*

Operations

The p-type emitter and junction 1 is forward biased, and a large number of holes enter the base region. These are minority carriers in the n-type base and the same will combine with majority of electrons. However, if the base is very thin, most of these holes will be swept through the base without recombination and cross junction 2, go into the p-type collector. Holes have become a part of emitter–collector circuit. A small increase in input voltage V_i, produces a large increase in current across junction 2. This large increase in collector current produces large increase in output voltage (across the load resistor). Therefore, a voltage signal V_i that passes through junction transistor experiences amplification and becomes V_0, as shown in Figure 18.16 (voltage–time plots).

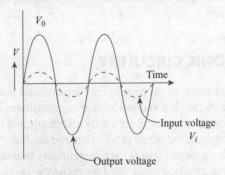

Figure 18.16 *Amplified Output Voltage*

Similarly, the operations of n–p–n transistor can be explained, but in this case electrons instead of holes are injected across the base into the collector.

18.10.2 MOSFET

In MOSFET, two small islands of p-type semiconductors are created within a substrate of n-type silicon semiconductor as shown in Figure 18.17. Two p-type islands are joined to a p-type channel. An insulating layer of silicon dioxide (SiO_2) is formed on the surface of silicon.

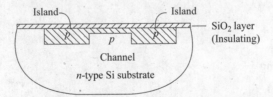

Figure 18.17 *MOSFET Transistor*

Connection of source, gate and drain are made on p island, p channel and p island as shown in Figure 18.18. The conductivity of the channel is changed by the presence of electric field applied on the gate. A positive field applied on the gate will drive charge carriers, i.e. holes out of the channel, and the electrical conductivity is reduced. Therefore, a small change in the field at the gate will produce a large change in current between the source and the drain.

Basic difference between the operation of junction and MOSFET transistors is that the gate current is very small in comparison to the base current in a junction transistor. Therefore, MOSFET is employed where the signal sources to be amplified cannot sustain a significant current.

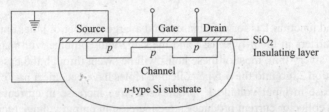

Figure 18.18 *Connection of Source, Gate and Drain*

In addition to their function in amplifying the input electrical signal, transistors and diodes are used as switching devices in computers.

18.11 MICROELECTRONIC CIRCUITRY

In microelectronic circuitry, thousands of electronic components and circuits are incorporated into a very small chip. Very small size of the chip and low power consumptions are the basic requirements in aerospace technology. Now, personal computers are easily affordable and integrated circuits are used in calculators, watches, communications, industrial production and control.

Microelectronics processes are grouped into (1) semiconductors as transistors, diodes, *pnp* switches and resistors and (2) thin film microelectronics used as resistors, capacitors and interconnectors of electronic circuits.

First of all, a single crystal is grown out of the melt doped with the proper element. At present, silicon and germanium are mainly used because their manufacturing technology is very well understood and established. Silicon is generally preferred over germanium, because of its greater energy gap and better thermal resistance. From a single crystal of silicon, thin wafers are cut with the help of diamond saws. Then from wafers, chips of rectangular shape are cut. A highly polished surface free of any surface damage is essential for the wafer. Each polished wafer constitutes a substrate on which typically 1000 integrated circuits can be located. Wafer is subjected to further processes as follows:

1. Oxidation
2. Photoengraving
3. Diffusion
4. Epitaxy
5. Chemical processing
6. Interconnection

Oxidation provides an insulating layer of silicon dioxide to isolate a number of pockets of a single-crystal semiconducting wafer. Photoengraving is used for cutting windows in the oxide layer. Diffusion forms *p*- and *n*-type areas. Epitaxy is the growth of a new layer having the same crystal orientations as that of the substrate. Within this layer, the components of integrated circuit are formed using diffusion, oxide isolations and again diffusion. Chemical processing involves the technique of etching and removing mask and oxide layers by chemical actions. Finally, interconnections are made by metalizing aluminium, which can be deposited readily by vacuum evaporation that forms an excellent band with silicon and silicon oxide surfaces. Aluminium has good conductivity and welds readily to gold attachment leads by thermocompression bonding.

18.12 APPLICATIONS OF SEMICONDUCTORS

Because of their applications in transistors and lasers, the search for new semiconducting materials and improvement in existing materials are important studies in material science.

Most commonly used semiconductors are crystalline organic materials. These materials are classified according to the periodic table groups from which their constituent atoms emerge.

Group III nitrides have high tolerance to ionizing radiations, making them suitable for radiation-hardened electronics. Group IV elemental semiconductors are diamond, silicon and germanium. Group IV compound semiconductors include SiC (silicon carbide) and SiGe (silicon germanide).

18.12.1 III–V Semiconductors

Following are few examples of III–V semiconductors:

1. Aluminium anti-monide (AlSb) containing aluminium and antimony (lattice constant is 0.61 nm). Indirect band gap is 1.6 eV at 300 K and direct band gap is 2.22 eV.
2. *Aluminium arsenide (AlAs) (lattice constant is 0.61 nm):* It has wider band gap than AlSb. It is hygroscopic.
3. *Aluminium nitride (AlN):* It has extremely wide gap of 6.2 eV. It has potential applications in deep ultraviolet optoelectronics.
4. Aluminium phosphide (AlP) along with other elements, used in devices such as light-emitting diodes (e.g. aluminium gallium indium phosphide).
5. *Boron nitride (BN):* Recently discovered boron nitride nanotubes have homogeneous electronic behaviour.
6. *Boron arsenide (BAs):* Solar cells are fabricated from this semiconducting material.
7. *Gallium anti-monide (GaSb):* It is used in devices such as microwave frequency-integrated circuits, infrared light-emitting diodes, laser diodes and solar cells.
8. *Gallium phosphide (GaP):* This is used in the manufacture of low- and standard-brightness red, orange and green light-emitting diodes. GaP has been used as an LED material since 1960.
9. *Indium anti-monide (InSb):* This narrow gap semiconducting material is used in infrared detectors, thermal imaging cameras, infrared astronomy and infrared homing missile guidance systems. InSb is sensitive to 1–5 μm wavelengths.
10. *Indium nitride:* It is a small band gap semiconductor material having potential application in solar cells and high-speed electronics.
11. *Indium phosphide:* This is used in high-power, high-frequency electronics because of its superior electron velocity with respect to more common semiconductors as silicon and gallium arsenide.

18.12.2 II–VI Semiconductors

A few examples of II–VI semiconductors are as follows:

1. *Cadmium selenide (CdSe):* Band gap is 1.74 eV at 300 K, and is used in optoelectronic devices, laser diodes, nanosensing and biomedical imaging.

2. *Cadmium sulphide (CdS):* Band gap is 2.42 eV. It has useful properties for optoelectronics, and is used in both photosensitive and photovoltaic devices and in photoresistors—electrical resistance changes with incident light levels.

3. *Cadmium telluride (CdTe):* This is a strong solar cell material. It is usually sandwiched with cadmium sulphide to form a *p–n* junction photovoltaic solar cell.

4. *Zinc oxide:* It has a direct band gap of 3.37 eV, and is commonly used in gas sensors, blue LESs, transparent TFTs and in transparent conducting oxide (TCO).

5. *Zinc selenide (ZnSe):* It is used in light-emitting diodes and diode lasers; it emits blue light. It is susceptible to *n*-type doping, by halogen element. *p*-type doping is more difficult, but can be achieved by introducing nitrogen.

6. *Zinc telluride:* It can be easily doped, and is used in optoelectronics.

18.12.3 Miscellaneous Oxides

Following are few examples of miscellaneous oxides:

1. Cu_2O*(cupric oxide):* Initially rectifier diodes were made from this material. Now silicon is used.

2. *CuO (cuprous oxide):* Application is in *p*-type semiconductor, and has a narrow band gap of 1.2 eV. It is an abrasive to polish optical instruments. Cupric oxide is used to produce dry cell batteries.

3. *Uranium dioxide (UO_2):* Band gap is 1.3 eV, and is used in very efficient solar cells. It can absorb five different wavelengths, including infrared. It is also useful for red-hard devices for special military and aerospace applications.

18.12.4 Organic Semiconductors

Both short-chain oligomers and long-chain polymers are known organic conductors. For example, oligomers are pentacene, anthracene and rubrene. Polymers are poly (3-hexylthiophene), poly (*p*-phanylene vinylene) and polyacetylene.

18.12.5 Magnetic Semiconductors

Magnetic semiconductors are materials that exhibit ferromagnetism (and a similar response) and have useful semiconductor properties. They are used in spin transistors.

Manganese-doped indium arsenide and gallium arsenide are examples of ferromagnetic semiconductor (at Curie temperature). Manganese-doped indium anti-monide becomes ferromagnetic even at room temperature, even with less than 1 per cent Mn.

KEY POINTS TO REMEMBER

❏ In intrinsic semiconductors, electrical behaviour is based on electronic configuration.
❏ In extrinsic semiconductors, electrical behaviour is based on impurity atoms.

- Silicon with $E_g = 1.1$ eV and germanium with $E_g = 0.67$ eV are most commonly used semiconductors.
- Electrical conduction,

$$\sigma = |e|\{n_e\mu_e + n_h\mu_h\}$$

where n_e is the number of free electrons, n_h is the number of holes, μ_e is the electron mobility and μ_h is the hole mobility.

- Temperature effect on intrinsic semiconductors

$$n = n_e = n_h = n_0\exp(-E/2kT)$$

where n_0 is a constant, k is the Boltzmann's constant and T is the absolute temperature.

- In n-type semiconductors, electrons enter an energy level in a donor state $E_d < E_g$.
- In p-type semiconductors, holes enter an energy level in an acceptor state $E_a > E_g$.
- Total charge carriers in p-extrinsic

$$n_t = n_a \text{ (acceptor)} + n_h \text{ (intrinsic)} + n_e \text{ (intrinsic)}$$

- *Hall effect:* When a magnetic field is applied in a direction perpendicular to the motion of charged particles, which exerts a force on the particles perpendicular to both magnetic field and direction of particle motion, Hall voltage is created.
- Hall coefficient,

$$R_H = \frac{\sigma}{\mu_e} = \frac{1}{n|e|}$$

- Intrinsic semiconductor

  Variation of conductivity σ with temperature

$$\ln\sigma = C - \frac{E_g}{2kT}$$

where C is a constant, E_g is the gap energy, k is the Boltzmann's constant and T is the absolute temperature.

- p–n junctions, when reverse biasing applied $I_R < I_F$ (i.e. the current when forward biasing is applied), effect of rectifier is obtained.
- Group III nitrides have high temperature to ionizing radiation. These are suitable for radiation-hardened electronics.
- Gallium anti-monide (GaSb) is used in devices such as microwave frequency-integrated circuits, infrared light-emitting diodes, laser diodes and solar cells.
- Indium anti-monide (InSb) is used in infrared detectors, thermal imaging cameras, infrared astronomy and missile guidance systems.
- Cadmium sulphide (CdS) is used in photosensitive and photovoltaic devices, and in photo resistors.
- Zinc selenide (ZnSe) is used in blue light-emitting diodes.
- Photoemission is produced by shorter and shorter wavelengths.
- Photoconductors are sensitive to visible light.
- If a temperature gradient exists in a semiconductor (otherwise having uniform distribution of charge carriers), free electrons and excess holes tend to move from hot end of a conductor towards a cold end.
- Transistors can amplify an electrical signal and in computers they serve as switching devices.

❏ *MOSFET (metal oxide semiconductor field effect transistor):* A very small change in the field at gate produces a large change in current between the source and the drain.

❏ *Microelectronic circuits:* Thousands of electronic components and circuits are incorporated in a very small chip. Small size and low power consumption are special properties of these chips.

MULTIPLE CHOICE QUESTIONS

1. Which is a correct statement?
   - (A) Extrinsic semiconductor properties are dependent on electronic configuration only.
   - (B) Behaviour of intrinsic semiconductor is based on electronic configuration of pure material.
   - (C) Band gap energy of Si is 0.67 eV.

   - (a) A and B
   - (b) B and C
   - (c) B only
   - (d) C only

2. Arrange the following semiconductors in increasing order of band gap energy.

   Silicon, germanium, gallium, arsenide
   - (a) GaS, Ge, Si
   - (b) Ge, Si, GaS
   - (c) Si, GaS, Ge
   - (d) GaS, Si, Ge

3. Arrange the following semiconductors in decreasing order of electron mobility

   Si, GaP, CdS
   - (a) Si, GaP, CdS
   - (b) GaP, Si, CdS
   - (c) CdS, Si, GaP
   - (d) CdS, GaP, Si

4. Resistivity of a semiconductor is 2.5×10^3 Ωm. What is its electrical conductivity in $(\Omega m)^{-1}$?
   - (a) 2.5×10^{-3}
   - (b) 2.5×10^{-4}
   - (c) 4×10^{-3}
   - (d) 4×10^{-4}

5. What is the band gap energy in indium antimonide (InSb) semiconductor?
   - (a) 2.27 eV
   - (b) 1.42 eV
   - (c) 0.17 eV
   - (d) None of these

6. What is the expression of Hall coefficient, R_H?
   - (a) $\dfrac{1}{n|e|}$
   - (b) $\dfrac{\mu_e}{\sigma}$
   - (c) $\dfrac{n}{|e|}$
   - (d) None of these

7. Under the influence of applied voltage, holes on *p*-side are attracted towards the junction and electrons on *n*-side are also attracted towards the junction. This statement is correct for which biasing in *p–n* junction
   - (a) Forward biasing
   - (b) Reverse biasing
   - (c) Neither (a) nor (b)
   - (d) Both (a) and (b)

8. If current in reverse biasing is I_R and in forward biasing is I_F, which is a correct statement?
   - (a) $I_R \gg I_F$
   - (b) $I_R = I_F$
   - (c) $I_R \ll I_F$
   - (d) None of these

9. Which of the following semiconductors has 6.2 eV as gap energy?

   Aluminium anitmonide, Aluminium Arsenide, Aluminium Nitride
   - (a) AlN
   - (b) AlSb
   - (c) AlAs
   - (d) None of these

10. In a semiconductor, thermoelectric effect is produced by
   - (a) Seebeck effect
   - (b) Peltier effect
   - (c) Thompson effect
   - (d) None of these

Answers

1. (c) 2. (b) 3. (a) 4. (d) 5. (c) 6. (a) 7. (a) 8. (c) 9. (a)
10.(c)

REVIEW QUESTIONS

1. What are intrinsic and extrinsic semiconductors. Explain. What are forbidden band gap, electrical conductivity, electron mobility and hole mobility?

2. Explain the temperature effect on behaviour of intrinsic semiconductors.

3. Describe n-type and p-type extrinsic semiconductors, explaining donor energy, E_d, acceptor energy, E_a and gap energy, E_g.

4. What is Hall effect? How it is determined? How electron mobility is measured?

5. Explain the variation of electrical conductivity with temperature in the case of extrinsic semiconductors.

6. What is p–n junction? What are forward biasing and reverse biasing voltages? How rectifying effect is obtained?

7. Name a few semiconductors for application in

   (a) Integrated circuits

   (b) Infrared light-emitting diodes

   (c) Solar cells

   (d) Nanosensing

   (e) Photovoltaic devices

   (f) Dry cell batteries

8. What are infrared detector and photoconductor? What is the difference in their principle of operation?

9. What semiconductor is used in thermoelectricity? Explain Thomson effect in a semiconductor-type thermocouple.

10. Explain how voltage is amplified by junction transistor.

11. Describe the preparation of a MOSFET.

12. Mention the achievements in microelectronic circuitry.

PRACTICE PROBLEMS

1. For intrinsic silicon, electrical conductivity at room temperature is $4 \times 10^{-4}\ \Omega\text{m}^{-1}$. The electron and hole mobilities are 0.1 and 0.05 m²/Vs, respectively. Complete the electron and hole concentrations at room temperature.

   Ans. $[1.316 \times 10^{16}/\text{m}^3]$

2. The electrical conductivity and electron mobility for aluminium are $3 \times 10^7\ \Omega\text{m}^{-1}$ and 0.0012 m²/Vs. Calculate the Hall voltage for an aluminium specimen that is 15-mm thick for a current of 20 A and a magnetic field of 0.6 tesla (imposed in a direction perpendicular to current).

   Ans. $[-2.53 \times 10^{-8}\ \text{V}]$

3. Phosphorus is added to high-purity silicon to give a concentration of $10^{23.5}$/m^3 of charge carriers at room temperature. If electron mobility of silicon is 0.139 m^2/Vs, calculate the room temperature conductivity of the materials assuming that $n_e = n_h$ for intrinsic material.

Ans. [7.33 (Ωm)$^{-1}$]

4. At room temperature of 25°C, the electrical conductivity of intrinsic germanium is 2.2 Ωm^{-1}. Estimate its conductivity at 200°C (473 K).

Ans. [274 (Ωm)$^{-1}$]

19

DIELECTRIC PROPERTIES

19.1 INTRODUCTION

A dielectric material is an electrically insulating material (non-metallic) and it exhibits an electric dipole structure. Electrically charged positive and negative dipoles are separated on a molecular or atomic level. The properties of dielectrics are due to polarization of the substance of dielectric. Due to polarization, dielectric stores energy and makes it available when electric field is reversed.

The effectiveness of a dielectric is measured by its ability to store energy and is expressed in terms of 'dielectric constant'. The ability of a dielectric to withstand electric field without losing its insulating property is known as 'dielectric strength'. Because of this ability, it is used in capacitance.

A good dielectric must retain a large percentage of energy stored in it, when the field is reversed. Dielectrics are characterized by high resistivity, negative temperature coefficient and a large insulation resistance.

Dielectrics with high dielectric constant are extremely useful in all branches of electrical engineering. Polymers like nylon, PVC, bakelite, polyethylene and ceramics like glass, mica, porcelain and steatite are commonly used as dielectrics.

19.2 DIELECTRIC BEHAVIOUR

A dielectric material is an electrically insulating material. It exhibits or can be made to exhibit an electric dipole structure. In a dipole, there is a separation of positively and negatively charged entities at atomic or molecular level.

A dipole may be induced or created in an atom or molecule, which is electrically symmetric. In a symmetric atom, the overall spatial distribution of electrons is symmetric in relation to the positively charged nucleus as shown in Figure 19.1.

Now, all the atoms constantly vibrate and cause short-lived distortions of electrical symmetry resulting in small electric dipoles as shown in Figure 19.2. One of these dipoles can produce a displacement of electron distribution of a nearby atom or molecule, which makes second one also to become a dipole.

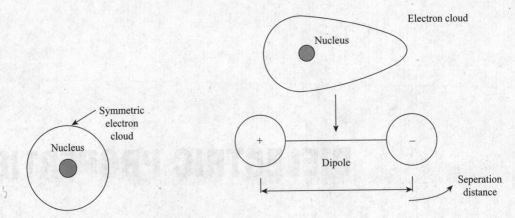

Figure 19.1 *Electron Cloud Around Nucleus*   **Figure 19.2** *Electric Dipoles*

A *dipole moment* arises from net positive and negative charges of a dipole. As a result of dipole interactions with electric field, dielectric materials are used in capacitors.

When an electric field is applied across a capacitor, one plate is positively charged and the other is negatively charged, with electric field directed from positive to negative.

Capacitance, $C = Q/V$, where Q is the quantity of charge stored on any of the two plates and V is the voltage applied across the capacitor. Units of capacitance are coulombs per volt or Farads (F).

Consider a parallel plate capacitor as shown in Figure 19.3. There is vacuum between the two plates. Electric field V is applied between the two plates as shown in Figure 19.3.

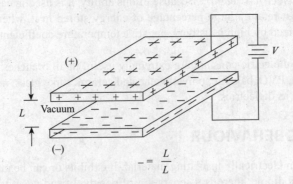

Figure 19.3 *Parallel Plate Capacitor*

Capacitance of a parallel plate capacitor, $C = \epsilon_0 A/L$, where A is the area enclosed between the two plates, L is the distance between the plates, ϵ_0 is the permittivity of a vacuum and a universal constant $= 8.85 \times 10^{-12}$ F/m. Now, a dielectric medium is inserted between the two plates as shown in Figure 19.4.

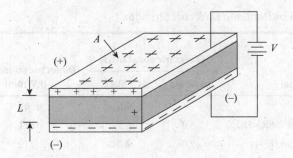

Figure 19.4 *Dielectric Medium Between Two Plates*

Capacitance, $$C = \epsilon A/L,$$

where ϵ is the permittivity of a dielectric medium, which is greater than ϵ_0.

Relative permittivity, $$k = \epsilon/\epsilon_0,$$

which is also called as dielectric constant.

Now, $k > 1$ represents the increase in charge storing capacity of a dielectric medium between the plates. The ability of a dielectric to withstand electric fields without losing insulating property is known as 'dielectric strength'.

Dielectric strength, $$\zeta = V/L, = V/m$$

Dielectric constant and dielectric strength (kV/mm) for some materials are given in Table 19.1.

19.3 DIPOLE MOMENT AND POLARIZATION

An electric dipole moment, p is associated with each dipole, which is equal to the charge on each pair × separation distance between positive and negative charge as shown in Figure 19.5. If $+q$ is the charge on one dipole element, $-q$ is the charge on another dipole and d is the separation distance, then

Dipole moment, $$p = q.d$$

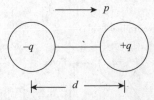

Figure 19.5 *Polarization Vector, p on a Dipole*

Dipole moment is a vector, p directed from negative to positive charge. In the presence of an electric field, $\zeta = V/L$ (voltage per unit distance between the capacitor plates), electric field acts on electric

Table 19.1 *Dielectric Constant and Dielectric Strength*

Material	Dielectric constant, k		Dielectric strength, ζ (kV/mm)
	at 60 Hz	at 1 MHz	
Mica	—	6.5	60
Steatite (MgO–SiO_2)	6.0	6.5	11
Soda lime glass	7.0	7.0	10
Porcelain	6.0	6.0	1.6–16
Fused silica	4.0	3.8	10
Air	1.0	—	3.0
Alcohol	26.0	—	—
Asbestos	2.0	—	2.0
Cellulose film	5.8	—	28
Ebonite	2.8	—	50
Dry paper	7.2	—	5.0
Quartz	3.5	—	13
Mica	8.0	5.0	—
Polymers			
Phenol formaldehyde	5.3	—	14
Nylon 6.6	4.0	3.5	16
Polystyrene	2.6	—	24
Polyethylene	2.3	2.3	18
Polytetrafluoro-ethylene	2.1	—	18
PVC	7.0	3.4	—

dipole to orient with the applied field. This phenomenon is known as 'polarization', which is shown in Figure 19.6. For a capacitor, surface charge density, D or the amount of charge per unit area (C/m²) is proportional to the applied electric field, $ζ$.

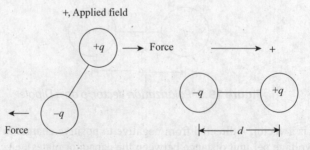

Figure 19.6 Polarization: *Final Dipole Alignment with the Field*

In a vacuum, surface charge density, $D_0 = \epsilon_0 \zeta$. In the case of a dielectric medium, charge density, $D = \epsilon \zeta$. For a capacitor containing n plates, the capacitance, $C = \epsilon_0 kA \, (n - 1)/L$, where A is the area between the plates, k is the dielectric constant, L is the separation between the plates and ϵ_0 is the permittivity of vacuum, which is equal to 8.85×10^{-12} F/m. Sometimes, D is also known as dielectric displacement. When a dielectric is introduced and an electric field is applied, the entire solid within the plates becomes polarized.

Surface charge density on the plates of a capacitor can be represented by, $D = \epsilon_0 \zeta + P$, where P is polarization.

$$P = D - \epsilon_0 \zeta = \epsilon \zeta - \epsilon_0 \zeta = \zeta(\epsilon - \epsilon_0) = \zeta \epsilon_0 \, (k - 1)$$

Units of P are the same as that of D, i.e C/m^2.

Example 19.1 Sodium chloride has a polarization of 4.33×10^{-8} C/m^2 in an electric field of 950 V/m. Calculate the dielectric constant k for NaCl.

Solution:

Polarization, $\qquad\qquad\qquad P = (k - 1)\, \epsilon_0 \zeta,$

$$k - 1 = \frac{P}{\epsilon_0 \zeta} = \frac{4.33 \times 10^{-8}}{8.85 \times 10^{-12} \times 950} = 5.15$$

Dielectric constant, $\qquad\qquad k = 6.15$

Example 19.2 A parallel plate capacitor has an area of 7.74×10^{-4} m^2, and a plate separation of 2.2 mm, across which a potential of 10 V is applied. Dielectric constant of the material is 6.02. Calculate (1) the capacitance, (2) magnitude of charge stored on each plate, (3) dielectric displacement and (4) polarization.

Solution:

Permittivity of dielectric medium,
$$\epsilon = k\epsilon_0 = 6.02 \times 8.85 \times 10^{-12} \text{ F/m}$$
$$= 53.227 \times 10^{-12} \text{ F/m}$$

Area of the plate,
$$A = 7.74 \times 10^{-4} \text{ m}^2$$

Separation,
$$L = 0.0022 \text{ m}$$

(1) Capacitance, $\qquad C = \dfrac{EA}{L} = \dfrac{53.227 \times 10^{-12} \times 7.74^3 \times 10^{-4}}{0.0022}$

$$= 1.874 \times 10^{-11} \text{ C}$$

(2) Charge stored, $\qquad Q = CV = 1.874 \times 10^{-11} \times 10 = 1.874 \times 10^{-10} \text{ C}$

(3) Dielectric displacement, $\qquad D = \epsilon \zeta = \epsilon V/L$

$$= \frac{53.227 \times 10^{-12} \times 10}{0.0022} = 2.4217 \times 10^{-7} \text{ C/m}^2$$

(4) Polarization, $\qquad P = D - \epsilon_0 \zeta = 2.4217 \times 10^{-7} - \dfrac{8.85 \times 10^{-12} \times 10}{0.0022}$

$$= 2.0194 \times 10^{-7} \text{ C/m}^2$$

19.4 POLARIZATION OF AN ELECTRIC FIELD

When an electric field is applied to a material, dipoles are induced within the atomic or molecular structure. During polarization, dipoles are aligned along the direction of the field. In addition, any permanent dipoles already present in the material are also aligned with the field.

Polarization, $P = N_c qd$, where N_c is the number of charge carriers, q is the electronic charge and d is the distance between the dipoles. $P = qd$, i.e. total electronic charge × distance between the dipoles.

There are three mechanisms that cause polarization. They are as follows:

1. Electronic polarization
2. Ionic polarization
3. Orientation polarization

19.4.1 Electronic Polarization

Electronic polarization is induced in all atoms. This polarization results from the displacement of centre of the negatively charged electron cloud relative to the positively charged nucleus of the atom by an electric field. It is found in all dielectric materials and exists under an applied electric field as shown in Figure 19.7.

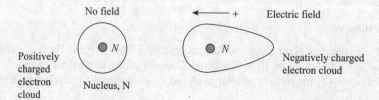

Figure 19.7 *Electronic Polarization*

19.4.2 Ionic Polarization

This polarization occurs only in ionic materials. An applied electric field acts to displace cations in one direction and anions in the opposite direction, which gives rise to a net dipole moment, p_i as shown in Figure 19.8.

Dipole moment on each pair, $p_i = q.d_i$, where d_i is the relative displacement and q is the magnitude of each dipole charge.

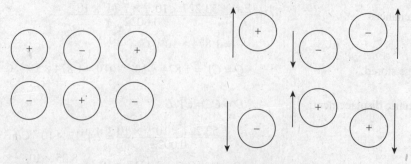

Figure 19.8 *Ionic Polarization*

19.4.3 Orientation Polarization

It is a temperature-dependent process in which hydrocarbon molecules align themselves in the direction of applied field. By increasing the temperature, the alignment becomes random. The CH_3Cl molecule carrying dipole moment gets aligned in this way even without an electric field. The positive and negative charges do not coincide in this molecule.

Some materials contain natural dipoles. When a field is applied, the dipoles rotate to line up with the imposed field. When the field is removed, the dipoles remain in alignment, causing permanent polarization. Figure 19.9 shows an orientation polarization.

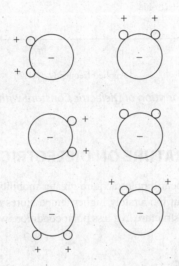

Figure 19.9 *Orientation Polarization*

19.5 FREQUENCY DEPENDENCE OF DIELECTRIC CONSTANT

In many applications, ac power is used and the applied electric field reverses direction continuously. Dielectric material is subjected to polarization by an ac electric field. With each reversal of voltage, the dipoles attempt to reorient with the field—a process that requires a finite time. Relaxation frequency is taken as the reciprocal of this minimum orientation time. A dipole cannot keep switching orientation if the relaxation frequency, f_r is less than the frequency of applied voltage, f_a. Under these circumstances, a dipole cannot contribute to the dielectric constant. Figure 19.10 shows dependence of k (dielectric constant) on field frequency, f_a for three types of polarization, i.e. orientation, ionic and electronic.

Figure 19.10 shows that the dielectric constant, k is independent of frequency in a particular range of frequencies for a certain type of polarization, but when polarization mechanism ceases to function, there is abrupt change in the dielectric constant.

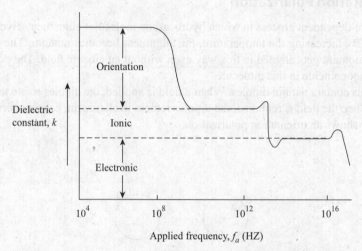

Figure 19.10 *Variation of Dielectric Constant with Frequency, f_a*

19.6 EFFECT OF TEMPERATURE ON DIELECTRIC CONSTANT

Under increased temperature, permanent dipoles acquire greater mobility and polarize more easily giving higher value of dielectric constant, but moderately higher temperatures may cause the dielectric to break-down and produce changes in crystal structure to a less polar condition, which greatly reduces polarization.

19.7 DIELECTRIC LOSSES

When a dielectric material is polarized in an ac electric field, some energy is dissipated as heat. The fraction of energy lost during each reversal is the dielectric loss. Energy loss is mainly due to the following factors:

1. *Current leakage:* Losses due to current leakage are low if the electrical resistivity is high.
2. *Dipole friction:* This occurs when reorientation of the dipoles is difficult as in complex organic molecules.
3. At lower frequencies, losses are high because dipoles have time to move. At higher frequencies, losses are low because dipoles do not move at all.

A frequency can be purposely selected so that the dielectric materials with permanent dipoles have high dielectric loss and the materials that polarize only by electronic or ionic means have a low dielectric loss. Consequently, the permanent dipole materials heat but other materials remain cool. Figure 19.11 shows the influence of frequency on dielectric loss.

Example: Microwave ovens are used to cure many polymeric adhesives while joining two materials. Adhesive has a high loss factor but the materials to be joined have low loss factor, and the heat produced in adhesive due to dielectric loss initiates the thermosetting reaction.

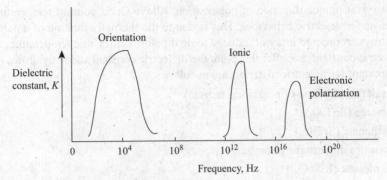

Figure 19.11 *Influence of Frequency on Dielectric Loss*

19.8 DIELECTRIC BREAKDOWN

The voltage per unit thickness of insulating material that can be sustained by an insulating material before it breaks down is known as 'dielectric strength' and a good insulating material must possess high dielectric strength.

Following factors are responsible for the breakdown of a dielectric:

1. *Intrinsic breakdown:* This occurs when electrons from valence band crossover forbidden gap, E_g, under the action of applied voltage and enter into conduction band. In this process, a large induction current and very high local field is created. This failure is known as Zener breakdown. Intrinsic breakdown can occur at lower voltage also if impurities are present in the dielectric material.

2. *Thermal breakdown:* If the heat dissipation is poor, heat produced by electrical energy gets accumulated and the dielectric may melt. This breakdown is more severe in dc than in ac field.

3. *Electrochemical breakdown:* If the leakage current increases due to larger mobility of ions at elevated temperature, the dielectric gets converted into oxides, decreasing the insulation resistance, for example, breakdown of rubber.

4. *Defect breakdown:* Due to detrimental effects of moisture and pores on the surface of the dielectric material, this type of breakdown occurs. Glazing of surface may eliminate this breakdown. Fire-proof silica and high-strength mica are used to provide good surface finish.

5. *Discharge breakdown:* This occurs due to the presence of gas bubbles in the solid and their collapse under the applied field. Gaseous atoms get ionized at lower potential than the solid atoms, causing deterioration.

Example 19.3 The dielectric strength of a natural rubber is 40 kV/mm at 60 Hz. Calculate the thickness of insulation on a wire carrying 25 kV to sustain breakdown.

Solution:

Dielectric strength, $\qquad \zeta = V/L = 40 \text{ kV/mm}$
Voltage in wire $\qquad = 25 \text{ kV}$
Thickness of insulation $\qquad = 25 \times 1/40$
$\qquad = 0.625 \text{ mm}$

19.9 FERROELECTRICITY

Ferroelectricity is a result of spontaneous alignment of electric dipoles, which exhibit a strong mutual interaction. A ferroelectric crystal lacks the centre of symmetry but must contain a unique non-equivalent direction necessary for unique direction of polarization. Above Curie point of temperature, ferroelectric crystal loses its ferroelectric behaviour. This is due to the thermal vibration of a particular amplitude, which destroys an ordered array of induced ionic dipoles. Until Curie temperature, there is sharp increase in dielectric constant, but after this point the dielectric constant suddenly drops.

The most important ferroelectric materials are as follows:

1. Rocheile salt (tetrahydrate of potassium tartrate)
2. Barium titanate ($BaTiO_3$)
3. Strontium titanate ($SrTiO_3$)
4. KDP (potassium dihydrogen phosphate)
5. Potassium niobate ($KNbO_3$)
6. Lead zirconate titanate ($PbZrO_3TiO_3$)

Whenever high dielectric constant is required, ferroelectric materials are used. When Lead zirconate titanate is used as a dielectric material for capacitors, size becomes much smaller in comparison to the capacitor made from paper or mica. Moreover, high value of electromechanical coupling constant of ferroelectrics makes them highly useful for piezoelectric transducers. But in frequency determination devices, still quartz is used. All ferroelectric materials are piezoelectric also, but not all piezoelectric materials are ferroelectrics. For example, quartz is a piezoelectric material but not a ferroelectric material. Ferroelectric lithium niobate is used as an electro-optic material, whose index of refraction is controlled by an electric field. Ferroelectrics are employed in the form of polycrystalline ceramics for most technical applications.

If a ferroelectric material is heated above its Curie temperature and then allowed to cool slowly in powerful electric field, then preferred orientation of the domains in each of the crystal is maintained. This type of material with a net permanent polarization acts like a pseudo-single crystal (Table 19.2).

Table 19.2 *Properties of Some Ferroelectric Materials*

Material	Polarization (C/m²)	Curie Temperature (°C)
KH_2PO_4	0.05	−148
$BaTiO_3$	0.25	122
$KNbO_3$	0.30	436
$PbTiO_3$	0.50	490

19.10 PIEZOELECTRICITY

When a crystal is strained, an electric field is generated in it. This phenomenon is known as 'piezoelectricity'. As a result of this field, a potential difference develops across the sample, which can be measured. The inverse effect is that an applied field produces strain in the sample, which has also been observed in a piezoelectric crystal. This piezoelectricity is very small. A field of 1000 V/cm in a quartz crystal (SiO_2) produces a strain of only 10^{-7}. Conversely, even a small strain produces enormous electric fields. The piezoelectric effect is often used to convert electrical energy into mechanical energy and vice versa. Piezoelectric crystal is used as a transducer. For example, an electric signal applied to the ends of a quartz rod generates mechanical waves in the rod. Quartz is the most commonly used piezoelectric material in transducer applications.

The microscopic origin of piezoelectricity lies in the displacement of ionic charge within the crystal. In the absence of any strain, the distribution of charge at the lattice sites is symmetric, and no electric field is present. But, when the crystal is strained, the charge is displaced. If the charge distribution is no longer symmetric, then a net polarization occurs and a concomitant electric field is developed.

19.11 DIELECTRIC MATERIALS

Most of the dielectric materials used for capacitors are classified into three categories as follows:

1. Liquids composed of polar molecules
2. Polymers
3. Ceramics

All these possess permanent dipoles that move easily in an electric field and have high dielectric constant. Water has a high dielectric constant but is corrosive in nature, relatively conductive and difficult to use in capacitors. Organic oils and wax are more effective. These materials contain long-chain molecules, which serve as dipoles and are easily aligned. Often these are impregnated into papers.

In amorphous polymers, segments of chains possess sufficient mobility to cause polarization. Capacitors very often use polyesters (as Mylar), polystyrenes, polycarbonates and cellulose (paper) as dielectrics. Glass is an amorphous substance used as dielectric material.

Polymers with asymmetric chains have higher dielectric constant, even though the chains may not align easily during polarization. Polyvinyl chloride and polystyrene have dielectric strength greater than that of polyethylene. For polymers, dielectric constant lies between 2.2 and 4.0.

Barium titanate ($BaTiO_3$), a crystalline ceramic, has a asymmetric structure at room temperature. Titanium ion is displaced slightly from the centre of the unit cell, causing the crystal to be tetragonal and permanently polarized. In ac field, there is rapid response of titanium ion to move back and forth to assure that polarization is aligned with the field. Barium titanate has extraordinarily high dielectric constant.

Ceramics provide excellent insulation because of their high dielectric strength and excellent thermal stability. Widely used ceramics are glass, alumina, quartz, mica and asbestos, which have a dielectric constant up to 12. The mineral rutile (TiO_2) possesses very high values of dielectric constant.

Piezoelectric materials include titanates of barium and lead; lead zirconate ($PbZrO_3$), ammonia dihydrogen phosphate ($NH_4H_2PO_4$) and quartz. Rochelle salt (tetrahydrate of potassium phosphate), strantium titanate ($SrTiO_3$), potassium dihydrogen phosphate (KDP) and potassium niobate ($KNbO_3$) are ferroelectric materials. Formvar is a suitable insulating material at low-temperature applications. It is the trade name of polyvinylformal.

19.12 PRACTICAL DIELECTRICS

Solid dielectrics are the most commonly used dielectrics in electrical engineering and many solids are very good insulators also. Common examples of dielectrics are porcelain, glass and many plastics. Air, nitrogen and sulphur hexafluoride are the three most commonly used gaseous dielectrics. Following are some other examples of dielectrics:

1. Industrial coatings such as parylene provide a dielectric barrier between the substrate and its environment.
2. Mineral oil is extensively used in electrical transformers as a fluid dielectric and to assist in cooling. Electrical grade castor oil is used in high-voltage capacitors to prevent corona discharge and to increase capacitance.

3. Since dielectrics resist the flow of electricity, the surface of the dielectric may retain stranded excess electrical charge. This may occur accidentally when the dielectric is rubbed (triboelectric effect). This is useful in Van de Graff generator, but destructive in electrostatic discharge.

4. Specially processed dielectrics called 'electrets' may retain excess internal charge or 'frozen in 'polarization'. They have a semi-permanent external electric field and are the electrostatics equivalent to magnets.

5. Some dielectrics can generate a potential difference, when subjected to a mechanical stress or strain. These materials are called 'piezoelectric materials'.

6. Some ionic crystals and polymer dielectrics exhibit a spontaneous dipole moment, which can be reversed by an externally applied electric field. This behaviour is called 'ferroelectric effect'. Ferroelectric materials often have high dielectric constant, making them useful for capacitors.

KEY POINTS TO REMEMBER

❑ A dielectric material is an electrically insulating material exhibiting an electric dipole structure.

❑ Positively and negatively charged dipoles are separated on atomic or molecular level.

❑ As a result of dipole interaction with electric field, dielectric material is used in capacitors.

❑ Capacitance, $C = Q/V$, i.e. the ratio of quantity of charge stored on any of the two plates and applied voltage.

❑ Capacitance, $C = \epsilon_0 A/L$, where ϵ_0 is the permittivity in a vacuum, which is equal to 8.85×10^{-12} F/m, A is the area between the plates, L is the distance between the two plates or thickness of dielectric.

❑ Dielectric constant, $k = \epsilon/\epsilon_0$, i.e. the ratio of permittivity of dielectric medium and vacuum.

❑ In a vacuum, charge density, $D_0 = \epsilon_0 \zeta$.

❑ In a dielectric medium, charge density, $D = \epsilon \zeta$, where ζ is the density of electric field.

❑ Polarization, $P = \zeta \epsilon_0 (k - 1)$ in C/m².

❑ Polarization, $P = N_c qd$, where N_c is number of charge carriers, q is electronic charge and d is distance between the dipoles.

❑ Electronic polarization results from the displacement of centre of the negatively charged electron cloud relative to the positively charged nucleus of an atom by an electric field.

❑ *Ionic polarization:* Applied electric field displaces cations in one direction and anions in opposite direction, giving rise to a dipole moment.

❑ *Orientation polarization:* When an electric field is applied, natural dipoles of some materials rotate to line up with the imposed field. After the removal of the field, the dipoles remain in alignment.

❑ When the frequency of the applied electric field is more than the relaxation frequency of dipoles, the polarization mechanism ceases to function.

❑ With increased temperature, the permanent dipole acquires greater mobility and polarizes more easily, resulting in higher dielectric constant.

❑ When a dielectric material is polarized in an ac electrical field, some energy is dissipated as heat. The fraction of energy lost during each reversal is the dielectric loss. The current leakage and dipole friction are the main causes of dielectric loss.

❑ The voltage per unit thickness of insulating material that can be sustained by an insulating material before it breaks down is known as dielectric strength.

❑ *Intrinsic breakdown*: Due to large induction current and very high local field.

❑ *Thermal breakdown:* Due to poor heat dissipation, electrical energy gets accumulated, causing melting of the dielectric.

❑ *Electro-chemical breakdown:* Due to elevated temperature, dielectric gets converted into oxide, resulting in decrease in insulation resistance.

❑ *Discharge breakdown:* Due to the collapse of gas bubbles present in the solid under the applied field.

❑ Ferroelectricity is the result of spontaneous alignment of electric dipoles, which has a strong mutual interaction. Rochelle salt, barium titanate, KDP, potassium niobate, strontium titanate and lead zirconate titanate are ferroelectrics.

❑ When a crystal is strained, an electric field is generated or vice versa, which is known as piezoelectricity. Quartz crystal is piezoelectric.

❑ Organic oils and wax are effective as capacitors.

❑ Polyester, polystyrene, polycarbonates and cellulose are used as dielectrics.

❑ Ceramics as glass, porcelain, alumina, quartz, mica and asbestos are excellent dielectric materials with excellent thermal stability and high dielectric constant.

❑ Formvar is a suitable insulating material for low-temperature applications.

❑ Electrets are specially processed dielectrics, which may retain excess internal charge or frozen in polarization.

MULTIPLE CHOICE QUESTIONS

1. Dielectric losses are due to
   (A) Current leakage
   (B) Dipole friction, which is a correct statement
   (a) Both (A) and (B)
   (b) Neither (A) nor (B)
   (c) Only (A)
   (d) Only (B)

2. If Q = charge, V = voltage, then capacitance C is given by
   (a) $Q.V$
   (b) Q/V
   (c) V/Q
   (d) None of these

3. Dielectric constant for mica at 60 Hz is
   (a) 8
   (b) 4.0
   (c) 2.6
   (d) None of these

4. If V is the voltage, ζ is the field density, ϵ_0 is the permittivity for vacuum, then in vacuum charge density, D_0 is
   (a) $\epsilon_0 V$
   (b) $\epsilon_0 \zeta$
   (c) V/ϵ_0
   (d) None of these

5. If the capacitance, $C = 2 \times 10^{-9}$ F, voltage applied is 100 V, then charge stored, Q is
   (a) 2×10^{-11} C
   (b) 2×10^{-8} C
   (c) 2×10^{-7} C
   (d) None of these

6. If f_r is the relaxation frequency and f_a is the applied frequency, then at what stage polarization mechanism ceases to function

    (a) $f_a < f_r$ (c) $f_a > f_r$

    (b) $f_a = f_r$ (d) None of these

7. Which of the following statements is correct?

    (A) At lower frequencies losses are high because dipoles have time to move

    (B) At higher frequencies, losses are low because the dipoles do not move at all

    (a) Both (A) and (B)

    (b) (A) only

    (c) (B) only

    (d) None of these

8. Match the lists of reasons and types of breakdown

I	II
I Poor heat dissipation	(A) Electrochemical breakdown
II Dielectric converted in oxide	(B) Discharge break down
III Collapse of gas bubbles	(C) Defect break down
IV Detrimental effect of moisture	(D) Thermal break down

	I	II	III	IV
(a)	A	D	B	C
(b)	D	A	B	C
(c)	D	A	C	B
(d) None of these				

9. Curie temperature of lead titanate is

    (a) $-148°C$ (c) $436°C$

    (b) $122°C$ (d) $490°C$

Answers

1. (a)   2. (b)   3. (a)   4. (b)   5. (c)   6. (c)   7. (c)   8. (b)   9. (d)

REVIEW QUESTIONS

1. What is the difference between a dielectric and an insulator?

2. Define the terms dielectric constant, dielectric strength and dielectric loss.

3. Explain polarization and describe three types of polarization with the help of neat sketches.

4. Discuss the phenomenon of polarization taking place in a capacitor connected to a dc supply.

5. Enumerate the factors leading to dielectric loss.

6. What is breakdown voltage of a capacitor?

7. What is spontaneous polarization?

8. State the difference between polar and nonpolar materials.

9. Explain the difference between ferroelectricity and piezoelectricity.

10. What is dipole moment and what is polarization?

11. With the help of a neat graph between dielectric constant and applied frequency, explain the effect of frequency on dielectric constant for three types of polarization.

12. Compare the dielectric constants of polymers and ceramics.

PRACTICE PROBLEMS

1. The polarization P of a dielectric material positioned within a parallel plate capacitor is to be 1×10^{-6} C/m^2.

    (a) What must be the dielectric constant if an electric field of 5×10^4 V is applied?

    (b) What will be the dielectric displacement D?

    Ans. (3.26, 1.44 $\times$ 10^{-6} C/m^2)

2. A charge of 3.5×10^{-11} C is to be stored on each plate of a parallel plate capacitor having an area of 160 mm^2 and a plate separation of 3.5 mm.

    (a) What voltage is required if a material having a dielectric constant of 5.0 is positioned within the plates and what is the capacitance?

    (b) What voltage is required if a vacuum is there in between the plates?

    (c) What is polarization in part (a)?

    Ans. (17.3 V, 2.023 $\times 10^{-12}$ F; 86.5 V, 0.404 $\times$ 10^{-12} F/m, $P = 1.75 \times 10^{-7}$ C/m^2)

3. A barium titanate crystal is inserted in a parallel plate condenser of plate dimensions 10×10 mm^2. A capacitance of 10^{-9} F is noticed when the plates are separated by 2 mm. Taking $\epsilon_0 = 8.85 \times 10^{-12}$ F/m, determine the dielectric constant of the crystal.

    Ans. (2260)

4. Capacitor has a capacitance of 0.019 F, when a wax paper ($\epsilon_p = 1.85$) between electrodes of aluminium foil is used. The wax paper is to be replaced by a plastic film ($\epsilon_p = 2.15$) of same dimensions. Taking the other factors to be equal, obtain the change in capacitance.

    Ans. (0.0117 F increase)

5. A layer of porcelain is 80 mm long, 20 mm wide and 1 μm thick. Calculate its capacitance taking $k = 6$.

    Ans. (0.85 $\times$ 10^{-7} F)

MAGNETIC PROPERTIES

20.1 INTRODUCTION

From the beginning of civilization magnet has been in the service of mankind as magnetite ore or lode-stone. But for the past 100 years, numerous applications of magnetization and magnetic materials have come up. In the more recent years, development of new magnetic materials has played important role in computer revolution.

Large powerful magnets are crucial for advanced technologies as magnetic levitation trains float above tracks using strong magnets. Powerful magnetic fields are used in nuclear magnetic resonance as a very useful diagnostic instrument used by doctors.

The magnetic forces are produced by the motion of charged particles such as electrons, which indicate close relationship between magnetism and electricity underlying the electromagnetic theory. The magnetic fields are used to control the path of charged particles.

This chapter discusses various types of magnetisms, magnetization and demagnetization processes including different types of soft and hard magnetic materials.

20.2 MAGNETISM

For the past thousands of years, magnet has been in use in day-to-day activities. A magnet is character-ized by attractive and repulsive forces, yet the phenomenon of magnetism is complex and difficult to understand. However, there are enormous contributions of magnetism in the service of society, which are as follows:

1. Computer, electric power generation, transformers and electric motors
2. Radio, telephone and television
3. Sound and video reproduction systems
4. Recorders and tape players using magnetic tapes
5. Compass to determine North direction
6. Magnetic latches

7. Use of magnets in healing several diseases
8. Computer memories fabricated using bubble domains
9. Magnetic levitation trains float above the tracks using strong magnets
10. Powerful magnetic fields are used in nuclear resonance imaging
11. Superconducting magnets—most powerful particle accelerator

20.2.1 Magnetic Behaviour

Iron, steel and naturally occurring lodestone exhibit magnetic properties. The magnetic force or forces arise from the movement of electrical charge. Maxwell's equation and Bio-Savart law describe the origin and behaviour of the fields that govern these forces. So, magnetism is observed whenever electrically charged particles are in motion. This can arise either from the movement of electrons in an electrical circuit resulting in electromagnetism or from the quantum mechanical spin or orbital motion of electrons resulting in permanent magnets. Electron spin is the dominant effect within the atoms and orbital motion of electrons around the nucleus is a *secondary effect*. The magnetic field can be best visualized within a magnetic coil (carrying electric current) as shown in Figure 20.1. The figure shows the imaginary lines of force drawn to show the direction of force in the vicinity of field source (a loop carrying current).

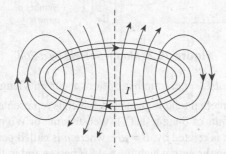

Figure 20.1 *Magnetic Field Around a Loop Carrying Current*

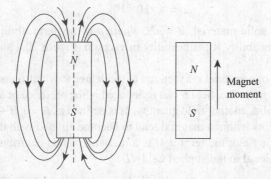

Figure 20.2 *Magnetic Lines of Force Around a Bar Magnet*

The magnetic field generated by a coil (current loop) is termed as magnetic field, H. Magnetic dipoles are found to exist in magnetic materials, which in some respect are analogous to electric dipoles. Magnetic dipoles consist of small bar magnets composed of north and south poles and magnetic dipole moment is represented by an arrow (south to north pole). Figure 20.2 shows the magnetic field distribution by lines of force for a bar magnet and a magnetic moment by an arrow.

20.3 MAGNETIC FIELD VECTORS

Figure 20.3 shows the magnetic field, H generated by a cylindrical coil. This magnetic field is dependent on the current, I, number of turns, n, and coil length, L. The units of H are Ampere-turn/m. The magnetic field, H is also termed as 'magnetic field strength'.

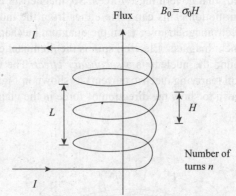

Figure 20.3 *Magnetic Field by a Coil*

$$H = n.I/L, \quad \text{i.e. (number of turns} \times \text{current)/length, } L$$

Due to external field H, an internal field is generated, which is represented by B, the magnetic flux density (or magnetic induction). Units of B are tesla (T) (Websters/m², or Wb/m²). Both H and B are vectors.

The magnetic field strength is related by, $B = \mu H$, where μ is called permeability, which is a specific property of the specific medium through which the field H passes and in this medium the flux density B is measured. Permeability, μ has a unit of Wb/A-m or H/m (Henry /meter).

In the presence of vacuum, magnetic flux density, $B_0 = \mu_0 \times H$, where μ_0 is the permeability of the vacuum.

$$\mu_0 = 4 \times 10^{-7} \text{ H/m}$$

The magnetic flux within a solid material, $B = \mu H$, where μ is the permeability of a solid. Moreover, $\mu = \mu_r x \, \mu_0$, i.e. relative permeability $\times$ permeability in vacuum. Figure 20.4 shows flux within a solid material (bar).

The relative permeability of a material is a measure of the degree to which a material can be magnetized or the ease with which a magnetic flux field B can be induced in the presence of an external field H.

For magnetization of a solid, another field quantity, M is defined as $B = \mu_0 H + \mu_0 M$. In the presence of field H, the magnetic moments within a material tend to become aligned with the field and to reinforce it by virtue of their magnetic field; the term $\mu_0 M$ is a measure of this contribution. The magnitude of magnetization, M is proportional to the applied field, H.

$$M = X_m H,$$

where X_m is called magnetic susceptibility, which is unit-less.

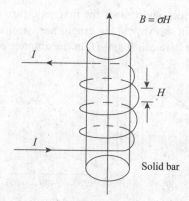

Figure 20.4 *Magnetic Flux in a Solid Bar*

$$X_m = (\mu_r - 1) = \text{relative permeability} - 1$$
$$= (\mu_r - 1)H$$

20.3.1 Magnetic Moments

Each electron in an atom has magnetic moments due to (1) orbital motion of electron around the nucleus and (2) spinning motion of the electron about its axis. Orbital motion around the nucleus, a moving charge on electron can be considered as a small current loop, generating a very small magnetic field, having a magnetic moment about the axis of rotation. Similarly, each electron can be considered as spinning around an axis, so other magnetic moment generates from an electron spin. Therefore, each electron in an atom is thought of as a small magnet having (1) permanent orbital magnetic moment and (2) spin magnetic moment.

Bohr has given magnetron, μ_B, the most fundamental magnetic moment of magnitude 9.27×10^{-24} A-m^2. For each electron, spin magnetic moment is μ_B, while the orbital magnetic moment is $m_l\mu_B$, where m_l is the magnetic quantum number of the electron.

Some of the orbital magnetic moments of some electron pairs cancel each other. Similarly, some spin moments are cancelled because spin-up moment will cancel spin-down moment. The net magnetic moment for an atom is the sum of the total magnetic moments minus the moments that are cancelled out.

For an atom having completely filled shells or subshells, when all electrons are taken into account, there is total cancellation of both orbital and spin moments. Therefore, the materials composed of atoms having completely filled electron shells are not capable of being permanently magnetized. For example, atoms of some inert gases like He, Ne and Ar in which shells are completely filled.

Different types of magnetisms are diamagnetism, paramagnetism and ferromagnetism. Subclasses of ferromagnetism are anti-ferrimagnetism and ferrimagnetism. All materials exhibit at least one of these types of magnetisms. The magnetic behaviour depends on the response of electrons and magnetic dipoles to the applied magnetic field.

20.4 MAGNETIZATION CURVES

The magnetic properties of a material are well understood by a magnetization or B–H curve, i.e. a curve between flux and magnetic field as shown in Figure 20.5(a)–(c).

These curves are all straight lines and drawn for magnetic flux density, B versus magnetic field strength, H. Negative values are not shown, but the graphs are symmetrical about vertical axis.

Figure 20.5(a) shows the curve between B and H, in the absence of any material, i.e., in a vacuum.

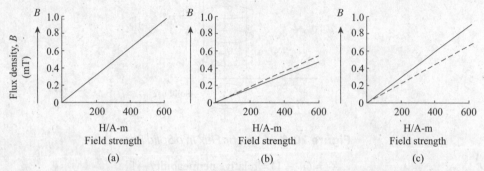

Figure 20.5 *Magnetization Curves (a) Vacuum (b) Diamagnetic Material (c) Paramagnetic Material*

The gradient of this curve is $4\pi \times 10^{-7}$ H/m, which corresponds to the fundamental physical constant, μ_0. Of greater interest is to see how placing a specimen of some material affects the gradient, μ_0. Manufacturers of a particular grade of ferrite metal generally provide this curve because the shape reveals how the core material in any component made from it will respond to changes in the applied field.

Every material exhibits magnetic properties when placed in a magnetic field, hence the materials can be classified according to their interaction with this magnetic field.

Diamagnetism is a classification used to describe materials that line up at right angles to a non-uniform magnetic field and are slightly repelled by the field. Diamagnetism occurs as a result of interference of magnetic field with the motion of electrons orbiting the atoms or molecules of an element or a compound. When a material is placed in the magnetic field, the magnetic force acts upon the moving electrons in the material, causing the electrons to speed up or slow down. The movement of electrons interferes with the motion of the magnetic field, so the atoms internally oppose the field, causing the material to be slightly repelled by the magnetic field.

Diamagnetism is a characteristic of elements or compounds that possess complete sets of valence electrons, which means that all their electrons are paired. Electrons orbit an atom while spinning about their own axis. If a spinning electron is orbiting singly, then its movement generates a magnetic field. But two paired electrons have opposite spins, so that magnetic field generated by each is cancelled out. So, when all the electrons of an atom are paired, the element will not have any magnetic field. When this element is placed in a magnetic field, it is repelled. The atomic dipole configuration of a diamagnetic material with or without magnetic field is shown in Figure 20.6. In the presence of a field, dipoles are induced and are aligned opposite to the field.

In the case of diamagnetism, relative permeability μ_r is slightly less than 1 and the magnetic susceptibility is negative, that is, the magnitude of magnetic flux B within a diamagnetic material is less than that in vacuum. The volume susceptibility X_m for a diamagnetic solid material is of the order of -10^{-5}. When placed between the poles of a strong electromagnet, the diamagnetic material is attracted towards a region where the field is weak. Table 20.1 presents relative permeability values of some diamagnetic materials.

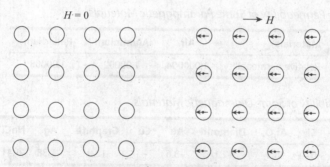

Figure 20.6 *Diamagnetic Material*

Table 20.1 *Relative Permeability of Some Diamagnetic Materials*

Materials	Bi	Ag	Pb	Cu
Relative permeability	0.99983	0.99998	0.9999983	0.999991

20.4.1 Paramagnetism

Paramagnetism generally occurs in elements or compounds possessing unpaired electrons. Many compounds consisting of iron, palladium, platinum and rare earth elements have single electron that generates a small magnetic field. In this case, atom acts as a small permanent magnet. If a substance containing such atoms is placed in a magnetic field, the field of the atom aligns with the applied magnetic field and causes the atom to be slightly attracted to that magnetic field. This attraction to an applied magnetic field is called paramagnetism. Figure 20.7 shows atomic dipole configuration with or without external magnetic field for a paramagnetic material.

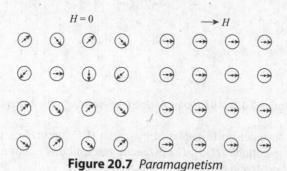

Figure 20.7 *Paramagnetism*

The dipoles align with the external field; they enhance it by giving rise to a relative permeability, μ_r, greater than 1 and to a relatively small but positive magnetic susceptibility. Table 20.2 gives relative permeability values of some paramagnetic materials.

Both diamagnetic and paramagnetic materials are considered to be non-magnetic as they exhibit magnetism only in the presence of an external field. Flux density B within them is almost the same as it would be in a vacuum, because relative permeability is either slightly less than 1 or slightly more than 1. Tables 20.3 and 20.4 demonstrate susceptibility of some diamagnetic and paramagnetic materials.

Table 20.2 *Relative Permeability of Some Paramagnetic Materials*

Materials	Air	Aluminium	Palladium
Relative permeability	1.000004	1.00002	1.00008

Table 20.3 *Susceptibility of Some Diamagnetic Materials*

Materials	Si	Al_2O_3	Diamond	Au	Cu	Graphite	Ag	NaCl	Zn
X_m, Susceptib	−0.41	−0.5	−2.1	−3.6	−	−12.0	−2.38	−1.41	$−1.5 \times 10^{-5}$

Table 20.4 *Susceptibility of Some Paramagnetic Materials*

Materials	$NiSO_4$	Fe_2O_3	$MnSO_4$	$FeCl_2$	Al	Cr	Mo	Ti	Zr
X_m, Susceptib	1.2	1.4	370	3.7	2.07	31.3	11.9	18.1	0.109×10^{-5}

20.5 FERROMAGNETISM

In ferromagnetic materials, there are permanent magnetic dipoles, even when no external field acts on the material; as a result, there is long and permanent magnetization. Figure 20.8 shows that when all dipoles are aligned and $H = 0$, applied field is zero.

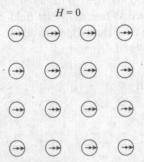

$H = 0$

Figure 20.8 *All Dipoles Aligned—Ferromagnetic Material*

This property of ferromagnetism is displayed by α iron (BCC structure), nickel, cobalt and some rare earth metals such as gadolinium (Gd). The magnetic susceptibility of this material is as high as 10^6, therefore, in this case, $H \ll M$ and the magnetic flux $M = \mu_0 M$.

1. Permanent magnetic moments in ferromagnetic materials result from atomic magnetic moment due to electron spin, which are not cancelled as a result of electronic configuration.
2. Interactions between adjacent atoms, called coupling interaction, cause the adjacent atoms to align with one another or causing the spin moments to align with one another.
3. The contribution of orbital magnetic moment is smaller in comparison to spin moments.
4. Origin of coupling forces is not well understood, but it may be due to the electron structure of the metal.

This mutual spin alignment (coupling) exists in a large volume of region of a crystal, called domains. At a temperature below Curie temperature, T_c, a ferromagnetic material is composed of small volume regions, in which there is mutual alignment of all magnetic dipole moments in the same direction. Figure 20.9 shows the domains in a ferromagnetic material. Arrow represents the atomic magnetic dipole moments.

Figure 20.9 *Domains of Aligned Dipoles—Magnetic Moments*

Within each domain, all the dipoles are aligned. When the external field is applied, all the magnetic dipoles in a solid piece are mutually aligned with the external field H, causing saturation magnetization, M_s, the maximum possible magnetization. Similarly, there is a corresponding value of saturation flux density, B_s.

Saturation magnetization,

M_s = net magnetic moments for each atom × number of atoms per unit volume.

For iron, cobalt and nickel, the net magnetic moment per atom is 2.22, 1.72 and 0.6 times the Bohr's magnetron, respectively.

Example 20.1 Calculate (1) saturation magnetization and (2) saturation flux density for cobalt, which has a density of 8.9 g/cc, net magnetic moment per atom is 1.72 × Bohr's magnetron and atomic weight is 58.93 amu.

Solution:

Bohr's magnetron per atom = 1.72

Saturation magnetization, $M_s = 1.72 \, \mu_B \times N$

$$N = (\rho \times N_a)/A_w = \text{(density} \times \text{Avogadro's number)/atomic weight}$$

$$= (8.9 \times 10^6 \times 6.023 \times 10^{23})/58.93$$

$$= 9.096 \times 10^{28} \text{ atoms/m}^3$$

$$M_s = 1.72 \times 9.27 \times 10^{-24} \times 9.096 \times 10^{28} = 14.5 \times 10^5 \text{ A/m}$$

Saturation flux density, $B_s = \mu_0 M_s = 4\pi \times 10^{-7} \times 14.5 \times 10^5 = 1.82$ T

where T Stands for tesla.

20.5.1 Anti-ferromagnetism

In ferromagnetism, the magnetic moment coupling in adjacent atoms or ions, i.e. dipole moments are parallel and in the same direction, but in anti-ferromagnetism alignment of spin moments in adjacent atoms or ions are completely in opposite directions (anti-parallel). For example, in MnO (manganese oxide) there are Mn^{2+} and O^{2-} ions.

1. No net magnetic moment is associated with oxygen ions as there is total cancellation of spin and orbital moments.

2. Mn^{2+} ions are arrayed in crystal structure so that the moments in adjacent ions are anti-parallel, i.e. opposing moments cancel each other.

3. Solid (MnO) does not possess any magnetic moment.

Figure 20.10 shows anti-parallel alignment of spin magnetic moments of Mn^{2+} ions.

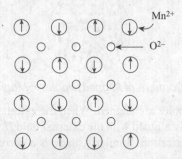

Figure 20.10 *Anti-parallel Alignment of Mn^{2+} Ions*

20.6 FERRIMAGNETISM

Almost every item of electronic equipment produced today contains some ferrimagnetic materials like loudspeakers, motor, interference suppressor, antenna rods, proximity sensors, recharge heads, transformers and inductors that are frequently based on ferrites.

Ferrimagnetic materials are oxides of iron compounded with one or more transition metals such as Mn, Ni and Zn, for example, $MnFe_2O_4$. Permanent magnets include barium.

Raw material is ground into a powder, which is then fired in a kiln or sintered to produce grey, hard, brittle ceramic materials, having cubic crystalline structure.

On an atomic scale, the magnetic properties depend upon interaction between the electrons associated with metal ions. Neighbouring atomic magnetic moments become locked in anti-parallel with neighbours (which contrast with ferromagnetism), but the magnetic moments in one direction are weaker than the magnetic moments in the opposite direction, resulting in overall magnetic moments. Garnets and ferrites show this behaviour.

Ferrites are compounds of two metallic oxides out of which one is invariably iron oxide. The other metal oxide may be of bivalent elements such as Ni, Mn, Zn, Cu or Fe. Symbolically, ferrites may be designated as $(MetO.Fe_2O_3)$ in which Met stands for metal and expresses the element. Magnetite, Fe_3O_4, is composed of $FeO.Fe_2O_3$. It has a cubic structure. Few examples of more common ferrites are Mn-Fe_2O_4, Nickel ferrite, $NiFe_2O_4$, Zn–Mn ferrite and Zn–Ni ferrite.

Ferrites are ceramic materials having the following properties:

1. Very high electrical resistivity

2. Lower power loss at high frequencies

3. Due to their spontaneous magnetism, suitable for both temporary and permanent magnet applications

They suffer from poor machinability and brittleness. The magnetization hysteresis loop of ferrite may vary from very narrow to very wide. Ferrites with *narrow hysteresis loop form soft magnets*, which is used in audio, TV transformer, gyration and inductance cores.

The Mn–Mg ferrites with almost square hysteresis loop are used in memory cores of computers. Barium ferrite ($BaO.6Fe_2O_3$) is used to make permanent magnets.

20.6.1 Spinal and Garnet Ferrites

Ferrites have three types of crystals as shown in Table 20.5

Table 20.5 *Three Types of Crystals of Ferrites*

	Structure	Symbol	Metals (M stands for metal element)
Spinal	Cubic	MFe_2O_3	Zn, Mg, Co, Cd, Cu, Mn, Ni
Garnet	Cubic	$M_3Fe_2O_{12}$	Sn, Tb, Ha, Lu, Tm, Y, Eu, Gd, Dy
Magneto plumbite	Hexagonal	$MFe_{12}O_{19}$	Ba

The spinal ferrite unit cell contains $8 \times MFe_2O_3$, where M is a bivalent metal ion. The iron and metal ions occupy octahedral and tetrahedral sites of the spinal lattice, respectively. Spinal can be normal or inverse. Zn ferrite ($ZnFe_2O_4$) is a normal spinal, while Magnetite (Fe_3O_4) is an inverse spinal. Curie temperatures of spinal ferrites are in the range of 700–860 K. The conductivity varies from 10^2 to 10^{-11} $(\Omega cm)^{-1}$.

Ferrites exhibit hysteresis during magnetization. The hysteresis loops of Cu–Mn ferrite and Mg–Mn ferrite are square, which is used in memory cores of the computers.

Ferrites are also classified as soft and hard ferrites. For example, lithium ferrite is a soft ferrite. It forms square hysteresis loop and has a low dielectric loss. It is mainly used in low-mobility semiconductors and in applications of microwave frequency.

Barium, strontium and lead ferrites exhibiting semiconducting behaviour are hard ferrites. A general-purpose Ni–Zn ferrite has a high relative permeability of the order of 10^4 and a high resistivity of the order of 10^7 Ω-m.

20.7 MAGNETOSTRICTION

The dimensions of a bar of a material change when it is magnetized. Depending upon the field, the length of the bar extends or contracts and its area of cross section decreases or increases, respectively. But, when the bar is subjected to a rapidly alternating magnetic field, there is rapid extension and contraction in the length of the bar. This phenomenon is known as magnetostriction. As a result of rapid extension/contraction, longitudinal vibrations are set up in the bar. The phenomenon of magnetostriction is used in audio-frequency oscillators at sonic and ultrasonic frequencies.

20.8 EFFECT OF TEMPERATURE ON MAGNETIC BEHAVIOUR

The magnetic behaviour of a material is very much dependent on the temperature rise as increase in temperature directly affects the saturation magnetization.

As the temperature of a solid is increased, thermal vibrations of the atoms also increase in magnitude and the increased thermal motion of the atoms tends to randomize the direction of magnetic moments. The atomic thermal vibrations counteract the coupling forces between the adjacent atomic dipole moments causing dipole misalignment in ferromagnetic, anti-ferromagnetic and ferromagnetic materials. The dipole misalignment results in decrease in saturation magnetization in ferromagnetic and ferrimagnetic materials.

The saturation magnetization, M_s is maximum at 0 K, because thermal vibrations at 0 K are minimum. So, with increasing temperature, the saturation magnetization gradually decreases and finally it becomes zero at Curie temperature, T_c. At Curie temperature, the mutual spin coupling forces are fully destroyed. For temperatures above Curie temperature, ferromagnetic and ferrimagnetic materials become paramagnetic. For iron, cobalt, nickel and Fe_3O_4, the Curie temperatures are 768°C, 1120°C, 335°C and 585°C, respectively.

The magnetization behaviour of Fe_3O_4 is shown in Figure 20.11. Magnetization, M_s becomes zero at Curie temperature and it is maximum at 0 K.

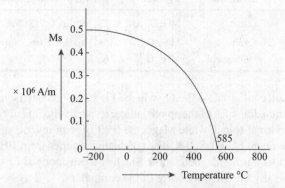

Figure 20.11 *Saturation Magnetization of Fe₃O₄*

By temperature variation, anti-ferromagnetism is also affected. The behaviour of anti-ferromagnetism vanishes at Neel temperature. At temperatures above Neel temperature, anti-ferromagnetic material becomes paramagnetic.

20.9 DOMAINS

At temperatures below Curie point, T_c, in ferromagnetic and ferrimagnetic materials, there exist domains, i.e. small volume regions in each of which there is mutual alignment of all magnetic dipoles in the same direction as shown in Figure 20.12.

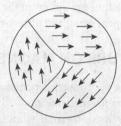

Figure 20.12 *Aligned Magnetic Dipoles in Each Domain*

On microscopic scale, there are several domains in each grain. But on macroscopic scale, considering a solid piece, there are multitudes of domains. There is magnetization in each domain. For a solid piece, the overall magnetization is the vector sum of magnetizations in all the domains.

Flux density, B and field density, H are not proportional to each other in ferromagnetic and ferrimagnetic materials. A curve between B and H is shown in Figure 20.13. As the external field H is increased, the flux density B begins to increase slowly (the flux B lags behind the applied field H) and more rapidly and finally the curve becomes asymptotic at saturation as shown. Maximum flux is B_s.

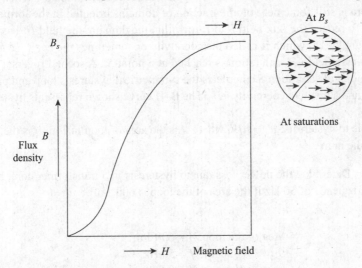

Figure 20.13 *Magnetic Flux Density Versus Magnetic Field*

As the field H is applied, domains change shape and size by the movement of domain boundaries. As the field H increases, the domains, which are favourably oriented grow at the expense of other domains that are not favourably oriented. As the process of magnetization continues, at saturation point in all the domains dipole moments are aligned with the external field, H as shown in Figure 20.13. The magnetic dipoles in all domains are aligned with external field, H.

20.10 HYSTERESIS

A hysteresis effect is produced in which the flux field, B lags behind applied magnetic field, H. At zero H, there exists a residual flux that is called remanence or remanent. Flux density, B_r (the material receives magnetization in the absence of external field H) is shown in Figure 20.14.

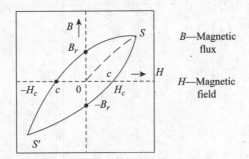

Figure 20.14 *Magnetic Flux Density B Versus Magnetic Field H*

The hysteresis behaviour can be explained by the motion of domain walls. From saturation, when the field is reversed, the process by which the domain structure changes is also reversed. First of all, there is rotation of a single domain in the reversed field, then domains having magnetic moments aligned with the new field form and grow at the expense of the former domains. When the applied field reaches zero, there is still some net volume fraction of domains oriented in the former direction, flux field $-B_r$, exists. To reduce the flux field B to zero within the domain, the field H_c has to be applied as shown in the Figure 20.14, which is called the coercivity or sometimes the *coercive force*. During the application of reverse field $-H$, saturation is reached at a point S'. A second reversal of the field ($+H$ direction) to the point of saturation S completes the symmetrical hysteresis loop and provides negative remanence ($-B_r$) and a positive coercivity $+H_c$. The B–H curve shown represents hysteresis loop taken to saturation.

Energy loss due to hysteresis, $U_h = AfV$, where A is the area of loop in J/m², f is the frequency in Hz and V is the volume in m³.

Example 20.2 Determine the power loss due to hysteresis in a transformer core, having a volume of 0.008 m³ at a frequency of 50 Hz if the area of the loop is 600 J/m².

Solution:

$$\text{Area of the loop, } A = 600 \text{ J/m}^2$$
$$\text{Frequency, } f = 50 \text{ Hz}$$
$$\text{Volume, } V = 0.008 \text{ m}^3$$
$$\text{Power loss, } U_h = 600 \times 50 \times 0.008 = 240 \text{ W}$$

20.11 SOFT MAGNETIC MATERIALS

The area within the hysteresis loop represents the energy loss per unit volume during magnetization and demagnetization cycles. Energy loss is converted into heat and the temperature of the specimen is raised. On the basis of energy loss in the loop, both ferromagnetism and ferrimagnetism can be classified into soft and hard magnetic materials. Soft magnetic materials are used in devices subjected to alternating magnetic fields such as in transformer cores, where the energy loss must be low (Figure 20.15).

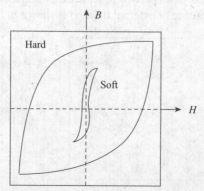

Figure 20.15 *Magnetization Curve for Soft and Hard Magnetic Materials*

Following are the properties of a soft magnetic material:

1. Area within the loop is small as shown in Figure 20.15.
2. High initial permeability.
3. Low coercivity.
4. Saturation magnetization is reached at low applied field H.
5. Easily magnetized and demagnetized.

The structural defects as voids and impurity particles tend to restrict the motion of domain walls and so increase the coercivity, H_c. Therefore, a soft magnetic material must be free from structural defects.

An electrical current may be induced in the material by a magnetic material and field varies in magnitude and time, resulting in eddy currents. The losses due to eddy currents must be minimized by increasing electrical resistivity of the material. To increase resistivity, solid solution alloys of Fe–Si and Fe–Ni are used.

In some magnetic amplifier and pulse transformer applications, a square hysteresis loop is desired, which can be obtained by proper heat treatment of the magnetic material. Soft magnetic materials are used in the following:

1. Generators
2. Motors
3. Dynamos
4. Switching circuits
5. Magnetic amplifiers
6. Pulse transformers

Table 20.6 gives composition, initial relative permeability, hysteresis loss area and resistivity of some soft magnetic materials

Table 20.6 *Soft Magnetic Materials*

Material	Composition	Initial Relative Permeability	Hysteresis Loss (J/m²)	Resistivity ρ (Ωm) × 10⁻⁷
Commercial iron	99.95 Fe	150	270	1.0
Si–Fe (oriented)	97 Fe, 3 Si	1400	40	4.7
45 Permalloy	55 Fe, 45 Ni	2500	120	4.5
Supermalloy	79 Ni, 15 Fe, 5 Mo, 0.5 Mn	75,000	—	6.0

20.12 HARD MAGNETIC MATERIALS

Permanent magnets are made from hard magnetic materials. They possess high resistance to magnetization. They also possess high values of remanence B_r, coercivity H_c and saturation flux density B_s. However, they have low initial relative permeability and suffer from high hysteresis energy losses as shown in Figure 20.16.

Energy product $(BH)_{max}$ corresponds to the largest area that can be constructed in the II quadrant of the loop. Larger the value of $(BH)_{max}$, harder will be the magnetic material.

There are two types of hard magnetic materials: conventional and high-energy hard magnetic materials. For conventional material $(BH)_{max} < 80$ kJ/m³ and for high-energy hard material $(BH)_{max} > 80$ kJ/m³.

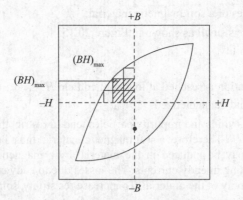

Figure 20.16 *(BH)*$_{max}$ *in II Quadrant, Magnetization Curve*

Hard magnetic steel employs tungsten and chromium as alloying elements. Hard precipitates of tungsten and chromium carbides obstruct the movement of domains. Table 20.7 gives the composition, remanent flux, energy product, Curie temperature T_c and resistivity of some hard magnetic materials.

Table 20.7 *Hard Magnetic Materials*

Material	Composition	Br (tesla)	(BH)$_{max}$	T_c (°C)	ρ (Ωm) × 10^{-7}
Tungsten steel	92.8 Fe, 6 W, 0.5 Cr, 0.7 C	0.95	2.6	760	3
Cunife	20 Fe, 20 Ni, 60 Cr	0.54	12	410	1.8
Sintered Alnico 8	34 Fe, 7 Al, 15 Ni, 35 Co, 4 Cu, 5 Ti	0.76	36	860	—
Sintered ferrite 3	BaO.6Fe$_2$O$_3$	0.32	20	450	—

20.12.1 High-energy Hard Magnetic Materials

These are permanent magnetic materials with an energy product > 80 kJ/m³. Two such alloys are commercially available.

1. Samarium–cobalt magnet (SmCo$_5$)

   Sm is a rare earth element and is expensive, exhibits the properties of high-energy hard magnetic material.

   $(BH)_{max}$ = 120–240 kJ/m³, B_r = 0.92, H_c = 720,000 ampere-turn/m, T_c = 725 and ρ = 5 × 10^{-7} Ωm.

2. Neodymium iron boron magnet (Nd$_2$Fe$_{14}$B)

   This is used in wide variety of applications. The coercivity and energy product of this alloy are more than those of SmCo$_5$ alloy.

A few applications of hard magnetic materials as follows:

1. Motors
2. No heat is generated during operation
3. Cordless drills and screw drivers
4. Automobiles, starters, window winders, wipers, washers and fan motors

5. Audio–video recorders
6. Clocks
7. Lightweight earphones, hearing aids
8. Computer peripherals

20.13 MAGNETIC STORAGE

There are wide applications of magnetic recording:

1. Storage of electronic information is in the form of audio tapes, VRSs, computer hard disks and floppy disks. A typical desktop computer now has a capacity of 40 Gbytes/disk. For magnetic data storage, the key parameter is electron spin, which is the fundamental origin of magnetic moments.

2. Recording and television industry rely on magnetic tapes for storage and reproduction of audio and video sequences. Transference to and retrieval from the tape or disk is accompanied by an inductive read–write head, which consists of basically a wire coil wound around a magnetic material core into which a gap is cut. Data are written by electrical signal within the coil, which generates a magnetic field across the gap. The field in turn magnetizes a very small area of the tape within the proximity of the head. When the applied field is removed, magnetization remains and signal has been stored.

3. There are two principal types of magnetic media: (a) particulates of iron oxide or chromium oxide and (b) polymeric thin film (for magnetic tape). The storage density of thin film is greater than that of particulate media.

Storage is permanent and magnetization reversal will result in a narrow range of applied field.

20.14 COMMONLY USED MAGNETIC MATERIALS

Commonly used magnetic materials are as follows:

1. *Permalloy:* Magnetic properties depend upon the percentage of nickel in the alloy. Increased percentage of nickel improves the magnetic properties. Low nickel permalloy with 40–50 per cent nickel is cheap, but high nickel alloy with 72–80 per cent of nickel is costly. Relative permeability of Permalloy is as high as 8×10^5.

2. *Alsifier:* It contains 9.5 Si, 5.6 Al and 84.9 Fe. It is hard, brittle and cheaper than Permalloy. It has a relative permeability of 1.0×10^4–3.5×10^4. It is used in magneto dielectric capacitors.

3. *Cammalloys:* Contains 66.5 Ni, 30 Cu and 3.5 Fe. It is a soft magnetic material. Its Curie point is 100°C.

4. *Magnetostrictive materials:* Pure nickel and some alloys of iron with chromium, cobalt and aluminium are magnetostrictive. They are used in audio frequency oscillators at sonic and sub-sonic frequencies.

5. *Magneto dielectric materials:* These are made from powders of carbonyl iron, alsifer and per-malloy. They reduce eddy current losses. These materials are used as cores in magnetic circuits in such instruments, which operate at very high frequencies.

6. *Powder magnets:* Pure iron is powdered by applying high pressures. These are kept in benzene to prevent from spontaneous combustion.

7. *Mumetals:* These are used to obtain huge flux densities in weak magnetic field in transformers. It contains some percentage of copper and eddy current losses are reduced. It has high permeability.

8. *Perminvar:* Sometimes it is necessary to have a magnetic material for which the permeability is independent of the field strength. Such materials find applications in chokes and transformers. Perminvar is an alloy of nickel, iron and cobalt. But the material is very expensive.

9. *Supermalloy:* It consists of iron and nickel alloyed with copper and molybdenum. It is characterized by very high purity and high permeability of the order of 10^5.

10. *Ferrites (Fe2O3.NiO.ZnO):* They are ceramic compounds of ferric oxide with NiO and ZnO. These oxides are finely powdered with organic binders. Binders burn out when fired at 1100–1400°C. The permeability of ferrites varies with field frequency. The resistivity is of the order of 10^2–10^7 Ωm.

Like semiconducting materials, their applications are in very high-frequency devices.

20.15 SUPERCONDUCTIVITY

As most of the high purity metals are cooled down gradually to temperature nearing 0 K, the electrical resistivity also decreases gradually approaching to a very small quantity. There are a few materials for which resistivity plunges down virtually to zero at temperatures very near to 0 K. Such materials are known as superconducting materials. The temperature at which they attain superconductivity is called critical temperature, T_{cs}. The critical temperature varies from 0.02 to 7.2 K for pure metals, from 10.2 to 23 K for compounds and alloys and from 92 to 153 K for ceramic compounds developed for super conduction.

The state of superconductivity results from attractive interaction between pairs of conducting electrons. The motion of these paired electrons becomes co-ordinated such that the scattering by thermal vibrations and impurity is highly inefficient. The resistivity that is proportional to the incidence of scattering becomes zero. There are two types of superconducting materials: Type I and II.

1. *Type I:* They are completely diamagnetic in superconducting state. Elements like Al, Pb, Sn and Hg belong to this group. All of an applied magnetic field will be excluded from the body of the material, i.e. Meissner effect, as shown in Figure 20.17(a). As field *H* is increased, the material

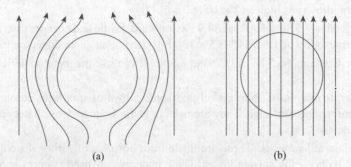

(a)   (b)

Figure 20.17 *(a) Exclusion of Body by Magnetic Flux (b) Magnetic Flux Penetration in Body*

remains diamagnetic until H_c magnetic field is reached. After this, conduction becomes normal and complete magnetic flux penetrates the body as shown in Figure 20.17(b)

2. *Type II:* Superconductors are totally diamagnetic at low applied fields and field exclusion is total-transition from superconducting state to normal state occurs between lower critical field, H_{c1} and upper critical field, H_{c2}. At H_{c1}, flux lines begin to penetrate into the body and at H_{c2} penetration is complete. Between the two critical fields, the material exists in a mixed state—both normal and superconducting states are present.

Three most commonly used superconductors are niobium–zirconium alloy, niobium–titanium alloy and niobium–tin alloy. Properties of these intermetallic compounds are given in Table 20.8.

Table 20.8 *Properties of Intermetallic Compounds*

Alloy	Critical Temperature (K)	Critical Flux Density (B_c)
Nb–Ti	10.2	12 T (tesla)
Nb–Zr	10.8	11 T (tesla)
Nb_3Sn	18.3	12 T (tesla)

Several ceramic materials, which are normally electrically insulative have been found to be super-conducting with higher critical temperatures. For example,

$$YBa_2Cu_3O_7 - T_c \text{ is } 92 \text{ K}$$

$$HgBa_2Ca_2Cu_2O_8 - T_c \text{ is } 153 \text{ K}$$

But these ceramic superconductors are brittle in nature, and cannot be fabricated in the form of wires.

20.15.1 Applications of Superconductors

Superconductors are mainly used in following fields:

1. Magnetic resonance imaging in medical field.
2. Electrical power transmission through superconductors, power loss is extremely low, and transmission at low voltage is possible.
3. Magnets of high-energy particle accelerators .
4. High-speed switching and signal transmission in computers.
5. High-speed magnetically levitated trains.

KEY POINTS TO REMEMBER

❑ Magnetic forces arise from the movement of electrical charge.

❑ Electron spin has a dominant effect and electron orbital motion has a secondary effect on the magnetic behaviour.

❑ Magnetic dipoles are found to exist in magnetic materials.

❑ Magnetic flux is generated within the coil/cylinder subjected to external field.

❑ Magnetic flux $B = \mu H$, = permeability × field

❑ Permeability in vacuum, $\mu_0 = 4\pi \times 10^{-7}$ H/m

❑ Magnetization,

$$M = X_m H$$

        = magnetic susceptibility × field

        = $(\mu_r - 1)H$, where μ_r is the relative permeability

❑ Flux, $B = \mu_0(H + M)$

❑ Bohr's magnetron, $\mu_B = 9.27 \times 10^{-24}$ A-m^2

❑ *Diamagnetism:* All the electrons are paired but with opposite spin. Diamagnetic material when placed in a magnetic field is repelled, and the relative permeability is less than 1.

❑ *Paramagnetism:* Electrons are unpaired. When magnetic field is applied, dipoles align with the external field, giving rise to a relative permeability greater than 1.

❑ *Ferromagnetism:* Permanent magnetic moments result from atomic magnetic moments; electron spins are not cancelled, and dipoles are aligned even when $H = 0$.

❑ *Domain:* Within each domain all the dipoles are aligned.

❑ Saturation magnetization, M_s = net magnetic moment for each atom × number of atoms per unit volume.

❑ *Anti-ferromagnetism:* Alignment of spin moments of adjacent atoms or ions is completely in opposite directions. MnO is anti-ferromagnetic.

❑ *Ferrimagnetism:* Atomic magnetic moments are locked in anti-parallel in neighbouring atoms. Magnetic moments are weaker in one direction than in the opposite direction, resulting in overall net magnetic moment. Ferrites are ferrimagnetic materials.

❑ *Magnetostriction:* Under applied alternating magnetic field, there are rapid extension/contraction in a bar, which starts oscillating.

❑ At Curie temperature, magnetization becomes zero as mutual spin coupling forces are fully destroyed.

❑ At saturation, dipole moments in all domains are aligned with the applied field.

❑ For soft magnetic materials, a narrow hysteresis loop and for hard magnetic materials, wide hysteresis loop is generated.

❑ Area within the hysteresis loop represents the energy loss per unit volume during magnetization–demagnetization cycle.

❑ Soft magnetic material $(BH)_{max} < 80$ kJ/m^3

❑ Hard magnetic material $(BH)_{max} > 80$ kJ/m^3

❑ Magnetic recording of sequences is done on magnetic tapes, computer hard disks and floppy disk.

❑ Superconductivity: Electrical resistivity of some high-purity metals approaches zero close to 0 K; power can be transmitted at low power loss and low voltage.

❑ Temperature at which superconductivity is attained is called critical temperature.

❑ For a pure metal, critical temperature is very close to 0 K.

MULTIPLE CHOICE QUESTIONS

1. Permeability of a vacuum is
    (a) $4\pi \times 10^{-6}$ H/m
    (b) $4\pi \times 10^{-7}$ H/m
    (c) $4\pi \times 10^{-8}$ H/m
    (d) None of these

2. What is the value of Bohr's magnetron?
    (a) 9.27×10^{-24} A-m^2
    (b) 7.29×10^{-24} A-m^2
    (c) 9.33×10^{-24} A-m^2
    (d) None of these

3. Susceptibility of a ferromagnetic material can be as high as
    (a) 100   (c) 10^6
    (b) 10,000   (d) None of these

4. Bohr's magnetron for iron is
    (a) 0.60   (c) 2.22
    (b) 1.72   (d) None of these

5. For MnO, an anti-ferromagnetic material, which of following statements is correct?
    (A) O^{2-} ions are arrayed in a crystal structure and moments of adjacent ions are anti-parallel
    (B) Mn^{2+} ions, moments of adjacent ions are anti-parallel and opposing moments cancel each other

    (a) Both (A) and (B)
    (b) Only (A)
    (c) Only (B)
    (d) None of the above

6. Special application of barium ferrite ($BaO.6Fe_2O_3$)
    (a) Transformers
    (b) Memory cores of computers
    (c) Permanent magnets
    (d) None of these

7. Which one of the following is a correct statement?
    (a) Cunife is the high-energy hard magnetic material
    (b) Si–Fe compound is a soft magnetic material
    (c) The losses due to eddy currents can be minimized by reducing the electrical resistivity of the material
    (d) None of these

8. Permanent magnets are made of
    (a) High-energy hard magnetic material
    (b) 45 Permalloy
    (c) Commercial iron
    (d) None of these

9. For transformer cores, which material is most suitable?
    (a) Soft magnetic material
    (b) High-energy hard magnetic material
    (c) Both (a) and (b)
    (d) Neither (a) nor (b)

10. For a hysteresis loop, area of loop is 120 J/m^3 and transformer core volume is 0.012 m^3 at a frequency of 50 Hz, what is hysteresis loss?

    (a) 144 W   (c) 14.4 W
    (b) 72 W   (d) None of these

11. For cordless drilling, which magnetic material is used?

    (a) Soft magnetic material
    (b) Hard magnetic material
    (c) High-energy hard magnetic material
    (d) None of these

Answers

1. (b)   2. (a)   3. (c)   4. (c)   5. (c)   6. (c)   7. (b)   8. (a)
9. (a)   10. (b)   11. (c)

REVIEW QUESTIONS

1. Explain the magnetic field, flux field and magnetic moment.

2. Define the following:
   Relative permeability, magnetization and susceptibility

3. What are spinning and orbital moments of an electron?

4. Differentiate between diamagnetism and paramagnetism with the help of sketches.

5. Explain ferromagnetism and ferrimagnetism with the help of sketches.

6. What are ferrites? What are the characteristics of ferrites? Name a few ferrites.

7. What are magnetostriction, Curie point and domains?

8. Explain B–H curve and show domains at saturation point.

9. Differentiate between soft and hard magnetic materials with the help of hysteresis loop.

10. Explain the following in the case of hysteresis loop
    Remanent, saturation flux and coercive force

11. Enumerate the properties of soft magnetic materials. Name a few soft magnetic materials with composition and initial relative permeability.

12. Name a few hard magnetic materials.

13. What do you mean by magnetic storage?

14. Write a short note on superconductivity.

PRACTICE PROBLEMS

1. Calculate the saturation magnetization and saturation flux density for nickel with a density of 8.9 g/cm^3. Bohr' magnetron per atom is 0.60 and atomic weight is 58.69.

Ans. $(5.08 \times 10^5 \text{ A/m}, 0.639 \text{ T})$

2. Determine the power loss due to hysteresis in a transformer core having a volume of 0.012 m^3 at a frequency of 50 Hz. The area of the loop is 550 J/m^3.

Ans. (330 W)

OPTICAL PROPERTIES
OF MATERIALS

21.1 INTRODUCTION

You might have wondered why some materials are transparent while others are opaque, some surfaces are good reflectors while others absorb all incident light. The various phenomena of light's interactions with materials fascinate us right throughout our lives and the sense of sight has been given the highest position among all other senses that we experience. However, light is only a narrow band of wavelengths that is sensitive to the human eye. The general name of such waves is electromagnetic waves and as the name suggests it contains two waves, an electric wave and a magnetic wave. Therefore, it is the whole spectrum of electromagnetic waves that is important as far as material science is concerned.

At the very small wavelengths the electromagnetic waves are called Gamma rays which are produced in the nucleus of the atoms of the radioactive elements. The next bands of wavelengths are called X-rays and these are produced by rapidly decelerating electrons. The ultraviolet and the optical wavelengths are produced by atomic transitions, the infrared by molecular transitions, microwaves by electronic devices called klystrons, still larger waves like that used in TV transmission mobile communications, radios are produced by oscillating currents in the devices called antennas. These waves are received by antennas amplified and fed to the appropriate devices after filtering all the noise that are also received. The larger wavelength waves are of less importance to materials but of immense importance for communications.

We would therefore study first the electromagnetic waves and their general characteristics before embarking on to study the interactions of electromagnetic waves with matter. We would then understand the basic physical quantities that are used to characterize the behaviour of all materials vis-a-vis em waves. Further in the chapter we would know about the production of laser, a very special type of light with extremely useful properties and the materials that are used for their production. In the final section we would describe the application of lasers in communication called optical communications.

Historically the understanding of the particle character of the electromagnetic waves came later than its understanding of wave character. We would describe the former first. That is because it is easier to understand and some of its results are used later in the section.

21.1.1 The Particle Characteristic of EM Waves

Max Planck while trying to explain the spectrum of black body radiation found that the spectrum can only be obtained if it is assumed that the energy associated with the waves is discrete. This is called the Planck's Law, and mathematically

$$E = hv \tag{21.1}$$

Where v is the frequency of the radiation and h is a constant called Planck's constant. The value of h is 6.626×10^{-34} J s or 4.136×10^{-15} eVs.

We should also note that energy packets which are called photons have momentum as high-energy photons scatter elementary particles like electrons. The famous relationship between energy (E) momentum (p) and rest mass (M) of the particle is given by Einstein as

$$E^2 = p^2 c^2 + M^2 c^4 \tag{21.2}$$

This will reduce to

$$E^2 = p^2 c^2 \tag{21.3}$$

as the rest mass of photon $= 0$.

$$p = E/c$$

Using the Plank's Law (Eq. 21.1), this reduces to

$$p = h/\lambda$$

As wave number

$$k = 2\pi /\lambda$$

$$k = p/\hbar \tag{21.4}$$

where $\hbar = h/2\pi$. The equation shows that the wave number is directly proportional to the momentum and is a vector too like momentum.

A beam of electromagnetic wave is composed of photons. The intensity, I which is the energy crossing a unit area per second is also given by

$$I = \text{(energy of one photon)} \times \text{number of photons crossing a unit area per second} \tag{21.5}$$

Further proof that light behaves as a packet of energy came from Einstein's explanation of photo electric effect. The maximum kinetic energy K_{max} carried by the electrons ejected from a metal surface after absorbing the kinetic energy of the photon ($= hv$) is given by

$$K_{max} = hv - \varphi$$

where φ is the work function of the material. Below threshold frequency given by

$$hv_{th} = \varphi$$

No electrons will be ejected no matter how intense is the light. In an experiment to study photo electricity, light shines on a metal surface in an evacuated tube and a stopping potential, V_s is measured. The stopping potential is the potential required to make the current zero in the external circuit.

By energy balance

$$eV_s = K_{max} = hv - \varphi \tag{21.6}$$

Example 21.1 Find the wavelength (in nm and A), frequency and momentum of 100eV photon.

$$1 \text{ eV} = 1.6 \times 10^{-19} \text{ J s}$$

Solution:

Using equation $E = hv$, $100 \times 1.6 \times 10^{-19} = 6.626 \times 10^{-34} \times v$

Giving,

$$v = 2.4 \times 10^{16} \text{ Hz}$$

Using $\lambda = c/v$

$$\lambda = 12.5 \text{ nm} = 125 \text{ Å}$$

Using $p = h/\lambda$

$$p = 5.3 \times 10^{-26} \text{ kg m/s}$$

We can also write

$$p = hv/c = E/c = 100 \text{ eV}/c$$

Example 21. 2 A light source produces 20W at the wavelength of 600nm. How many photons are produced per second?

Solution:

Using equation $E = hv = h c/\lambda$

$$E = \frac{6.626 \times 10^{-34} \times 3 \times 10^8}{600 \times 10^{-9}}$$

$$E = 3.3 \times 10^{-19} \text{ J}$$

Is the energy associated with each photon.
Number of photons radiated per second = (energy radiated per second)/ (energy of each photon)

$$= \frac{20}{3.3 \times 10^{-19}}$$

$$= 6.06 \times 10^{19} \text{ photons/s}$$

Example 21. 3 In a photo electric experiment, the stopping potential measured is 2.0 V for light of wavelength 400 nm. Find the work function of the material.

Solution:

Using the Eq. (21.6) $e V_s = K_{max} = h v - \varphi$

$$\varphi = h v - e V_s$$

$$\varphi = h.c/\lambda - e V_s$$

$$= \left[\frac{4.136 \times 10^{-15} \times 3 \times 10^8}{400 \times 10^{-9}} - 2.0 \right] eV$$

$$= (3.1 - 2.0) eV$$

$$\varphi = 1.7 \text{ eV}$$

21.1.2 Waves of Electric and Magnetic Fields

First time James Clerk Maxwell wrote a set of four comprehensive equations that govern the characteristics of electric field (E) and magnetic fields (H) and are called the Maxwell's equations. Out of the four Maxwell's equations two equations are coupled in the variables E and H. In free space (vacuum) these are as follows:

$$\text{div } E = 0 \tag{21.7}$$

$$\text{div } B = 0 \tag{21.8}$$

$$\text{curl } E = \frac{\partial B}{\partial t} \tag{21.9}$$

$$\text{curl } H = t_0 \frac{\partial E}{\partial t} \tag{21.10}$$

The Eq. (21.9) is the famous Faraday's Law while the Eq. (21.10) is modified Ampere's Law with zero current. Decoupling these two equations by using one equation into the other we can obtain equations which contain only one variable either E or H. These are

$$\nabla^2 E = \mu_0 \varepsilon_0 \frac{\partial^2 E}{\partial t^2} \tag{21.11}$$

$$\nabla^2 H = \mu_0 \varepsilon_0 \frac{\partial^2 H}{\partial t^2} \tag{21.12}$$

Surprising that the two equations resemble the general wave equation with velocity

$$u = \frac{1}{\sqrt{\mu_0 \varepsilon_0}} \tag{21.13}$$

the velocity of light, 2.99×10^8 m/s. ($\varepsilon_0 = 8.85 \times 10^{-12}$ F m^{-1} $\mu_0 = 4\pi \times 10^{-7}$ H m^{-1})

Solutions of Eq. (21.11) and (21.12) in one dimension are

$$E = E_0 \sin(\omega t - kx) \tag{21.14a}$$

$$H = H_0 \sin(\omega t - kx), \tag{21.14b}$$

which are simple harmonic plane waves propagating in the x direction.

From this Maxwell concluded that light too is a kind of electromagnetic waves. Some general characteristics of these waves are as follows:

1. The waves are transverse in nature i.e. the direction of E vector and H vector are perpendicular to the direction of propagation. The direction of propagation is direction of the vector k which is the wave number of the wave (= $2\pi/\lambda$).

2. The vectors E and H are perpendicular to each other.

3. The vector E, H and k form the three axes of the right-handed Cartesian coordinate system (Figure 21.1). That is if we place a right-handed screw along the k vector and rotate the screw from E to H the screw will move forward along k.

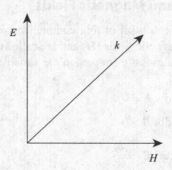

Figure 21.1 *Vector E, H, and k*

4. In vacuum there is no phase difference between the wave of the electric field and the wave of the magnetic field. The ratio

$$\frac{E}{H} = \left[\frac{\mu_0}{\varepsilon_0} \right]^{1/2} \qquad (21.15)$$

5. The cross product of vector E and the vector H give the energy flow per unit area per unit time.

$$S = E \times H \,[\text{W/m}^2] \qquad (21.16)$$

The vector S is called the pointing vector which is in the direction of k.
6. Generally the light and other electromagnetic waves are unpolarized that the planes in which the electric oscillations are taking place are random and different from photon to photon. This is because the waves emitted from different atomic transitions are uncorrelated.

In Figure 21.2 we have shown the electromagnetic wave nature in vacuum.

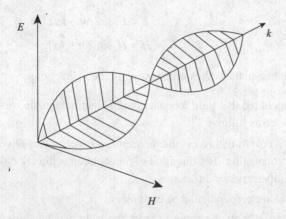

Figure 21.2 *Electromagnetic Waves in Vaccum*

Example 21.4 If the incident solar energy is 1.33 kW/m², calculate amplitude of electric field associated with the sunlight.

Solution:

$$S = E \times H$$

$$|S| = (E_0/\sqrt{2})\,(H_0/\sqrt{2})$$

$$= 1330 \text{ W/m}^2$$

Replacing H_0 by the equation

$$H_0 = \left[\frac{\mu_0}{\varepsilon_0}\right]^{-1/2} E_0$$

We obtain,

$$E_0 = 996.8 \text{ V/m}$$

21.2 ELECTROMAGNETIC WAVE PROPAGATION IN SOLIDS

Every medium is characterized by the following physical parameters that determine the nature of the waves in that medium.

1. The permittivity, ε
2. The permeability, μ
3. The conductivity, σ
4. The angular velocity of the wave, ω.

For free space,

$$\sigma = 0,\ \varepsilon = \varepsilon_0,\ \mu = \mu_0$$

For perfect dielectric

$$\sigma = 0,\ \varepsilon = \varepsilon_r \varepsilon_0,\ \mu = \mu_r \mu_0 \text{ and } \sigma << \omega\varepsilon,$$

For good conductor

$$\sigma \rightarrow \infty,\ \varepsilon = \varepsilon_0,\ \mu = \mu_r \mu_0 \text{ and } \sigma << \omega\varepsilon$$

We have studied the propagation of em waves in free space. In perfect dielectric the em wave has similar character except that its velocity is

$$u = [\varepsilon \mu]^{-1/2} \tag{21.17}$$

As

$$\varepsilon > \varepsilon_0, \text{ and } \mu > \mu_0$$

its velocity is lower than that in free space.

In good conductor the character of the waves is completely different. The E wave and H waves travel with a phase difference between them. In a perfect conductor this phase difference is 45°. The intensity of the wave rapidly decreases as it travels in the medium. The amplitude of the electric vector varies as

$$E(x) = E_0 \exp(-\alpha x) \tag{21.18}$$

At the value of $x = 1/\alpha$ the amplitude remains $1/e$ of the original value. It's called the skin depth of the medium, and given by

$$\delta = \frac{1}{\alpha} = \frac{1}{\sqrt{\pi f \mu \sigma}}$$ (21.19)

where f is the frequency of the wave. The skin depth measures the exponential damping of the wave as it travels through the conductor. The skin depth decreases with the increase in the frequency of the wave.

The small value of skin depth in good conductor finds many applications. The outdoor TV antenna is made hollow instead of solid. The waveguides are coated with a thin layer of silver. Signal carrying wires protected by an outer wire mesh that eliminates the outer noise is another important application. This is known as electromagnetic shielding.

21.3 REFLECTION AND REFRACTION AT THE INTERFACE

When a plane wave travelling in one medium meets a different medium, it is partly reflected and partly transmitted at the interface. The parameters ε, μ and σ of the two media and angular velocity of the wave govern the part of energy reflected wave and refracted wave will carry. If the second medium is a metal the transmitted wave is heavily attenuated. Most of the energy is reflected back into the first medium. Metals are therefore good reflectors.

For oblique incidence at the boundary of two dielectric media it can be shown that,

$$n_1 \sin\theta_1 = n_2 \sin\theta_2$$ (21.20)

where θ_1 and θ_2 are the angle of incidence and the angle of refraction.

$$n_1 = c\sqrt{\varepsilon_1 \mu_1} = \frac{c}{u_1}$$ (21.21a)

$$n_2 = c\sqrt{\varepsilon_2 \mu_2} = \frac{c}{u_2}$$ (21.21b)

are called the refractive indices of the material 1 and 2.

From the energy consideration it is obvious that the incident energy is divided into three parts namely the energy of reflected ray, energy of refracted ray and the energy absorbed by the medium.

Refractive Indices of Some Common Transparent Materials for Sodium D Line

Medium	n_D
Borocilicate crown	1.50
Light flint	1.57
Dense flint	1.62
Fused quartz	1.46

(Source: Jenkins and White, Fundamentals of Optics, McGraw Hill)

Therefore
$$R + T + A = 1$$

where R the fraction of intensity reflected, T the fraction of intensity carried by the refracted ray and A the fraction of intensity absorbed by the medium.

21.4 THE ELECTROMAGNETIC SPECTRUM

Light is only a narrow part of the electromagnetic spectrum which extends from few km long radio waves to extremely small waves gamma rays. In Figure 21.3, we have shown the whole range of electromagnetic spectrum. Note that the visible part of the spectrum is very narrow. In the longer side (right side of the Figure 21.3) the radio waves are the longest waves which can be bigger than a few football fields. In the shortest side (left of the Figure 21.3) we have waves as short as 10^{-12} m which are gamma rays. The visible side extends from 380 nm for violet to about 750 nm for deep red.

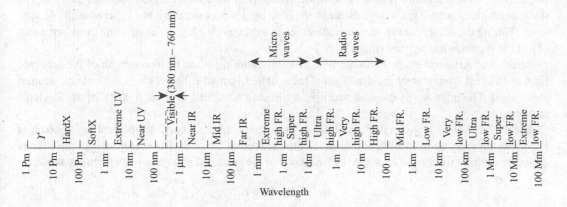

Figure 21.3 *Spectrum of Electromagnetic Waves*

21.5 ABSORPTION AND SCATTERING

The intensity of electromagnetic waves will decrease when it travels through a material medium. This is due to absorption. If the electromagnetic wave does not have the right wavelength then it will pass through the medium without absorption. Long wavelength electromagnetic waves are not affected by solid bodies in its path. For example, radio waves pass easily through the human body and even through walls of the buildings. As we come down to the infrared wavelengths it starts showing effect. The infrared is absorbed by the skin.

Absorption occurs because light quanta raise the electrons in the atoms to excited states. In this process the entire photon may be absorbed by the atom. If the photon's energy is in excess of the energy required to make the electron free (called the ionization energy) the excess energy will be carried by the free electron. The freed electron is called photoelectron and the process is called photoemission. Many metals and metal oxides emit electrons when exposed to light of appropriate wavelength.

A photon will not be absorbed unless its energy is equal to one of the excitation energies of the absorbing atom. For example, hydrogen atoms at the ground state are transparent to visible light. Recall that the Lyman series, which are the spectral lines that are due to transition from the higher states to the ground states ($n = 1$), is in the far ultraviolet region. Scattering is another process by which the intensity of the wave attenuates as it travels through a medium

21.5.1 Scattering

Light scattering is a common phenomena occurring in nature. In elastic scattering of light the wavelength of the scattered light is the same as that of the incident light. This is known as Rayleigh scattering. Rayleigh studied such type of scattering in air and he observed that the molecules of air are responsible for this scattering. In this scattering the light's particle properties are not revealed and the light behaves more like a wave. The molecules behave like dipoles by which the electromagnetic waves get scattered. A mathematical analysis shows that the intensity of the scattered light is inversely proportional to the fourth power of the wavelength. Therefore the light of shorter wavelengths are scattered more than the longer. The sunlight appears yellow because the blue part of the spectrum has been scattered out. The sky appears blue because in all other direction the blue light is prevalent as it has suffered multiple scattering. During the sunset the sun appears red as the sunlight travels a larger distance and even larger part of its blue region is lost by scattering.

Raman and Krishnan studied another type of light scattering when the wavelength of the scattered light is different from that of incident light. This is called Raman Effect. This is the inelastic scattering of light. The intensity of the scattered light by Raman scattering is about 0.001% of the Rayleigh scattering.

The explanation of the Raman Effect follows from the Quantum theory. An incident light photon of energy hv impinges upon an atom or molecule of the scattering medium. The energy state of the atom or molecule changes from E_1 to E_2 while the frequency of the scattered photon is v' then we can write,

$$hv - hv' = E_2 - E_1 \qquad (21.22)$$

Raman Effect has been utilized for non-destructive chemical analysis of substances by using high-powered laser beams as the scattered light is characteristic of the medium.

A smaller wavelength of ultraviolet and X-ray scattering occurs by the electrons which results in scattered radiation having smaller frequency than the incident wave. Such scattering is called Compton scattering. The energy $hv - hv'$ is transferred to the electrons.

The gamma rays are highly energetic and are capable of damaging human tissues resulting in damaging the chromosomes. These also pass through light metals; only heavy metal like lead of sufficient thickness is capable of stopping these rays.

Example 21.5 The Bohr model gives the energy of the nth level for hydrogen atom,

$$E_n = -\frac{E_1}{n^2} \text{ eV}$$

where E_1 is the energy of the ground state $n = 1$.

(a) Calculate its ionization energy i.e. the energy required to liberate the electron from its ground state, if the shortest wavelength in the Balmer series is 365 nm.

(b) Calculate the wavelength of the photon corresponding to the ionization energy.

Solution: The shortest wavelength of the Balmer series corresponds to the transition from $n = \infty$ to $n = 2$.

Using the given equation,

$$E_2 = -\frac{E_1}{4} = h\nu$$

or

$$h\left(\frac{c}{\lambda}\right) = -\frac{E_1}{4}$$

$$E_1 = -\frac{4 \times 4.136 \times 10^{-15} \times 3 \times 10^8}{365 \times 10^{-9}} = -13.6 \text{ eV},$$

which is the ionization energy.

Using

$$E = \frac{hc}{\lambda} \Rightarrow \lambda = \frac{hc}{E} = \frac{12.408 \times 10^{-7}}{13.6}$$

$$\lambda = 91.2 \text{nm}$$

21.5.2 Selective Absorption

Some materials like dyes absorb only part of the spectrum. This is called selective absorption. In general all material will have high absorption on some narrow part or parts of the electromagnetic spectrum but the absorption remains almost the same over a wide range of wavelengths. In selective absorption, strong absorption of certain wavelengths causes their larger attenuation. This causes the effect of colour. For example, a red glass plate absorbs the green part of the visible light. As green is complimentary to red the transmitted light will appear red.

21.6 COLOUR

Spectral light evokes in the human eye sensation of a particular colour depending on the wavelength of light involved. They are grouped into seven primary colours listed in Table 21.1.

Table 21.1 *Wavelength Ranges of Different Colours*

Wavelength (nm)	Colour
780–605	Red
605–590	Orange
590–560	Yellow
560–500	Green
500–470	Blue
470–430	Indigo
430–380	Violet

The colour sensation depends on the spectral composition of light incident on eye and properties of vision. Because the eye has the property of integral sensitivity same colour sensation can be produced by mixing different spectral components. New colour sensation can be produced by two processes. The first process, called additive, light of different hue illuminates a white screen resulting in new colour sensation. The second is subtractive, examples of which are pigments that absorb other colours except the one they reflect. The colour television uses the additive method while the colour printing uses the subtractive method.

21.7 FLUORESCENCE, PHOSPHORESCENCE AND LUMINESCENCE

Fluorescence is a process in which an atom is excited to a higher energy state by a high energy photon. The atom releases a photon of smaller energy, generally after a time interval that may be less than a micro second. This happens because the atom de excite in several steps releasing visible light in each of the transition. The method is used for production of efficient fluorescent tube lamps. Mercury vapour produces ultraviolet radiation when an electric discharge passes through it. The inner surface of the lamp is coated with a fluorescent material that absorbs the UV radiation but de excite by releasing visible light. These materials are also used in cathode ray tubes.

Some materials contain metastable state. The atom if excited to the metastable state will return to the normal state after spending little longer time. Such material gives persistent light that may last several hours, after the external excitation has been removed. The phenomenon is called phosphorescence. They are used in glow in dark toys.

Luminescence is a general term that is used for light emission occurring at low temperature in contradistinction to incandescence which is light generated at high temperature. Luminescence can be due to various processes some of which are listed below:

(a) Chemo luminescence, results from a chemical reaction.

(b) Bioluminescence by living organism.

(c) Photo luminescence, absorption and re-radiation of photon which we have described earlier.

21.8 LASER

Lasers are artificially produced light beams abbreviated from the words Light Amplification by Stimulated Emission of Radiation. These are finding applications in almost all areas of engineering and technology. We would first study the theory of laser.

As we know all atoms and molecules have the ground state which is the lowest energy state and the excited states. If the electrons are raised to the excited states they return to the ground state by emitting a light photon. The atom remains in the excited state for a very short duration of time. In some atoms or molecules there are states, called metastable state in which the atom stays for a little longer duration of time if it is raised to such states. In a collection of atoms if a large number of atoms are raised to this metastable state there is a possibility of population inversion. In this situation larger proportion of atoms may be in the metastable state than the ground state.

Now the transition in the atoms are of two kinds. In the first called spontaneous transition the atom makes a transition to the ground state without any external stimulus. In the second called stimulated transition the atom makes a transition to the ground state or a lower excited state by another photon of

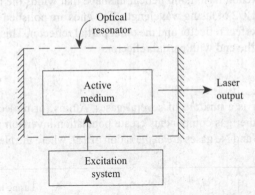

Figure 21.4 *Schematic Diagram of a Laser System*

same frequency. This is termed as stimulated emission. If any one of the excited atoms emits a photon by making a transition from the metastable state it will induce stimulated emission in another atom. This process will soon result in increasing number of photons giving increasing intensity of the beam.

Therefore the process of building a laser beam is the following. An appropriate material that contains metastable state or states has to be found. This is called the active medium. A system of excitation that provides mechanism of obtaining population inversion by pumping the atoms or molecules of the active centres to the excited state. Confining the photons to move back and forth in the lasing medium by an optical resonator that selects the photons of correct wavelength produced by the laser transition. Figure 21.4 shows a schematic diagram of the essential elements of lasing system.

The following types of active mediums are used:

(a) Gases or mixture of gases

(b) Crystals and glasses doped with special ions

(c) Liquids

(d) Semiconductors.

According to the type of medium the lasers are named as gas laser, solid state laser, liquid laser or semiconductor laser.

21.8.1 Ruby Laser

An example of solid state laser is the ruby laser, consisting of ruby crystal (Al_2O_3 doped with Cr^{+++} ions, 0.05 to 0.5%) which is cylindrical in shape 3 to 20mm in diameter and 5 to 30 cm long (Figure 21.5). The

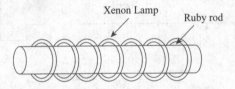

Figure 21.5 *The Ruby Rod with Xenon Flash Lamp*

optical pumping system is a xenon flash lamp helical in shape that winds the rod. The crystal length is adjusted and made multiple of $\lambda/2$ of lasing wavelength. The ends are polished and mirrored by depositing thin films, with one face perfect reflector and the other partial reflector. This acts as optical resonator. The laser light emerges from the end with partial reflector.

21.8.2 HeNe Laser

Active medium of a gas laser is a mixture of several gases. Atoms (or molecule) of one of the gases are active centres while the other gas components create population inversion in the active centres. For example, in the HeNe laser He and Ne gases are in the ration of 1:9, where the Ne atoms are active centres.

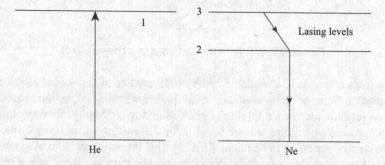

Figure 21.6 *Atomic States for He and Ne Participating in Laser Action*

A dc glow discharge produces accelerating electrons that excite He atoms to the state 1 as shown in the Figure 21.6. The excited He atoms collide with the Ne atoms raising them to the state 3, which is very close to the state 1 for the He atoms. There is another short-lived state for the Ne atoms close to the state 3 shown as 2 in the Figure 21.6. The Ne atoms make lasing transition from state 3 to 2 from where they go to the ground state. The laser transition produces photons of wavelength 632.8 nm. The ends of the tube are fixed with two mirrors, one perfectly silvered and the other partially silvered with distance between them an integral multiple of $\lambda/2$.

The output of HeNe laser can range from 1mW to 80mW. Essential elements of HeNe laser have been shown in Figure 21.7.

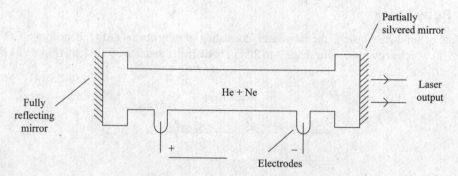

Figure 21.7 *Essential Elements of HeNe Laser*

21.8.3 CO₂ Laser

One of the earliest gas laser invented was the CO_2 laser by C.K.N. Patel in the Bell Labs in 1964. The active medium consists of CO_2 (20%), N_2 (20%), H_2 (a few percent) and rest He depending on the power output. CO_2 molecules are the active centres. Nitrogen molecules are excited by electrons. These nitrogen molecules in turn transfer energy to the carbon dioxide molecules creating a population inversion. The output laser is in infrared region and therefore special materials are needed for their construction. The windows are made of germanium or diamond which are transparent to infrared wavelengths. They give high power output and find applications in cutting, welding and also in surgical procedures.

21.8.4 Dye Laser

In dye laser the active medium is an organic dye dissolved in a solvent. Dye laser has the advantage that it is tunable i.e. we can vary its frequency by varying the dye, the pumping light and the angle of the mirrors.

21.8.5 Semiconductor Laser

When a p-n junction is forward biased the electrons and the holes move in the opposite direction. An electron and a hole can combine resulting in the emission of photon. The energy of the photon will be equal to the difference of energy between the valance band and conduction band. A device operating this way is called a light emitting diode or a semiconductor laser. The end faces of such a diode are polished to obtain reflective surfaces. Such a diode is generally operated with large forward biasing that results in a large number of holes and electrons moving in opposite direction near the junction creating a situation like population inversion.

21.8.6 Properties of Laser Light

1. It is monochromatic, that is it consists of a single wavelength.
2. It is coherent. By coherent, we mean that the photons constituting the beam are in phase with each other. It is due to this property that a laser beam can deliver more power to the target than in case of ordinary light beam. As ordinary light beam is incoherent, interference will result in less power delivered to the output.
3. Highly directional and can be obtained as polarized light.

21.8.7 Applications of Laser

1. *Laser in surgery:* LASIK one of the first application of laser in surgery was applied for correcting vision as an alternative to wearing eye glasses or contact lenses. This pioneering work was done by Mani Bhaumik an alumni of IIT K. Further developments of laser surgery have taken place and laser is being used for tumour removal to welding of the retina in retinal detachment.
2. *Laser in mechanical engineering:* The laser light can be focused to an extremely high energy density. High powered laser beams obtained from CO_2 laser is being used for laser machining, cutting of metal sheets etc.

3. *Laser in electronics industry:* Laser is used in the microelectronics for cutting, welding and drilling.

4. *Plate tectonics:* Astronauts (in 1969) placed a laser reflector on the surface of the moon. This reflector enables scientists to measure the distance between earth and moon within few inches. Minute motions of earth's plates are being detected by using laser beams sent from American Pacific coast, and Japan giving valuable information regarding the motion of plates constituting the earth's crust.

5. *Laser in civil engineering:* Because of its excellent directionality lasers are used extensively for surveying. It is used in the construction industry for checking and correcting alignment of large structures like bridge or tunnel using the laser beam as reference.

6. *Laser in defense:* Laser target finders on guns, laser guided missiles, laser fitted missiles (that penetrated thick walls of bunkers in Iraq War) are some of the weapons that are being used in recent wars.

7. *Laser in fusion research:* Because of its ability to deliver very high energy density pulsed lasers have been developed to induce fusion reaction.

8. *Laser holography:* Holography is a technique of reproducing three-dimensional image of an object. It is done by recording interference pattern of a scattered beam and a reference beam that memorizes the phases of the scattered waves from the object. This photograph when exposed to laser beam reproduces the image of the object in three-dimension. It is finding applications in Biology and Medicine.

9. *Laser in lighting:* Light emitting diodes (LED) are increasingly being used for lighting as it is highly efficient in converting the input electrical energy into light.

10. *Laser in communication:* Optical fibre communication will be discussed in detail in the next section.

21.9 THE FIBRE OPTIC COMMUNICATION

The development of optical fibre has proven to be the key element in optical communication. The optical fibre is long glass or plastic fibre with circular cross-section that has a structure as shown. It has the core and the cladding, the outer layer. The refractive index of the core is larger than the cladding. Therefore a ray of light meeting the interface with larger than the critical angle will be reflected back. Such a ray will be confined into the fibre as it will travel suffering multiple total internal reflections at the interface of the core and the cladding. The fibre acts as optical waveguide (Figure. 21.8). The advantages of using such fibres in comparison to that through the atmosphere for communications are less attenuation of the

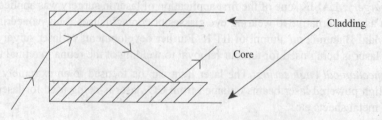

Figure 21.8 *Optical Fibre Showing a Ray*

intensity. Its advantage over the copper cable is practically no possibility of interference with the noise. Its advantages over microwave are lower attenuation, very large number of channels and is secure. It is because of these advantages more and more critical areas such as railways, defense and broad band internet lines are provided with optical fibre communication links.

Initially the loss in the fibre was high but progress in material science has brought down the loss down to about 10 dB/km.

To enable several pieces of signals to be transmitted simultaneously, it is superimposed on a carrier signal. The process is called modulation. The message which is primary composed of low frequency is encoded onto reference signals of high frequency. For example, speech and music in range of 20 Hz to 20 kHz is transmitted by using radio waves which are of frequency 100 kHz or MHz. range. We can see why light will be of advantage for transmitting the signal. Typically light in the visible part of the spectrum has frequency of 100 THz. It has million times more capacity to encode messages onto it.

Several forms of modulation, based on analogous or digital methods are used for communication. The amplitude modulation which is simple to understand the amplitude of the high frequency carrier wave is modulated by the message. In recent technology the digital modulation called pulse code modulation is increasingly used because of its advantages over amplitude modulation. In digital communication the signal can be recovered more easily as it's free from the noise unlike in amplitude modulation. A signal consisting of a series of equal amplitude pulses is easy to recover even when they are distorted.

In Figure 21.9 we have shown schematically the essential elements of optical fibre telephone link. Transmitter terminal consists of light source and modulator. Mechanical sound waves are converted to electrical signal. The message is superimposed on the carrier wave. The fibre optic cables are the transmission medium. The signal suffers attenuation due to leakages. In order to amplify the signal on the path regenerators are employed. At the receiving terminal there is a photodetector that converts the light signals back into electrical signals. Finally a demodulator retrieves the input signal.

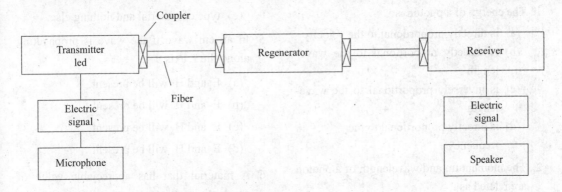

Figure 21.9 *Essential Parts of Optical Fibre Communication Link*

KEY POINTS TO REMEMBER

❏ Light is a kind of electromagnetic wave.

❏ The electromagnetic waves contain oscillating electric and magnetic fields.

❏ The electric field and the magnetic fields in em waves are perpendicular to each other and perpendicular to the direction of propagation of the wave.

- ❑ The vectors E, H and k form right-handed coordinate system.
- ❑ In em waves in vacuum there is no phase difference between E vector and H vector.
- ❑ The velocity of em waves in vacuum is $\dfrac{1}{\sqrt{\varepsilon_0 \mu_0}}$.

  The ratio $\dfrac{E}{H} = \sqrt{\dfrac{\mu_0}{\varepsilon_0}}$
- ❑ Radio waves can pass through all materials except metals.
- ❑ EM waves are heavily attenuated inside a conductor.
- ❑ The skin depth in a conductor is the distance at which the amplitude of the em wave drops to 1/e times the original.
- ❑ The essential elements of a laser system is an active medium, optical resonator and excitation system.
- ❑ The lifetime of a metastable state is large compared to a normal excited state.
- ❑ Population inversion is the situation when larger numbers of atoms or molecules of the active centres are raised to the metastable state. This is achieved by optical pumping.
- ❑ In a stimulated emission photons of appropriate wavelength trigger a transition from an excited atom in the metastable state releasing another photon of same wavelength.

MULTIPLE CHOICE QUESTIONS

In each of the following choose the correct option.

1. The energy of a photon is
   - (a) is directly proportional to the velocity
   - (b) is directly proportional to the wavelength
   - (c) is inversely proportional to the wavelength
   - (d) is directly proportional to the frequency.

2. The momentum and wavelength of a photon are related as
   - (a) $\lambda = \hbar/p$
   - (b) $\lambda = h/p$
   - (c) $\lambda = p/h$
   - (d) $\lambda = p/\hbar$

3. The energy of a photon is given by
   - (a) pc
   - (b) p/c
   - (c) c/p
   - (d) hc

4. The photoelectric work function of a material depends on

   - (a) the frequency of em wave
   - (b) the wavelength of the em wave
   - (c) type of material and nothing else.

5. In an em wave if the wave is propagating along the Z axis
   - (a) E_x and H_y will be present
   - (b) E_y and H_z will be present
   - (c) E_y and H_y will be present
   - (d) E_x and H_x will be present.

6. A material that has appreciable value of conductivity, the em wave will travel in the medium
   - (a) with decreasing amplitude
   - (b) with constant amplitude

7. Which one is not one of the properties of laser
   - (a) coherent
   - (b) directional
   - (c) monochromatic
   - (d) convergent

Answers

1. (c) and (d)   2. (b)   3. (a)   4. (c)   5. (a)   6. (a)   7. (d)

REVIEW QUESTIONS

1. What are the basic features of the em waves in vacuum?

2. What is photoelectric effect? How can it be used to determine the value of Planck's constant, h?

3. What are different kinds of scattering of em waves? In which type of scattering the particle character of em wave is revealed?

4. What is the difference between phosphorescence and fluorescence? Discuss some of their applications.

5. Explain why modulation is necessary to transmit a signal.

6. Describe with the help of schematic diagram essential elements of fibre optic communication system.

PRACTICE PROBLEMS

1. Find the energy (in J and eV) and momentum of 600 nm photon.

    (Ans. 3.21×10^{-19} J, 2.06 eV, 5.3×10^{-26} kg m/s)

2. A radio station uses 100 MHz waves and 100kW of power. How many photons are emitted per second by the radio station?

    (Ans. 1.5×10^{30} photons/s)

3. Potassium has work function of 2.21eV. Find its threshold wavelength.

    (Ans. 564nm)

4. Calculate the first two longest light wavelengths that will be absent in the absorption spectra of hydrogen. [Hint: It will be the first two lines of the Balmer series, from level 3 to 2 and from level 4 to 2. Use the equation in the worked example]

    (Ans. 656 nm, 487nm)

5. Calculate the skin depth for 2 MHz em wave through copper.
    Given $\sigma = 5.8 \times 10^7$ Si, $\mu = 4\pi \times 10^7$ H/m

    (Ans. 4.67×10^{-5} m)

INDEX